Successful Marriage

Successful Marriage

A MODERN GUIDE TO LOVE, SEX, AND FAMILY LIFE

EDITED BY MORRIS FISHBEIN, M.D.

FORMER EDITOR, "JOURNAL OF THE AMERICAN MEDICAL ASSOCIATION"; CONTRIBUTING EDITOR, "POSTGRADUATE MEDICINE"; CHIEF EDITOR, "EXCERPTA MEDICA"

AND ERNEST W. BURGESS, Ph.D.

PROFESSOR AND CHAIRMAN EMERITUS, DEPARTMENT OF SOCIOLOGY, UNIVERSITY OF CHICAGO

NEW AND REVISED EDITION 1955

Doubleday & Company, Inc., Garden City, N.Y.

LIBRARY OF CONGRESS CATALOG CARD NUMBER 55–5953

PRINTED IN THE UNITED STATES AT
THE COUNTRY LIFE PRESS, GARDEN CITY, N.Y.
DESIGNED BY ALMA REESE CARDI

Contents

Part One: Preparation for Marriage

Part Three: Conception, Pregnancy, and Childbirth

Part Four: The Child in the Family

Part Five: Social Problems of Sex and Marriage

Illustrations

Introduction

by Robert W. Laidlaw, M.D.

PAST PRESIDENT, AMERICAN ASSOCIATION OF MARRIAGE COUNSELORS

"Marriage Counseling" and "Marital Adjustment" have become common phrases in the American vocabulary of today. They are frequently used with little realization of the multiplicity of problems they include, of the differences between competent and incompetent counseling, and of the availability or dearth of counseling facilities. Many misconceptions have arisen. Much literature on marriage has been written for popular consumption. Often such literature deals only with one phase of counseling, each writer stressing his favorite aspect of a much larger specialty. Correlation of existing facts and clarification of current theories must be presented if the most adequate type of service is to be rendered. This book has been conceived with full realization of the responsibilities inherent in the total field of marriage counseling.

One of the most common misconceptions is that a successful marriage must meet a certain norm, with little or no allowance for individual variations. There is a search for a magic formula, application of which will solve all current and future marital problems. Some people look on marriage counseling as a desperate kind of surgery for marriages that are already moribund. Many professional and non-professional people firmly believe that all marital problems are primarily based on sexual maladjustment. Since all maladjustments in the individual will color to some extent his effectiveness in the sexual relationship, this difficulty is a concomitant part of the problems brought to the counselor. It would be a grave error, however, to insist that adjustment in this phase of marriage is an isolated problem.

A secure and well-adjusted family unit is the desired outcome of marriage. The extent to which the counselor can aid in the creation of such a unit varies conversely with the time at which his assistance is enlisted. The longer an ill-adjusted situation has existed, the more difficult the problem and the less that can be done about it. Marriage counseling is at its best and offers its most promising results in the field of preventive medicine.

Premarital counseling affords the counselor the maximum leverage in helping in the creation of a real marriage. At this time the various factors making for success or failure between the two people concerned are in a relatively plastic state and can be molded or changed in the hands of a skilled counselor in ways leading toward a mature adjustment in marriage itself. The counselor must search out unresolved conflicts in the past, particularly those of a psychosexual nature, and attempt to resolve guilt reactions that arise from these conflicts. He surveys the individual's fund of sexual information, *taking nothing for granted,* and orientates him correctly from a mature and objective point of view. As part of the broader aspect of counseling, he inquires into the whole concept of marriage itself held by the person who consults him; he looks into the depth of understanding and tolerance existing between the two prospective partners and into the purposefulness with which they view their future lives.

This mutual evaluation of each other's potentialities and limitations does much to eliminate the "moonlight and roses" concept of marriage where, once the marriage ceremony is performed, the couple is expected to "live happily ever after." Marriage is to be viewed as a dynamic relationship between two people, with rough spots as well as smooth spots to be realistically anticipated. Tolerance, understanding, and good humor are more valuable assets in marriage than a starry-eyed idealization of the other partner. Occasionally the counselor will encounter in one or both prospective partners emotional maladjustments that demand long-term treatment. He would do well under such circumstances to advise postponement of the marriage until such hazardous factors have been adequately treated. If the counselor is not himself a psychiatrist, referral to such a specialist is in order.

THE OSTRICH ATTITUDE TOWARD SEX

American society has long maintained an ostrich-like attitude toward sex. In a typical family sex is rarely, if ever, mentioned in the home. There is a widespread fallacious belief that by ignoring the subject completely— pretending that it does not exist—the problem is thereby eradicated. Parents naïvely believe that preadolescent children are sexless and that the longer they can be kept so, by keeping them in a sexual vacuum, the better. They fail to recall the active curiosity, the early outcropping of sexual drive, and the various types of sex play which characterized their own childhood. Such memories are pushed aside, as they are disturbing, because of the inadequacies in sex education passed on to them by their own parents, and are replaced by this bland, wishful-thinking concept of childhood "innocence." This unrealistic attitude exists not only in parent-child relationships. It is present also between adults in our supposedly grown-up world. Even in the most intimate and personal of human relationships—marriage—we only rarely find a frank and open discussion of problems of sex.

This is a cultural pattern which permeates, to varying degrees, all strata of American society. It is based on a curious confusion of sex with obscenity. There is a feeling that there is something intrinsically evil about sex. The highest type of life has been held to be one in which all sexual thought and all sexual expression are eliminated. We have inherited this concept from creeds and dogmas many centuries old. Despite any superimposed intellectualizations to the contrary, there is still a basic feeling in our culture that sex is bad.

Such a deeply rooted attitude cannot be lightly set aside. The alteration of this cultural pattern constitutes the greatest challenge in the preventive aspects of marriage counseling. So long as this pattern remains, the counselor is handicapped at every level of his work. He would like to see a wholesome type of sex education start in infancy rather than at a premarital level. He would like to see parents so orientated in the norms of sexual behavior of infants and children that the costly mistakes arising from unwise parental handling of sexual problems would never be made. He would like to see a thoughtful system of sex education integrated into the school system from primary grades onward, each integration being in terms of the child's stage of development at the time. These desires are, however, far from being realized. A start has been made, as the sections in this book dealing with sex education indicate, but it is an uphill fight. We are still up against this cultural pattern: "There is something intrinsically bad about sex." Because of this there is a dead weight of resistance in most religious, educational, and political circles to any program sponsoring the wider dissemination of scientifically orientated sexual information. With such widespread resistance, progress will be slow and uneven.

What would our country be like in a few years if every child were to be brought up with a completely healthy attitude toward sex? Some people would shudder at the thought. In such a situation they could only imagine a state of utter sexual license. They would say that once the repressive bonds were lifted there would be no limit to all forms and varieties of sexual activity. I believe that just the opposite would be the case. I believe that with an optimum system of sex education man (and woman) would be more mature, more socially orientated in sexual expression than ever before. There would be far less prostitution, far less venereal disease. Illegitimacy, juvenile delinquency, and crimes of sexual passion would decrease. We would have, I am sure, a far less neurotic society because of the increased closeness and understanding in parent-child and teacher-child relationships. Such children would reach maturity without having painful lessons to unlearn. They would be more grown-up than preceding generations and more capable of becoming responsible citizens in the modern world. This lessening of inner conflicts in the sexually integrated individual would diminish his aggressive tendencies and would make for a more peace-loving society. Yet everywhere there is resistance, individual and organized, to bringing such a program to pass.

The contention that such benefits would follow from such a widespread system of sex education is based on the belief that the more man knows about himself the better he is able to cope with his various instinctive drives and to lead a life on a more truly mature level. Knowledge is power in this field as in many others. Man has spent centuries gathering knowledge about the world around him and has only recently turned the spotlight of attention upon himself. This spotlight must be one based on facts, not theory, and one which calls on findings gathered through the use of scientific method.

A RESEARCH STUDY ON SEX LIFE

The outstanding example of objective factual data gathered in the field of sex is the series of studies being made by Dr. Alfred C. Kinsey and his associates at Indiana University. With grants from the Medical Division of the National Research Council and the Medical Division of the Rockefeller Foundation, this series will ultimately report on the sex behavior of 100,000 individuals of both sexes, of all age groups, of all social, economic, and educational levels, chosen from all geographical areas of the United States.

The first two volumes of this series of nine contemplated volumes have already been published—i.e., *Sexual Behavior in the Human Male* (1948) and *Sexual Behavior in the Human Female* (1953). A storm of controversy has followed their publication. Critics have questioned the validity of the findings, claiming that there are defects in the statistical methods employed and in the types of individuals studied. Many outstanding scientists, however, who have closely followed Dr. Kinsey's work from its beginning, are convinced as to its validity and as to its unique and immense value in indicating the range and variety of sex activity in contemporary America. Out of these findings is emerging a true picture of how people in this country actually behave sexually. Only upon such a factual basis can a valid program of sex education be founded.

HOW THE MARRIAGE COUNSELOR HELPS

Postmaritally the counselor is often confronted with the problem of belatedly offering guidance which would much better have been sought prior to marriage. The diversity and complexity of many of these postmarital problems are ably discussed by a number of the contributors to this book. Many postmarital conflicts are remediable in the hands of a skilled counselor, but the principle still holds that the longer the problem has been in existence the greater the task of treatment. There is a need for early consultation before the pattern has become crystallized, for it may become so fixed that counseling is of no avail. When after ample study this proves to be the case, the counselor still has a service to perform. It is within his province to discuss with the individual or with both partners to the marriage the question of the wisest course to pursue in an irremediable situation. Often the best available answer is divorce.

DIVORCE

The marriage counselor does not like divorce. His concern is with helping people to make their marriages really work. But at times circumstances are too heavily weighted against success. To continue to struggle against such odds, to insist stubbornly on trying to hold together a marriage which is bursting apart at every seam, is the act of a zealot, not of a scientist.

The counselor can do much, however, to ease the impact of divorce on the couple concerned and help them to agree on the procedure to be followed. The rancors, the tensions, the accusations and counteraccusations that are so prevalent in divorce actions can often be largely avoided with the help of a competent counselor. His role is to help the two people to face the fact that their marriage has failed beyond hope of repair, that it must be terminated and terminated in as fair and as mutually considerate a manner as possible. He can also help them to understand the causes of this failure, to grow and to mature by passing through this experience, and to become potentially better candidates for some marriage in the future. In so doing the counselor is rendering a real service.

The counselor may also be called upon to render skilled assistance in helping people to adjust to the current complexity of economic and vocational demands. However, there are many more sources of help available for these types of problems. Social agencies, vocational advisers, economic specialists, plus a vast array of technical literature, may be consulted outside of the marriage-counseling field. The counselor should, however, be well orientated in these subjects and should be ready to give help in them when needed. He should also be familiar with matters related to fertility and sterility and should have a working knowledge of gynecological and urological conditions. Much of such work he will refer to appropriate professional colleagues, but he must himself be sensitive to indications for referral.

A counselor is not intuitively prepared to handle the wide range of difficulties presented to him. There is an imperative need for specialization in training for counseling. Recent developments in this training program have indicated that undergraduate work with a firm foundation in the social sciences is of primary value. This should be followed by training on a graduate level with specific reference to the demands of this new specialized field. It is particularly important that the counselor have expert knowledge of the anatomy, physiology, and psychology of human sex behavior.

It has been found feasible to consider the personal qualifications of the potential counselor during his period of undergraduate work and to rule out early those aspirants who are obviously lacking in their own adjustments and who are incapable of objectivity of approach, of inspiring confidence, or of maintaining the human approach in interpersonal relationships. It is still a moot question whether marital status is a prerequisite to marriage counseling, but it would seem logical that those seeking counsel would prefer to deal with a person who has experienced marriage and parenthood. Short cuts to training are dangerous and are not to be encouraged. Particularly to be deplored are correspondence courses in marriage counseling (which actually exist!), which give their ill-trained "graduates" an opening to set themselves up as "therapists."

I refer in the previous paragraph to the non-medical counselor. It should be stressed, however, that the medical man is not qualified as a counselor just on the strength of his M.D. degree. He, too, requires a broader background than is at present obtainable in medical schools in order to be sensitive to the special needs of this field.

Granted the availability of competent counselors, there is still the question of what types of organizations can best render counseling service. This requires a careful consideration of the needs of the area to be served. The co-operation of the local community must be enlisted in a program which takes into consideration the social standards of both majority and minority groups. In some instances it may prove more feasible to create such a service within already existing community services rather than build an entirely new organization. In any event, the counselor and his organization must be thoroughly familiar with local sources of referral for problems exceeding the specialty of marriage counseling.

In a recent survey of creditable marriage-counseling facilities in the United States, the American Association of Marriage Counselors has found a dearth, in proportion to the need, of both trained counselors and organized services. This is not surprising when one considers that marriage counseling as a specialty is comparatively new and that the opportunities for the training of counselors at graduate levels are rare. A further handicap has been the lack of standardization of criteria for adequate counseling and a lack of uniformity in organization. Because of this want of a yardstick for acceptable counseling, there has been ovelapping of services in communities instead of an efficient co-ordination of all community endeavors.

QUALIFICATIONS FOR MARRIAGE COUNSELORS

In 1949 a Joint Sub-Committee on Standards for Marriage Counselors, made up of representatives from the American Association of Marriage Counselors and the National Council on Family Relations, submitted recommendations for the training of marriage counselors of the future. This report stated:

Marriage counseling is here regarded as a specialized field of family counseling which centers largely on the interpersonal relationship between husband and wife. It involves many disciplines and is interprofessional in character. Those who wish to enter this field however, whether physician, clergyman, psychiatrist, or social worker, require a common body of scientific knowledge, techniques, and qualifications.

Standards for acceptable and recognized marriage counselors are herewith presented in terms of:

1. ACADEMIC TRAINING
2. PROFESSIONAL EXPERIENCE AND QUALIFICATION
3. PERSONAL QUALIFICATIONS

1. ACADEMIC TRAINING
   a. Every marriage counselor shall have a graduate or professional degree from an approved institution as a minimum qualification. This degree shall be in one of the following fields:

Education	*Psychology*
Home Economics	*Religion*
Law	*Social Anthropology*
Medicine	*Social Work*
Nursing	*Sociology*

b. Whatever the field of major emphasis, there shall be included accredited training in:

 Psychology of personality development and interpersonal relations
 Elements of psychiatry
 Human biology, including the fundamentals of sex anatomy, physiology, and
  genetics
 Sociology of marriage and the family
 Legal aspects of marriage and the family
 Counseling techniques

2. PROFESSIONAL EXPERIENCE AND QUALIFICATIONS

 a. The candidate shall have had at least three years of recognized professional experience subsequent to obtaining his degree.

 In addition, he shall have had actual experience as a clinical assistant in marriage counseling under approved supervision.

 b. A candidate's qualifications shall include: (1) Diagnostic skill in differentiating between the superficial and the deeper-level types of maladjustment and the ability to recognize when the latter type requires referral to other specialists. (2) A scientific attitude toward individual variation and deviation, especially in the field of human sex behavior, and the ability to discuss sexual problems objectively.

3. PERSONAL QUALIFICATIONS

 a. The candidate shall possess personal and professional integrity in accordance with accepted ethical standards.

 b. The candidate shall have an attitude of interest, warmth, and kindness toward people, combined with a high degree of integration and emotional maturity.

 c. The personal experience of marriage and parenthood is a decided asset.

It is vitally important that the counselor should have no platform of his own toward which he tries to lead his clients. He should see their problems in the light of their own backgrounds. Maintaining a non-moralistic attitude of acceptance of individual variations, his role is to help them to work out solutions particularly geared to their own needs and circumstances. To do so requires a close working relationship between a clear head and a warm heart.

A glance at the advertising columns in the press, current magazines, or classified telephone directories, or a turn of a radio dial, indicates the number of people who stand ready to solve one's problems. A recent study[1] has shown these so-called "counselors" to be largely ignorant and commercially minded people who are fattening on the woes of American society. These studies also indicate that the majority of problems brought to such people are related to love and marriage. The self-styled "specialists" and

---

[1]Lee R. Steiner, *Where Do People Take Their Troubles?*, Boston, Houghton Mifflin Co., 1945.

"consultants" who are capitalizing on the unlicensed field of psychological practice are a motley crew—marriage brokers, astrologists, graphologists, palmists, spiritualists, numerologists, and even beauticians who claim they "cure" inferiority complexes. This study is cited as an objective indication of the number of people seeking help on personal problems in America today. For such a large number of dishonest or incompetent "counselors" of all types to flourish, there must be a vast clientele.

Counseling services of an accredited nature are thinly distributed in the United States. They are to be found mainly along the Eastern seaboard, in the large centers of the Midwest, and along the West Coast, but many areas comprising many hundreds of square miles in other parts of the country are completely without resources. It is no wonder, therefore, that so many people respond to the extravagant promises of advice and help found in advertising columns.

It is understood that none of the contributors to this book is regimented in writing, so that some variants in points of view and some overlapping of material are to be found. In addition, there are inevitable and often regrettable limitations on candid discussion of some intimate elements of psychosexual behavior in a volume not limited to professional and scientific circles. Such restrictions on full frankness in facing actualities will remain until a new generation insists on completely straight talk.

With this paucity of available services in relationship to a much greater demand for qualified counseling, the value of informative literature in this field is at once apparent.

At one time it might have been thought that repressive laws would have an undesirable impact on books such as this. But in recent years, the courts have correctly taken their cue from physicians and other experts in the field. They have held in a series of outstanding opinions that:

". . . accurate information, rather than mystery and curiosity, is better in the long run and is less likely to occasion lascivious thoughts and ignorance and anxiety . . . . We have held that an exposition of the relevant facts of the sex side of life in decent language and in manifestly serious and disinterested spirit cannot ordinarily be regarded as obscene."

It is to be hoped that this book will find wide circulation. It can be of help to the counselor, the student counselor, and especially to the person in need who has no one to whom to turn. Such a person may learn for the first time from the pages of this book that his problem is not unique to him alone. It is remarkable how frequently in counseling one encounters this concept of "uniqueness" and how often the reassurance as to the actual commonplaceness of the problem will have a therapeutic effect.

In the practical discussions of the many phases of married life the reader may find many leads for the working out of a better adjustment. This will be particularly true if husband and wife will both read the book and then discuss it together. By so doing a situation which may have been passed over in silence between them may be brought out, with all the resultant benefits coming from such mutual facing of a common problem. Many couples are so basically uncommunicative in regard to fundamental elements in their married life! With its many approaches to the marriage-counseling field, more than have ever before been contained within the cover of one book, this volume may act as a catalyst in bringing areas of difficulty out into the open so that the couple, perhaps for the first time, is in a position to deal with them effectively.

The contributors to this book have made recognized contributions in their own fields and are thoroughly competent to present the material offered. In addition to their professional standing, they are known among their colleagues for their factual accuracy, their progressive thinking, and a humility of approach to the responsibilities incurred in serving individuals in their most personal needs.

Preface

Thirty-four out of every one hundred marriages end in divorce. Many such divorces are preventable, undesirable, and unnecessary. In developing this book and in editing it I have had the aid of Professor Ernest W. Burgess, with whom I have been more or less associated at the University of Chicago. He participated in the selection of authors and in passing on the manuscripts as they were prepared. His advice was invaluable in choosing authoritative writers who were widely known for their published research on the topics assigned to them.

Marriage counseling is essentially a new profession but one which, nevertheless, is rapidly advancing. Sex education is one of its most important departments. Marriage counseling involves sociological, psychological, and physiological problems.

In the past marriage counseling was primarily a function of clergymen, doctors, and lawyers. Recent years have seen the growth of so-called marriage-counseling centers, including, for example, the Association for Family Living in Chicago, and the consultation centers in New York and in Philadelphia.

This book is developed, as will be apparent from the table of contents, in various parts devoted to specific phases of the whole problem. Both logically and chronologically it begins with a statement concerning the profession of marriage counseling, considers next the questions that arise related to falling in love, choosing a mate, and marriage. The book then considers the sexual problems of marriage and describes the anatomical and functional considerations, also the necessary premarital examinations—both physical and psychological. Another section concerns disturbances of married life, then conception, pregnancy, and childbirth. A fourth part is concerned with the child in the family, and the fifth portion with the many social problems that disturb marriage from many points of view. While material on certain phases of marriage is presented in an objective fashion, it is acknowledged that the moral aspects are also important.

The volume is in no sense of the word intended as propaganda in behalf of any other objective than successful marriage. The persistent increase in divorce indicates, as already mentioned, that at least one third of marriages now contracted are not successful. The percentage is too great for continued maintenance of the family as the center of life and living; maintenance of the family is basic to continuation of democracy in our government.

In the editing of the volume we have been greatly aided by Robert W. Laidlaw, Robert L. Dickinson, and Abraham Stone.

MORRIS FISHBEIN, M.D.

1954

Successful Marriage

PART ONE

Preparation for Marriage

Chapter 1

HOW CAN YOU TELL IF IT IS LOVE?

by Henry A. Bowman, Ph.D.

CHAIRMAN, DIVISION OF HOME AND FAMILY LIVING, STEPHENS COLLEGE, COLUMBIA, MISSOURI

WHY THE QUESTION ARISES

Marriage, as we know it in the United States today, is different from the marriage of the not-too-distant past; for some years marriage has been changing. The changes apparently involve the way the marriage works out, rather than the form, although the instability of modern marriage is relatively new.

Marriage was formerly an association between two people—in which the economic, reproductive, protective, and societal aspects were most important —with the personal relationship between husband and wife also important but secondary. Nowadays there is a tendency to consider personal relationships and satisfactions of first importance, with the other aspects of marriage relegated to a secondary position. Marriage is moving from an association of unequals to an association of equals. The husband is no longer the master, the "head of the house" in the old sense of the term.

When marriage was consummated under previous conditions, the prerequisites for success were, with the exception of ability to have children, readily observable before the wedding by the prospective spouses, their families and friends. It was relatively easy to measure these requirements. The man's social status, ambition, economic condition and prospects, conduct and moral standards, and his stability were readily observable. The woman's domestic inclinations and ability and her social behavior were equally apparent. The preparation that either sex needed for marriage was afforded by the family life, home activities, folkways, and mores of the group in which they lived.

Today, with primary emphasis on the personal relationship of husband and wife, the picture has changed. The prerequisites for success in marriage are not readily obvious. They are not measurable in the light of accepted factors. Judgment has become highly individualized. It rests in large part upon the attitudes, tastes, and emotional responses of the parties concerned. Parents and friends play a minor role. Folkways and mores play a part, but these are changing. Family life and domestic activities do not contribute to the individual's preparation for marriage in the way they formerly did. The old factors that counted in marriage, like home and family and emphasis upon stability, are not now dominant. Increased freedom of individual choice stimulates young people's aspirations, colors their idealism, and influences their judgments without furnishing adequate means for distinguishing between real and counterfeit prerequisites for successful marriage.

With the guideposts of the past no longer adequate and contemporary guideposts not yet clearly established, many young people are raising queries about love. In one form or another they are asking: How can a person tell whether or not he is really in love? How can he distinguish between love and infatuation? Is there such a thing as love at first sight? Can you love two or more persons at the same time? Is love the one and only basis for marriage? Do most people fall out of love soon after the wedding? Are there any people who cannot fall in love?

What young people are asking is: With marriage considered primarily a personal relationship between husband and wife, with love considered the first prerequisite for success in that relationship, with nothing to guide him, in the last analysis and in making the final decision, except his own judgments of his own responses, how can anyone determine whether or not he has this essential prerequisite? This serious question deserves serious consideration. Modern young people are to be commended for asking it so frequently, for it indicates an attitude toward marriage and the means of making it succeed for which they are not always given credit.

The question is difficult even for a marriage counselor; frequently the person who asks it wants a simple, ready-made answer, or he wants the counselor to make a judgment. But a simple, ready-made answer is impossible. There is no formula, no sleight of hand, no ability to foresee the future by which the question may be answered. Ultimately the solution depends on self-analysis. You must make your own judgment. A counselor cannot make it for you.

How, then, can you tell whether or not you are in love? There are several things you may do in attempting to solve the problem, but there is no way of guaranteeing that you will arrive at an answer if you do them. First, you may analyze yourself to determine, if possible, whether or not it is likely that you are prepared to fall in love at all. Second, you may be sure that you understand the differences between love and infatuation. Third, you may examine the contemporary social scene and attempt to determine the degree to which factors in it have influenced your thinking. Fourth, you may analyze yourself in the light of certain questions and conditions that may play a part in your decision.

PERSONS NOT PREPARED TO FALL IN LOVE

Romantic love, the love into which we fall, the love that prefaces and carries over into marriage, is distinguished from other types of love— filial, parental, brotherly—by the fact that it grows out of an awareness of and response to sex differences. Its focus is a person of opposite sex who is considered an outlet for sexual urges, a stimulator of sexual responses, and an objective of marital aspirations. It leads to a profound and permeating type of sharing found in its most fully developed form only in the marriage relationship. There are persons who are not likely to be in love, in this sense of the term, although they may exhibit some of the superficial, external symptoms or are themselves inclined to place the label of love on their own emotional experiences.

The exceedingly immature person is that type. He may consider himself deeply in love. He may manifest the stereotyped pattern of behavior, phraseology, letter writing, idealizing. Yet his immaturity suggests that his experience has been so limited, his knowledge of the opposite sex and of marriage so meager, and his attitudes so undeveloped that he is infatuated rather than in love. Sometimes the violence of the throes of his emotions contraindicates love. This is usually called "puppy love."

The person who is a victim of a parent fixation—too deeply attached to a parent—cannot readily love anyone else, since he "loves" only his parent and does that in infantile fashion. He may seem to love someone who resembles the parent or who may become a substitute for his parent. In so doing, however, he merely transfers his "love" from his parent to the other person; he does not fall in love with the other person.

The narcissistic individual, whose "love" is turned in upon himself, so that in a sense he is both subject and object of it, cannot readily love another person. If he seems to do so, it may be only because the other person's attractiveness, devotion, favorable responses, and complimentary remarks are a mirror in which he sees himself reflected.

The person who has a predatory or exploitive attitude toward members of the opposite sex cannot easily experience true love. In such a case the other person is not a love object in the better sense of the term; rather the other person is a means of self-gratification. The person who has never learned to share may fall into a similar category. The person who, because of fear of sex, marriage, or the opposite sex, hesitates to "let himself go" can hardly share sufficiently to be in love. Yet such a person may exhibit the outward symptoms of love because he is eager to fit into the social pattern.

Anyone who feels inferior, insecure, or unattractive may have a strong desire to love and be loved. Whenever any interest in him is shown by a member of the opposite sex, he hastily concludes that he is in love. Without being fully aware of it, he is afraid that each manifestation of such interest may be the last. This makes his love of a compulsive nature. Hidden deeply within him is "I must love somebody, but I am afraid no one will love me." Nearer the surface this becomes "I must love this person." At the surface it becomes "I do love this person."

A person in rebellion against his parents or eager to escape an unpleasant situation may leap to a hasty conclusion that love is the solution to his problem, when actually he is not in condition either to fall in love or to make a judgment about it. A person who has been disappointed in love and soon thereafter transfers his feelings toward the first person to a second person is not thereby in love with the second. Such a person must recover from his unhappy experience before he can fall in love again. His judgments made on the rebound are not likely to be sound.

A person whose leanings toward his own sex are stronger than his leanings toward the other sex can hardly fall in love as a first step toward marriage. Whether such leanings represent retarded emotional development or a full-fledged homosexual fixation, true love of someone of the opposite sex is excluded, at least for the time being.

LOVE AND INFATUATION

In attempting to distinguish between love and infatuation, one of the first considerations is that of time. Love is not a separate entity, something that exists independently of the personalities involved. It is not something that may suddenly be attached to them or patched upon the pattern of their lives. Love is an attribute of two personalities which bear a relationship one to the other. It is an outgrowth of their association with and appraisal of each other. Every living thing that grows is subject to the influence of time, and love is no exception. Love implies a reorientation of each personality with the other as a new focal point. It grows out of association in a variety of circumstances and an estimate of all a person's known characteristics. Infatuation, however, may come suddenly. It is the result of attaching self-generated feelings to another person, of projecting ideals upon him, of oversimplifying the elements in the association of the two individuals. It may result from contact in relatively few situations, or even only one. It may be an outgrowth of an estimate based upon only a few of the other party's attributes.

Love tends to produce a feeling of oneness on the part of the couple. They tend to feel identified with each other. A boy or girl who is infatuated tends to think of the other party as a means of self-gratification. Since love tends to produce this "pairness," this oneness, this sense of identification, genuine love is centered upon only one person. It cannot be divided between two persons so that the person loves them simultaneously. I have found in counseling people about marriage that the one who claims to be in love with two persons is usually not in love with either and frequently marries a third person not in question at the time the problem of love is raised.

Love tends to give the person who is in love a sense of security and trust when the total situation and the other person's total personality are considered. It does this because when such an appraisal is made the assets outweigh the liabilities. The latter are assimilated into the thinking of the person making the appraisal. Infatuation tends to produce a false sense of security based upon wishful thinking. At times, also, infatuation produces a sense of insecurity that may manifest itself as jealousy.

Since love is other-person-centered, the person in love tends to direct his behavior toward the welfare and happiness of the other party. Their future relationship together is considered in part an opportunity to contribute to the loved one's happiness. Since infatuation tends to be self-centered, the infatuated person often loses his ambition and his interest in the ordinary affairs of life. The infatuated one becomes absorbed in daydreaming about the other party or in contemplation of his own misery at being separated from the one with whom he is infatuated. This self-centeredness also tends to produce a feeling of urgency in connection with getting married and an inclination to set aside or gloss over possible barriers to the wedding. A couple in love may greatly desire marriage, but they are willing to allow sufficient time for preparation. They face and try to solve the problems that may stand in the way of their getting married. They do not evade them.

It is impossible to be completely objective and impersonal regarding a loved one. There is always some idealization, more of course in some cases than in others. When a couple are in love, however, the idealization tends to grow out of their relationship and their estimate of each other. When a couple are infatuated the idealization tends to be projected onto the other person.

"The path of true love never runs smoothly," says the old adage, and there may be some truth in it. All couples have their "ups and downs" during the period that their love is growing. One by one they are solving the problems of adjustment that are inevitable in their relationship. Love, however, tends to be a dynamic, living, growing thing. It also tends to be durable and lasting. When it changes, as it does in some cases, the change tends to be the result of alterations in the personality or behavior of the other person. Infatuation, being the outgrowth of self-generated feelings and attitudes, may change suddenly and without any apparent reason. The one who is infatuated may suddenly feel repulsed by, rather than attracted to, the other, although the latter has not changed.

An expression of affection has more meaning when a couple are in love and often comes relatively late in their association. A couple who are infatuated may express affection very early in their association. Their affection tends to be an end in itself rather than a symbol of what they mean to each other.

INFLUENCE OF SOCIAL FACTORS

There are certain factors in our modern society that play a part in making it more than ordinarily difficult for the young person to distinguish between love and infatuation. One of these factors is the current over-emphasis upon premarital romance and upon sex appeal. Books, magazines, plays, radio, television, and movies help to keep these emphases alive. Young people are given the impression that the prerequisites for love are largely physical and that they may be recognized shortly after two persons meet. The other qualities that contribute to successful marriage are either not taken into account or are assumed to be identical with those that are involved in physical appeal. Screen personalities are both a reflection of and a pattern for the particular types of youthful beauty considered to be most highly desirable and against which many potential boy or girl friends, fiancés and spouses must compete. Young people who cannot distinguish clearly between "reel" life and "real" life assume that, if the superficial aspects of their relationship resemble those of admired stars in the "movies," the great gaps of preparation, experience, and growth will somehow be filled in for them. The demands of dramatization take care of these factors in the motion pictures.

The current world situation is a factor leading some persons to confuse infatuation and love. In the face of this situation many young people have a tendency to be pessimistic about the future. Military service may interrupt a boy's education and may occur at a time when he feels he is at the age for marriage. Thus young couples must choose among three alternatives: (1) marry before the boy enters military service; (2) marry while he is in the service; (3) postpone marriage until he is discharged, perhaps even until he completes his education. The last involves a long delay during which there may be relatively little opportunity for contact and thus for getting better acquainted, while there is ample possibility that the couple may lose interest in each other and drift apart. Thought of this contributes to a sense of insecurity. This, in turn, leads many young people to want to "nail down" their relationship as soon as possible. Hence it is not surprising that some of them leap to the conclusion that any emotional response they have toward each other must be love. If circumstances do not provide the time and opportunity for love to develop, then it becomes easy to rationalize and to assume that love can develop in a shorter period and with less acquaintance.

Let us speculate on another rather subtle part that the military situation may play in leading young men to confuse infatuation and love. Many young men anticipate military service with regret, dislike, disgust, even fear. A term of service, coming as it does "in the middle of everything," an imposition on a young man's life and involving the upset of his pattern of living, so often unrelated to anything in his civilian life either preceding it or following it, and usually anticipated with anything but eagerness and pleasure, in a sense constitutes a crisis, especially as the young man looks forward to it. In times of stress, of crisis, it is not unusual for people to fall back upon relatively primitive and elemental urges, desires, and behavior. With the typical young man's sexual urge rather prominent in his life anyway, thus making it difficult for him to distinguish between physical appeal and love, this problem is intensified under the stress of crisis produced by the military situation.

OTHER CONSIDERATIONS

The Loved One's Relationship to Other People. A person is unlikely to fall in love if he has a parent fixation, if he is retarded in his emotional development to the point of preferring the company of members of his own sex, or if he has definite homosexual tendencies. Sometimes girls or boys will say that they are in love, yet at times prefer the company of some other person of the same sex as themselves rather than the loved one. This makes it doubtful that they are really in love.

The judgments of other people are important. If the loved one is not liked or accepted by your friends or family, it may be because the friends and family do not know him well enough to like him in spite of his apparent unattractive qualities. In addition they may appraise him more objectively and without romantic or amorous coloring; therefore, their evaluation may be more nearly correct.

If you have an attitude of what might be termed "temporary permanence" concerning the love object, this may indicate that true love does not exist. If, for example, you feel that the other person is "at the head of the list" at the moment but are not sure that he will remain there because each new attractive person is considered a possible competitor, then it may be doubted that the reorientation of your thinking and the refocusing of your urges have progressed sufficiently to establish love.

Since true love is other-person-centered and is considered a highly private matter, there is doubt about the love of a person who carelessly and chronically lets intimate details become public property through unrestrained conversation, uncontrolled reading of letters, or conspicuous necking or petting.

The Relation of Love to Things Connected with the Loved One. In a case in which anyone expressed certainty of being in love yet is hesitant about letting friends or family meet the loved one and is occasionally ashamed of the loved one's manners, language, appearance, or ideas, the presence of true love may be questioned. Moreover, many young people confuse their attitude toward wealth, the excitement generated by expensive gifts, new cars, promises of travel, the prestige of family or position with love.

Negative, Critical, or Doubtful Elements in the Couple's Relationship. All couples have some conflict at some stage in their relationship. The presence of conflict, as such, is not so important in determining love as the nature of the conflict, the sources from which it rises, its frequency or duration, and the means used to resolve it. The way you make up after a quarrel or difference, the means by which your relationship is re-established, furthered, or blocked, the degree to which you hold grudges, who takes the initiative, who makes concessions, are all significant. Conflict taking the form of surface skirmishes over inconsequentials is less important than conflict of longer duration over fundamentals, unless the frequency of the "spats" becomes a problem in itself. In that case the apparent causes are probably only precipitating causes. They bear the same relation to the basic cause of the conflict that a trigger bears to the shooting of a bullet.

I have already mentioned the compulsive nature of love in some instances. There is also the type of case in which a person "fights against" love. In such an instance there may be a tug of war between physical appeal and intelligent judgment, and the presence of love may be doubted.

In counseling people about marriage I often see young persons who say they are in love, yet catalogue fault after fault of the other party with the assertion that such faults will make no difference in marriage or will readily be changed or else they cannot be accepted. In such cases the faults are merely listed; they are not assimilated into the thinking of the person concerned. Hence only a fraction of the other person is the object of love.

The Concept of Roles. To love another person you must be able to conceive of that person and yourself as working out a pattern of life that is acceptable to both. To an acceptable degree the other person must fit your concept of the role to be played in marriage by a person of that sex. If, for example, a man conceives of the role of the wife in terms of full-time home-making, child-rearing, a complementary relationship between husband and wife, his apparent falling in love with a woman who disliked homemaking, wanted no children, insisted upon combining career and marriage would be open to question. In such a case it would be unlikely that he was in love with a total personality. In counseling I have encountered many instances in which a girl has a rather clear-cut concept of the husband's role in marriage, thinking of it in terms of support, stability, economic ambition, thoughtfulness and consideration, love of home and children, yet says she is in love with a boy whose characteristics are exactly opposed to the items mentioned.

The Pattern of Development of the Couple's Relationship. In order to determine the presence or absence of love, more is needed than a cross section of the couple's feelings and relationship at a given moment. How they arrived at their present attitudes, feelings, relation to each other is also important. The order in which steps in the development of their relationship were taken is significant. Whether a couple's relationship has grown through repeated contacts relatively close together or has grown through infrequent contacts with the intervening periods "filled in" by the imagination, wishful thinking, and idealizing is an important consideration.

The Interests and Activities Associated with the Other Person. When a couple seem to have common interests that constitute one of the factors drawing them together and making them attractive one to the other, it is important to know when and why these interests developed. They may have been individual interests before association made them common. They may be bona fide outgrowths of the couple's association. They may represent an interest in each other of such nature that each adopts the other's interests. They may represent merely apparently acceptable excuses for being together. They may represent a confusion of interest in each other with interest in each other's interests. In each case there will be a difference in the durability of the interests and in their value as one partial criterion for determining love.

Elements in Environment. The effect of crisis on the individual's love and the couple's relationship is important. If a crisis tends to draw them more closely together and give them a sense of security in each other's presence and trust, this fact may indicate love. If, on the other hand, a crisis seems to drive them apart or if during the crisis each reacts as an isolated person with nothing gained from their mutual love and trust, this fact may suggest the absence of love.

Without overemphasizing the physical aspects of their relationship, a couple in love tend to have sufficient resources to make their association interesting, stimulating, and satisfying without "external" stimuli. If a couple become bored, dissatisfied, "lost," disinterested unless there are "external" stimuli, such as other people, music, movies, dancing, to maintain their interest, the presence of love may be questioned.

An individual is an entity. He has, or perhaps it would be more nearly accurate to say *is,* one personality. Yet under different circumstances he may exhibit different traits or play different roles. For example, he reacts in one way when he is ill, in another way when he is well; in one way at work, another at play. He assumes one role with his family, another with friends of his own sex, another with his fiancée. If love has seemed to grow through association under only one or few types of circumstance, we may wonder whether the boy and girl can know each other's total personality well enough to make the over-all judgments necessary for love to be established.

Location Relative to Each Other. Love tends to be constant whether the couple are separated or together, because love rests upon a broader base than merely physical presence or physical appeal. If an individual seems to be in love when he is with the other party but seems to be less in love when they are separated for a period, it may indicate that when they are together overwhelming physical appeal beclouds judgment and overshadows other considerations, while when they are separated judgment is more objective and the physical element is less intense. If the reverse is true and they seem to be more in love when separated and less when together, it may indicate that during separation there is too much idealization, while when they are together a more accurate appraisal of personal traits is possible.

Because of military service or attendance at different colleges or other circumstances making for temporary separations, there are numerous instances in which a couple are apparently in love when they part, only to find themselves doubtful, seemingly unacquainted, embarrassed, when they are reunited months or years later. In the meantime, however, there has been little or no indication of change. The reason is probably that love had not developed before the parting, that during the separation idealization was substituted for personal contact, and that at reunion there is a quick reappraisal of each other against a background of new experience. Hence there is disillusionment.

The Role of the Counselor. Finally, only the person himself can determine whether or not he is in love. No simple, numerically scored test can give a cut-and-dried answer. No simple formula can solve the problem. A marriage counselor may help define the problem, may give an opportunity for talking about it, may suggest ways to analyze yourself; but a counselor cannot make final judgment. In some cases the marriage counselor may, in his own thinking, decide that the one seeking advice is probably not in love, but a counselor cannot decide that an individual *is* in love, nor can he help the person much by expressing his judgment.

When you decide that you are in love and get married on the basis of your decision you are taking part in one of the most important processes of your entire life. The decision should never be approached lightly or be based upon ignorance. Young people take it seriously. Marriage counselors should do likewise. If a problem is considered serious enough to be brought to a marriage counselor's attention, no matter what the problem may be it is *ipso facto* serious enough to be given careful and sincere attention. The marriage counselor who labels such a problem "silly," who laughs at the young person in the throes of "puppy love," who gives dogmatic answers to questions about love, or who resorts to such evasions as "It's up to you" or "If you have thought it through and considered all angles, use your own judgment" is not counseling in any accepted sense of the term. Many young people are afraid they will be thought silly. "Puppy love" can be a trying and painful experience. Dogmatic answers can never be individualized, and they suggest lack of understanding, overconfidence, or "moralizing." Evasions add nothing that the hesitant person did not know before he came for a conference.

The marriage counselor may assist the young person in defining the problem. He may give assurance that an intelligent solution is possible and that the doubtful one is not the victim of powers beyond his control. The counselor may encourage the young person to wait or to delay a decision, if this is indicated. If the one seeking advice is in a vicious circle of indecision because he is trying to reach a conclusion with insufficient data, he may be encouraged to get more data through experience and contact with the other person, and while doing so to suspend judgment. The counselor may assure the boy or girl that, if what he experiences is true love, it can stand both analysis and the passage of time. If it is not true love, the sooner this fact is discovered, the better.

Chapter 2

THE WISE CHOICE OF A MATE

by *Ernest W. Burgess, Ph.D.*
PROFESSOR EMERITUS OF SOCIOLOGY, UNIVERSITY OF CHICAGO

You make two great choices in life: one, the selection of a profession or trade; the other, the choice of a mate. When you decide on a profession, business, or trade, you usually act rationally; you try to secure all the training and education necessary or feasible in order to prepare yourself for it.

When you marry, however, you are likely to behave in a romantic rather than a practical way. Some people still believe that success in marriage is guided by Providence; to others, the whole procedure appears to be a great gamble. Most people still regard marriage as a romantic experience through which a man or woman is mated with his affinity. Only a few today utilize science as a guide to the wise choice of a mate. Almost no one considers preparation necessary for success in marriage in the same serious and thorough way as for a trade or profession.

In earlier times in many countries, marriages were based on prudential considerations. Parents, rather than young people, arranged marriages. They limited the union of their children to partners of the same social class and to those who belonged to the same cultural, educational, and religious groups. Parents rated economic considerations high; the bridegroom was frequently much older than the bride. In some countries of the Orient, the young people might not even see each other before marriage or, at most, for a brief period in the presence of other members of the two families. In colonial New England the Puritans arranged the marriages of their children with more stress on financial considerations than on the personal preferences of the young people. The pioneer situation, however, favored early emancipation of youth from parental control because of the abundance of free land and the opportunity for setting up a new household.

In modern American society young people have freedom to make their own selection of marriage partners. In the modern manner parents do not impose their preferences or interfere arbitrarily in their children's choice of a mate. Only when the young people are underage, as variously determined by the laws of different states, is it legally necessary for them to secure the consent of their parents to the marriage.

The change from marriages arranged by parents to those entered into by young people on their own initiative has not increased the stability of marriage. Judging by the increase in the divorce rate, free choice seems to have had the reverse effect. Divorces were practically unknown in the colonial period. Since the Civil War the divorce rate has been steadily rising. In 1951 one divorce occurred for every four marriages. This increase in the instability of marriage cannot, however, be attributed to the fact that marriages are arranged by young people rather than by their parents. It is due to certain long-time factors which have made the selection of mates increasingly difficult. The five of greatest importance are (1) urbanization, (2) individualism, (3) the emancipation of women, (4) the secularization of life, and (5) the growing conception of marriage as a companionship.

1. *Urbanization.* In 1790, 95 per cent of the population of the United States was rural. Since then, in every decade except one, the proportion of city population in the United States has increased; in 1950 only 36 per cent of the people lived in communities of under 2,500 population. Even more significant has been the growth of urbanization which has accompanied the development of industry. Economic, educational, recreational, and religious activities have been transferred to agencies outside the home. The intimacy and friendliness of the rural neighborhood have been superseded by the formal, impersonal, and disinterested relationships of city life. In the city the primary controls over behavior, personified by Madam Grundy, have broken down in the anonymity and secondary contacts especially of the rooming-house and apartment-house neighborhoods.

2. *Individualism.* Living in cities has encouraged the development of individualism; one of the chief manifestations is the self-expression of the individual. The consequent accentuation of the individuality of the members of society promotes the complexity of selecting a mate. In the rural community the occupation, the interests, the ideas and ideals of all were practically the same. In the city these are widely divergent. Another manifestation of individualism is the decrease of control exercised by society over its members. Consequently the person who is dissatisfied with his mate is less inclined to conform to the social controls which would prevent the dissolution of a marriage in the country.

3. *The Emancipation of Women.* In the United States the trend has been toward greater freedom for women. Increasingly they participate in the

economic, social, educational, and political life of the country. This greater freedom, in conjunction with the other factors mentioned, has inclined women more and more against enduring an unsatisfactory marriage; they now seek release when conditions are unsatisfactory. The emancipation of women has also tended to make them more discriminating in selecting a husband.

4. *The Secularization of Life.* One aspect of city living has been the trend toward the secularization of life accompanied by a decline in the religious sanction of marriage and the family. In recent generations the role of religion in the family has diminished. Religious observances in the home, such as family prayers and grace at meals, have declined in use. Most marriages are still solemnized by the clergy, but they no longer are protected by as strong religious sanctions as in the past. The stand of certain Protestant churches against divorce has weakened, as indicated by the greater number of marriages of divorced persons performed by ministers. Mate selection takes place to a larger degree than previously outside of the home, the Sunday school, the young people's society, and the church.

5. *Marriage as a Companionship.* The trend in the United States has been away from the conception of marriage as a contract sanctioned by law and community pressure toward that of an interpersonal relation expressive of companionship. Marriage as a legal and institutional arrangement was held together (1) by external forces, such as the law, custom, and community opinion; (2) by the authority and superiority of the husband and the subordination and inferiority of the wife; (3) by rigid discipline; and (4) by the sense of duty of husband and wife. Marriage as a companionship is bound together (1) by internal forces, such as affection and comradeship; (2) by consensus based on the equality of husband and wife; (3) by sympathetic understanding; and (4) by the personal happiness realized in the union. The transition from the institutional and authoritarian type of marriage to the companionship and democratic form has often tended to increase the instability of the family. In the long run, however, the realization of the ideal of companionship in marriage should increase its stability.

The five factors that have been discussed—city living, individualism, the emancipation of women, the loss of religious influences, and the growing conception of marriage as a companionship—have all increased the risks involved in making marriage a success. They have made it easier for people to enter into marriage and to abandon a union with which they have become dissatisfied. They have made it more difficult for husbands and wives to become and remain adjusted to each other, particularly if they were not well suited to each other in personality, interests, and ideals. The increase in the divorce rate has demonstrated the bankruptcy of the romantic theory that "love at first sight" was sufficient guarantee for "live happily ever after." The interest is growing in the possibilities of finding a solid foundation for successful marriage in the wise selection of a mate.

How can a young man or woman improve chances of a happy marriage by utilizing the knowledge that is now available? Psychological and sociological research has given us new information on the conditions and factors that make for success in marriage. This knowledge can be helpful to young people. Here are five main points that every candidate for marriage ought to consider: (1) the intelligent utilization of dating and courtship, (2) the favorable combination of the social and cultural backgrounds of the couple, (3) their compatibility in temperament and personality, (4) their common interests and values, and (5) the measure of success achieved by them in adjustment during the engagement.

1. DATING AND COURTSHIP

Today in American society five stages in the relationship of the sexes finally culminate in marriage. If any one of these is omitted or slighted the chances for a happy marriage may be correspondingly decreased. These five stages in the courtship cycle include dating, keeping company, going steady, private understanding, and engagement.

1. *Dating.* Dating is a relatively new custom; it is one of the great social innovations of our time. It arose, as many changes do, out of a new social situation. No one person devised it. It arose as a new practice which permitted freer association among the sexes in the new age of the automobile.

In the old-time rural community, selection of a mate was limited to the distance you could travel with a horse and buggy. After World War I the area of selection expanded, both in the city and the country, to the distance you could cover with an automobile. Dating gives young people an opportunity to become acquainted with a large number of persons of the opposite sex before selecting a mate. Pairing can be deferred until the best preliminary choice is made from a wide circle of contacts.

Dating also implies that each date is rated in terms of a prospective partner in matrimony. The date, of course, is an end in itself; there may be no further involvement. You try a date; if you don't become interested you can decide then and there to stop.

Dating is not utilized wisely if it merely multiplies superficial social contacts. The value of dating for selecting a mate is enhanced to the degree that it enables a couple to determine in a preliminary way whether or not they are compatible in temperament and have similar interests.

Dating is important to the teen-agers as the basis for boy-and-girl friendships. During this time of emotional and social immaturity dating should not pass into pairing too early.

2. *Keeping Company*. Dating is the prelude to keeping company. Keeping company means that you concentrate your dates on one person, but you are still free to have dates with others. Keeping company is an expression of active preference. You can make comparisons before becoming involved in a more serious commitment. Teen-agers should not try to shorten this period.

3. *Going Steady*. Keeping company signifies mutual preference which may represent only friendship and not love. Going steady indicates a stronger attachment, at least on the part of one member of the couple. Both have made an agreement that they will limit their society to each other.

Going steady should be utilized by the couple as a period of exploration. The couple can find out if they are in love. They can test their temperamental compatibility, the satisfaction of their personality needs, their common interests, and their ideals.

4. *Private Understanding*. The private understanding is a mutual avowal of love by the couple. This new development in the relationship is generally kept secret or shared only with close friends. Often at this time the young man and the young woman are introduced to each other's families in order to secure an appraisal from parents and other relatives. The function of the period of the private understanding is to permit a further test of the certainty of one's choice before becoming committed to a formal and public engagement. The private understanding may be terminated without the embarrassment that attends a broken engagement.

5. *Engagement*. The engagement period is the final test before marriage of the couple's compatibility in personality and temperament, congeniality of interests, and agreement in ideas and ideals. On the average, at least one year is the minimum time required for this purpose. Of course the sheer passage of time is not important. What is significant is the utilization of this period by the couple to resolve any difficulties between them, to make any needed adjustments to each other, and to build a deeper relationship of mutual confiding and common understanding.

Dating, keeping company, going steady, private understanding, and engagement, if utilized intelligently, should contribute greatly to the wise choice of a mate.

II. SOCIAL BACKGROUNDS

In recent years several investigations have shown what factors in the social background of the couple are of importance in selecting a mate. These are:

(1) family relationships, (2) number of friends, (3) membership in organizations, (4) educational level, (5) religious participation, and (6) economic status.

1. *Family Relationships*. Family relationships are most important in mate selection. When the marriages of the parents of both bride and groom are happy, a high proportion of the marriages of the young people are happy. Conversely, if the marriages of their parents are unhappy, a large percentage of the children's marriages will turn out unhappily. Close attachment to both parents and a corresponding absence of hostility toward them in childhood are associated with a higher than average prospect of success in marriage. When the discipline of the parent has been kindly but firm, the prospect of a child's adjustment in marriage is more promising than in those cases when it has been too severe or too lenient, or, worse still, has fluctuated between leniency and severity. Young people who report that their parents gave them sex information—even if it was rather inadequate—are happier in their marriages than those instances when the knowledge of the facts of life came from other sources.

The status of the family in the community and the similarity of the family backgrounds of the young people in terms of socioeconomic status, type of occupation, religious affiliation, and nationality stock are also of great importance in successful marriage.

2. *Number of Friends*. The number of friends of the couple is definitely related to happiness in marriage. The matrimonial risk of the husband is better if before marriage he has several or many men friends and several women friends; that of the future wife is higher if she does not lack men friends and has many women friends. The sociable person appears to be a better marital prospect than the one who has few or no friends.

3. *Membership in Organizations*. You have a higher probability for success in marriage if you have been a member of three or more organizations. Actual research proves that social contacts increase the probabilities of marital happiness.

4. *Educational Level*. The higher the amount of formal education, the greater the likelihood of adjustment in marriage. For both the future husband and wife a high-school education is better than the grade-school level; college superior to high school. Graduate and professional education in universities provides the highest proportion of successful unions.

5. *Church and Sunday-School Attendance*. The better the record of a person in his church and Sunday-school attendance, the higher his chance of making a successful marriage. This is measured by the number of years that he has attended Sunday school, by attending church three or more times a

month, and by his activity in church before marriage. Being married by a minister and having the wedding in church or parsonage seem to be associated with marital success. The basic factor here is the degree of religious interest of the person.

6. *Economic Status*. Happiness in marriage comes most frequently to people in those occupations that have a moderate but stable income, that require considerable educational preparation, and that are lacking in mobility. A man with a steady job is a better matrimonial risk. The prospects of good marital adjustment for the wife are increased if she worked before marriage or engaged in civic or social activity, if she was employed at an occupation the same as, or similar to, the one she prefers. The husband with savings at time of marriage is a superior risk.

Young people are inclined to select their mates according to their similarity in certain of these background interests. They marry within the same social class, at the same or similar level of education, and with others of about the same economic status. Wide differences in cultural background appear to make for unhappy unions. Where young people are attracted to each other despite, or perhaps because of, cultural differences, they should attempt during the process of courtship to find out if they can successfully bridge their divergences so that these will not constitute serious problems in marriage.

III. TEMPERAMENT AND PERSONALITY

Compatibility in temperament and personality is essential to a happy marriage. During dating, keeping company, and even while going steady, young people are likely to be on their best behavior and so do not fully reveal their basic personality characteristics. The intimacy of the period of private understanding and engagement makes it feasible for the couple to find out how well or how poorly they are matched in temperament and personality. Scientific research has established some important facts on the relation between personality and marital adjustment.

1. *Favorable and Unfavorable Personality Traits*. Certain personality characteristics may be listed in pairs as making for and against happiness in marriage. A person with an optimistic temperament is more likely to be happy than one with a pessimistic temperament. Emotional stability makes for, and emotional unstability against, marital adjustment. Submissive tendencies are favorable, while dominating and domineering behavior is unfavorable to success in marriage. A considerate and sympathetic person is a better matrimonial risk than the critical and inconsiderate person. Self-confidence, especially on the part of the husband, is a more desirable characteristic than lack of self-assurance. A person who is emotionally dependent

has a better chance for marital happiness than the self-sufficient person, who tends to face trouble alone and to avoid asking advice from others. Evidently, it is most desirable in mate selection for both the young man and the young woman to possess the favorable trait of any of the pairs listed and least desirable for both to have the unfavorable one. The person with the unfavorable trait may raise his chances of marital happiness by selecting a partner with the desirable characteristic. For example, two sympathetic persons are happier in marriage than two critical people; but the union of a critical and a sympathetic person has, on the average, an intermediate state of happiness.

Certain other personality traits have little or no relation to marital happiness. Whether the person is outgoing or withdrawing in his behavior, whether he likes or dislikes the company of other persons, whether he gives or does not give much thought to what impression he makes upon others, whether he finds or does not find it uncomfortable to be "different," whether he is impulsive or deliberate seem immaterial to his chances of success in marriage.

2. *Emotional and Social Maturity.* Marriages at too early an age result in a high proportion of unhappy unions. Yet census statistics indicate that the average age for marriage is becoming lower. From the point of view of marital happiness the optimum age for marriage is from 22 to 30 years. Chronological age, of course, is only an index of a person's emotional and social maturity; those are actually the factors to be considered. Too many young people in their early twenties, as well as in their late teens, are still adolescent in their emotional and social development. To be successful in mate selection and marriage, they need to have passed into the adult stage where they are no longer emotionally dependent on their parents or subject to the control of their age group, but able to make their own decisions and to be responsible for their obligations.

3. *Emotional Interdependence.* Compatibility in temperament and other personality traits is in great measure a question of the degree to which the married couple complement each other in the fulfillment of their personality needs. Persons differ widely in their demand for sympathy, understanding, and encouragement. Whatever their emotional needs may be, their happiness in marriage depends to a considerable degree on the capacity of their mate to satisfy these needs.

Typically in courtship people unconsciously seek either to continue an emotional relationship which was satisfying when they were children in association with their parents, or to establish a satisfactory affectional relationship which they missed when they were children. The boy and girl are successful when they find they can realize this relation in their association with another person. You often hear them say: "Our personalities seemed to click," "It seemed we had known each other a long time," and "I feel more at ease with him than with any of the other fellows."

4. *Affection and Sex.* Falling in love, with modern couples, is either infatuation or companionship. In infatuation the emphasis is on physical and romantic attraction. This is often called love at first sight. In infatuation, emotional reactions predominate. The pair tend to be isolated from others, to be in a state of high mutual suggestibility, and to be indifferent or hostile to the advice of parents and friends. Unions of this type are frequently between persons of widely different social background and social class. But infatuation in love is blind to the factors that should be considered in selecting a mate. An elopement or some other form of hasty marriage is likely soon to be followed by disillusionment and the disruption of the union.

Affection of the companionship type is based on friendship deepening into love. After marriage comradeship is still an important, if not the most important, element. Husbands and wives are in agreement in reporting that companionship is the chief gain that they have obtained from marriage. Modern courtship gives the young people an opportunity to develop and to test the satisfactions which they secure in companionship with each other.

Sex is included under the discussion of personality because sexual adjustment in marriage depends largely, first, upon the attitude of the person to it and, second, upon the interaction of two personalities to each other. Persons are more likely to be well adjusted and happy in their marriage if they have received sex instruction from their parents, if their parents had a frank attitude toward early sex curiosity, if they have no disgust or aversion toward sex in their premarital attitudes, if their sexual desires are of equal, or about equal, strength, and if they have not been sexually promiscuous.

IV. COMMON INTERESTS AND VALUES

Since companionship is the great value that modern young people seek to obtain in marriage, the presence or absence of common interests and values is of prime importance in selecting a mate.

1. *Leisure-time Preferences.* During courtship and engagement the couple find out not only what recreational interests they have in common but also the possibility of developing other activities that both can enjoy.

If the ways in which they prefer to spend their leisure time differ too greatly the union is likely to be unhappy. The chances for a happy marriage are highest where both enjoy home activities, intermediate when both would rather "step out," and lowest where one prefers to stay at home and the other to be on the go.

For a happy union the prospective husband and wife must participate together in a sufficient number of activities that ensure companionship. Their mutual activities and interests may be in sports and games, literature, music and art, or religion and a social cause. Sports and games provide mutual enjoyment and a sense of companionship. Literature, music, and art tend to bind the couple together. Religion and interest in the same social causes are particularly binding. Divergences in preferences for spending leisure time may be a source of conflict especially in the latter two groups of interest. Differences in religion and politics are well known as destructive of friendship, and this applies with particular force to marriage. If difficulties exist here, they should be resolved during the period of courtship and engagement. A common core of mutual interests and activities leaves room for a certain range of diversity. In fact, such differences may be stimulating to the couple and so increase the satisfaction of the relationship.

2. *Desire for Children.* A strong desire for children, expressed by both members of the engaged couple, shows a higher association with success in marriage than a mild desire, no desire, or a mild objection. The disagreement in desire between the two is correlated with a high proportion of unhappy unions. This suggests that the couple should come to an agreement if possible before marriage on their wish for children. Contrary to general belief, the results of investigation show that the engaged young man is only slightly less interested in having children than his fiancée.

3. *Friends.* Agreement on friends makes for adjustment both in engagement and in marriage. Frequently the engaged couple share the same circle of friends and the same attitudes toward them. In a considerable number of cases, however, each has his own set of friends, and one or both may be critical of the friends of the other.

Where there is disagreement the couple should seek to find out if the objections are valid and to determine on the standards by which they should retain their old friends and choose new ones. On the basis of this mutual understanding much of the conflict which might otherwise occur may be avoided. In this way there would be more toleration of the old friends of the other and any tendency toward jealousy would be diminished by a sense of greater security in the relationship.

4. *Domestic Interests.* The degree to which a person is domestic in his interests and activities makes him a better matrimonial prospect. Domesticity is indicated in many different ways. It is evident, first of all, when a young man or woman places the values of home and family above other considera-

tions. Affections and desire for children is a second index. Interest in gardening and in fixing things up around the house on the part of the man is still another indication. The girl who likes housekeeping, cooking, and sewing will probably make a contented and happy wife.

Couples are more likely to settle down to the enjoyment of married life if both of them prefer to live in a single house rather than in an apartment when they are married and when, even before marriage, they are making plans to buy or to build their own home.

5. *Life Values and Career.* For successful marriage it is important that the couple have the same philosophy of life or at least have discussed their different convictions of what is most worth while in life and have arrived at a sympathetic appreciation of the other's point of view. The life values of the two persons should be sufficiently harmonious so that serious difficulties will not develop later. One of the arguments against marriage at an early age is that the ideals and objectives of the person have not yet crystallized and that in the future they may become so widely divergent as to disrupt the union.

Particular important for mate selection is the career interest of the person. The conception which he has of his role in life, especially in relation to his occupation, is often a decisive selective factor in the choice of a marriage partner. A young minister, for example, wishes for a wife a girl who is idealistic and who has other qualities which will make her a good minister's wife. A rising young businessman desires as a bride a girl with social graces and aspirations. The combination of qualities which each seeks in the other is more complex than these illustrations suggest. What the person may actually desire is the possibility of finding a companion with whom he can express the major roles he would like to play in life.

Too often the process of courtship is telescoped into so short a time that the association of the couple before marriage remains on the superficial level. Even where there is a sufficient period of time between first acquaintance and marriage it is often not adequately utilized by the couple to determine the vitality of their common interests, to appraise the significance of divergent points of view, and to arrive at a mutual understanding which will serve as a secure basis for a lifelong companionship.

V. ENGAGEMENT ADJUSTMENTS

So far the wise choice of a mate has been considered largely as the result of factors over which the couple have little or no control. But to a greater or lesser extent they themselves can influence the outcome. The engagement period is or can be used to improve the probabilities of the happiness of the prospective union. There are five ways in which couples may realize this objective: (1) achieving adjustment in engagement, (2) determination to make marriage a success, (3) adaptability, (4) preparation for marriage, and (5) premarital counseling.

1. *Adjustment in Engagement.* Research has shown that the adjustment secured by the couple in engagement is correlated with their adjustment in marriage.[1] There is also evidence that problems in the relationship are generally more easily solved before rather than after marriage. Accordingly, couples should discuss and try to settle the important issues in their relationship, such as children, in-laws, finances, religion, and philosophy of life, before the wedding date. It is generally a vain hope to expect to reform a mate after the marriage ceremony.

The positive aspect of adjustment during engagement is the building of a companionship to constitute a solid foundation for the marriage relationship. The materials essential for its construction are to be found in the breadth and depth of love for each other, significant shared experiences, the degree of mutual confiding, and sympathetic understanding.

2. *Determination to Succeed in Marriage.* Other things being equal, success in marriage depends on the degree of the determination of the couple to achieve this objective. Not infrequently couples with unfavorable factors in their social backgrounds or in their personality characteristics succeed in marriage because of the additional effort that they are willing to invest in effecting adjustments both in engagement and in marriage. Determination alone, however, is insufficient for this purpose unless both members of the couple are intelligent, are adaptable in attitudes and behavior, and are willing to prepare for marriage and to benefit by premarital and postmarital counseling.

3. *Flexibility.* Young women, in general, enter marriage with the realization that they must make adjustments. The great majority of young men have little or no idea that they have any important adjustments to make. The happiness of marriage could be greatly increased if husbands as well as wives realized that they also must make adaptations in marriage.

There are, of course, great individual differences in flexibility. But adaptability is a trait that can be developed. In a society characterized by social change and growing complexity, the flexibility of the person becomes of signal value. A large element in adaptability is the acceptance of the attitude that adjustments in marriage are necessary and desirable. Persons are likely to be good mates if in the discussion and decision upon an issue both are willing to meet the other not merely halfway, but more than halfway. Flexibility in marriage is increased to the degree that one or both develop sympathetic understanding of divergent attitudes and behavior in the other. Under these conditions the risks involved in marrying a person who in some respects is different from one's self are lessened. In the wise choice of a mate one accepts a life partner as a personality with his own particular combination of traits. Many marriages are wrecked because either the husband or the wife plans to reform the other after marriage. There is an old saying that it never pays to marry a man to reform him.

4. *Preparation for Marriage.* Young people today in increasing numbers are demanding preparation for marriage as part of their education. This is particularly true in colleges and universities, where they have demanded the introduction of courses in marriage, sometimes against the opposition of members of the faculty. Today courses in preparation for marriage and family living are also being taught in high schools and to some extent in the elementary schools.

Young people are eager to know the results of research on marriage. Now there are many books and pamphlets with this information. Many couples devote a considerable portion of the engagement period in reading together books and articles on preparation for marriage.

5. *Premarital Counseling.* Most articles on marriage, while of great value, have one serious limitation: they present general knowledge applicable to all couples. What John and Mary, however, wish and need specifically to know are the probable difficulties which *they* will face in their own marriage, what is the best way to prevent them, and, if this is not possible, how to deal with them.

In our larger cities counseling services are now available which provide this kind of premarital guidance. Sometimes the counselor explains to the couple the crucial difficulties that are likely to arise in their relationship and how they may best avoid or treat them. Or the counselor assists the couple in identifying the problems that exist, perhaps in incipient form, and in stimulating them to find their own solutions.

Young people can greatly reduce the probability of serious difficulties in their marriage if, in the engagement period, they learn the important principle which is common to the fields of physical and mental health. If difficulties arise which do not easily and quickly yield to home treatment, consult a specialist. Many couples in the engagement period adopt the plan that they will settle each day any problem that may arise in marriage. When this program fails they should turn without delay to a marriage counselor for help. Otherwise, any unresolved difficulty, even a seemingly trivial one, may develop into a tension which becomes more difficult and is possible to cure only with expert assistance.

Throughout this discussion it has been assumed that the problem of selecting a mate would be solved if one found an ideal partner. But it is just as important that the person himself be a good marital choice.

The wise selection of a mate is not completed once a choice is made. On the contrary, it is a process of development in the interaction of the two persons. It begins in dating, it continues through courtship and engagement, and it reaches its culmination in the shared experiences of marriage.

NOTES

[1]Ernest W. Burgess and Paul Wallin, *Engagement and Marriage,* Philadelphia, J. B. Lippincott, 1953, pp. 547–49.

BIBLIOGRAPHY

Adams, Clifford R., and Packard, Vance, *How to Pick a Mate,* New York, Dutton, 1946.

Burgess, Ernest W., and Cottrell, Leonard S., Jr., *Predicting Success or Failure in Marriage,* New York, Prentice-Hall, 1939, Chaps. 6–15, pp. 75–312.

Burgess, Ernest W.; Wallin, Paul; and Schultz, Gladys D; *Courtship, Engagement and Marriage,* Philadelphia, J. B. Lippincott, 1954.

Mead, Margaret, *Male and Female,* New York, William Morrow, 1949, Chap. 14, pp. 281–95.

Strauss, Anselm, "Personality Needs and Marital Choice," *Social Forces,* 25, 1947, pp. 332–35.

Terman, Lewis M., *Psychological Factors in Marital Happiness,* New York, McGraw-Hill Book Co., 1938.

Wile, Ira S., *The Man Takes a Wife,* New York, D. Appleton-Century Co., 1936.

Winch, Robert F., *The Modern Family,* New York, Henry Holt, 1952.
(See also Bibliography, Chapter 3.)

Chapter 3

COURTSHIP AND ENGAGEMENT

by *Evelyn M. Duvall, Ph.D. (Mrs. S. M.)*
AUTHOR OF "FACTS OF LIFE AND LOVE," "FAMILY LIVING," "WHEN YOU MARRY"
(WITH REUBEN HILL)

There was a time when a young man interested in a young woman around town walked her home from church and met her father. Father had a talk with the fellow which was based on two questions: 1. "What are your intentions?" This was designed to ward off the men who were out for only a good time and to make sure that anyone hanging around had ultimate intentions of marriage. This careful supervision of parents saved many girls from "the fate worse than death" in those days.

The second question raised with the potential suitor was, "What are your prospects?" This covered the realm of the young man's visible assets, how many acres of land he owned or would fall heir to, whether he had a house or the prospects of one, and how he planned to earn a living that would support the girl in the manner to which she had become accustomed. Parents were responsible for seeing that a girl's husband-to-be would be a good "pervider." This was essential in the days when women were entirely dependent on their menfolk for economic security. When Grandma "made her bed" she must "lie in it," even though it was a hard one.

Grandpa had some practical purposes in his selection too. He might be attracted by a shapely figure or a slim ankle, but when he came to the place where he was announcing serious intentions, he made sure that the girl could cook. "Can she bake a cherry pie, Billy boy, Billy boy?" was a serious question in the days that preceded the corner delicatessen, the commercial foods companies, and the ubiquitous restaurant. A man needed a woman around the house to cook and sew and garden and can and lay her hand to the hundred and one home industries that produced just about everything the family needed to keep going.

Nowadays courtship is much less frequently subject to parental approval, is under way far more casually, and is burdened with many fewer practical considerations. For marriage itself today is contracted not so much for the mutual economic dependence of man and woman as it is for purposes of companionship.

DATING

Today's teen age couples go out togther just for the fun of it. This pairing off for an evening's entertainment at a movie, a dance, a game, or a party is called "dating." Dating is distinguished from courtship in the older sense in that there is no commitment of either girl or boy for the future, there is relatively little parental evaluation of the young man's eligibility, and the young people themselves choose each other more in terms of desirability for the occasion.

The young person who "rates" as a date is one who ranks high in dating desirability in the particular group. The tendency is for high-ranking girls to date the high-ranking boys in any given community or campus.[1] The rivalry tends to be keen, and the rating assigned by the group is often mercilessly without regard for such factors as stability, character, and real worth of the person. Rating by the group is done in "bull sessions," around "cokes" after parties, and over malted milks at odd hours. Indications are that the more important factors are (1) *Physical attractiveness*[2] ("He is so handsome"; "She is cute-looking"), (2) *Personality factors* (vivacity, friendliness, social poise), (3) *Reputation* among others ("They think she is swell"; "He was big shot at camp last summer"), (4) *Participation* in activities ("He is captain of the team"; "She was president of the Glee Club last term"), (5) *Social status* ("He is a big fraternity man"; "She is one of the Ritzeys, you know").

In any given community, except those where the ratio between the sexes is skewed, there is usually a considerable number of both boys and girls who do not date.[3] This is often a source of distress and anxiety to the non-daters, who may feel that something is wrong with them if they do not get dates. Sometimes the lack is covered up consciously or unconsciously by devotion to home duties, absorption in school, work responsibilities, attention to a hobby, or the development of a talent. There are situations where special interests or budding genius keeps the youth so busy that he has literally no time for dates. This seems to be far less frequent than the use of a preoccupation as a rationalization for not dating.

The people who get the dates in most groups are those who have three qualifications: First, *they rate* (they enjoy a favorable place in the dating hierarchy assigned by the rest of the crowd). The standards vary considerably from group to group. The "country-club set" in most towns has different standards and values than those found across the tracks or in the "Sunday-school crowd." A young person moving from one neighborhood to another may find himself rated quite differently. Rating standards differ within a set from time to time. Tryon,[4] who studied adolescents for the National Research Council, pointed out the changing standards among young teen-agers, who begin by expressing their preference for the "nice" girl, well-mannered, quiet-spoken, pleasing to teachers, and a few years later turn to the daredevil, active, vivacious type of girl. Later still other standards appear and disappear as the young people mature and ready themselves for marriage.

The second qualification is related to social and emotional maturity. Here, too, there are wide variations among young people. Chronological age is not a reliable gauge of the emotional maturity of a boy or a girl, or even of his or her physiological age. Some girls menstruate as early as eleven years of age. Others, still within fair range of the normal, experience the first menstruation at sixteen or even later. Investigators Stone and Barker[5] compared the attitudes and interests of young girls before and after menstruation. They found that maturing sex interests, feelings, and concepts of self in a sex role *follow* physical maturation. Thus we find an early-maturing girl of twelve already setting out on dates while her late-maturing neighbor of sixteen has not even started to date.

Boys mature later than girls. It is not unusual for two thirds of the eighth-grade girl graduates to be already into their puberal cycle while two thirds of the boys in the same age-grade have not yet begun their maturation.[6] This is why girls at this age tend to be taller and heavier than the boys. It also explains why girls through junior high and high school tend to be in advance of the boys in social interests. On the whole, girls are ready for dating, dancing, and courtship before the boys of their own age group. The girls must launch the parties, plan the dances, and teach the boys to dance in the average high-school community. This is sometimes hard on the boys who are forced into social situations for which they are not quite ready developmentally. And it isn't always easy for girls to take so much of the initiative in boy-girl affairs. But it has a sound basis in developmental fact and must be accepted as one of the realities of the early dating situation.

The third qualification for dating is a measure of social competence.[7] It is the socially skilled who date most readily. The boys and girls with conversational ability, ease in dancing, adequacy in the more common sports such as swimming, skating, and tennis, competency in some musical form, poise in a restaurant, on the dance floor, and in each other's homes get dates most easily. Behind these special skills lie the social poise and maturity that are characterized by such qualities as a genuine friendliness and liking for others, the ability to make other people of both sexes and various ages feel comfortable, and the relegating of selfish, ego interests to second place in preference to the common interests and loyalties of the group.

Social competence keeps dates from falling into the stolid patterns of a movie, a coke, and home again. Couples with initiative and originality practice a give and take of hospitality in a variety of dating patterns. Picnics, hobby interests, whole group activities, "smart" dates, and dates at home offer a wide variety of dating experience planned by either the boy, the girl, or both together.

Schools and community agencies such as YMCAs, YWCAs, church youth groups, scouts, settlements, and other social clubs can do much to assist young people to meet each other and to gain poise and social skill. Attention to such needs for social development appears to be imperative from the recent surveys of high-school populations which reveal that less than half of the boys and girls are dating regularly.

Too often dances and parties for teen-age youth are poorly planned, with too few mixers and too little competent guidance to assure adequate social opportunities. Consequently even in schools that do provide some such social affairs, only the more socially expert attend, and those youths who most need the learning experience are left out.

Social affairs which promote social development are planned to elicit wide participation of all potentially interested youth. Active working committees that have real responsibility for specific details of the occasion are helpful. A few of the more frequently recommended activities are picnics, skating, folk games, interest groups, etc., which allow boys and girls to be near each other, sharing in the fun, without too long intervals in which they are required to maintain a high level of social competence. In contrast, ballroom dancing requires a girl and boy to keep up an interesting conversation, observe the elaborate courtesies of the dance floor, execute the intricacies of the dance, and move in step with the music all at the same time; a combination often overwhelming to the beginner, the shy boy, or the inexperienced girl. This is one reason why stag lines become stagnant and why so many girls do not brave the affair at all.

Families can help by providing their children with graduated social experiences from childhood on into young man- and young womanhood. Having friends in for meals or for overnight, being a "drop-in" home where the crowd can congregate after an affair, going to camp, doing things together with others as family and neighborhood groups all help. The socially active family rarely produces a permanently socially handicapped youth. Non-participating young people often come from relatively isolated families with few opportunities for meaningful social contacts through childhood.

Many young people use outlets through the church, the YMCAs, the YWCAs, the scout troop, or other neighborhood clubs for the step-by-step progress into social maturity that only experience with other people provides.

Dating is a learned skill that is acquired, as are all learnings, through the actual process of the activity itself. We learn by doing in our friendships as in anything else.

Now that chaperones and parental supervision of courting young people are rarely heavily restrictive, the responsibility for the relationship lies increasingly with the young people themselves. The many varieties of background of young people in the average American community complicate the setting and keeping of common standards of dating behavior. Some young people are "fast." They go in for petting, thrills, and excitement. Others are "slow," dull, uninteresting, or kill-joys to the fast set, and "salt of the earth" to others. Finding other young people who share one's values and standards is often a difficult task, especially when the young person himself or herself has not clearly defined his or her own position in the confused and changing patterns of moral conduct.[8]

Dating is sometimes a touch-and-go affair, with a different partner every date or so, on a quite superficial plane. Other couples date with each other to the place where they are recognized as "going steady" by the rest of the set.

GOING STEADY

A couple is said to go steady when the others of the social group expect them to appear together at social affairs and when varying degrees of possessiveness are felt by the members of the couple involved. A couple may go steady for many reasons:

1. They mutually prefer each other to others who might be dated at the time.
2. They are "in love"; caught in emotional involvements that make being together a highly desirable end.
3. They cling to each other for social reasons. She can be sure of a date; he does not risk being stood up if they are going steady.
4. They are thrust into going steady by group expectations and demands. After a date or two together the others hang back and expect the two to date only each other. This is particularly pronounced in some schools and colleges. Often the custom is regretted by men and women alike but, once established on a campus, is hard to break.
5. They go steady because it is cheaper and easier than "playing the field." It costs less money and time to go together time after time than it would to

impress a new date every time. Couples accustomed to each other can do simple things together that neither would dare suggest to a newly acquired companion.

6. They establish the fact of their social success by hanging onto the frat pin or the other symbols of having acquired a steady of high rāting in the competitive hierarchy of dating. In order to date at all on some campuses a girl must hold a steady or a series of steadies. Before letting anyone go she must be sure of her ability to attract a man of at least the same dating ranking, or she loses ground socially.

7. They go steady preliminary to getting engaged and being married. Mutual exploration of each other's tastes, habits, values, backgrounds, ambitions, fears, and hopes can be done without the interference of intruding competitors. As interest in each other deepens, the steady date readies itself for the understanding that precedes engagement.

It is not infrequent to find young people of junior-high and high-school age going steady with each other. Many adults and some young persons are concerned over this tendency to go steady so early. They point out that going steady too soon provides less opportunity for knowing the many other eligible young people of the other sex who might be dated were it not for the possessive restriction of the going-steady relationship. Another danger of going steady too soon is that the scope of self-understanding may be limited. Different people call forth different responses in a person. Various friends draw forth a variety of responses, feelings, and roles. One boy may make a girl feel roguish and coquettish, another make her feel quiet and subdued; one may make her feel maternal, while still another makes her feel like a little girl enjoying the protection of a big father-figure. It is possible that in the process of growing up both a girl and a boy should have the opportunities of playing many of these emotional roles with each other, in order that they may learn from experience the kinds of boys and girls that there are and achieve a deeper understanding of their own emotional repertoire, from which they may more intelligently choose the partner who will be most harmonious.

Still another problem of going steady too soon is that of an uneven commitment of the members of the couple. One of the pair may take the relationship seriously, while the other sees himself or herself much less seriously involved. This problem becomes acute when the less involved partner wishes to withdraw and is able to do so only by hurting the other and feeling a burden of guilt himself. This has been known to be so serious that couples poorly suited to each other have been precipitated into marriage simply because the courage for breaking off with a clinging "steady" has been lacking.

Breaking off with a steady can be a difficult and uncomfortable procedure. Loosening the hold of an unpromising relationship is bound to involve some hurt and often is full of heartache and anguish for one or both of the pair. Recognizing these factors, the initiator of the break will do well to choose a method that will soften the blow for both. There are several procedures which may be considered. The first is the sudden complete severance of the relationship. The steady who was so reliable one day just isn't there the next. If the woman is the initiator of the break she doesn't answer his telephone calls, she is "out" when he drops by, she is "busy" when he does catch up with her, she begins to appear at social affairs with other girls or fellows. The male aggressor stops calling, does not appear, asks for no further dates, and soon is out with another woman. This method has the advantage of being quick, easy, and effective. Its disadvantages are that it causes the one who is being sloughed off needless pain and bewilderment, which in turn boomerang on the more active member of the pair in feelings of guilt and fear of being faced with his or her duplicity.

The other extreme is the long agonizing discussion of "How washed up we are," "Why don't you love me as you used to?"; and the unanswerable questions: "What has happened? What did I do? Why can't we be friends again?" These scenes are apt to be extremely uncomfortable to both the man and the woman. The raking over of dead embers of a love very rarely causes it to burst into flame again, nor does it usually bring much insight as to what has happened and what the break means.

A middle ground is that of easing off. Couples who have gone steady on dates three and four times a week begin to taper off to once or twice a week. Their ardor in expressing affection cools. Possessiveness begins to dwindle. One may suggest to the other double dates with mutual friends; or the attractiveness of another companion may be called to the other's attention. Some understanding and acceptance of the impending break helps each to release the other and to redefine the relationship on a more casual plane. Basic to the success of this procedure is a realization of the place of dating and going steady in final mate selection and its particular function in weeding out incompatible and uncongenial prospective mates. Before a couple become engaged they should have mutually established the fact of their ability to please each other, feel comfortable with each other, and be the kind of people who are sufficiently compatible to build a lasting and satisfactory union.

Going steady has as its chief values that of allowing opportunities mutually to explore each other as two whole persons and of facilitating the selection of promising mates. It is not unlikely that patterns established during this "keeping company" stage of courtship carry over into engagement, very much as engagement adjustments preview the marital adjustments yet to be.[9]

ENGAGEMENT

A couple become engaged when they have a mutual understanding of intention to marry. This is viewed differently by different people. Some high-school and college engagements are little more than formalized "steadies." A boy "hangs his pin" on a girl much as a prospector will stake out a claim, which holds others off while he explores its possibilities. Girls sometimes accept an engagement ring that means little more than a symbol of their being able to "catch" a highly desirable man in the competitive race for social recognition. She may wear the ring for very much the same reason that others wear a Phi Beta Kappa key; as a mark of achievement.

People more often think of engagement as a prelude to marriage. The engagement period has several recognized functions that are important for the success of the marriage. One of these functions is to place the couple as a pair in the eyes of their friends and families. The parents "get used to" the idea of the serious involvement of their son or daughter. Friends invite the couple as a pair. The crowd the couple go with may shift to those others who are engaged and looking ahead to marriage rather than just "playing around." A "we feeling" develops within the couple in which each is increasingly included in the other's plans, supported by the recognition and acceptance of the engagement by the others round about.

The engagement period further provides the time and the privacy for becoming basically and understandingly acquainted with each other. Sharing past experiences, relating the important and the trivial episodes in one's life history and how one felt about them, within the permissiveness and encouragement possible with the affianced, are highly significant ways of getting through to each other. Such insights, understandings, and sympathies are imperative for two people who are to share a life together as mutually loving companions.

Sharing the present is another important function of the engagement period. Not only the good times, but the troubles, the disappointments, the dreams, and the ambitions of each of the pair can be shared to the advantage of the total relationship. Learning to talk freely and frankly about things which may be cloaked with reticence in more casual contacts is a powerful cement in the pair unity. Working together in common interests and purposes weaves a bond that has promising durability and strength.

Establishing patterns of mutual giving and receiving of affection is a vital part of engagement. Society encourages more freedom and privacy for the engaged couple than is approved for less seriously committed couples. So each couple is left to find its own best ways of loving and being loved.

Couples should approach marriage ready for the full intimacy of the marriage relationship. How best to achieve that full union of man and woman both physically and emotionally is a highly disputed question today.[10] There are some sophisticated young people and adults who argue for complete sexual exploration before marriage. They point to the importance of sex compatibility and imply that premarital experience allows the couple to discover whether or not they are physically satisfying to each other. Much of the research on this subject indicates premarital sex experience is *not* conducive to good marital adjustment. The psychic atmosphere of the premarital relationship is not at all that of the married pair. Elements of fear, anxiety over exposure, guilt, suspicion, and jealousy occur frequently enough in cases of premarital exploration to indicate that many, many couples simply cannot get this far away from what people in general will stand for.

Furthermore, a large number of very happy marriages do not achieve satisfactory sexual adjustment until some time after the marriage was first consummated.[11] Most couples must learn to orient themselves to each other sexually, so that each achieves satisfaction and gives to the other the degree of pleasure that makes for a satisfying union. For most people the indications are that these specific learnings are best learned *after* marriage, when the sense of belonging, permanence, and social approval support the process of mutual accommodation.[12]

"What degree of intimacy is wise for an engaged couple?" Surely there is no argument that the extreme reserve and prudery of the Victorian era are not conducive to wholesome happy marriages today. The engaged couple can safely be encouraged to express their affection in many ways not allowed their strait-laced ancestors. The good-night kiss, the enthusiastic embrace, the caressing and fondling that lovers find pleasure in have won a degree of social approval and encouragement unknown a couple of generations ago. As the same time there can be reassurance that the full physical experience can wait, and that petting and fondling that arouse sex excitement in either or both of the pair may be postponed in favor of the tender, lighter caresses which before and after marriage convey a depth and beauty of affection that is highly conducive to stability of the relationship.

Engagement may be seen as a period of planning ahead for the marriage that is to be. Before marriage many of the marriage plans can be discussed most fruitfully.[13] Questions such as, shall the wife work? and for how long? and on what basis? can far more easily be faced before than after marriage. The financial basis of the partnership: Can they live on the man's earnings? Will some help from parents be acceptable? Is his further education worth sacrificing for? Who will hold the purse strings? Will there be an attempt to live always within the income, or is some indebtedness justified? These questions are all relevant and important for consideration before the actual contingencies arise. The attitude of the couple about becoming parents is significant. Do they agree on the number of children they want to try to have? Is there a comfortable consensus on the way the children shall be cared for, disciplined, trained, and introduced to life? The way each feels about his and the other's family is important. In-law troubles rank high in complaints of newlyweds. Emotional dependencies and immaturities are better faced before than after marriage. Some understanding of the place of the members of the extended families in the partnership is helpful. What constitutes a good time, attitudes toward friends, recreation and social participation are another whole area for consideration and understanding that is well undertaken before the marriage takes place. The balance of power, who shall be boss, and when, can be explored both verbally and in behavior to the great advantage of the settling down of the partners into comfortable patterns of mutually desirable dominance and submission.

Courtship and engagement can be seen as somewhat similar to the casting and rehearsals for the real drama of marriage. Potential mates are cast and recast in the complex of modern dating, going steady, and getting engaged. Mutual adjustments and planning before marriage establish patterns carried over into the permanent relationship. It is therefore not surprising that studies[14] have found that the longer the period of acquaintance and engagement, the more stable and happy the marriage. Conversely, the hastier the marriage, the sooner the divorce.

Courtship and engagement today are not at all the rigid, formalized, supervised affairs they once were. Today's young people must take their own responsibility for making them the kind of relationships that are conducive to personal fulfillment and marital stability.

NOTES

[1]See Reuben Hill's revision of Willard Waller's *The Family: A Dynamic Interpretation*, New York, Dryden Press, 1951, pp. 150–55.

[2]Arnold Green and Stuart Loomis, "The Pattern of Mental Conflict in a Typical State University," *Journal of Abnormal and Social Psychology*, July 1947, pp. 342–55.

[3]The Purdue University Opinion Panel for Young People reports that 48 per cent of the boys and 39 per cent of the girls 12–20 years of age in their national sample seldom have dates. H. H. Remmers and C. G. Hackett, *Let's Listen to Youth*, Chicago, Science Research Associates, 1950, 49 pp.

[4]Caroline Tryon, "Evaluation of Adolescent Personality by Adolescents," *Society for Research in Child Development*, Vol. IV, No. 4, National Research Council, 1939.

[5]Calvin Stone and Roger Barker, "The Attitudes and Interests of Pre-menarcheal and

Post-menarcheal Girls," *Pedagogical Seminary and Journal of Genetic Psychology*, **LIV**, March 1939, pp. 27–71.

⁶Lois Hayden Meek, et al., *The Personal-Social Development of Boys and Girls with Implications for Secondary Education*, New York, Progressive Education Association, 1940, p. 35.

⁷For a fuller development of this point see Evelyn Millis Duvall, *Facts of Life and Love*, New York, Association Press, 1950, Chaps. 5, 6, 7, 8.

⁸See the section on "Changes in Courtship Patterns" in Evelyn Duvall and Reuben Hill, *When You Marry*, New York, Association Press, and Boston, D. C. Heath and Co., 1953 revision, pp. 79–80.

⁹See especially Ernest Burgess and Paul Wallin, "Predicting Adjustment in Marriage from Adjustment in Engagement," *American Journal of Sociology*, 49, 1944, pp. 324–30; and their full report, *Engagement and Marriage*, Philadelphia, J. B. Lippincott, 1953.

¹⁰Note the extensive research reported by Alfred Kinsey et al. in their *Sexual Behavior in the Human Male*, Philadelphia, Saunders, 1948, and *Sexual Behavior in the Human Female*, Philadelphia, Saunders, 1953; as well as the widespread discussion of their findings throughout the popular and professional presses through the years since the appearance of the first report.

¹¹Judson Landis, "Adjustment after Marriage," *Marriage and Family Living*, May 1947, pp. 32–34.

¹²Lewis Terman and others in their *Psychological Factors in Marital Happiness*, New York, McGray-Hill, 1938, report, "in general those husbands and wives who were either virgins at marriage or had had intercourse only with each other tend to have higher mean happiness scores [in marriage] than the other groups" (with premarital experience with others than spouse), p. 329. For a detailed analysis of other research studies of the effect of sexual behavior upon the person, see S. M. Duvall, *Men, Women, and Morals*, New York, Association Press, 1952.

¹³Read particularly, S. M. Duvall, *Before You Marry: 101 Questions to Ask Yourself*, New York, Association Press, 1949, as well as any of the marriage texts appearing in recent years that deal competently with these questions. See Bibliography for a starter listing.

¹⁴Ernest Burgess and Leonard Cottrell, *Predicting Success or Failure in Marriage*, New York, Prentice-Hall, 1939, p. 167; Lewis Terman and others, *Psychological Factors in Marital Happiness*, New York, McGraw-Hill, 1938, p. 198; and Harvey Locke, *Predicting Adjustment in Marriage*, New York, Henry Holt, 1951, pp. 91–96.

BIBLIOGRAPHY

Bowman, Henry, *Marriage for Moderns*, New York, Whittlesey House, second edition, 1948, Chap. 8.

Burgess, Ernest, and Locke, Harvey, *The Family: From Institution to Companionship*, New York, American Book Co., 1945, Chaps. 12, 13, 14, 15.

Burgess, Ernest, and Wallin, Paul, *Engagement and Marriage*, Philadelphia, J. B. Lippincott, 1953, 819 pp.

Cavan, Ruth, *The American Family*, New York, Crowell, 1953, Chap. 13, "Courtship and Engagement," pp. 330–66.

Christensen, Harold, "Dating Behavior as Evaluated by High School Students," *American Journal of Sociology*, May 1952, pp. 580–86.

Connor, Ruth, and Hall, Edith, "The Dating Behavior of College Freshmen and Sophomores," *Journal of Home Economics*, April 1952, pp. 278–81.

Cuber, John, "Changing Courtship and Marriage Customs," *The Annals of the American Academy of Political and Social Science,* September 1943, pp. 30–38.

Duvall, Evelyn Millis, *Facts of Life and Love,* New York, Association Press, 1950, 360 pp.

Duvall, Evelyn, and Hill, Reuben, *When You Marry,* Boston, D. C. Heath, revised edition, 1953, Chaps. 3, 4, 5.

Duvall, Sylvanus, *Before You Marry: 101 Questions to Ask Yourself,* New York, Association Press, 1949, 171 pp.

Folsom, Joseph, *The Family and Democratic Society,* New York, Wiley, 1943, Chap. 16.

Kirkpatrick, Clifford, and Caplow, Theodore, "Courtship in a Group of Minnesota Students," *The American Journal of Sociology,* September 1945, pp. 114–25.

————, "Emotional Trends in the Courtship Experience of College Students as Expressed by Graphs with Some Observations on Methodological Implications," *American Sociological Review,* October 1945, pp. 619–26.

Koos, Earl Lomon, *Marriage,* New York, Henry Holt, 1953, Chaps. 6, 7.

Landis, Judson, and Landis, Mary, *Building a Successful Marriage,* New York, Prentice-Hall, 1948, Chaps. 4, 8.

Locke, Harvey, *Predicting Adjustment in Marriage,* New York, Henry Holt, 1951, Chap. 5, "Courtship and Engagement," pp. 86–105.

Magoun, F. Alexander, *Love and Marriage,* New York, Harper's, 1948, Chaps 6, 7.

Merrill, Francis, *Courtship and Marriage,* New York, Sloane, 1949, Part I, "Courtship," pp. 3–107.

Nimkoff, Meyer, *Marriage and the Family,* New York, Houghton-Mifflin, 1947, Chap 12, "Courtship," pp. 365–98.

Taylor, Donald, "Courtship as a Social Institution in the United States, 1930 to 1945," *Social Forces,* October 1946, pp. 65–69.

Waller, Willard, and Hill, Reuben, *The Family: A Dynamic Interpretation,* New York, Dryden, 1951, Chaps. 10, 12.

Winch, Robert, *The Modern Family,* New York, Henry Holt, 1952, Chap. 16.

Wolford, Opal Powell, "How Early Background Affects Dating Behavior," *Journal of Home Economics,* November 1948, pp. 505–6.

Chapter 4

PREMARITAL SEX RELATIONSHIPS

*by Anna O. Stephens, M.D.**

FORMERLY DIRECTOR, COLLEGE HEALTH SERVICE, PENNSYLVANIA STATE COLLEGE

The term "premarital" might mean anything from childhood up to the actual date of marriage or, in the permanently unmarried, throughout life. Here it means the period from the beginning of interest in the other sex in early adolescence until the date of marriage. "Sex relationships" means actual physical contact between the sexes and includes everything from holding hands and other rather usual and ordinary contacts, on through "petting," to and including that most intimate of all relationships, coitus or sexual intercourse.

Premarital relationships may include three more or less well-outlined stages. The period of acquaintance or friendship, though most commonly associated with adolescence, may extend throughout life in those who do not marry and between a married person and members of the opposite sex other than the mate. During courtship the boy or girl is definitely looking for a mate, whether or not such a purpose is acknowledged by either of them. This second period usually leads to and is terminated by the third period: "engagement." Engagement does not necessarily coincide with the limits of the formal engagement period but should be considered to begin at such a time as a boy and girl have definitely decided on a specific mate and have committed themselves to each other by promises to marry—with or without the accompaniment of fraternity pins, rings, parties, or public announcements. The engagement period is presumed to terminate at the wedding. Some engagements, because of unforeseen complications such as change of interest, physical disability, family responsibilities, economic problems, or untimely death of either party, may be broken. Usually, however, engagement leads to marriage.

---

*Dr. Stephens died before preparation of this latest revision of *Successful Marriage*. The chapter has been edited by Dr. Morris Fishbein.

The problem of premarital sex relationships has become increasingly important in our modern world partly because more or less equality is accorded to women by men. As a result there is freedom in the mingling of the sexes in our social life. The custom of postponing marriage long beyond the point of physical maturity to permit longer periods of education or the achievement of an economic status believed to be of value in establishing a home also contributes to the problem. Surely no one wishes to solve our problems by returning to the primitive society in which these factors did not exist. We find too much of value in our present way of life to wish to go back even one generation. We should use our increasing information, our technics of education, in helping the modern boy and girl to learn how to handle the problems of sex relationships so that there will be fewer "unmarried mothers," less venereal disease, fewer divorces, fewer juvenile delinquents, fewer neurotics, more happy homes, more well-integrated and happily adjusted men and women in a society that is moving forward on the moral plane as well as technologically.

EARLY FRIENDSHIPS

During early adolescence boys and girls seem to prefer groups rather than dates with one person. Their personal contacts are more often in the nature of "roughhouse" or "fooling around" than of a more intimate nature. And yet every physician, welfare worker, and school principal has seen some unfortunate girl who is pregnant in early adolescence. These youngsters do get into trouble, now as in the past.

In reading *Romeo and Juliet* the modern reader may not be aware that these young people would be juvenile delinquents according to present standards! In most states Juliet would be too young to get a marriage license, even with parental consent. Had the marriage laws of that time required a "waiting period," perhaps their untimely deaths would have been prevented. The experience of these well-known young lovers stresses that the early adolescent has capacity for mature sexual experience without accompanying maturity of judgment. Ordinarily these youngsters in their gangs "playing around" are assumed to be harmlessly engaged in getting acquainted. Never forget, however, that in all such contacts the ever-present possibility exists of more specific sex interest being aroused. These young people need to be given adequate sex information and education before the need for its use arises.

Whether or not these boys and girls have had proper instruction, it is certainly wise to encourage their meeting in groups where adequate facilities for play make friendship possible without encouraging intimacy. The boy or girl who has been used to this sort of relationship progresses to the more personal relationship of courtship easily and naturally. For those who never marry these early friendships pave the way for ease in dealing with persons of the opposite sex in business and social relationships throughout life.

COURTSHIP

Although courtship can take place at any age, it occurs most commonly during middle or later adolescence. Physiological maturity and the ability to have sexual intercourse occur in early adolescence, while social and economic maturity are delayed until early adult life in our present state of civilization. The usual custom is to demand a certain degree of social and economic maturity as a prerequisite for marriage. Marriage is discouraged until education has been completed and the financial means of establishing a home have been acquired. In other words, although physiological maturity may be established at a relatively early age, marriage is postponed until early adult life or even later, thus unnaturally prolonging the period of courtship. This long period of time must be passed by these adolescents in the more or less constant presence of the opposite sex, with opportunities for intimacy increasing as their freedom increases. They are subjected on all sides to an advertising campaign and to music, movies, and literature which place emphasis on sex appeal and glamour as highly desirable factors in personal charm. Since they are inadequately informed as to the significance of these sex attitudes and contacts, many young people find it difficult, if not impossible, to maintain the ideals of society regarding the importance of preserving chastity until marriage. True, since the beginning of World War II there has been considerable lowering of the economic standards for marriage, with a great number of marriages taking place at a much younger age. Although marriage before economic independence is reached or education is completed may help to solve some problems, it poses others which may in the end be even greater than those solved. This tendency to younger marriage has continued into the postwar period, but whether or not it will persist indefinitely is problematical. Should a period of economic stress such as a depression intervene, marriage would probably again be postponed until more mature years.

PETTING

The adolescent is especially interested in two activities—in being popular with his or her own group, and in being grown up. The former is often promoted by appearing to be the latter. For the time being he is willing to sacrifice family standards, economic status, physical well-being, and even to some extent his personal ideals in order to obtain the much sought after status. Every parent is familiar with juvenile attempts to convince others of their maturity by such superficial means as wearing bright nail polish, disregarding parents' instructions, spending money too freely, staying out late, monopolizing the family car. Many teen-agers would be helped in the solution of their problems if they were given an opportunity to share in mature responsibilities. Young people of rather tender years grew up rapidly during the recent war when they were permitted to hold jobs, to enlist in the Army, or to share household responsibilities with an employed mother. In this struggle to grow up, "petting" may be tried because it is considered to be mature behavior. This, unfortunately, like reckless driving of the family car, may lead to serious difficulties before the much-desired maturity has been achieved by the slow natural process of continuing growth and development. Once having started to "pet" for whatever reason, the habit easily grows until for many it is practically the only form of entertainment expected on a date.

Webster states that to pet is "to fondle; to caress." Bowman, in his excellent text, *Marriage for Moderns,* defines petting as follows: ". . . physical contact for pleasure which is an end in itself, arising from sexual desire in one or both parties but stopping short of coitus, and of such nature that in one or both there is produced an increased sexual sensitivity and response, a stirring up of sexually colored emotions, and an increased tension that can be relieved immediately only by coitus or some substitute therefor. In the absence of relief, the tension has a tendency to persist for a time."[1] This definition seems to be complete. The physical contact with which it deals usually takes the form mentioned by Webster—caressing and fondling. Such "caressing and fondling" is normally part of the love-making that precedes sexual intercourse in married life. This period of petting helps to create sexual desire and to make physiological preparation for the completion of the sex act. When unmarried young people pet without understanding this biological effect of petting they may unexpectedly find themselves so stimulated that it is difficult for them to stop short of coitus. What is commonly called "heavy petting" usually means caressing of the more intimate parts of the body such as the breasts and the thighs. Young people who indulge in "heavy petting" often learn to reach a sexual climax or orgasm as a result of this manual contact rather than by coitus. Since the physiological mechanism set in motion by petting normally leads to sexual intercourse the young couple should understand this biologic fact: The more intimate petting becomes, the more dangerous it is to the couple who do not wish to carry the sex act to completion.

Many adolescent girls begin to practice petting at the request of their boy friends because they believe that it is the only way to be sure of getting another date, or of demonstrating that they are grown up enough to continue dating, or because they have been led to believe that they owe it to the boy who has given them a pleasant evening. Only after the practice is well established do they learn its real physiological significance. Then it is difficult to establish a new pattern of behavior unless both the environment and the boy friend are also new. The young boy may begin petting because he thinks girls expect it of him or that they will be impressed with his maturity thereby. In many instances he recognizes the sex urge before he begins to pet or at least much earlier in the process than the girl does. Believing that the girl shares his sexual stimulation, he assumes that her reasons for continuing the process are the same as his. As petting becomes more intimate the girl may be bewildered by his ardor and insistence while he is confused by her resistance or her surprise at his intentions. The result is often unhappy for both of them. Whether coitus results sooner than one or both had wished or intended, whether friendship is disrupted by misunderstanding over the matter, or whether petting is discontinued after physical desires have been aroused and the friendship is difficult to re-establish on any other basis, the situation is unfortunate. Young people from junior-high-school age on need to have a thorough understanding of the physiological implications of petting.

Since the temptation to make petting a major part of courtship will inevitably arise, young people, assisted by those who advise them, should be resourceful in planning interesting ways of spending their time together. A generation or two ago adults, children, and young people alike found their recreation in their homes. Many young people now find that homes, their own or their friends', are the center of their lives. Yet homes cannot fully meet the need. Many young people are employed away from home. Many homes are so small, so crowded with other activities, or so inhospitable to the enthusiasm of youth that young people find it difficult to spend their leisure there. How this need of youth for adequate opportunity for recreation is to be met will depend on the resourcefulness of both the young people and the community. At considerable effort many communities provided through the USO or other agencies for the entertainment of the soldiers so recently in their midst. Many of these same communities have large numbers of employed young people as truly in need of such facilities as were the soldiers. Add to this the large group of young people who because they are still in school have little money to spend for recreation and it can readily be seen that every community has some obligation to provide for its youth. The young people themselves need to understand that marriage is based primarily on friendship and a deep underlying unity of spirit of which sexual relationships are an expression rather than a cause. They need to see the great importance of being able to do many things together for pleasure before sharing sexual experience. If opportunity for some of the more popular activities is provided at a time and place and for a price that is convenient to the young couple, they may be helped to postpone petting as their chief "indoor sport." The average community has limited facilities at the disposal of young people. They can attend movies, many of which are sexually stimulating; go to public eating places, which is expensive; go to church, which is usually limited to certain hours on Sunday; or walk in the park, which is either dark and cold or warm and moonlight, neither of which condition can be long endured by the average couple without problems arising. A few communities have bowling alleys enough to provide for an extremely small per cent of their population and which are assigned to certain organizations at any hours that the usual "date" would wish to use them. Then, of course, they could visit libraries and museums; but even adults do not find them really exciting for long, and besides, they are usually closed evenings when young people are dating.

Anyone who watches young people skiing or skating or playing tennis or picnicking or making candy or playing records together knows that young couples are eager for shared experiences in many fields of activity. The community is not without obligation to provide more adequately for these needs. Whether the school, the service clubs, the church, or some independent organization will be the first to attempt to meet the need will depend on the people who make up the particular community.

A "super-chaperone" will not suffice to keep present-day independent youth from making grave errors in the struggle for popularity and maturity. The independent youth, if shown the pitfalls and if given even meager equipment, is capable of building himself a program of activity which will be worthy of our scientific age.

What about the boy or girl who is faced immediately with the problem of petting? The girl asks, "How far can a 'good' girl go?" "What can you do after a movie if your boy friend is emotionally aroused?" "Should you refuse to kiss a boy on your first date with him?" "What about cocktail parties before a dance?" The boys ask, "What does a girl expect of her date?" and "Why does a girl lead us on if she doesn't mean it?" Without moralizing, it is possible to point out pitfalls. These must first be seen clearly and unemotionally. Girls need to know that many, if not most, men are relatively easily stimulated sexually by suggestive dress, behavior, movies, or even a pretty face or figure. If more girls realized this fact they might learn to anticipate the development of a too-intimate mood. Boys need to learn that most girls, in spite of appearances to the contrary, are usually eager to please their boy friends and hence often submit to petting for that purpose only. If more boys realized this fact they might not feel called upon to make physical advances so early in courtship. Both boy and girl need to learn that when physical contacts pass beyond the realm of the casual hand holding or good-night kiss to the more exciting experience of caressing the more intimate parts of the body, such as the breasts and the thighs, they are playing with explosive situations. The situation may get so far without warning that it may be difficult, if not impossible, for them to stop short of mutual orgasm by fondling or even coitus. Inexperienced young people do not understand veiled language and adroit references.

HINTS ON DATING CONDUCT

Both boys and girls need to recognize that persons of different social, educational, and cultural backgrounds have different averages in ideals and standards. Many are helped by being shown that the same standards apply when selecting friends of the opposite sex as when choosing those of one's own sex. Men in uniform may look alike, but they represent a wide range of home backgrounds. Neither do all college girls represent a uniform high standard of conduct. Among friends of the same sex it is usual to find more or less similar cultural background and experience. It is helpful to choose friends of the opposite sex from this same group. Boys and girls reared in the same home will usually have similar ideals and standards. It is reasonable then to find one's dates among the brothers or sisters of one's friends or among the friends of one's brothers and sisters, so that wide cultural differences will not complicate the relationship. This suggestion is perhaps more helpful to the younger age group.

Another important point for all young people is the need for deciding one's standard of conduct ahead of time. Many young people, having their emotions aroused by petting, are suddenly faced with the question of how far they shall go. Since they are on a "hot spot," it is no time to make a cool-headed decision. This decision must be made in the peace and quiet of one's own room before the temptation arises. Each young person should ask himself, "Where do I stand on the matter of chastity?" "What is ideal marriage?" "Does it permit premarital sex relations?" "If it comes to the point of deciding between premarital sex relations or losing the friend I've been dating, do I still plan to maintain my standards?" "Shall I go all out for virginity, or do I admit extenuating circumstances?" Once this decision has been made and is clear cut so that the boy or girl is convinced in his own mind as to the ideal he holds and the price he is willing to pay for that ideal, the whole problem is simplified. Having decided that marriage is worth waiting for, the problem becomes how to handle courtship so as to avoid or reduce the temptation to compromise this ideal. As friendship leads on to courtship and as affection develops during courtship it is important that the emphasis in this growing relationship be placed on shared experiences other than the physical. Later on physical intimacy develops readily on the firm basis of this enduring friendship. When emphasis is placed on the physical early in the relationship it becomes increasingly hard to distinguish between love and infatuation, so that an unhappy marriage is more likely to result. Excess petting which constantly stimulates sexual desire may lead a couple to marry prematurely, before either party is ready to assume the responsibilities of marriage and a home. Dating time spent in working and playing together and in exploring one another's interests and abilities is never time wasted.

Another important suggestion regards drinking on or before dates. Alcohol is a depressant, not a stimulant. Even one drink may affect judgment, especially if a boy or girl is emotionally aroused. The best rule is: Don't drink when dating, not even a little. This applies equally to boys and girls.

The custom of blind dating raises special problems. While love at first sight may be possible, the blind date that turns out to be a bore at first sight, or at least after the first hour, is much more probable. The situation is then likely to deteriorate into a petting party. This hazard can be reduced somewhat by insisting that all blind dates be double dates. This is especially important in the case of girls going out with strange men. If a girl insists that the other girl in the foursome be one whom she knows and who shares her ideals and standards of conduct, she can avoid the difficult position of being the only dissenter at a heavy petting party. Two girls who stick together in their opposition to conduct of which they do not approve can usually win.

Petting is so largely dependent on mood that many difficult situations can be anticipated and avoided. Such a simple thing as the urge to go get something to eat may break up a petting session. A couple who after a sexy movie or an especially stimulating dance decide to park on a dark road or seek a secluded bench in a garden are setting the scene for "heavy" petting. Such an occasion calls for eating with a crowd or some other activity where it is light and where there are other people, so that the sexual urge will diminish in intensity.

ENGAGEMENT

As courtship leads to the definite selection of one person as the object of affection and as the prospective mate, the relationship of the young couple will naturally increase in intimacy. During courtship the partner selected for one or a series of dates may be dropped as soon as a more interesting partner is available. Even couples who "go steady" at a rather early stage in their acquaintance may later break up. In this respect the engaged couple are quite different. Engagement signifies a mutual pledge and the occupation of one's interest with the betrothed alone. The period of engagement, be it short or long, is filled with definite preparation for marriage. The young couple during this period are engrossed in plans for everything from the size of their anticipated family, whether the wife shall be employed, how money matters shall be handled, and what church they shall attend, to such remote events as where they wish to live when they retire, or where they will travel if they ever can afford to travel!

Since affection is the basis of this new relationship, it is natural and in order that this affection should be expressed not only by candy and flowers but by petting. If we assume that chastity until marriage is a valid standard, then it is obvious that the amount of petting that is desirable during engagement will vary under different circumstances. In general these circumstances include the length of time the couple must wait until marriage can take place, the ease with which either party becomes sexually aroused, the amount of time that is spent together; the frequency of seeing each other, the privacy from interruptions, and the readiness of each for marriage. If by early training (or lack of it) either party is hesitant about entering into the marriage relationship, then surely it is important that the expression of affection during the engagement period should awaken desire sufficiently to make the sexual relations of marriage seem a natural and right next step. If, however, the couple are physically fully ready for marriage, physical contacts may have to be limited severely during the engagement in order that they be not too strongly tempted to disregard any idea of continence before marriage. This is especially so if the marriage is to be postponed for some time. Many couples, as they approach their wedding date, will find that the temptation for them to consummate their relationship before their wedding becomes very strong. If each understands the problem of the other they may help one another to avoid the situations which make the temptation real and vivid. It may take considerable determination on the part of one or both to find ways of doing things together and at the same time of avoiding complete intimacy. There are so many things that can be done together which demand physical activity or are done with other people or at least permit a lighted room and a certain degree of independent activity that a couple who really desire to avoid sexual intercourse can usually do so. Here again it should be emphasized that the couple must have adequate information and understanding of the physical factors involved. Many girls and a few men do not understand the relationship of petting to sexual desire. This understanding must be clear if the couple are to handle their problem intelligently.

SUMMARY

Each young person must decide what his standard of conduct is to be. Young people need to be prepared by sex education for the problems associated with physical maturity before they are called upon to make a decision in a particular situation as to whether or not to relinquish their chastity. This can be done only by the co-operation of all the resources of our community life in providing straightforward education, instructions, student counseling, premarital advice and adequate opportunities for recreation. Attention must be given to the needs of youth during the periods usually occupied with heterosexual group acquaintances and growing friendships among individuals as well as during courtship and engagement. It is important to stress common interests and mutual participation in work and play as a basis for the later development of affection and its natural expression by physical means. Since the too early development of the habit of stimulating sex desire by petting or other physical means may impair happiness in marriage, it is desirable that young people find other means of enjoyment of one another in their usual daily contacts and dates until such time as marriage is seriously contemplated. The avoidance of such sex-stimulating activities as petting should not be accomplished by threat or fear but by concentration on the positive elements in friendship developed through work and play together. In the present state of our social organization, adequate opportunities for such work and play together are not provided in most communities. Adults and young people alike should bend every effort to find new and better ways of meeting the recreational needs of youth in order that our society may continue to develop toward a higher plane of moral and spiritual life. The problems of young people who are engaged and contemplating marriage are related to the experience of each, the length of time until marriage will take place, the frequency with which they see one another, and the degree to which their affection for one another has developed. They may be helped to limit the degree of intimacy desirable for them by encouraging them to put first emphasis on the solving of other problems related to their anticipated marriage, such as finances, religion, and similar subjects, and to limit the expression of affection to such petting as does not bring undue temptation to either.

NOTE

[1]Henry A. Bowman, *Marriage for Moderns,* New York, Whittlesey House (McGraw-Hill Book Co.), 1942, pp. 208, 209.

Chapter 5

PREMARITAL PHYSICAL EXAMINATION

by Lovett Dewees, M.D.

CONSULTANT TO MARRIAGE COUNCIL OF PHILADELPHIA; CONSULTING PHYSICIAN, BRYN MAWR HOSPITAL

The premarital interview and examination in a doctor's office may be something of an initiation, like a preparation for joining a club. It is important because helpful. This is a discussion of several possible phases of it, from the briefest legal requirements to its varied instructional and practical aspects.

We assume that most people will marry, and they do. They assume that they will have children, and most of them can. But 14 per cent or more of couples will presently seem to be unable to have children. Of these, nearly half can be helped to some degree of fertility by medical aid, and the others will remain childless. The causes of infertility (sterility) are occasionally single, but often multiple or complex. Couples may show as many as four factors hindering or lowering fertility, and of these a little less than half are in the man, and more than half in the woman. Injury, infection, inflammation, surgical operation, queer anatomy, growth defects, glandular imbalance are among the commoner causes of childlessness in either husband or wife. Further discussion of sterility will be found in Dr. Dickinson's chapter on anatomy and physiology.

As knowledge of these matters increases among doctors and becomes known to people generally, a small but growing number of thoughtful young people think of finding out about their ability to have babies before marriage. The first young man who ever asked me for a semen evaluation before marriage was a Chinese student. He expected to go back to China and "found a family."

While doctors may advise premarital examinations in the light of the knowledge they have, the average young people come for more obvious and immediately pressing reasons. They come because the marriage-license clerk demands a medical certificate, or for advice about contraception, or the timid for reassurance, the enlightened for more information. A certain concept of the premarital medical examination is being developed and taught in college and other "marriage courses." It includes not only examination but discussion. An effort is being made in some medical schools and medical journals to prepare doctors for their part. Special natural aptitudes and training are needed. A medical education cannot make a good premarital counselor of every man. His own emotional life must be sound and his approach to intimate matters dignified. I tell medical students never to forget that young people getting married are idealistic and need "adequate authoritative information with a minimum of disillusionment." The less wise counselor may try to tell you too much, something you don't need now, something disturbing. Try to find if you can a sensitive, understanding physician, trained and experienced in this field, with time to talk and listen. Then use what intelligence you have, what frankness you can summon; get your questions answered or your fears dispelled. If you get something to read, get it under advice, if possible, and suited to your needs. The flood of books about marriage includes some quite general and good, some specialized and of limited use for special purposes. Your counseling physician may use judgment in suggesting reading as much as in what he talks about. At any rate, build up your self-assurance and marry with confidence. Dr. Dickinson says, "Success in marriage and in parenthood is teachable."

It used to be said that we bring up our boys to think they know everything and our girls to think they know very little. Certainly there is much for each to learn when married. Premarital sex experience may be of little help or some hindrance. People differ. Skill as a sexual partner is not innate or instinctive, but may be achieved in time by a couple who have first established a good personal relationship. A counseling physician may contribute much toward good sex hygiene and happy adjustments. The facts he gives may be necessary. The attitude, the emotional balance he has and tries to impart may be even more useful. My compulsion to teach and write as I do comes from long experience in premarital counseling of young people who felt sure they were helped. Individual needs will vary greatly, and not every interview will be satisfactory to patient or doctor. But help can be given and received, difficulties forestalled. Postmarital counseling of maladjusted people uncovers troubles which seem to have been at one time preventable. At any rate, one often hears: "I wish I had known this when I married."

Working near a city where there is a marriage council,* I am impressed by the intelligent attitude of patients who have been there first. The council

*Marriage Council of Philadelphia.

aims to include for young people information and discussion of attitudes. It is education at its best, often eagerly accepted by receptive clients, whose need is immediate. A service like this, or sometimes the work of a minister or family society counselor, can do much to interpret the medical examination, can make the doctor's work shorter and more effective. The patient is better prepared. On the other hand, the doctor may uncover emotional problems which, if he cannot handle, he may refer for additional help to a counseling service. A few people may need a psychiatrist's help.

CERTIFICATES REQUIRED

Forty states, three territories, and parts of Canada now require a medical certificate of fitness for marriage before granting a license. Laws of this type are all fairly recent, and more states are likely to enact them. The broad purpose is always to prevent the marriage of people who have a transmissible disease which might be passed on to spouse or offspring. More specifically, they are the outcome of a comprehensive program of the United States Public Health Service to find cases of syphilis and bring them under treatment. In further search for this disease, in some states the law requires and it is everywhere good medical practice to have a blood test early in pregnancy, because it is possible to treat a syphilitic expectant mother and thus prevent the birth of a syphilitic child.

The statutes vary in different states. In general the more recent ones are better as experience accumulates. A typical provision is that each applicant for a marriage license must bring a certificate of medical examination (both physical examination and laboratory blood test) stating that the applicant is free from syphilis or gonorrhea. Sometimes other communicable diseases are specified. The diagnosis of syphilis in any applicant is not a matter of public record. The certificate simply states that the applicant is medically fit for marriage. Those found unfit, by reason of positive blood test (less than 1 per cent of all applicants), do not get their medical certificate and so do not apply for a marriage license until sufficiently treated. Unfortunately, from the public health point of view, a few states have less satisfactory premarital health requirements, a few have none. Crossing a state line to marry without health tests is sometimes possible, but wrong from any point of view.

PREMARITAL EXAMINATION OF A MAN

Premarital examination of a man will begin with getting a history of any relevant illness or operation he has had. Two examples of occasional and possibly surprising findings are that mumps may, in a few cases, have left permanent injury to testicles, or that a childhood operation for hernia may have interfered with the blood supply and nutrition of these glands. The male sexual fluid derives from three separate organs, and each may be examined and evaluated. Transmissible disease of the sex organs or of any organ must be searched for and ruled out. Many men need information or reassurance as to the possible effect of previous illnesses or personal experience on success in the new venture. It is a fair general statement that earlier masturbation need not cause worry as to sex adjustment in marriage.

PREMARITAL EXAMINATION OF WOMEN

A woman's examination also will include inquiry as to fears, anxieties, or unreasonable attitudes. Then a thorough physical examination will answer at least three questions.

1. Is she ready for intercourse?

2. Is she likely to be able to conceive readily and bear a child by normal labor?

3. How can she best control conception?

She is fortunate, or the couple is fortunate, if they are ready to start the first child when they marry. Contraceptives are a nuisance, and it is pleasant to get used to the new relationship without the nuisance. It is good also to be assured that one *can* have a child. There is a real experience of completing maturity, experience in further personality growth, for a woman who passes from potential to actual motherhood. Considering physical fitness and adaptability, childbearing is best begun in the years from 19 to 25. But in recent years, especially during depression or wartime, postponement of childbearing from one to five years after marriage has been almost the rule in large groups of the population. Indeed, innumerable marriages are undertaken only on the confident assumption that conception can be controlled. The reason for delay is often economic. But there is also the feeling in many thoughtful couples that a marriage should have time to ripen and prove its stability before children are invited.

I have made a study of the findings in 650 premarital examinations of women in a middle-class suburban practice. These show convincing reason for urging women to be examined and to have the examination weeks or even months before marriage. They show that 59 per cent were anatomical virgins, but only about 30 per cent had had some experience of coitus, of sexual intercourse. About 10 per cent, though without sex experience, had a relaxed or elastic hymen with adequate opening. Three per cent had some gross disturbance (tumors, cysts, or anatomical defects needing surgery). This 3 per cent included the 2 per cent who had to be told they would never bear children. This information is disconcerting to the prospective bride and may or may not stop the marriage, but certainly is better known beforehand. More than 20 per cent had the less common though still normal posture or position of the uterus called retroversion. This means a uterus (womb) with its larger end leaning toward the back instead of toward the front. All of these were told of it, but were told they were normal and might expect normal experience as to conception and pregnancy. About 35 per cent had some degree of redness or abnormal color or texture of the covering membrane or skin of the cervix, that part of the uterus which can be felt at the deep end of the vagina. Of these 35 per cent, two thirds had an abnormal kind of amount of moisture in the vagina, called a "discharge" or leukorrhea. A few of these had to be warned of possible lowered fertility from "cervicitis," or inflammation of the opening of the uterus.

Should women with doubtful or lowered fertility be told of it? Each case is unique, and its particular answer must be found. We can rarely be absolutely sure of sterility without extensive tests. Some physicians will feel and express the hope that persons with doubtful fertility will not use contraception, or not for long. If it seems likely that only one or two pregnancies can be achieved, and they may take time, there is reason for trying soon if circumstances justify it. It may be quite annoying, it may seem tragic, to use contraceptives most carefully for two or three years, then try to conceive and fail. A final fertility rating may be arrived at only by actual trial over many months. But some factors that might influence fertility can be found and considered before marriage. There surely will be increasing interest in this phase of the physical examination.

CONTRACEPTIVES AND ABILITY TO HAVE CHILDREN

An important question is: Will the use of contraceptives lessen fertility? The evidence is sufficient now to justify the general statement that they will not. If we consider the use of condom, jelly, diaphragm, as now generally taught, a couple will be just as fertile after several years of using them as they would have been at that time without having used them. If fertility rating changes it will be from something else that happened during the passing of time, not from the use of contraceptives. These statements refer to preventives used for each occasion of intercourse. A permanent intra-uterine device may produce irritation or worse, and if ever justifiable is certainly not for the beginning of marriage.

LEUKORRHEA

The management of leukorrhea deserves further discussion. When is it a "discharge" or when is it normal vaginal moisture? The vagina is a collapsed or deflated elastic tube, which is the female organ of copulation and also the birth canal. Its lining membrane or skin must for comfort be normally moist and slippery with mucus. When annoying amounts of mucus are frequently felt, or found on the clothing, a medical consultation and possibly treatment are needed. The commonest source of "discharge" is the abnormal cervix. It is often a matter of misgrowth, more rarely of infection, by no means always "venereal" infection. Douching is rarely curative though sometimes brings transient relief. A discharge which causes itching or burning or soreness may indicate invasion of the vagina or cervix by infectious disease or parasites. The premarital examination also finds some minor troubles which might have been relieved years before. There are convincing reasons for routine annual or occasional pelvic examinations of teen-age girls. Abnormalities may be found and corrected early. Such examination should help establish wholesome natural attitudes about the genital organs. It should accustom the girl to a natural co-operative relation with the examining physician. Such examination need not disturb the hymen as evidence of virginity, and the procedure should be detached from any lingering suggestion of impropriety.

VIRGINITY

In much of our cultural background great importance is given to anatomical virginity. Objective evidence of virginity is in the hymen, a thin double fold of mucous membrane which narrows or makes smaller the opening into the vagina. The conventional assumption is that girls will grow up and not know a man sexually until marriage. They will expect the hymen to be torn or hurt a little with the first sexual experience and need some time for comfortable adjustment to the physical side of marriage. Innumerable women have been through this experience cheerfully and without great pain and accepted it as normal or even desirable. Far too many have dreaded it, sometimes without reason. A significant minority have met difficulty or real distress. Married virgins are occasionally found in any doctor's experience. Pregnant virgins also turn up, married or unmarried, though they are rare.

Sperm cells from semen must go four to six inches from the cervix mouth, up through the uterus, and out through the Fallopian tubes. The vagina from hymen to cervix may in very rare cases be traversed by cells vigorous enough to go on from there to fertilize an egg. Now, more and more, physicians and other counselors are advising physical preparation for coitus before it is attempted. This is usually advised in college courses in preparation for marriage. Several different procedures have been developed for it, depending on the preference of the patient, the time available, and the experience and skill of the physician.

Of the women without previous sex experience, 10 per cent or more will need an extended period (weeks) of preparation before marriage. This may rarely include a small incision of the hymen under local anesthetic, but after incision stretching is still needed. In complete contrast, another 10 per cent will be found to have an elastic hymen with adequate relaxation and may be assured there will be no difficulty in coitus. The average or middle group of 80 per cent are advised to have preparatory stretching but may choose (1) to be stretched in attempts at intercourse, and then some instruction as to posture and procedure will help, or (2) they may elect a rapid stretching in the doctor's office with the help of a local anesthetic, or (3) they may elect a more gradual procedure of self-stretching with methods taught by the doctor to be used at home. Choice of these last two methods has been greatly promoted by the recent interest in the use of the vaginal occlusive diaphragm for contraception. See further discussion of the hymen in the chapter on anatomy and physiology.

Premarital teaching of contraception has become so common that many a girl thinks it is the chief purpose of the premarital interview. The choice of method will depend on several factors, the couple's attitude or prejudice, the woman's anatomy, the doctor's experience. The condom is still a good method, but the vaginal diaphragm with jelly has overtaken and passed the condom in popularity in the twenty-odd years since it became generally available. A contraceptive jelly alone seems simpler to some and, though a little less safe, is much used. A woman fitted with a diaphragm when she has had no coitus or very little should be refitted three or four months after marriage. A possible 20 per cent will then be a little safer with a larger size. Obviously many virgins will need the hymen stretched to practice with the diaphragm, but this practice, this acquaintance with one's anatomy, this getting used to the concept of space in the vagina has often made the beginning of sexual intercourse much easier. I have, in three or four cases of hesitant women over 25, been unwise in urging or allowing the use of the diaphragm in the beginning of marriage. On the other hand, I have had a large number of grateful patients reporting satisfaction with this type of physical preparation and this contraceptive for the beginning of marriage. For a more complete discussion of control of conception, see Dr. Stone's chapter later in the book.

BIBLIOGRAPHY

Shafer, J. K., *Premarital Health Examination Legislation*, Public Health Reports, 69:487, May 1954.

Illinois Department of Public Health, *Premarital Health Examination*, Educational Health Circular No. 62, 1940.

Harper, F. V., *Problems of the Family*, Indianapolis, Bobbs-Merrill, 1953, pp. 226–28.

Chapter 6

THE MARRIAGE COUNSELOR

by Paul Popenoe, Sc.D.

DIRECTOR, AMERICAN INSTITUTE OF FAMILY RELATIONS, AND AUTHOR OF "MARRIAGE BEFORE AND AFTER," "MODERN MARRIAGE," ETC.

Why should anyone consult a marriage counselor? Most persons who do not have special preparation for marriage will benefit by getting specific help when it is needed. No one nowadays supposes himself able to pilot an airplane without any training. Even those of us who have driven our automobiles successfully for a quarter of a century find occasions when we need to call for help. Certainly the establishment and maintenance of a marriage are not any simpler matters than handling a car or plane.

Why do so many persous who would not hesitate to consult a mechanic or plumber feel reluctant to consult a specialist in the problems of marriage? Often they say that "if a man can't solve his own problems no one can solve them for him." To appeal for help in such cases involves, they assert, some peculiar humiliation or degradation. The hesitation is not due to any unwillingness to tell the story; the same woman who refuses to consult an expert has probably already told her story to a dozen friends and relatives. Every chapter in this book furnishes ample evidence that such reluctance is quite out of place.

Someday a marriage counselor will probably be consulted before any marriage is definitely planned. The counselor is pleased when someone comes in and says, "I am looking forward to marriage. I do not have a prospective partner in mind, but I figure that the time to get help is before I do select a mate. I want to get all the information I can that will help me to choose a mate wisely and, still more, to be the kind of partner whom someone else would want to choose." In such a case there are often questions, common in fact to a large part of the human race, which may be answered. The inquirer can be referred to authoritative books on marriage. He can thus learn to understand himself better. He will be able to dismiss any doubts that may bother his mind, as, for instance, about something in his family history. He will get intelligent ideas as to how to go about the job of finding a mate without being swayed too much by the overromantic pictures that come daily from the popular agencies of education, such as the movies, radio, and the short stories in magazines.

When you have actually selected a partner the need of preparation is no less important but still more urgent. Even persons with the best general education are certain to feel as they approach the time of marriage that there are a good many things that they ought to know but don't. They have seen friends and relatives enter matrimony with the same high expectations and the same prospects of success. They have seen these friends and relatives unexpectedly fail. Where is the trouble? How can one avoid such difficulties? Are they avoidable or are they the results of blind forces that are quite outside of human control? Now is the time for the prospective husband and wife to get the best scientific assistance available.

After marriage innumerable problems arise from time to time that have not been foreseen. It is a mistake to suppose that these problems will solve themselves if ignored. Each additional year of marriage brings new situations for which previous experiences have not given preparation. First, perhaps, it is the personal adjustment of husband and wife. Then there are in-laws whose attitudes seem to become quite different from what they were before the wedding. Soon the first baby arrives or is in prospect. The wife may find herself cut off from many activities which she enjoyed before marriage and may not know how to enrich her life satisfactorily without neglecting her husband. All such questions and a hundred others may appear one at a time and demand attention.

People often make their own situation more difficult by imagining it to be more difficult than it really is. "It's no use for me to see a counselor," a woman will declare, "because my husband won't co-operate. I asked him to go with me, but he refused." In that case she should go alone. Most counselors would prefer, naturally, to see both partners—but separately, since few counselors want to see husband and wife together at first. But the marriage can often be saved by seeing either one and helping that one to help the other. The marriage counselor concentrates on the marriage rather than on the individual partner, and he can approach the marriage from either side. No matter how desperate the situation seems to the husband or wife, it will probably not seem quite so hopeless to an outsider who is not emotionally involved and who is used to studying such situations. He knows what complicated and far-reaching results proceed from simple causes and, conversely, he has seen these results disappear when the simple causes were removed. No family situation is desperate enough to justify anyone in saying, "I won't seek any help." It is much better to seek help before the situation has become desperate. But, whatever the nature of the problem, those involved may save much time and trouble by turning for information and guidance to someone who is a specialist in the field.

MARRIAGE-COUNSELING ORGANIZATIONS

In a few large cities there are now organizations set up particularly for marriage counseling. Every large city also has a Family Service Association, maintained by the Community Chest, where trained assistance is available. This, however, may have limitations, such as taking only persons who live in a certain area that is covered by the Community Chest, or persons below a certain level of income. Such an organization, easily found in the telephone book, will be able to make an intelligent referral if unable to give direct help.

The clergyman, the Christian Association, or comparable agency will be able to tell whether any other special organization in your city is available for your purpose. If not, they may at least know of some person skilled in counseling who may be associated with an organization that has some other primary purpose.

Every large city has a variety of counselors, psychologists, and professionals in "guidance." A choice cannot be made profitably at random. Many counselors are skilled in their own work but not particularly qualified in marriage counseling, which is definitely a specialty on its own account.

HOW TO SELECT A COUNSELOR

First, ask yourself exactly what kind of help you need. What is your problem? Do you want help in dealing with your own personality, or with family finances, or with child guidance, or with sexual adjustment, or with recreational opportunities, or with some point of law? Do you need fundamental education as to what marriage really means? Think this through and determine exactly what sort of help you ought to have, ideally at least, before you begin to inquire about what kind of help you can get. It will be much easier for anyone to refer you intelligently with this information.

If you hear of someone who is doing marriage counseling make some further inquiries on your own account. Has this counselor himself had some experience of successful marriage? Is he of high standing in the community so far as character and reputation are concerned? Do not be guided as much by college degrees as by what you can learn of the personality and experience of the proposed counselor. The fact that one has certain degrees gives evidence of certain formal training, but it may not be training for what you particularly want.

Do not expect any one superman or superwoman to be able to deal equally with all the problems that can arise in marriage and family life. Try to select a counselor who has the background of information that you particularly need, after you have decided exactly what you do need. It may turn out, of course, that what you really need is not what you thought you needed. But at least you are going to save yourself some time and wasted motion if you set up a goal and head for it.

If any choice among counselors is available, remember that personality and experience are more important than training in any particular specialty or adherence to any particular "school" of psychology or anything else. Many interesting studies in recent years have shown that equally good results are attained by counselors with widely divergent backgrounds and affiliations. Counseling is as much an art as a science, and the artist is judged by the quality of his work, not by the label he attaches to his style or the reputation of the institution in which he once studied.

Some people are deterred from seeking a counselor by the fear of expense. This is quite unwarranted. Fees of marriage counselors are usually less than those of other professional people—sometimes not more than five or ten dollars an hour. They are usually less than those of divorce lawyers! If you save your marriage by working with a counselor, the expense will be far less than that involved in getting a divorce—and you'll have something to show for your money.

Historically, counseling has been a function of the clergy more than any other one profession. The Roman Catholic Church has always considered this a particular responsibility of its leaders. One Protestant denomination after another is now emphasizing the importance of strengthening family life in this way and is providing special training for its ministers. For a long time to come it seems certain that professional marriage counselors will be found mainly in large cities. People living elsewhere are more likely to find satisfactory help from a qualified clergyman than from any other source.

If you have a problem of heredity take it up with the biology or science teacher at your local high school. If your problem is one of personality the teacher of psychology (provided the high school is large enough to have one) will probably be able to give some practical suggestions. In household management, budgeting, and the economics of homemaking, almost every high school has a home-economics teacher who is qualified to give specific help. In general matters of adjustment of personalities the pastor may be the best prospect. In cases of sexual maladjustment the inquirer's first thought is usually to consult a physician. This will be successful if the problem is primarily a medical or surgical one. In many rural areas there are also innumerable county, state, and federal officials, from the home-demonstration agent to the public-health nurse, and from the director of the 4-H Club to the county probation officer. There is no reason why one who needs help should not appeal to these persons provided they are people with whom some of your secrets are safe from gossip. At least such individuals are likely to be much better able to refer you to competent assistance than is the neighbor over the fence.

The first step in the search for counsel in marriage problems or in anticipation of marriage problems is to get clearly in mind just what type of help is needed. Then one should canvass the community to hunt for such advice. The kind and amount available in a community are usually found to be greater than was thought possible, however disguised, and, short of individual guidance, books and pamphlets are commonly within reach.

PART TWO

The Marriage

SECTION I

Chapter 1

ANATOMY AND PHYSIOLOGY OF THE SEX ORGANS

by Robert L. Dickinson, M.D.*

FORMERLY HONORARY CHAIRMAN, NATIONAL COMMITTEE ON MATERNAL HEALTH;
AUTHOR OF "HUMAN SEX ANATOMY," ETC.

Mating is an activity in which instruction can foster needed skills and forestall grievous blunders. This holds particularly for the mismanaged physical relation oftenest leading to divorce as a result of "leaving it to nature." Indeed, for every occupation save one, examination for fitness is the rule. That one is the most vital and worth while of all—marriage and parenthood—and for it, someday, routine preliminary examination will come to pass, through custom, into code.

First we must sift attitudes toward sex response. Next comes search for physical factors making for distress in intercourse or for frigidity. These disabilities are found in something like one sixth of the maladjustments, with some analyses reporting one half or more of all complaints loaded thereon by unhappy wives and husbands. Yet such discords are largely or wholly preventable.

The mechanical physiology of sex intercourse would seem rather simple. Given affection and eagerness, here is a cylindrical passage, elastic and lubricated, receiving an organ with taper point and tender cover in a quickening rhythm inciting to mutual ecstasy. Nothing would appear less complicated for two persons who have never been indoctrinated with shames or repulsions and are free from fears of conception, infection, or detection. With the anatomical normalities that are usual, happy accord thus hangs on preamble and timing, on gentleness and considerateness. And a certain amount of information about each other's anatomy!

Understanding of this anatomy is only possible through description accompanied with diagram or picture in which the names of the parts are in those medical terms—mostly euphonious—that often lack equivalents in

---

*Dr. Robert L. Dickinson died recently. This chapter has been edited by Dr. Morris Fishbein.

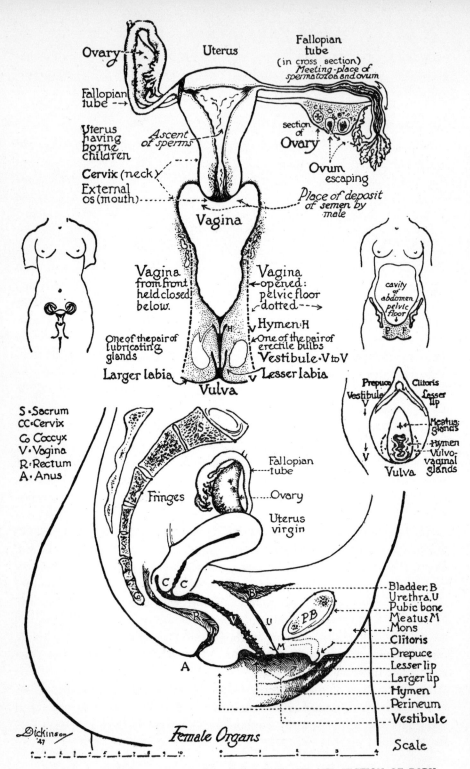

Ovary

Uterus

Fallopian tube
(in cross section)
Meeting-place of spermatozoa and ovum

Fallopian tube --→

Ascent of sperms

section of Ovary

Uterus having borne children

Cervix (neck)

External os (mouth)

Ovum escaping

Vagina

Place of deposit of semen by male

Vagina from front held closed below.

Vagina opened: pelvic floor dotted --→

cavity of abdomen pelvic floor

Hymen·H

One of the pair of lubricating glands

One of the pair of erectile bulbs

Vestibule·V to V

Larger labia

Lesser labia

Vulva

Prepuce

Clitoris

Vestibule V

Lesser lip

Meatus glands

Hymen

Vulvo-vaginal glands

Vulva

S·Sacrum
CC·Cervix
Co·Coccyx
V·Vagina
R·Rectum
A·Anus

Fringes

Fallopian tube

Ovary

Uterus virgin

C C

B

PB

Bladder·B
Urethra·U
Pubic bone
Meatus·M
Mons
Clitoris
Prepuce
Lesser lip
Larger lip
Hymen
Perineum

V

U

M

A

Vestibule

Dickinson '47

Female Organs

Scale

FIGURE I.   FEMALE ORGANS: FRONTAL VIEW AND MID-SECTION OF BODY

everyday English. Without diagrams it is impossible to explain any mechanism; the youth we seek to teach would be the first to ridicule prudish evasion.

THE FEMALE GENITALIA

The flexible channel, the vulvovaginal canal, slants upward and backward to the womb, the uterus, the rounded mouth of which, the cervix, dips into it at right angles (Fig. 1). From each upper corner of the flattened pear-shaped uterus (Fig. 1) a thin, expanding tube runs out to the ovary, to bring down an egg each month for more than thirty years. The widened top of the vagina is the space where the male organ, the penis, deposits millions of sperms, in order that some may ascend through uterus and tube to reach the egg, the ovum. We conveniently divide the female sex organs into two groups: those external parts making up the vulva, and the internal comprising the vagina, the uterus that nests the ovum and grows the baby, and the tubes that loop around the hanging ovary—with the hymen standing at the meeting point. In Figure 1 the front half of the uterus and of one tube and ovary are removed to show interiors. The ovum is escaping from its follicle into the egg trap of the outreaching fringes of the tube, and the neighboring puckered egg sac is its aftermath that, by its secretion, effects the nesting in the uterus. Closure of the bristle-sized tubal channel at the inner end, or gluing together of the mobile fringes, produces about a third of the sterilities.

The portal of entry, the vulva, is closed in a lengthwise cleft between two rounded, tapering cushions covered with fine hair, called the outer or larger lips or labia majora. Above where they broaden and join is the pubic area, at the base of the abdomen, with its crosswise hillock named the mons, covered with its hair shield of triangular shape. As these outer labia are drawn apart there appears an arched recess an inch in depth and two in length known as the vestibule. The vestibule is lined with smooth mucous membrane kept moist by a pair of glands called the vulvovaginal glands. The ducts of these glands open just outside the hymen and furnish abundant lubrication during sex excitement in order to facilitate entry. The vestibule supplies the funnel of access for the douche tube and the menstrual tampon, for the cervix cap in control of conception and the penis during sexual intercourse. On the inner aspects of the larger labia, on each side of the archway, the inner or lesser lips or labia converge above as hanging skin folds. They vary markedly at times in size and shape and surface and projection. They meet over the top of the clitoris to form its cover, called, as in the male, the foreskin or prepuce. The clitoris, not unlike a miniature penis without its water passage, is the external center of erotic sensation. Its rounded end, the glans, is endowed with closely packed nerve ends. This tip is about the size of a pea, or a quarter inch across as average. It has no visible shaft and may enlarge and harden and darken in erection, but erection is relatively infrequent. Erectility, as a somewhat tense filling of veins, is found more often in the little sausage-shaped bulb of the vestibule on each side and in the veins of the walls of the vagina, high up laterally, both shown in Figure 1. Under the prepuce the trifling white material is not secretion but shed surface cells.

On the rear wall of the vestibule, under the overhang of the clitoris, is a tiny slit, the meatus, the opening of the urethra, exit channel from the bladder. The meatus has two tiny pockets, as the second favorite resort of the gonorrhea germ. Below this is seen the slight projection of the crescent of the hymen as puckered pink foldings of delicate mucous membrane, thinner and softer than the lower eyelid, and hiding the entrance to the vagina. In the virgin the hymen admits the owner's full forefinger as an average, or is an inch in diameter deployed. This is ample for douche tube or commercial tampon, provided the sensitiveness is lessened or lost by douching or gentle placement. The hymen is easily rendered elastic by careful repeated stretching, so that there is rarely reason for cutting or notching or for forcible dilation by the doctor preceding marriage.

The back rim of the vestibule fully drawn open is a thin cross fold of skin (unless there has been some damage in childbirth) with the name of fourchette. An inch farther to the rear, set back in the groove between the buttocks, lies the anus, the opening from the bowel, with its radiating folds.

In the drawing of the mid-section of the body (Fig. 2) the bones are the solid sacrum that continues the spinal column down to its hinged little tip, the coccyx, and the narrow strip of the front part of the girdle of the bony pelvis, the symphysis, from which hangs the clitoris. Across this opening or outlet in the bones stretches a remarkable supporting structure called the pelvic floor (Fig. 1). In the standing posture it holds up all the interior organs. Yet it has three gaps that must close themselves securely and automatically except for the times of the four escapes, namely, the voiding of urine and bowel contents, the slow trickle of blood and mucus during the menstrual days, and finally the escape of the baby after a long softening and enlarging process.

This mechanism is concerned in voluntary and involuntary activities and particularly in the climax and the throb of sex relations. The main element of this structure is muscular, in edge-to-edge loops or slings in thin layers, called the levator group, together with the accompanying sheaths and connective tissues and some filling pads of fat. The whole resembles, in form and thickness, one's two hands held with interlacing fingers, palms upward, curved cupwise. The vaginal entry has a thin muscle loop of its own, but this is feeble compared with the twin circle, the anal double sphincter. It is the sweep of the levators, in a loop like four thin fingers, along the sides and rear of the lower vagina, and with front attachments, that keeps the vagina a flattened passage. The loop can resist entrance either by voluntary contraction or involuntary cramp. Whereas the upper and much wider half of the vaginal tube, its front and rear walls in contact, (accounting for the expanded appearance in Figure 1), is an elastic bag around the projecting lower tip of the uterus. The dotted upright side lines show the passage stretched as during intercourse. Moreover, it is important to remember that the uterus is so suspended by India-rubber-like bands called ligaments that it (with the bladder) can readily move up and away or aside with each to-and-fro thrust of the penis. This synthetic resiliency of Nature is so well distributed for happy mating that the short six inches of the vulvovaginal receptacle readily accommodate the long six inches of the penetrant. The anterior vaginal wall is about two and one half inches long, the posterior three and one half, while from hymen to outside of the larger labia averages one and one half inches.

In a certain number of women orgasm is accompanied by rhythmic contraction and relaxation of these muscular bands looping around the lower vagina, and this has been labeled the acme of "real" orgasm. The most intense climax, however, may lack such activity. This limitation to one special form of reaction is an excellent example of the dogmatic definitions that often appear in all sex literature.

The vagina is not furnished with glands to provide secretion, yet is moist. This is due to the mucus coming down from the inch-long canal of the cervix with its generous equipment of glands, especially active during sexual excitement.

Erotic Response. Erotic response can originate or even center in almost any part of the body. The chief focal points are in the front of the vulva and in the lower vagina. The tips of certain nerve ends that respond in excitement and orgasm, while concentrated in numbers in the visible, touchable part of the clitoris, are distributed freely in the lesser labia and the lower vagina, as on its front wall, while absent higher up in the passage. Systematic study of the variety of areas sensitive to sex play discovers the variations in different persons. Habit may develop restriction to some particular spot, but any statement that one location of pleasure or orgasm is "normal" and satisfactory, while other regions are not so or less so, belongs in the category of the unscientific and manufactures unwarranted disappointments. The avoidance of finger play within the hymen before marriage in those whose active ovaries awaken them sexually early in life tends to fix attention on the clitoris region. Here any habit of rhythmic pressures may produce various labial enlargements that demonstrate which nerve ends answer in this person. It is the husband's technique to discover such area and rhythm of self-relief in order to ensure mutual timings. Long repeating of friction on the clitoris tends no more to enlarge this organ than the same practice enlarges the penis. Size has little relation to function in either. There are steady averages in genital anatomies, but there are also variants, all within satisfactory activity. However, the injuries of labor, not properly stitched, and some relaxed tissues may defeat felicity until repaired. A small vulva of the persistent juvenile type may require special massage before marriage. All these and the easily freed adhesions of the prepuce are remediable when diagnosed at the premarital physical examination.

Statistics on Menstruation. Each month from the age of thirteen to nearly fifty the uterus prepares its lining to nest an egg. When a fertilized ovum does not come down out of the tube the top layers of this thin mucous membrane are shed in minute fragments in an ooze of blood and mucus for four or five days, to the amount of two to four ounces or up to a half cupful, as an average. Although twenty-eight days is the commonest type of repeat, the cycle may run between twenty-three and thirty-six, but even with those who consider themselves regular a range of eight days is found. During the thirty-five years or so of fertility, pregnancies in the first six or seven and in the last eight or nine are much less desirable, so that a third of the capacity for conception is excessive. Even with four children and absence of periods during full nursing, there may well be four hundred menstruations. The beginning and ending of the function may show irregular intervals, and fertility is at times low at the start and usually so toward the "change of life." Illness, anxiety, travel, and excessive tire may upset the timing.

Ovulation. At the start of the monthly cycle the tiny master gland at the base of the brain, the pituitary, sends chemical orders along the blood stream (the hormone estrogen) to the ovary. Hence, of the 25,000 potential ova ready, one outstrips the others, to ripen, by the midmonth, into a speck in the clear dewdrop on the surface of that olive-shaped organ. A spurt tosses it into the egg trap made by the seizing fringes of the tube (Fig. 1). This occurs about fourteen days before the next period is due, ranging from the ninth to the sixteenth day of the cycle, counting from the first day of the period, but illness or strain may affect the orderly procedure, so that verily no day of the whole series is an impossible one for the egg to be fertilized.

Thus, within the outer end of the tube a pin-point target is up for about one day, while a barrage of sperms may attack for some two days, with a single cell allowed to penetrate. Then the empty pocket whence came the ovum fills with blood and proceeds to manufacture a chemical (another hormone, progestin) which stirs the uterine lining to prepare itself to nest the egg. Developing on its travel inward, down the maze of tubal channels (Fig. 1), the egg pauses to select its site within the week of the start and, if sound, has nearly nine chances out of ten of producing a living child. The defectives Nature rejects, and thus one third to one half of the interruptions of pregnancy are spontaneous endings. Intercourse for conception is therefore timed by studying some months of intervals to find when this fourteenth day occurs, and covers it by sperm deliveries on the tenth, twelfth, and fourteenth days. The idea that orgasm produces ovulation is only true of a few animals, nor does orgasm bear any proven relation to successful conception. Twins occur about once in eight births from the release of two ova, with fraternal twins often unlike, or from a single ovum with the twins identical.

The second function of the ovary is the giving out of the hormone that develops bodily sex characteristics and sex forms, and its activity persists after it no longer produces ova and after menstruation ceases. Another chapter amplifies this.

COMMENT ON THE SAFE PERIOD

A simple method by which a woman could detect her day of ovulation would have two important bearings. First, she could arrange for conception at the time wisest in her marriage and finances. Second, she could postpone or cancel pregnancy very nearly at will. Research with this object in view is persistently under way, but the only present symptom is in rare individuals who show the sign of mid-period pain called *Mittelschmerz*. However, by checking on a printed chart the menstrual days during eight to twelve months, the degree of regularity is calculated, with the estimate for the fourteenth day preceding the period. As an accompaniment, the temperature by mouth, vagina, or rectum is taken exactly on waking and carefully noted as it is put down on paper or chart in tenths of a degree, any upset or cocktail party being noted. A consistent rise, month after month, at or close to a certain day in the cycle, gives many women the time of ovulation as checked up by the physician who specializes in birth-control advice. Furthermore, someday a self-test for spotting the special variety of limpid mid-month mucus from the cervix, of the kind hospitable to sperms, may yet be found. The changes in the lining of the vagina in a series of microscopic tests can give evidence offered by the shed cells that make up the normal white discharge, the slight "natural leukorrhea." Also, minute samples of the lining of the uterus taken by the doctor in his office (biopsy) give information, especially when there is doubt whether ovulation skips or is absent. Once a means is discovered of self-diagnosis for the fertile and non-fertile parts of the interval between periods—the latter called the "safe period"—provided no disturbance of one's living has occurred, then measures for control of conception will be needed during part of the month only. If pregnancy starts, the temperature stays up for the omitted period and is confirmed by a standard morning urine test when ten days overdue.

THE MALE GENITALIA

The parts related to reproduction and sex play in man and those filtering water and waste products from the body conjoin and interlock. In one of the upper diagrams of Figure 3 the cut-open kidney is brought down from above and shows its collecting funnel, the pelvis, leading to its drainpipe, the ureter, which droops in long curves to enter the bladder from the rear. From this reservoir for urine its outlet, called the urethra, is seen distended and terminating at the opening in the tip of the penis, the meatus whence both urine and semen are delivered. Glands along this tubing lubricate it and secrete the clear mucus at its outlet in erotic excitement. In the diagram (Fig. 2), the testicle on the right, hanging in the rear of the penis, is shown with its sac of flexible skin, the scrotum, while on the left the two-inch twin oval is opened up to suggest its compartments of microscopic tubings. This gland is the factory for the male cells, the sperms or spermatozoa, as well as for the male sex hormone or activator of maleness in body forms and sex urges. Its annex, the epididymis, is the finishing shop and also a part of the storage space for these cells. Up from each of the latter organs a pipe line rises through the spermatic cord (Fig. 2) with its many tortuous veins. This is the vas, with a pin-sized channel and strong muscular layers that shunt the minute product, hour by hour, upward through the groin into the body. Then the vas runs round behind the bladder to its base, to end in an elongated expansion, the ampulla, which forms the chief storage space for sperms. This reservoir, not yet commonly recognized as such, is one and one half inches long, has a fine nozzle leading into the upper urethra, the ejaculatory duct. Close to the ampulla, and the size of a flattened testicle, lies a laboratory, the seminal vesicle, for producing mucus which, with that of the prostate, forms the part teaspoonful which sweeps the sperms along at ejaculation and initiates and activates their swimming vigor. Its outlet joins that of the ampulla as it penetrates the prostate, the solid gland like a big horse chestnut beneath the bladder and circling its outlet. Such crowding

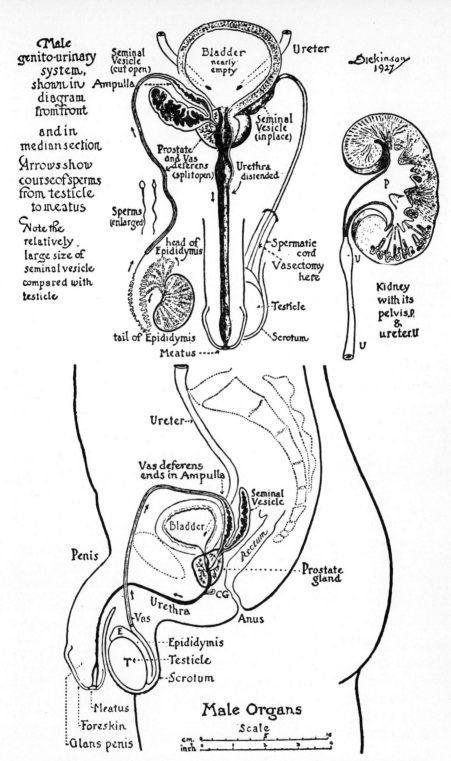

Male genito-urinary system, shown in diagram from front and in median section

Arrows show course of sperms from testicle to meatus

Note the relatively large size of seminal vesicle compared with testicle

Seminal Vesicle (cut open)

Ampulla

Bladder nearly empty

Ureter

Dickinson 1927

Seminal Vesicle (in place)

Prostate and Vas deferens (split open)

Urethra distended

Sperms (enlarged)

head of Epididymis

Spermatic cord

Vasectomy here

Testicle

Scrotum

tail of Epididymis

Meatus

Kidney with its pelvis, P. & ureter, U

P

U

U

Ureter

Vas deferens ends in Ampulla

Seminal Vesicle

Bladder

Rectum

Penis

Prostate gland

Urethra

CG

Vas

Anus

E

Epididymis

T

Testicle

Scrotum

Meatus

Foreskin

Glans penis

Male Organs

Scale

cm.

inch

FIGURE 2.   MALE ORGANS: FRONTAL VIEW AND MID-SECTION OF BODY

activity helps carry these rotating, whip-tailed tadpoles through the uterus to their destination, to the rendezvous with the ovum in the outer end of the tube (Fig. 1). The ampulla holds four to six rations, the earlier deliveries each from two to six hundred million sperm cells—cells so diminutive that it takes two to span a thin hair.

The penis is here shown relaxed, with its somewhat conical top, the glans, protected by the foreskin, or prepuce, the thin, elastic cover which is wholly or partly absent in those who have been circumcised. The white substance found under the foreskin is made up of shed cells. When quiescent, the length of the penis, along its upper surface, averages some four inches in the white adult, with a range of variation, while its diameter is about one and a quarter inches. Erect, our recent figures (curiously enough the only considerable series of observations on this pivotal problem) give the average measurement on the upper border as six and a quarter inches, starting from its base, with the tissues there compressed against the bone. The largest grouping of diameters is one and a half inches.

At the climax of the sex act in the male—that is, at orgasm—ejaculation drives out in spurts the three elements that make up the total half teaspoon-ful up to a teaspoonful (less than most suppose), first the sperms, then the prostatic secretion and that of the seminal vesicle, to mix together in what old English dubbed "the seed" and we label "semen." In ten to twenty min-utes after deposit in the upper vagina the whirling crisscross of sperms begins to penetrate mucus on and within the cervix, the rate of drive seen under the microscope being an inch in eight minutes. Therefore, to study conditions favorable or unfavorable to conception, one step is to draw by long dropping tube from within the channel some of the mucus for the doctor to view through the high-power lens.

The duration of the act of sex intercourse varies widely with individual desire and skill, but series of reports show averages running from two to five minutes intromission, with an average for orgasm of fifteen seconds, or a quarter minute—an oblivion too intense for any count until our statistical era—and with the same wide range in ability to repeat at long or short intervals.

No bodily function of human beings compares with sex intercourse for far-reaching effects from a single act, or for manifold implications based on total time of action. New life or no life hangs on seconds. The sum of the average activity of a twelvemonth—exclusive of foreplay—runs only to a few hours—less than the dark of one day, and the span of climax adds up to a half-hour a year.

For frequency of intercourse the average in certain series of studies among

American white adults runs above twice a week. The range covers gaps of days and weeks and months at one end and coitus daily or oftener at the other—any of these with good health accompanying the practice. There is no standard or "normal" because of this wide difference in endowment and capacity among individuals, because of the variant habits and mores at different economic and social levels, and by reason of the diversity of welcome between the partners, and in consequence of decline at older ages. Erection in boys from babyhood and orgasm long before ejaculation culminate in adolescence in masturbation. Self-relief is nearly or quite universal in the male, and in some degree in the female, in a third to orgasm, in another third short of climax, in one large series among the well-educated. In both sexes homosexual play is the substitute or deviation most concealed but infrequently leading to permanent addiction. The great disparity lies in the male's biological power and urgency and frequency as compared with that of the woman, with her education in reactions of shame and fear and the risks of pregnancy. The facing of actuality, sane sex education, and knowledge of techniques and protection can, in time, bring better balance and happy adjustment.

Posture during intercourse has its basis in the anatomy of the biped, together with the distribution of the special nerve endings. The method commonest in our culture under the very early ecclesiastical prescription is with the wife reclining and the husband above. (His weight is carried on elbows or hands.) This attitude may be reversed for her to regulate pressures, rhythms, or duration. Avoidance of abdominal pressure, as in pregnancy, may foster rear entry. Side-by-side positions favor prolongation. Across the lap permits casual affection. In any of these the closeness that yields clitoris seizure and excursion by the two pubic areas is a consideration, whenever this is the main focus of feeling. Variety and adaptation in techniques and adventure in environment belong to all loving.

CONFORMING TO EACH OTHER: THE HYMEN

The doctor, in examining two or three weeks or more before the wedding, bears in mind the shapes and measurements given in the preceding pages. He knows how husbands and wives adapt to each other. In the case of the patient who has been delivered of a child or of children with proper care, the vulvovaginal entrance readily admits his two examining fingers in their thin rubber gloves, or even three. With the wife who has not had a child but regular satisfactory intercourse, two fingers enter full length without discomfort, owing to the recurrent stretch and massage of happy marriage. With the virgin he finds an average opening that admits two joints of the lubricated gloved forefinger, or a one-inch diameter (Fig. 1). Secondly, he finds a sharp edge. Lastly, tenderness. There are many variants, but this is the most usual record for anatomical virginity.

These three criteria call for clear understanding of modifications. No other part of the body has developed more crises or curiosities than this gauge for marriage. None has focused such guesses, lacking all systematic study or competent depiction, until recent times. For this little crescent is susceptible of progressive elastic distensibility under certain circumstances without loss of continuity of edge and with quick resumption of its puckered form. The use of the douche and the narrow menstrual tampon remove tenderness and favor dilatability. A doctor's careful local treatments needed for the virgin with inflammation of the cervix (comparable to her sore throat in frequency and innocency) does stretch the circle somewhat. The third of our educated class of women with normally strong sex sensation who secure relief by finger play include some who add to the surface rhythmic pressures a finger entry within the hymen. Long engagements with petting to orgasm may develop this practice. With all such instances the digital examination or calibration with a cone gives the clue and tells the degree of further stretching required to forestall any pain or unnecessary damage on the wedding night. The only issue is the decision when we elect to begin to be honest, or to hide behind the still accredited tale of girls born without hymens or possessed of the hypothetical hymen of athletics or accidents. I have recorded premarital dimensions for several decades but I am still searching for a case of a hymen broken by a picket-fence or a bicycle.

For the tight hymen the doctor advises one of three treatments. The first is adapted to almost any girl or woman. Gradual finger stretch by the patient herself, begun in the hot bath or following a douche to render surfaces insensitive, is repeated with good lubrication and painlessly for one to two weeks or thereabouts, according to the results—attainment of her three-finger entry without surface break or notch or irritation. Dilators are sometimes suggested, like graded test tubes or the rubber forms available. The penis as a dilator after marriage is a possible but somewhat defective mechanism, with a thickness of one and one half inches to enter a one-inch thin membrane clumsily. Office dilation is often recommended, especially when the wedding is but a couple of days from the consultation. Although the local anesthetic renders this painless, raw surfaces result and the husband's active honeymoon attentions keep them open. This is timing as poor as the old standard first-night rape for the sake of the red evidence. Actual cutting is needed only with the unusually thick hymen, the one that resembles the whole bridge between the thumb and forefinger. Moreover, this is no real "operation" but merely scissor snips for notches, two or three, not more than an eighth or quarter inch deep. Deplorable words have always gone with these tiny injuries, even in the writings of counselors. The stock terms are "rupture," "breaking," "tearing," and "hemorrhage." "Dilation" or "dilatation" should be our title and procedure and absence of tenderness our test.

The partitioned hymen is a rarity, the closed hymen still more so, as discovered when menstrual fluid is retained at puberty.

THE VAGINA

The vagina varies in form and depth, but its elastic character in the upper parts, combined with the free displaceability of the organs previously described, yields fewer problems among the married. One woman in five may have some degree of backward tip of the uterus and thus a shorter passage. In the absence of inflammation or swelling or symptoms this retroversion or retroflexion need not be classed as a disorder to be treated or operated upon. Forward bend of the uterus may also shorten the passage, especially if it is part of defective local development or infantilism. Unless the walls are really basically short, regular intercourse does the stretching, the point of the penis by-passing the cervix into the upper pocket of the vagina. The S-shaped pessary that holds a backward displaced uterus in place is out of the way of the penis. As to the lower vaginal canal, the loop of muscles we described may, through spasm that is involuntary or through fear or refusal or pain from inflammation, hamper entry. The athletic woman may have thick muscles hereabouts, but excitement relaxes these. And in some there is definite throbbing. The upper vagina lacks nerve ends which might render deep thrusting painful, except in the presence of swellings or infections. After the change of life some shrinking of the walls may be found in the wives neglected, and the lining tends to grow thin and pale in any case. Happily, certain suppositories restore the hormone balance so well that the lining returns to previous receptive stages.

THE BONY PELVIS

The compartment holding or supporting all these organs is the circle of bone between the sockets of the hip joints, built to let us stand upright. This rigidity pays one penalty. The baby must make a roundabout exit through a curved passage of irregular form, long behind, short in front (Fig. 1), with entry or exit occasionally twisted. The doctor, at the premarital examination, can spot any definite deformity or narrowing of the interior of the bones. Late in pregnancy pictures by X ray yield clear measurements which show just how much room there is for the child's head to pass, molded as it will be from ball shape to egg shape by the pressures of the contractions of the uterus.

Finally, it takes some understanding of this bodily machinery for love to express itself happily in enduring ultimate intimacies. With sex education, familiarity must breed not contempt, but content.

THE ANATOMY OF STERILITY

One marriage in eight or ten is infertile, however steadily the couple may try for years. Early search for reasons and special skills in relief are rather recent. The average wait before consulting a doctor is two or three years, yet the average start of a pregnancy, in the absence of birth control, is three or four months. Even when under way, in about a tenth of pregnancies Nature may reject defectives or ill health of the mother may bring interruption—in conditions often curable. All barren marriages used to have the cause laid at the door of the wife and in some cultures barrenness was ample reason for divorce. Indeed consent of childless husbands to be examined dates back but a few decades, with the initial general American openmindedness. Because a man possessed full vigor in sex relations he was certain he was fertile. Now, however, examination begins with the husband because over a third of the faults belong to him, while, with a given couple, among the usual two or more reasons for delay or impossibility, some of the responsibility is likely to be his. Also, it is simpler to discover male than female factors.

Sperm meets egg. When both are sound, and the way is clear, and the timing is right, male cells travel through bristle-sized channels upward from the testicles (Fig. 4), and—when deposited at the mouth of the womb—travel outward from its cavern (Fig. 1) through tubes of somewhat like caliber, in order that one cell may enter the ovum to start a new life. Closure of either of these canals accounts for a large part of sterility—indeed in woman for about a third of her share. Whether the obstruction be in epididymis or vas or in Fallopian tube, these blockades constitute the most difficult—or the incurable—set of conditions to attempt to conquer. To understand this geography we need to consult anatomical maps like Figures 3, 4 and 5.

The sperm factory must turn out good product. Full-sized testicles may be disqualified by old infections, as from gonorrhea or other inflammations or from a complication of mumps. The commonest male fault is the finding of the following defects in the spermatozoa, either singly or in combination. The shapes may be defective or showing immaturity or deformity (Fig. 5); the activity may be sluggish or entirely absent; the numbers may be

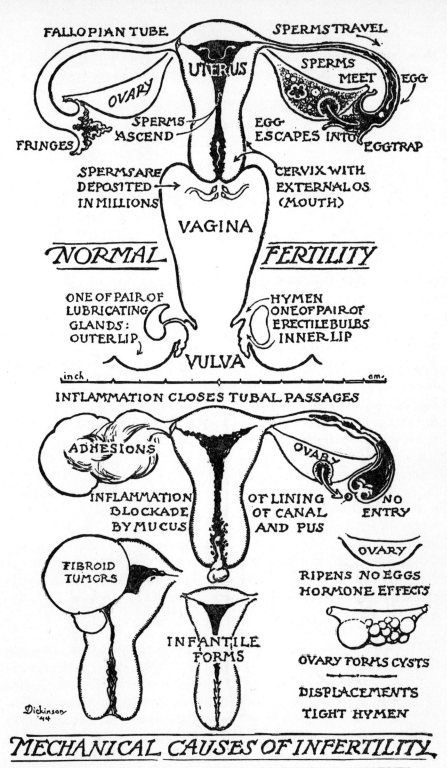

FALLOPIAN TUBE   SPERMS TRAVEL

UTERUS

OVARY   SPERMS MEET   EGG

SPERMS ASCEND

FRINGES   EGG ESCAPES INTO   EGG TRAP

SPERMS ARE DEPOSITED IN MILLIONS   CERVIX WITH EXTERNAL OS (MOUTH)

VAGINA

NORMAL FERTILITY

ONE OF PAIR OF LUBRICATING GLANDS: OUTER LIP   HYMEN ONE OF PAIR OF ERECTILE BULBS INNER LIP

VULVA

inch   cm.

INFLAMMATION CLOSES TUBAL PASSAGES

ADHESIONS   OVARY

INFLAMMATION BLOCKADE BY MUCUS   OF LINING OF CANAL AND PUS   NO ENTRY

FIBROID TUMORS   OVARY RIPENS NO EGGS HORMONE EFFECTS

INFANTILE FORMS   OVARY FORMS CYSTS

Dickinson '44   DISPLACEMENTS TIGHT HYMEN

MECHANICAL CAUSES OF INFERTILITY

FIGURE 3.   NORMAL FEMALE FERTILITY AND CAUSES OF INFERTILITY

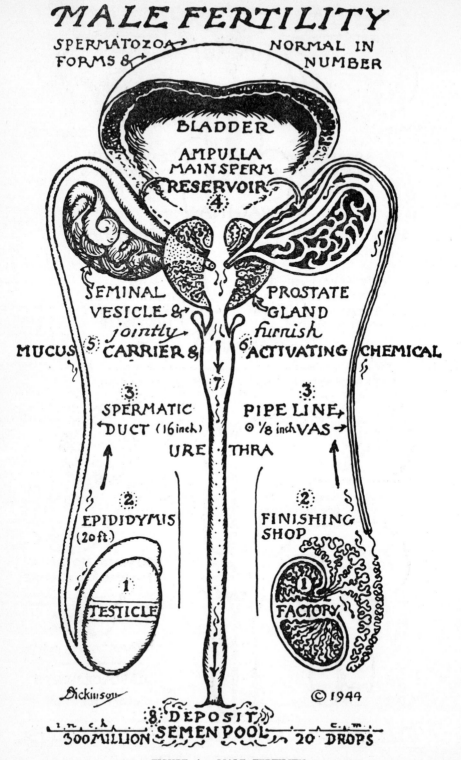

FIGURE 4.   MALE FERTILITY

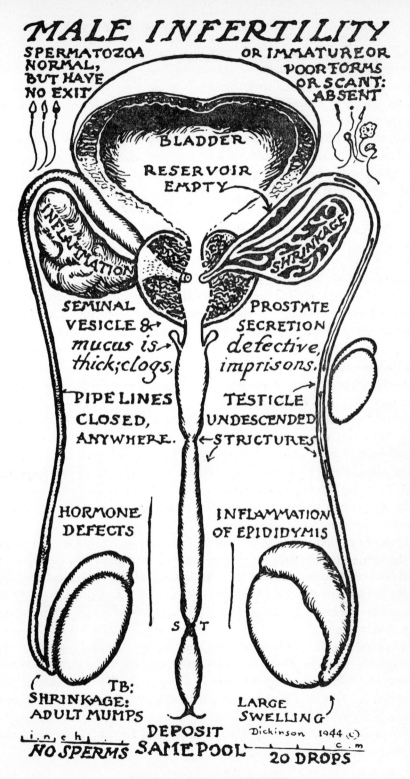

FIGURE 5. MALE INFERTILITY

small or, with full quantity of ejaculate, there may be no sperms at all. Judgment concerning quality of sperms and sperm counts are new accomplishments, for of old any lively swing across the field under the microscope was supposed to guarantee fertility. Now numbers and forms are counted, swarming is studied hour after hour. Soon after intercourse, a drop of mucus is sucked out of the canal above the mouth of the womb by a long dropping tube and is studied with a microscope. In a few puzzling instances a speck can be nipped out of the testicle to make the final decision on good or bad machinery in that workshop.

The fault may be with the ovary. Monthly ripening of eggs may fail from poor health, lack of some one hormone as from thyroid incompetence or a low vitamin. Inflammation can imprison ova (Fig. 3). The tubes are often offenders. Their flaring fringes may be glued together by inflammation (Fig. 3) or their branching inner gullies cemented. This follows some hard labors or fevered convalescences afterward, or from inexpert abortion operations or from gonorrhea or other inflammations, as during a neighboring appendicitis perhaps not acute enough for operation. A number of such closures yield to persuasive air pressure applied through the uterine cavity, but few operations for reopening or reimplanting closed tubes succeed.

To grow the egg the uterus must be of adult development (Fig. 3). We saw that its linings undergo striking changes every few days between the menstrual periods, by chemical blood orders called hormones. The ovum, when fertilized, comes into the flat cavern and hunts about for a spot for attachment. For the sperms to have reached that ovum from the vagina the canal of the cervix must not be pinhole size at either end of that important inch. Nor may this canal be clogged by viscid mucus or unhealthy discharge (Fig. 3), though such catarrh is not uncommonly encountered. Fibroid or ovarian tumors may call for removal.

Lack of erection sufficient to prevent entry into the vagina for the deposit of the sperms is rare. Still more so is the lack of descent of the testicles in fetal life into the scrotum (Fig. 5). The opening of exit—the meatus—along under the base of the penis is a curiosity. Such also is a closed hymen, discovered by the distress of banked-up blood in a postponed start of menstruation. The absence of uterus or ovaries is revealed by absent periods. When a vagina is missing it may be fabricated, and best by inward push and stretch of a pocket into the double-walled partition found between urethra and rectum (imagining the vagina absent in Figure 1). This is far simpler than dissecting a cavity in this partition with a lining that is borrowed from some nearby surface.

When the husband has no sperms at all or they persist in poor quality after careful treatment, adoption is recommended. If this is refused, one means remains that is besought by thousands of couples in these days. At the time of ovulation, into the mouth of the womb or at its mouth a slender tube places a little sperm from a donor selected with all care. His identity is never known to the couple or theirs to him. His health and heredity, his mind and race and religion, even his resemblance, are taken into account. This is called artificial insemination. With the expert and conscientious specialist success is reported in three out of four to four out of five fertile women, say within three months of three trials each, with some at once and a few over longer time. The birth is in charge of a different, uninformed doctor, who can therefore sign the birth certificate. Thus the baby belongs and time banishes memory of method.

In this matter of sterility there is hope that in some not too distant future incurables will be discovered early. This will be when the custom of adequate examination prevails, and at a time preferably before the wedding day is chosen, and still better before the engagement is announced.

The Anatomy of Early Pregnancy. The egg is particular where it nests in the uterus. It avoids the crevices at the sides of the cavern, and rarely hangs from the roof, but chooses the flat walls, near and front. This pinpoint speck draws such nourishment from the mucous lining as speedily to multiply the vast variety of cells which build themselves into all parts and organs of a new being.

The time of spontaneous abortion runs under a third in the second month and below half in the third, with actual death of the embryo usually weeks earlier. Therapeutic or elective abortion required to save the life or health of the mother is done before the third month, preferably before the second period, with its cherry size and softness of that time (Fig. 8).

Physiology and Continence. In the foregoing pages the vital midparts have been linked to function—to behavior. The function called fertility has little flexibility in the most healthy. Thus the usual test for chastity is abstention from sexual intercourse until marriage. For advocates of this criterion who are honest their program calls for frankness in study of substitutes and weighing acceptance of alternatives. For from adolescence onward the male has a rhythm of release of continuously manufactured seminal constituents a certain number of times each week. Involuntary emission being a method incomplete for relief, and generally rejected, proponents of physical chastity can hardly avoid facing the self-relief of recurring tension nearly universal among men, or mutual sex play, or petting to climax. For the woman this convention confronts any inherited endowment of sex capacity and its developed rhythm under the widely varying circumstances of her upbringing.

We may no longer evade that strange overplus of sex urge and fertility which Nature of old was forced to foster to secure survival. With an unparalleled mass of new data in process of coming before us, we dare not longer side-step logical biological reasoning. We face the hard fact of a gap of eight to twelve years between puberty and the age of marriage, and that it is just in this gap that the highest recurrences of sex gland activity are now found to belong in the male, by Kinsey. Nor this alone. The possibilities of extensive expanding function for the female arrive with the impending protection from the former triple penalties on sex expression.

That continence pays no penalties, as constantly claimed, is making denial of accumulating evidence, such as the conditioning of the abstinent man of forty or thirty-five to impotence or incompetence and mental blockades. Even those who teach the doctrine of suppress and sublimate often approve many of the newer freedoms among unchaperoned young people and the healthiness of the newer relatively naked fashions of hot-weather clothing or sun bathing, yet seek to keep to the sexual restrictions of the days when no "lady" showed an inch of stocking above her high buttoned shoetop. This is to endorse opportunity and to deny its temptations. This is to create a need for a new dividing line. This is to provide the most difficult of all problems to the student of the interlocking of healthy body function with emotional and spiritual equilibrium.

The alternative to abstinence until marriage involves many gradations, often labeled promiscuity. This is common practice even when coitus is far from casual but restricted to the fiancée, as in long engagements, to lover or trusted friend.

Weighing the pros and cons in the matter may not overlook the three conditions bearing on standards which are relatively recent. These are freedom from conception, infection, and detection-with-condemnation. While birth-control measures in general supply protection that is about 85 per cent effective, intelligent instructed methods consistently carried out yield almost sure immunity, of which the remarkable scarcity of pregnancy among college students running these risks will be shown. The general availability of one of the two most effective means, the condom, the rising value of jellies steadily advertised, and the adaptations to individual conditions are becoming generally known to young people, with no other possibility than widening access to this knowledge and material.

The second condition has to do with the condom as practically sure protection against venereal disease; the immediate prophylaxis after exposure that helps; the sulpha drugs and penicillin that cure in a few days—information that is spreading fast. Moreover, the increase of self-protection on the part of the commercial prostitute will have to be reckoned with, and her persuasion that the need for her professional services is lessening.

The third condition, petting to mutual orgasm, is substantially the substitute for coitus in the upper social-educational levels. This must be faced in discussions of chastity to define its status. For it seems to be a sufficient test of sexual responsiveness in any subsequent marriage without the need of vaginal entry to discover the degree of physical incompatibility. Silence on any of these three crucial points in any plea for avoidance of sexual intercourse before marriage is some ground for citation for evasion or disqualification as informed authority.

Toward all sex feeling and activity there is a holdover without parallel. Asceticism is the sacrifice of something especially loved in order to promote or attain spiritual growth or strength of character. This kind of self-deprivation of tasty food or comfortable bed or warm dwelling is no longer considered all-important to the good life. This ascetic principle is advocated almost solely in its application to sex. Perhaps because the keenest ecstasy, the mutual love embrace, shows, in its surrender, the topmost sacrifice. Such teaching involves the saintliest in foregoing any propagation of their kind. Indeed there seems to be no more curious contradiction in history than that celibates should have dictated the law on sexual behavior, which is as if the deaf were adjudicated to evaluate symphonies and the blind to allot standards for pictorial art.

The status of premarital coitus as a valid test of postmarital physical-emotional adjustment depends upon circumstances. Two opposites may be cited. Long engagement or steady keeping company that piles up opportunities; convenient privacy of his or her room, walk-up apartment or empty home; late-hour returns; security against pregnancy; agreement on secret or open marriage if "caught"; mutual trust and convictions assuring peace of mind—these can gauge degree of such adaptation after marriage. Conversely, hurried and worried sex intercourse that is casual, occasional, and hampered, with deceit and remorse, constitute no test, or even defeat possible happiness.

Companionate marriage has not had social approval. The Denver plan involves early marriage; safeguarding against start of a family until the couple has had time to learn whether their ingrained habits and beliefs or their flexibilities were such as to fit them to raise children or for lifelong partnership; lastly, with conviction of impossibilities, approval of divorce. Thus the chief calamity of a divorce, the broken-home child, is avoided, even though the other radical objection holds its place that the younger the couple the more frequent the misfit.

Chapter 2

TECHNIC OF MARRIAGE RELATIONS

by G. Lombard Kelly, M.D.

PROFESSOR OF ANATOMY, UNIVERSITY OF GEORGIA

Men and women both have been supplied with organs intended to make the marital relation mutually enjoyable. Especially sensitive microscopic nerve endings are present in the head of the penis and of the clitoris, and in the areas near these centers. Proper stimulation of these end organs under optimum conditions will result in that intense consummation of love, the climax of sexual feeling technically known as the orgasm. When this occurs there are rhythmic involuntary contractions in the muscles of the male causing ejaculation of semen from the urethra. The throbbing contraction and relaxation that is rhythmic in nature which takes place in some women has helped to give rise to the false belief that woman also ejaculates during her orgasm.

There is a flow of mucus just at the vaginal orifice, but this occurs during sexual excitement preceding the act of coitus. The purpose is to lubricate the vulva in order to facilitate the entrance of the penis, or intromission. The amount of this flow varies considerably in different women. In a few it is so abundant that it wets the inner side of the thighs; in others it is so scant that some artificial lubricant must be used to make introduction easy, though none compares with the mucus for lack of greasiness or stickiness or stain. In addition to the mucus provided by the glands within the vulva close to the vaginal orifice (Fig. 1) there is a considerable amount derived from the glands in the neck of the womb, pouring out freely during sexual excitement, thus lubricating the interior of the vagina, which itself rarely has mucous glands of its own.

Since the male organ is normally dry, it is necessary for easy introduction that the vulva provide adequate lubrication or that a lubricant be used. It may be applied by either partner. Artificial lubricants comprise vaseline, surgical lubricating jelly that seems preferable, and a number of jellies and creams advertised for "feminine hygiene"—which means contraception when injected into the vagina. All come in collapsible tubes obtainable in drugstores.

THE FIRST SEXUAL ACT

The ease of the first entrance will depend on absence of disproportion between the two partners. If the opening of the hymen is of average virgin size, unstretched as preamble to marriage, it cannot admit the penis. Days of gradual, gentle, painless stretching with fingers or smooth conical dilator by the bride-to-be (or the new husband) can be depended on in almost all instances to avoid the enlargement done by the doctor in his office after numbing with a local anesthetic. With very thick hymens he nicks or notches the edges. Hymens that are elastic enough to permit entry without discomfort have been described in the chapter on anatomy.

It is certainly not too much to ask that the bridegroom be the personification of tenderness. The bride should be courted and petted to the state of active passion, and any fears she might have should be allayed. The first embrace to be completed will depend on her being fit for response after recovery of the fatigue from the usual wedding. Also on their knowledge of each other's readiness. Her climax may come at once or soon, but many wives—particularly in the upper educational and social levels—are found to require weeks or months or longer to develop capacity for full and spontaneous orgasm.

Meanwhile the husband searches and finds out what counts with her. She wants darkness or dim illumination, where he likes light. She rouses to endearments in the beginning of the caresses but must have silence absolute to concentrate on climax. She has times and seasons of awakening, such as before and after the period. There are signs he learns or teaches her to tell. Patience pays large dividends.

A bridegroom who is selfish and cares only for his own satisfaction will certainly offend and disappoint a sensitive bride. If the woman is not quite apt and does not reach a climax easily she may remain in an unsatisfied state, with a resultant congestion of her generative organs and an unrelieved nervous tension. If this one-sided kind of marital act is persisted in the wife may tire of the disappointments and the nervous tension and turn against the act entirely. In short, the husband who does not take the necessary steps to make his relations with his wife mutually enjoyable and satisfactory may eventually ruin his marriage.

Fortunately it is no longer necessary in the large majority of cases for wives to remain frigid. Either injections or pellet implantations of androgenic hormones will bring about spontaneous orgasm in most women within approximately two months, provided, of course, that the husband does not suffer from premature ejaculation (which can often be successfully treated by application of a local anesthetic ointment). The hormone treatment for frigidity may cause some hair growth on lip or chin or possibly elsewhere, but this will disappear after treatment. The husband and wife may well tolerate a little extra hair growth for a while in consideration of the vast improvement of their marital happiness.

SEAT OF FEMININE SENSATION

The fact that the orgasm in woman is felt chiefly in the clitoris does not mean that this organ is by any means the only part of her body capable of erotic feeling. The dilation of the vaginal orifice by the erect penis gives the average woman the most voluptuous sensation; the penetration of the erect organ to its full length into the vagina accentuates this pleasurable feeling. The breasts are erogenous zones to a marked degree, and most women can be highly excited by proper attention to them before or during coitus. It is possible to fondle them in many positions of intercourse. In the face-to-face position, with the woman sitting on the man's lap, it is easy to fondle or kiss them alternately. Some women are excited by such fore play as the deep and prolonged kiss or biting the neck or lobes of the ears or finger play in various areas of the skin surface, such as the inner thigh or the breasts, but the goal is always the same: stimulation of the genital area, preferably by the erect penis, toward the end point of sexual orgasm. Some authors lay chief stress on what they call the vaginal orgasm. They may go so far as to claim that any woman, no matter how passionate, who fails to attain a climax by his vaginal rhythmic thrusting, but requires massage of the clitoris to reach this release, does not compass real orgasm and is in some degree frigid.

Proponents of the "vaginal" orgasm, who claim that the clitoris is predominant in children and adolescents but that the vagina "takes over" completely in grown women, are adherents of the Freudian school. Their claim that every woman who does not have a "vaginal" orgasm and perceptible contractions of the sphincter muscle at the orifice during orgasm is frigid simply does not conform to the vast array of statistics to the contrary. Possibly 10 or 15 per cent of women require the sensation of the erect penis in the vagina during orgasm.

The notion that fluid secretion from one or another set of glands produces orgasm by "squirting" through ducts has been handed down from generation to generation. Actually orgasm occurs without ejaculation in boys who produce full and repeated orgasm by masturbation well before puberty.

POSITIONS IN SEXUAL INTERCOURSE

The important variations of posture in this ultimate intimacy between husband and wife, together with the advantages of each, are as follows:

Man-Above Position. At the first approach the virgin assumes a recumbent attitude and the man stretches out above her. This combination has been called the Instinctive, the Habitual, and the Normal with us, because it has been the standard for Western cultures and theological prescription as well. Under the most favorable circumstances the woman lies flat on her back, spreads her thighs until there is room between her knees for those of the man, flexes her legs slightly on her thighs, and assumes as relaxed an attitude as her mental state will permit. In this position complete intromission, with proper contact of the penis with the clitoris, is possible.

In this position the man will ordinarily lie between the woman's thighs, but he can place one or both of his outside of hers. This is a satisfactory variation in prolonged intercourse. If the woman holds her thighs close together after entrance it is claimed that a small penis is kept erect by pressure of the feminine parts; also that a long penis will not enter too deeply and cause pain.

Woman-Above Position. This position may be accomplished by rolling over from the one just described, but this requires considerable care to prevent withdrawal of the penis. Experienced couples accomplish it by having the man lie flat on his back while the woman kneels over him and settles backward upon his middle. She then straightens out her legs and lies full length, with her thighs between or outside those of her partner. At first the man will have to guide the penis into the vagina, but later the woman will be able to feel the end of the penis with her vulva and envelop it as she settles backward and downward.

This position has at least two distinct advantages. It enables the woman to adjust herself to the penis in such a way that full contact with the clitoris and other most responsive areas is obtained and kept. In addition the woman has complete freedom of movement and can seek her own satisfaction in an abandon of motion that would be impossible with the weight of the man's body pressing on hers. This position is usually advised when the woman is considerably shorter or lighter than the man, but it is an excellent variation for couples with builds that are not disproportionate.

While in the woman-above position the woman can rise to a sitting posture by bringing her thighs up alongside the man's body, at the same time he can flex his thighs and support the woman's back. The clitoris gains excellent contact with the penis itself and its base in this way, but there is a tendency for the penis to penetrate too deeply and cause some discomfort. This is sometimes called the astride position. Its principal value is as an adjuvant to sex play.

The partner above, man or woman, should seldom lie dead-weight on the other, but should support the weight of the body by resting on the elbows. Only the weight of the hips should be imposed on the one beneath. The connubial bliss of many a small or medium-sized woman has been marred by the thoughtlessness of a heavy partner lying dead-weight upon her. In the woman-above position the same unpleasant experience could befall a small or medium-sized man with a partner considerably heavier.

Lateral or Side Position. The act of coitus may begin in this position, in which the man and woman lie on their sides facing each other. The woman places her upper thigh over the upper thigh of her partner in order to give him freedom of entry. This position may be attained by turning on the sides from either the man-above or woman-above postures. It is recommended by some during advanced pregnancy and also when the couple like to fall asleep after completion of the act with the organs still in contact.

Rear-Entry Position. The man and the woman may both lie on their right or left sides, with the woman's back against the front of the man's body. The man will have to lie well behind the woman's buttocks for good intromission, but for him this position is quite satisfactory. For the woman this posture is deficient in that the penis, entering from the rear, is "upside down" in the vagina and does not touch the clitoris. The man can easily reach the clitoris with his fingers and by stroking it during the progress of coitus can bring about simultaneous orgasm. This position is recommended during pregnancy and in any condition in which it would not be wise for the man to place his weight upon his companion's abdomen.

In the other rear-entry position the woman assumes the kneeling posture or even the knee-chest position. The man kneels behind her and after intromission is able to caress his partner's breasts or her clitoris. The penis does not come into contact with the clitoris in this posture, and unless the woman can reach the climax from strong passion it will likely be necessary to fondle the clitoris to bring her to the orgasm. This position has been advised during pregnancy, but it is easier for both when lying on their sides as described in the preceding paragraph.

Sedentary Positions. With the man using an armless chair the woman sits across his lap, intromission taking place as she settles down on him. The woman can get perfect contact of the clitoris with the penis and the cushion above it in this position, especially if she arches her back a little and leans forward on her partner and produces the desired sweep to and fro. The man does not have so much freedom of movement by this method but all that is necessary. When a chair is used, the height must be suitable for the woman, so that she can support her weight on her feet and take the active part when she desires. This posture is quite comfortable for both participants and it is thoroughly effective. When desired the man can massage the clitoris satisfactorily.

Standing Position. When there is not too great a disproportion between the heights of the man and the woman it is quite possible to bring about entrance with the partners facing each other while standing. It is necessary, of course, for the man to have a good erection and for the woman to place her feet apart and open her thighs.

The positions described are fundamental ones. Some authors describe many postures, with some claim for true variation. This writer once purchased a small, highly touted, but disappointing book which described scores of positions, differing as slightly as bending the knee of one leg. This, of course, approached the absurd. It is conceivable that male and female gymnasts might effect sexual union in a wide variety of postures, even while standing on their heads. There is a distinct difference between body positions during coitus (that is, the actual relation of one body to the other) and where the two bodies may be (as being in bed, across bed or table, sitting on a chair or standing up). Since each individual has only one front and one back and can only lie, sit, stand, or kneel, the fundamental possibilities in this regard are definitely limited.

The clitoris is located, as shown in Figure 1, an inch to an inch and a half from and above the vaginal orifice. It hangs on the front of the pubic bone, suspended by a ligament or band which allows an excursion, as it is swept by pressure or stroked, to the extent of an inch or two or three, in that type of action upon it which procures the climax. And its neighboring parts have much the same reaction, as shown by the enlargements of the labia in those women who are given to a habit of friction for self-relief. During intercourse with the man in a somewhat high position compared with that assumed when fully within, the upper surface of the penis can glide back and forth against the clitoris and the labial folds, in normal rhythms, to secure the explosion of feeling. With complete burying of the penis within the vulvo-vaginal canal that cushion of flesh at the base of the penis that is covered with hair, called the mons, with his pubic bone underneath it, makes the to-and-fro pressures, the clitoris being effectively caught between the two structures for the caress. The circular muscle at the vaginal entrance can be contracted voluntarily by some women, and husbands may ask them to do it for its voluptuous effect.

With the majority of couples each can learn to detect the signs of approaching climax in the other and with the exercise of control attain the state of orgasm together. If the woman is unduly slow the man can caress her clitoris gently with the rhythm of intercourse until she arrives with him. It is easy to insert the middle finger into the upper crevice of the vulva, even when the penis is deeply in place. It is true that some women cannot reach orgasm in normal intercourse, no matter how long or how vigorously continued, but many such women can reach a climax once or more by patient massage of the clitoris. As time passes, quicker response occurs until no finger play is needed, in many instances. Unfortunately, there are still other women who cannot reach a climax under any circumstances, while some women are satisfied with excitement alone.

To reach a climax, intercourse is not always necessary. There are imaginative women who can attain orgasm by mental stimulation, either by thoughts of attractive men or by being in their presence. These are, of course, exceptional.

How often may sexual intercourse be practiced with satisfaction and without immediate and eventual harm to one or both individuals? The consensus seems to center on twice a week for normally healthy persons, although many factors may alter this general average upward or downward.

Some of the most important items bearing upon frequency of intercourse are health, degree of mutual happiness obtained in the act, temperament, and age. Naturally, illness or poor health will militate against sex desire and also against the ability to indulge in it. It is assumed that men as a rule reach a satisfying climax, but this is by no means true of women. A woman who is not satisfied may be willing to repeat the act after a shorter interval than if her needs had been amply taken care of. If consistently disappointed, however, she may eventually turn against intercourse and refuse any longer to be left "hanging in the air."

Many women are thwarted in their ardent desires to achieve sexual satisfaction because of premature ejaculation of the husband. Women as a rule are slower than men in preparation for the climax of sexual excitement, requiring often ten, fifteen, or more minutes to reach the orgasm. In his book, *Sexual Behavior in the Human Male,* Kinsey states (p. 580), "For perhaps three quarters of all males, orgasm is reached within two minutes after the initiation of the sexual relation, and for a not inconsiderable number of males the climax may be reached within less than a minute or even within ten or twenty seconds after coital entrance." I regard this estimate as too high, but my researches on premature ejaculation and its treatment with an anesthetic ointment applied to the head of the penis, carried on now for eight years, attest to the great frequency of the failing as well as to the large number of broken marriages that result when it is not corrected by proper treatment. Since age is accompanied by degenerative changes it can be expected that a gradual slowing up of sexual expression will take place. This does not mean that many men fail to remain virile to advanced age, but frequency of intercourse will lessen appreciably in nearly every case. In many women after the childbearing years there is an accentuation of desire to such an extent that they may crave sexual union more often than their husbands. One of the principal reasons for this, as a rule, is cessation of the fear of becoming pregnant.

Minor factors influencing frequency of intercourse are mode of life, climate, diet, mental or nervous strain and worry, as well as general attitude toward sexual matters. Some of these factors may at times cease to be minor and greatly affect sexual desire or performance. Exhaustion from overwork or from much worrying is a strong inhibitory factor. Inhibition in sex matters as a result of repressive upbringing may affect sensitive women to the point of sexual frigidity.

Sexual intercourse is not too frequent if it does not produce any undesirable aftereffects in either partner. Some individuals are far more passionate than others, and husband and wife may vary widely in this respect. In such cases a mutual agreement based on love and common sense is essential. It is possible for either partner to arouse desire in the other by fondling the appropriate organs. In each act, however, the complete satisfaction of both must be striven for and attained if at all possible.

Sexual excesses may not cause immediate damage, but the eventual result may prove disastrous to a happy union. The act may become commonplace, and interest may be lost. Excess on the part of one partner may turn the other's affection away and ruin a marriage that restraint could have preserved.

Recent researches covering thousands of marriages show a variation of frequency from the so-called "sexual athletes" who have intercourse regularly once or more a day to others who have sexual union once or twice a year. Couples between twenty and forty years of age were found to have sexual relations about twelve times a month, or about every second or third day. The extremes in this group were from once a day to once a week.

Frequency of intercourse is considerably greater in newly married couples than in those married for a period of years. It can be safely assumed that normal persons can determine without difficulty how often they desire complete intimacy with each other. They are not likely to go wrong if each act is an expression of love to the point of mutual orgasm and entire satisfaction. The quality of the embrace is more important than the intervals between repetitions of it. And sex play short of orgasm has its place, where both enjoy it.

Masculine Sex Hygiene. A man may well wash his penis every day with soap and warm water, dry it with a cloth or absorbent paper, and even powder with a good grade of scented talcum. In the uncircumcised this will prevent the accumulation of white, bready material that tends to form beneath the foreskin after a few days. This secretion, known as smegma, has an objectional odor.

The warm, moist incubator underneath a long foreskin may foster development of germs of venereal disease. The occasional individual who has a long foreskin with a small opening that hinders or prevents complete retraction ("skinning") may develop accumulation of smegma calling for circumcision.

Young boys occasionally suffer from an annoying inflammatory condition around the head of the penis and just back of it. This is readily amenable to treatment with soap and water, followed by drying and application of talcum powder. Ointments, such as vaseline, can be used, but the dry powder treatment is quicker and better.

Feminine Sex Hygiene. The woman who requires it should have either a fountain syringe with a vaginal nozzle (long, slightly curved) or a large vaginal bulb syringe. In some women a douche is advisable after each menstrual period. The natural secretions from the cervix present in the vagina and the whitish cells of the shed lining have a characteristic odor. In some women odor is not perceptible, while in others it is objectionable. A certain amount of caressing or fondling of the female genitals is part and parcel of normal sex play, and while mucus of excitement is odorless as a rule, in other cases it does have odor and a man washes his hands and parts after coitus.

The douche material may be warm water. Many proprietary products are widely advertised for use in maintaining "feminine hygiene," but under this label most are intended for contraception, however ineffective. Such products are too expensive for use as cleansing agents, and for this purpose they are not better than good soap and water or vinegar, two tablespoons to the quart, as this latter matches the normal slight acidity of the vagina.

Many women, if indeed not all of them, show more or less of this whitish secretion derived from the slight steady shedding of the surface layers of the passage, just as our skin is constantly invisibly peeling its surface cells. If this is considerable it may appear at the vulva or after intercourse. If a man withdraws temporarily, as in play of one kind or another, and sees a little "leukorrhea," it might seem to him a "discharge." Cleansing the external parts, the vulva, with soap and water should thus be done daily. There is little that is more attractive than daintiness. And there is little that leads more happily to this loving closeness in marriage than knowledge that brings liberation from the old blockades of shame and repression—to train expertness and variety in mutual satisfactions.

I have satisfaction and a sense of accomplishment when seeing a formerly frigid woman who has received androgenic hormone treatment enter the office with a telltale smile on her face, showing clearly that "the something" has happened. Also, there are few expressions of gratitude that come to medical advisers or other marriage counselors that are more keen and enduring than those which are the outcome of perfected—or corrected—adjustment of the interlocking spiritual, mental, and physical act of love between husband and wife.

Chapter 3

SEXUAL ADJUSTMENT IN MARRIAGE

by O. Spurgeon English, M.D.

PROFESSOR OF PSYCHIATRY, TEMPLE UNIVERSITY SCHOOL OF MEDICINE, PHILADELPHIA

Nearly everyone agrees that people need to know much more about sexual adjustment in marriage. Such difficulty is by no means the only cause of divorce and separation. Yet the increasing separation and divorce rates, as well as the increased amount of extramarital sexual indulgence, are an indication that many married couples are not finding sexual compatibility and happiness. Some authorities blame the woman and her lack of interest in sex and her failure to have any response in feeling to the sexual advances of the male. Others say the man is chiefly responsible because of his inadequacy as a lover. Conservative estimates report that less than half of the marriages show sexual compatibility. Less conservative ones indicate that not one marriage in ten has a satisfactory sexual relationship.

Today's woman is doubtless by reason both of biological endowment and sociological training less prone to physical response. But the father of the daughter today is conditioning somebody's wife of tomorrow. We rarely meet an American man who isn't doing his best to discourage the development of any sexual interest in his daughter toward other men of her age and class. Not only can the man be indicted as an inadequate lover with his own wife, but he is also working to perpetuate what he complains most bitterly about— i.e., the sexual frigidity of the American woman.

We have the woman complaining that her husband never shows any interest in her or any tenderness toward her unless he desires sexual relations. He is unappreciative of her daily activities. When he does desire sexual relations he does not take time enough to excite her through caresses, kisses, and endearments. When intercourse begins he is not enough interested in the position assumed, the timing and technique of bringing his wife to orgasm, or in his verbal appreciation of her as a love partner to make her happy.

The man in turn complains that his wife is never interested in sex relations, or can't be made interested often enough, or is not appreciative enough of his advances. Or in sex relations she is physically inactive, emotionally unresponsive, takes too long to come to orgasm, or has no orgasm at all. She may even be critical of him as "low," "bestial," "brutal," "lustful," "unaesthetic," "ungentlemanly," or "lacking the proper appreciation of her" in wanting to have intercourse with her.

Millions of married people want to love and appreciate each other, and they are able to do so in every other way, but they disapprove of each other in sexual relationships which potentially hold the greatest joy for each of them.

WHY THESE FAULTY ATTITUDES?

Why is the sexual situation so faulty at present? The difficulty seems to begin in childhood when the mind is being formed. Adults have so much fear of the sexual impulse—far more fear than is warranted. There are two basic urges in mankind—sensual gratification and aggression. The former is no more dangerous to society than the latter; in fact, less so. Yet aggressive impulses are not feared as the sexual impulses are. Fighting is discouraged among children, but it is not taboo. In fact, sports and games are encouraged and even open fistic encounters among boys are regarded as desirable to the child's development. Even murder, while condemned, can be discussed with children and they are allowed to see it in the movies and the comics and hear about it on the radio, but that same child must not hear of sex. Is sex more powerful or more malicious to man's welfare than aggression? We think not. Yet sexual activity—the only means of complete physical expression of love —is tabooed and punished from the earliest days onward. It is assumed we have the power to control aggression but that we cannot control our sexual desires.

Now the fact is we haven't controlled our aggressive impulses. But we are at least wise enough to admit we have them. We have various agencies working at modifying our aggressions—racial, religious, industrial, and even those leading to war waged country against country. This is progress, and we must be equally progressive in the realm of sexuality. We must admit we have sexual impulses and needs; that they have a purpose; that they can be misused; but that they can also be controlled and used constructively. In fact, we haven't begun to tap the reservoir of value that lies in more wholesome and satisfying body relationships. This is true not only between man and wife but also between mother and child and even father and child. We have been made afraid and ashamed to be close to one another and enjoy one another. Until we overcome this great handicap in our thinking it is doubtful if we shall ever bring our aggressive and destructive forces under satisfactory control.

THE INFANT AND ITS MOTHER

The infant likes to be close to the mother—to enjoy the warmth and touch of her body and nurse from her breast. This is all-satisfying and gives him a sense of well-being. It is the forerunner of happiness, tolerance, magnanimity, gentleness, and generosity. Even when the child has given up the breast for other foods he will want to snuggle up to the mother in a gradually diminishing amount for several years. In fact, it hits a minimum only around the age of ten, to break forth afresh at puberty, but now directed, instead of toward the parent, toward a member of the opposite sex of his own age. This is the rhythm of life; this is psychosexual development. It needs guidance and fostering rather than the taboo, criticism, and silence which has prevailed for so long. As the child leaves the nursing period and goes through toilet training he need not be made ashamed of these functions in order to have the training completed. Co-operation in these as well as other social obligations can be achieved without invoking shame, anxiety, and criticism. This is most important because love is made with the organs associated with excretion. Put morbid emotional attitudes around the excretory organs and you have involved the organs of love. True love is expressed with the eyes, the lips, the hands, and with a clothed embrace, but in marriage the ultimate expression of love must be with the unclothed body and a union of the genital organs. If the latter are regarded as shameful, disgusting, or otherwise unaesthetic, the sexual union can never be an act of happiness or beauty for that person. The man who said, "I cannot think of anything more horrible and revolting than a man on top of a woman in sexual intercourse," expresses a lurking feeling common to most humans, even in the minds of some of those who feel themselves most sophisticated about and in accepting sexual relations. It is inconsistent twaddle for adults to talk about the beauty and sanctity of the marriage relationship (meaning the sexual relation in marriage) if they haven't given the child some glimpse of this possibility during his formative years.

During or soon after his toilet training period the child is going to meet two critical episodes of his sexual development. These are (1) when he begins to ask questions pertaining to the human sexual relation and (2) when he discovers that he can obtain pleasure from touching his own body, particularly the genital region. It is a wise and well-adjusted parent who can answer his child's questions calmly, sensibly, factually, and stick to what the child wants to know. It is inherent in adults to feel that "knowing" will do the child harm or that "his mind is too weak to integrate such strong stuff," or "with his lack of judgment he will surely misuse it." The answer to these attitudes is that knowing won't do him harm, sex isn't a bad or dangerous thing to absorb (it is only the adults who have come to think so), and any lack of judgment he has about using sex knowledge should be neutralized by some positive useful philosophy about when and how sexual expression is acceptable and desirable. As for touching himself for pleasure, we feel this offers no serious threat to health, morals, or aesthetic standards. It is a natural phenomenon, necessary to awaken the genital area to a capacity for sensation and pleasure, and never produces any problem in the child who is (1) on good terms with his parents and (2) has playmates and wholesome interests for his age. Around the age of three the child of either sex is likely to pass through a stage of frequently touching the genitals. Nothing need be done about this except keeping the child occupied and happy and it will pass. Occasional manipulation of the genitals for pleasure may and probably will occur up to marriage, carried on in privacy. The chief concern of the parent should be (1) that the child has no guilt or fear over the activity and that (2) he or she is so interested in his work, play, and social activity that he does not fall back upon his own body too frequently as a source of satisfaction. The good life is a useful, creative, and loving life, and overpreoccupation with unnecessary burdens of guilt defeats the avowed purposes of religious wholeness.

SEXUALITY IN THE CHILD

The acceptance and tolerance of manifestations of sexuality in the young child is most important. Let no one erroneously assume that sexual activity does not begin this early in the human being. At this time the basic attitudes toward sexual feeling and functioning are established. If children are made to feel fear or shame or even if their interest has never been allowed to gravitate toward sex, then we allow to develop one of the most difficult conditions a physician has to treat or any husband or wife to change or any counselor to modify. Moreover, once the parent has failed to play his role adequately in this early period of attitude building—if he has been too severe or has ignored the subject—the child is prone never to turn back to the parent and take a trusting attitude toward him on this subject. He falls prey to the misinformation and the gutter information and values of the "crowd" who perpetuate the very thing we want to change. The morbidly curious or even the uninformed child between the ages of five and fourteen who hasn't been given the wholesome truth about sex from his parents is likely to gather much of the worst and little, if any, of the best about the subject during these years.

SEX ADJUSTMENT AT PUBERTY

At puberty a new situation prevails. The sexual glands become active, sending their hormonal secretions throughout the body and adding a greater impetus to the general desire for body contact and release of sexual energy through the orgasm. In addition to this activity there is a social factor at work also. Adults push the young people of both sexes together in order that they gain poise and find mates, while the social environment of movies, radios, and magazines predisposes to heightened imagination and fantasy surrounding sex.

In general the adult attitude toward sex at this age is no wiser than before. Parents and children are generally farther apart at this age than ever and more self-conscious with each other about the sex subject. Many parents delay discussions of sex until the teens, when the child supposedly needs it. By this time both parties are so embarrassed that neither can carry on a satisfactory conversation on the subject. So the talk is indefinitely postponed or tried unsuccessfully and ends in a sense of futility for both. Without parental guidance the child has to struggle with his sex desires himself. He may be in conflict about masturbation; in any case, he has to undergo more of what is called repression—pushing the dangerous subject out of consciousness by various means. Some of these phenomena of repression are quite healthy and valuable. The young person unable to gratify his love needs directly may become an exceptionally good student, athlete, musician, actor or actress, or inventor. But others less well motivated can become overpreoccupied with religion, using it not as a means of a fuller, more meaningful life but as an escape from the realities of life. In other words, to avoid the evils of sex they avoid everything constructive. Or they may take flight from life through a great deal of daydreaming in which they achieve exceptional merit and imagine so much love and prestige that they do not have to resort to home and family life for emotional satisfaction. In fact, they often look upon the home with its day-to-day physical problems in which body needs are so much concerned (eating, sleeping, bathing, elimination, sex, illness) as unaesthetic, uninteresting, and unworthy of the interest and enthusiasm of a remarkable person like themselves. Or, never having been taught that they must play a part in these activities with pleasure, they retain a childish attitude which, put into words, would be something like this: "Well, those things are for Mother or Father to do or for the servants to do but not for me; I should be allowed to be a privileged character and remain aloof from these crass realities. I shall enjoy only the clean, well-ordered, already arranged, neat, gay, glamorous things of life, but nothing which has to do with the body, dirt, or that which requires persistent effort or painful thinking."

WRONG ATTITUDES TOWARD SEXUAL ADJUSTMENT

The majority of parents have two or more of the following attitudes which interfere with the maturing of their children into emotionally mature young adults. They fear that (1) their adolescent child will have sexual experience and become morbidly unhappy over it, or (2) that he or she will have it and be a party to an unwanted pregnancy, or (3) that he will be a participant in the sexual relation and be found out and suffer some degree of social condemnation, or (4) that he will have the experience and contract a venereal disease, or (5) that he will have some pleasurable experience the parent himself has missed. Now most of these are definite matters of concern and should be faced and discussed as such rather than remain an unverbalized barrier which spoils the friendship and value of closeness in the important years of adolescence. Millions of parents and their adolescent children are on bad terms all during this important period just because the parent is frightened and suspicious and does not understand why he is distrustful, suspicious of, and restrictive toward the child.

It would seem to be a mistake to try to train our children to go through adolescence without conflict about sex or without sexual desire. To attempt this leads to a suppression of the sexual impulses; fantasy results, as do exaggerated discussions and in some cases excessive petting. In order to have enough sexual desire to be reasonably normal during the adult years it is inevitable that the adolescent have sexual desire. Moreover, having it isn't ncessarily painful or unpleasant or dangerous. It is healthy and human. We should accept it and also the responsibility of making the children such good friends of ours that they will control it reasonably well if we show them why they should. It is a sad commentary on many intelligent parents that they never seem to think of using a positive education in connection with sex by telling the child the facts and then asking him to adapt himself to conventional standards and live up to a certain ideal of behavior in the setting of a full social existence. The formula would look like this: Facts of sexuality, plus personal social ideals, plus a well-balanced work and recreational program equal morally good, happy, and responsible citizens. In contrast to this: No facts of sexuality, plus no personal or social ideal, plus a restricted and empty work and recreational life (out of the parent's fear of the child's coming into contact with temptation) equal unhappiness, inefficiency, poor marital adjustment, neurosis, and personality defects contributing to alcoholism, delinquency, psychosis, and suicide.

THE NEED FOR COMMON SENSE AND THOUGHTFULNESS IN CASES WHERE ADJUSTMENT IS GOOD IN THE BEGINNING

Few people today realize the long history of the development of the sexual emotions. They are present at birth and have to be integrated into the rest of the personality during the whole period of growth from infancy to the day of marriage—and even thereafter. Anyone who assumes that the sexual emotions can be ignored for a lifetime and that they will start functioning satisfactorily on the day the marriage ceremony is read is truly living in the dark ages of thought regarding the welfare of human beings. This historical perspective of individual sexual development, as it struggles to unfold in an unsympathetic world, applied to any married person will give some indication as to whether he can make love pleasurably with his body or not. The love emotions (including the physical expression of them) must be in some continuous interaction with other people who are receptive. Through late childhood and adolescence some, though not all, of the physical must be withheld until marriage. This takes continuous wise and kind counseling —not rejection. But it is also true that there are few people after marriage who do not need counsel. In the best marriages, where sexual adjustment is harmonious, the partners accept the fact that they need to help each other to derive the most pleasure from their contacts together. They need to guide and advise each other upon how the satisfaction of each can be obtained.

SEXUAL ADJUSTMENT IN THE NEWLY MARRIED

Each newly married couple should realize that a good sexual adjustment is necessary to a happy life. It is more than a luxury to be accepted if present but ignored if absent. For each married couple there are years of hard work, responsibility, and at times a variable amount of hardship and suffering ahead. To neutralize the adverse effect of life's conflicts and struggles upon the mind a man and woman should do everything they can to find what happiness they can enjoy with each other. They need a close communion and sympathy which is so much easier to achieve if they can give each other the ecstatic happiness of frequent sexual relations. Pleasure begets gratitude, and the thoughtfulness which makes one capable of giving pleasure begets respect and love. Such a state of mind existing between man and wife is worth working for, but it *does* have to be worked for. There is probably no young couple so well adjusted sexually that they won't have to keep working to retain that adjustment. They must feel free to talk about their sexual desires and feel free to say when and how each derives the greatest pleasure. Here is where one partner must avoid the dangerous attitude of seeming to have, from some obscure source, an innate knowledge of what is proper, aesthetic, or good. For instance, one of the partners may want to have intercourse in the daytime or early in the evening, but the other feels that sex relations take place only late at night in bed, the last thing before going to sleep. Actually they can take place any time, any place, if mutual happiness is the goal. One of the partners may want a different position other than the usual one of the man lying on top of the woman, between her thighs. Naturally any position is acceptable which makes the partners happy. The woman may like the man to caress her a great deal in order to become aroused before the act begins, yet the man is impatient of caresses—perhaps regards caressing the woman's breast as childish. He should realize that when he fails to please her he runs the risk that in some way sooner or later she will fail to please him. Less common than the kissing of the breast is the desire to kiss other parts of the body before the act begins. The wife may desire this when it does not appeal to the man. In either case the thing for each to remember is that no laws prescribe what is good or bad for those who, loving each other, want to bring happiness to each other. They should avoid getting blocked by a feeling of "It isn't done," "Nice people don't do it," or even the more smug statement, "I may not be able to say who condemns it, but I have an instinct for decency and I know it isn't right." Such convictions in matters of sexual activity preclude mutual adjustment and are unfortunate.

If a young married couple have a good sexual adjustment to begin with they must take care not to disturb it through selfishness in behavior. For instance, the husband should continue to be tender and affectionate during menstruation. He should be thoughtful and willing to endure abstinence graciously during illness, the last month of pregnancy, and the first few weeks after the birth of a child. The wife should be considerate in her demands if the husband is overtired from work, but in her defense we must point out that the husband should not continuously be too tired. If such is the case, he is either in the wrong job or working too hard. Or it may be that he is organically ill or is suffering from a neurosis in which chronic fatigue is one of the symptoms.

Neither partner should be averse to giving the other orgasm manually should they desire it in any situation where normal relations are temporarily not possible. In short, plain human consideration on the part of two reasonably well-adjusted people should keep a good adjustment working. The importance of consideration cannot be overemphasized, however, as many people let a good adjustment deteriorate through carelessness, thoughtless-ness, and laziness until counseling on the part of an expert and much hard work on their own part have to be done to get things in order again.

THE NEED FOR OPEN-MINDEDNESS

There is a great tendency for the person with a difficulty in sexual adjust-ment to avoid facing it and doing something about it. There are many reasons for this. Having been brought up to think of sex as a shameful, dirty, unbecoming aspect of one's behavior, he is reticent to discuss it. Never hav-ing dealt with sex openly, he feels justified in keeping it a "personal" mat-ter and therefore hidden from others. Since in the popular mind the capacity for sexual enjoyment also connotes vigor and strength of a kind, the one who is unable to function adequately would like to keep his weakness hid-den. It stands as an evidence of imperfection, and he finds it hard and sometimes impossible to face any imperfection in himself. For example, a wife says, "John, I feel I might obtain orgasm if you could retain erection a little longer." Instead of replying, "Well, I wonder how that might be ac-complished. Is there any source of help for that?"—instead of seeking out that help—he feels criticized, is wounded, pouts, withdraws, won't admit he may be at fault, and insists upon continuing the present status, disregard-ing his wife's lack of pleasure. Or the husband might say, "Jane, I feel you don't give any thought to or allow any room in your mind for physical love-making. You make yourself very busy with other things, all of which are important, but you ignore my recurring need of enjoying your body and your enjoying mine." Instead of accepting this as a helpful suggestion and thinking about its truth and why it is so, she feels criticized, cries, defends herself, says her work is not appreciated and that he is just a nasty man with a low sexy mind.

Before marriage husbands and wives feel they are marrying the cleverest, the wisest, the most agreeable, co-operative person in the world, but find after marriage how hard it is to believe that the person they married ever says anything helpful or worth heeding. So the first plea to husbands and wives with a problem in sexual adjustment is to have an open mind, some degree of humility, and a continuous conviction that the other may be help-ful if listened to. If the one with the greatest problem could just admit he has a problem and humbly ask for and use the help of the partner many difficulties in sexual adjustment could be solved by the husband and wife themselves. Each could act as counselor for the other. For example, the com-mon problem of disinterest or frigidity of mild degree in the woman is best described, tersely, by one husband as follows: "I can never get my wife to be interested in enjoying herself sexually with me unless I take her away from home for a few days on a holiday." The fact that she can enjoy sex away from home indicates that her frigidity is not too deep. If such a woman would realize that such a state of affairs is not good and say to her husband, "What do you think I can do about it?" then he could say something as follows: "Be less absorbed in cleaning the house and having everything in such perfect order all the time. Give some thought to what I would like from you rather than being constantly prepared for some unexpected visitor who never arrives. Relax and read a little romantic literature once in a while. Change your idea of how a decent married woman behaves and be a little sexy and seductive with me and see if my appreciation doesn't repay you for the effort you make." A woman, to profit by this, would have to have more respect for her husband and his needs than for her parents' values which made her the way she is, but that capacity for learning new attitudes and values constitutes the means and practically always the *only* means of improving sexual adjustment. Happiness in physical love is a gift which husband and wife give each other. A few people give it easily and naturally all their lives, but they are exceptions. Most couples have to keep trying to improve upon it as they grow older. Generally people improve on their ability to do things as they get older, but in love-making in marriage the common trend is more toward deterioration in the love relation.

For the husband who is deficient in precoital tenderness, affection, caresses, and comes to ejaculation too soon, the very acceptance of the defect itself and making a resolution to do something about it are the first steps toward remedying the condition. Certainly he *can* control the affection, tenderness, and caressing. If he will do this and endeavor to be more considerate of his wife's needs in between the times of intercourse, he should achieve a better love relationship for both.

The preceding remarks may be too optimistic about what can be done by husband and wife themselves in improving their sexual relations. But we hope not. More and more people are becoming enlightened on the fact that difficulties in sexual adjustment are rarely due to organic disease or hereditary defects. They are practically always developmental defects in the personality and remediable to the degree that people are willing to work on themselves to correct wrong habits in thinking and feeling. In any case it is better to be optimistic than pessimistic in what people may accomplish with a little information and encouragement.

The findings and conclusions of Dr. Kinsey and his associates in their studies of the male and female can be of great value in helping a couple have a clearer understanding and perspective on their sexual adjustment.

(*Sexual Behavior in the Human Male,* Saunders, 1948; *Sexual Behavior in the Human Female,* Saunders, 1953.) Dr. Kinsey's studies have pointed up some definite differences in the personality make-up of men and women. For instance, while practically all men are sexually aroused by the female body dressed or undressed, very few women are aroused sexually by sight of the male body clothed or unclothed. Similarly, men respond to pictures, stories, jokes, and exotic clothing, while women seem to respond only somewhat to a romantic movie, chivalrous attention, and even to touch itself.

Preliminary courtship, according to Dr. Kinsey, seems to mean much to women and little if anything to men. Women want and value home, affection, and children to a higher degree than men. Men are more interested in adventure, conquest, and success. Women are much less likely to be troubled by sexual urges when alone than men. Men are intrigued by the more tangible aspects of sex, such as burlesque shows, musical comedy, and pin-up girls, while their equivalents do not excite women.

Husbands and wives, then, knowing these variations, should try to understand their mates better and try to compensate for these differences. These findings could mean, for instance, that a husband should be more affectionate and attentive to his wife all of the time and woo her more gradually to the point of intercourse. He should understand additionally that kissing, caressing, and sex play should be used to arouse his wife to the point of sexual excitement and that this will make sex relations more enjoyable. *He should not ignore or neglect this throughout his marriage.* (An exception to this might pertain if his wife, over a period of time, proved to be completely frigid and requested that love-making, to which she could not respond and which she found unpleasant, should be discontinued.)

The average wife, on the other hand, should try to realize that her husband has greater sexual spontaneity and a more frequent urge for sexual relations than she and be willing to participate in intercourse somewhat more frequently than she might feel to be ideal. The husband should bear in mind that out of all the women (nearly six thousand) studied by Kinsey, one third said they responded by orgasm only a small part of the time, another third responded more or less than half of the time, and the final third responded a major part of the time. Only a few equaled or surpassed the male in the desire for frequency or capacity for pleasure. Which seems to mean, therefore, that each partner of the marriage must try to meet the other halfway to improve the quality of their sexual relations and neither can set as a goal the idea that orgasm in the woman shall always take place. Such an ideal is unrealistic and may cause dissatisfaction or self-reproach in both partners. Much more mutual happiness is possible, bearing in mind these differences and striving for a more realistic and attainable ideal. Trying to make the partner act and feel like oneself can be a disillusioning endeavor.

It would seem that the quality of sexual happiness has improved between men and women over the past few decades, measured in terms of physiological response and mutual understanding, but there is farther to go in this direction and knowledge, patience, and understanding of the sexual nature of the opposite sex offer the best hope of bringing about this improvement.

THE USE OF PHYSICIAN OR MARRIAGE COUNSELOR

For those husbands and wives who in spite of information and good will cannot help each other we suggest a marriage counselor without delay. Once a problem is known to exist, the longer seeking help is postponed, the harder it is going to be to eradicate it. This is partly due to the fact that bad attitudes tend to get fixed and rigid, but also because good will—i.e., patience and friendliness—in both husband and wife are so necessary to effect a change. Hence a couple should not wait until these important qualities have become dissipated in either or both partners.

Since it is so hard for husbands and wives to help each other with these problems the solution is made easier by consulting a third person who has had some training in the science of human relations and who can impart the necessary information, appeal for new attitudes, encourage and give approval for accomplishment, and act as referee when questions arise as to which one of the partners should defer to the other. The same rule cannot be applied to every couple, since in some marriages the woman will need more consideration than average or in another marriage the husband will need more tolerance and understanding than average. While in marriage complete partnership and equality in giving each his own way should be the usual goal, there is no getting around the fact that some marital partners have more to give than others, and this may be either the man or the woman.

When counsel is sought it should be of the best quality available. Many people take their marital problems to a friend or some advertised adviser, and this is dangerous. It is an unusual occurrence to find a friend with the objectivity to be helpful. More physicians are receiving training in their medical-school courses or after for helping with these problems. Within the last ten years many cities have set up marriage-counsel organizations with people especially trained for helping with marriage problems. The Planned Parenthood Federation is taking a greater interest in marriage counseling, and a committee has worked out optimum standards for those who work in this field. A counselor, whether he be physician or layman, must have as much experience with life as possible, be as unprejudiced as possible toward either sex, not to mention being unprejudiced in regard to race, religion, political belief, and sexual expression in any form or under any condition. He or she should preferably be married, although this is not the most important qualification. He should be optimistic and be able to expect and *get* the best from people; in other words, be good at inspiring, encouraging, and getting people to work together as well as being an expert analyst on what is wrong. So, after choosing a counselor in whom they have confidence, a couple should work as hard as they would in class, or at a golf or tennis lesson. Surely marital harmony is worth as much time, effort, and practice as is put into learning a new sport or hobby. This may seem an undignified comparison, but the fact is that people are less prone to exercise their "mental and emotional muscles" than they are their physical muscles.

CASES REQUIRING A PSYCHIATRIST

There are some individuals who will be unresponsive to ordinary counseling. As might be inferred, these are cases with a much more profound personality disturbance. The psychopathology is so marked, so unconscious, or requires the combination of so much time and so much skillful handling to effect a change that the services of a psychiatrist are needed. One such type is that in which there is so much love of self that the patient finds it extremely hard, if not impossible, to think of anyone's feelings but his own. He has been starved of love as a child and hence has none to give anyone else. He has been given neither wormth nor affection nor had any example of it shown him. So during his period of growth he has had to give whatever love he possessed to himself. He knows no other way of behaving—when he hears of altruism and devotion being shown he feels that such a person is a "sap," a "sucker." Such women are calculating and frigid, are determined to be kept, waited on, served by men, without giving anything in return. Such men feel women are out to exploit them, and they reflect this feeling in their every conversation. They feel that tenderness and affection are "silly rot." They have a conviction that there isn't anything that can't be bought with money, if one has enough. Both sexes are relatively disinterested in children. A man and woman of this type, each one needing so much and disinclined to give, usually avoid each other and hence usually pair off in marriage with a type of mate who can give them more.

These people are referred to in psychiatric terms as narcissistic. They are often attractive and glib and hide their emptiness behind an articulate expression of their good intentions and a statement of what they feel they deserve. Their explanations usually sound well until the other partner has been heard. Then their emptiness, coldness, and inability to give become apparent. Their sex problem may be simply stated. The woman may be "just frigid" or the man "just unable to maintain erection." But this one symptom can harbor beneath the surface a lifetime of coldness, self-centeredness, stubbornness, ungenerosity, irritability, criticism, and lack of social interest which will take two to three years of continuous psychiatric treatment to modify, and which may not be modifiable at all. The woman will never feel any vaginal warmth or pleasure until she learns to be warm and friendly to all. The man will never be able to have and hold an erection until he has modified the character traits enumerated. If this can be accomplished at all it can be done best by two to three years with a Freudian psychoanalyst. Some of these people cannot be changed even with such intensive treatment. After a three to six months' trial treatment this may become clear and the couple should be told the outlook and the decision left to them as to whether they continue living together or not. There is already so much separation and divorce that any counselor is reluctant to suggest more. Yet it must be kept in mind that living in an atmosphere of affection, including physical affection, is necessary to the health and well-being of most people. If we can be reasonably sure the patient cannot change and the continued emotional and sexual coldness is going to be detrimental to the other partner, we owe it to both parties to make the situation as regards the future as clear as possible. A physician would not expose a man or woman to live with a spouse with active tuberculosis without warning of the danger. The same holds for sexual and emotional frigidity.

Akin to this narcissistic type and almost a variant of it is the man or woman who is really in love with his or her own sex. These people are latent homosexuals or, psychologically at least, bisexual in nature. They, too, have little love to give to the opposite sex. What isn't being used up in loving themselves goes over to their own sex. These cases are serious and require plenty of strenuous psychologic study. They must come to understand the nature of their delayed emotional development and learn to love in a more altruistic way. It can be seen that if love isn't in the mind it doesn't find its expression through the genital organs. There are women who envy the man his role in life and his sexual organs and psychologically refuse to submit to him or to feel or show any pleasure his sexual organ might give them. There are men who envy the woman her role and who refuse psychologically to play the male role. They do not wish to give a woman an orgasm, children a home, or any of the things a woman receives from a man. They want to be the recipients of these things themselves. If this unconscious psychologic constellation is strong enough it is surely going to interfere with the man's ability as a lover.

There are some men and women who, deep within them, just can't get over a feeling of sin or wickedness connected with sex or a fear that they will be hurt, punished, or have to suffer in some terrible way for sex pleasure. Naturally the changing of these attitudes takes considerable work with a psychiatrist.

Sexual maladjustments vary in severity, depending on the severity of the personality disturbance behind them. They are all too numerous. We should think of preventive treatment through better sex education, as we can never treat the large number of cases through individual treatment. Fortunately the younger clergy are taking an active interest in better personality adjustment, including the sexual adjustment. This will help to neutralize the strong sense of sin and guilt so long associated with sex. We need more education for marriage in the high school and college, including teaching about the sexual side of marriage adjustment.

THE USE OF BOOKS AS AN ADJUNCT TO COUNSELING

In the course of counseling the more normal couples or those with mild maladjustment or even some of the moderately severe cases, the interview can be supplemented by reading. *Marriage and Sexual Harmony,* by Oliver Butterfield, published by Emerson Books (1943), is a brief, concise, inexpensive, and excellent guide to the physical aspects of sexual adjustment. *Ideal Marriage,* by T. H. van de Velde, published by Random House (1926), and *Preparing for Marriage,* by Clifford R. Adams, published by E. P. Dutton & Co. (1951), are larger, more inclusive, and more expensive but valuable for those who need more than Dr. Butterfield's pamphlet. *The Happy Family,* by John Levy and Ruth Munroe, published by Alfred A. Knopf (1938), and *A Marriage Manual,* by Abraham Stone, M.D., published by Simon & Schuster (1952) are excellent books to stimulate that tolerant thinking of each other which is so necessary to happy marriage and the mutual understanding necessary in the background for good sexual adjustment.

Love cannot survive without its physical expression. Every effort made to achieve a happier, more satisfying sexual adjustment is an effort toward healthier, more harmonious living everywhere.

Chapter 4

MARITAL ADJUSTMENT AND ITS PREDICTION*

by Lewis M. Terman

PROFESSOR EMERITUS OF PSYCHOLOGY, STANFORD UNIVERSITY, CALIFORNIA

I. MEASURING THE HAPPINESS OF A MARRIAGE

Identification of the factors that make for successful marriage without some kind of criterion as to what constitutes marital success is obviously impossible. One criterion is whether the marriage proves to be permanent or is later broken by divorce or separation. This criterion is useful, but it has three shortcomings: (1) it is an all-or-none score and measures only the extreme degree of marital adjustment; (2) it is a criterion that cannot be applied without a wait of several years; (3) the likelihood of ultimate resort to divorce is determined not only by degree of marital dissatisfaction but also by the presence or absence of religious and moral scruples.

Early investigators solved the problem roughly by having subjects rate their marriage on a five-point scale as very happy, above average in happiness, average, below average, or definitely unhappy. Hamilton[1] improved the method by using a numerical index of marital satisfaction based on the answers to thirteen questions. The more elaborate techniques employed by Burgess and Cottrell[2] and by myself are merely improvements upon that devised by Hamilton.

The test we are concerned with in this chapter calls for information on fifteen aspects of the marriage, as follows:

1. Proportion of outside interest the spouses have in common.
2. Rated amount of agreement in each of ten different fields.

---

*The investigations summarized in this chapter were financed in large part by grants from the National Research Council on the recommendation of its Committee for Research on Problems of Sex, Robert M. Yerkes, chairman.

The author wishes also to acknowledge the valuable assistance rendered by Dr. Winifred B. Johnson in the selection and formulation of many items in the psychometric techniques which have been used.

Some of the material in this chapter has been more fully treated in Chapter XVIII of the volume by Terman and Oden.[5]

3. Method of settling disagreements that arise.

4. In a list of forty specific activities respondent
 (a) checks once those he (or she) enjoys doing, and
 (b) checks twice those enjoyed with the spouse.

5. Regret of marriage.

6. Choice of spouse if life could be lived over.

7. Contemplation of separation or divorce.

8. Admission or denial of present unhappiness.

9. Preference for spending leisure with spouse.

10. Gaiety and happiness when spouses are alone together.

11. Extent to which the spouse irritates or bores respondent.

12. Rated satisfactoriness of the spouse's personality.

13. Degree of certainty that no other spouse would have been so satisfactory.

14. Subjective rating of happiness of the marriage on a seven-point scale.

15. In a list of thirty-eight common faults respondent
 (a) checks once those that the spouse has, and
 (b) checks twice those that have affected the happiness of the mar-
  riage.†

The marital-happiness test in its present form was given in 1940 to 643 members of a gifted group and to their spouses. Their average age at the time was about 30 years. All the gifted subjects in childhood had IQs in the top one per cent of the school population and when retested for intelligence in 1940 they averaged close to the 99th percentile of the adult generality. The intelligence scores of their spouses in 1940 averaged considerably lower than those of the gifted subjects themselves but were about on a par with scores of typical college graduates.

The score weights (credits) assigned to the individual items and to the various possible responses to each item were based upon experimental work with several sets of tentative weights. Those finally chosen were weights which gave a suitably high correlation of each item with the sum of the remaining scores and which also gave a wide distribution of total scores. The intent was that the test as a whole should have a high degree of internal consistency and thus get at the same general factor of happiness from different angles. That this result was accomplished is demonstrated by the fact that the total scores have a reliability coefficient of .89 for each sex. Moreover, the score distributions which the test yields are much less skewed toward the high end of the scale than the distributions yielded by previous measures of marital adjustment.

The possible range of total scores is from 0 to 100, and the scores of the gifted subjects and their spouses extended over almost the entire range. The

---

†For exact wording of the test items see Appendix of the volume by Terman and Oden.[5]

mean for husbands was 63 and for wives 66. Although this difference is numerically small, it is statistically reliable (critical ratio=3.8). The difference could mean either that wives on the average tend to be a little better satisfied with their marriage than husbands are, or that wives are more willing to give verbal expression to their satisfactions.

The mean happiness score was almost exactly the same for gifted wives and the wives of gifted husbands, but the mean for gifted husbands was a little below the mean for husbands of gifted wives. In the case of each sex the two distributions were sufficiently alike to justify combining all husbands into a single distribution and all wives into another.

The total score gives a fairly reliable measure of the marital happiness at a given time, but it does not tell how the same person would score on the same test years later. One purpose of the test is to enable an investigator to follow the happiness trends of marriages over an extended period.

It is extremely significant that a test of this kind does not yield a high correlation between the happiness scores of husband and wife. For these subjects the husband-wife correlation was only .52. Marriage is evidently a venture in which the two principals cannot be guaranteed an equal share of the proceeds. A low happiness score on the part of either spouse is predictive of divorce or separation, and the wife's score appears to be somewhat more predictive than the husband's.

II. SEX ADJUSTMENTS IN MARRIAGE

The subjects who took the test of marital happiness also answered a number of questions on specific sexual adjustments in their marriage. Information requested from both spouses included usual frequency of intercourse, frequency preferred by the respondent, an estimate of the average duration of intercourse, a rating of the relative passionateness of the spouses, and a rating of how well mated they were sexually. Three additional questions asked the wife for information regarding her experience of the sexual orgasm, the degree of the satisfaction (release) which she obtained from intercourse, and the amount of pleasure and/or pain which she experienced at her first intercourse.

A sex-adjustment score for each subject was computed by assigning weights to the various possible responses to each of the sex items. A response given most often by subjects of high happiness was considered a "good" response and was weighted more heavily than a response less associated with happiness. The maximum sex-adjustment score possible was 23 for husbands and 30 for wives, the higher maximum for wives being due to the fact that more questions were asked of wives than of husbands.

Amazingly close agreement was found between the present group of gifted subjects and the less selected group of 792 couples. There was, in fact, no very significant difference between the two groups. This appears to warrant two conclusions: (1) that the subjects in both groups were probably reporting the facts as accurately as they could; and (2) that intellectually gifted persons are just as normal in their sex adjustments as persons less selected for intelligence and education.

The total score on sex adjustment correlated with marital happiness to the extent of .40 for husbands and .43 for wives. As we shall see presently, the sex-adjustment score is much less predictive of later divorce or separation than is the score on marital happiness.

III. THE TEST OF MARITAL APTITUDE

The test of marital aptitude to be described here is the result of several years of search for correlates of marital happiness. The work of Burgess and Cottrell[2] has emphasized the importance of factors in the childhood and family background and of facts and circumstances in the immediate background of the marriage. My own data confirm in large part the conclusions of those investigators but suggest that factors of personality and temperament play an even more important role. The test given to the gifted subjects and their spouses included most of the items which Burgess and Cottrell had found predictive and all the items which had shown some evidence of validity in my earlier study. The items fall into three categories, including (1) 117 relating to personality and temperament, (2) 33 on childhood and family background, and (3) 30 on the background of the particular marriage in question. The items in the first two categories can be used with any adult subject, married or single, but those in the third category can be used only with subjects who are married.

The test was given in 1940 not only to the married gifted subjects and their spouses who took the test of marital happiness, but also to 371 gifted subjects who had not yet married. The purpose of the test was disguised by labeling it as a test of personality and temperament.

Consider first the validity of individual items in predicting scores on the happiness test. This was judged by the extent to which the item discriminated between subjects with high happiness scores and subjects with low scores. The "high" group used for this purpose was composed of 150 couples who had scored high in happiness, and the low group was composed of 150 couples who had scored low. Valid items are those showing a reliable difference between the two groups of a given sex.‡ The following data illustrate the method.

	HUSBANDS			WIVES		
	HIGH	LOW	CR	HIGH	LOW	CR
	%	%		%	%	
Do you frequently feel grouchy?						
Response: No	78	47	5.8	81	61	3.9
Do you often ignore the feelings of others?						
Response: No	67	47	3.6	79	64	2.9
Amount of conflict with mother.						
Response: None	52	31	3.7	44	25	3.5

Responses which yielded differences having a critical ratio as high as 2.0 but less than 3.0 were given a score weight of one point; responses yielding a critical ratio of 3.0 but less than 4.0 were given two points; those with critical ratios of 4.0 or higher were given three points. A subject's total score on the test was the sum of the score weights carried by all the responses the subject had made.

Weights for Category 1. Personality and Temperament. There were four sets of items in this category, as follows: (1) 53 items of the type used in the Bernreuter personality inventory; (2) 34 items from the Strong vocational interest test; (3) 16 items on the subject's opinions about the ideal marriage; and (4) 14 items calling for self-ratings and ratings by the subject's spouse on fourteen traits of personality.

About three fourths of the 53 items of the Bernreuter type were predictive of happiness. The following carry a score weight of either two or three points for each sex, unless otherwise specified:

Do you daydream frequently?	Credit for No
Do you often feel just miserable?	Credit for No
Are you touchy on various subjects?	Credit for No
Do you often experience periods of loneliness?	Credit for No
Do you usually try to avoid arguments?	Credit for Yes

One point for men; two points for women. It is apparently more important that women should not be argumentative.

Do you often feel lonesome when you are with other people?	Credit for No
Do you try to get your own way even if you have to fight for it?	Credit for No

---

‡Another check on validity was made by comparing the mean happiness score of subjects who gave a particular response with the mean happiness of subjects who gave a different response on the same item. The general principle is the same as in the high-low comparison.

One point for men; two points for women. Such aggressiveness is less objectionable in men than women.

Do you frequently feel grouchy?   Credit for No
    Three points for men; two points for women.

Are you frequently burdened by a sense of remorse or regret? Credit for No
    Men two points; women one.

Do you lack self-confidence?   Credit for No
    Men two points; women none. Lack of self-confidence is
less serious for women.

Do you worry too long over humiliating experiences?   Credit for No
    Men two points; women one.

*Do your feelings alternate between happiness and sadness
without apparent reason?*   Credit for No
    Men two points; women three.

Do you lose your temper easily?   Credit for No
    One point for men; two points for women. Apparently
men are allowed a little more leeway on this trait than are
women.

*Do you think most religions do about as much harm as
good?*   Credit for No
    Two points for men; one point for women.

*Is it harder for you to be serene and cheerful than it is for
most people?*   Credit for No
    Two points for men; one point for women.

*Do you usually feel that you are well dressed and make a
good appearance?*   Credit for Yes
    Men three points; women two points.
    Surprising reversal of what one would expect.

*With the opposite sex do you tend to be dominant and
have your own way?*
    No score weight for men; women get two points for the
response No. Dominance with the opposite sex is permissible to men but not to women.

There are 19 other items in this list with a weight of one point for one or
both sexes.

Only a few of the 34 items from the Strong vocational interest test were
predictive of happiness with this group of subjects. Men get one point for
liking picnics, Bible study, public speaking, writing letters, conservative
people, and women cleverer than themselves. Women get one point for liking picnics, teaching children, contributing to charities, emotional people,
Negroes, or old people. The only weight of two points for men is for liking
old people and the only one of two points for women is for liking women
cleverer than themselves!

Of 16 items on opinions about what constitutes the ideal marriage, all but one proved to be predictive of happiness in greater or lesser degree. Opinions about which subjects were asked to express themselves concerned such issues as whether the husband should be some years older than the wife, whether the husband should "wear the pants," whether vacations should be taken together, whether marriage should be postponed until income is comfortable, whether the wife should be financially independent of the husband, whether the wife should have a definite budget, whether children should be given religious instruction, importance of the single standard of sex morals, and similar subjects. The fact that so many items in this list were predictive indicates that one's happiness in a marriage is definitely influenced by the attitudes one brings to it.

The traits rated were happiness of temperament, freedom from moodiness, caution vs. impulsiveness, self-confidence, freedom from emotionality, conformity to authority and the conventions, how easy to get on with, enjoyment of social contacts, persistence in accomplishment of ends, integration of life toward a definite goal, inferiority feelings, vanity and egotism, exclusiveness of friendships.

Trait ratings of this kind had not previously been used as indicators of marital aptitude. They proved to be among the best in the entire battery, all but one of them carrying score weights of two to three points for one or both of the sexes.

Weights for Category 2. Childhood and Family Background. Items which are not predictive of happiness for either sex in this group include birth order, number of sibs, number of opposite-sex sibs, report of having experienced a sex shock, amount of "petting" during the high-school period, and rated attractiveness of the same-sex parent. Items which justify the highest score weights for these subjects include the following:

Rated happiness of childhood, two points to men for "extremely happy"; women two points if "above average."

Childhood punishment, score weight of two points for men and one point for women if there was little or no punishment.

Attitude of parents toward the child's early sex curiosity gets a weight of two points for men if it was described as "frank and encouraging"; no weight for women.

Denial of having experienced any desire to be of the opposite sex gets two points for men and one point for women.

Lack of conflict with the father gets two points for men and one for women. On attachment to father, the husband gets two points if the response was either "very strong" or "none," and the wife one point for either of these responses.

Rated attractiveness of the opposite-sex parent gets a maximum of two points for each sex, the favorable condition being attractiveness rather than the reverse.

High rating on happiness of the parents' marriage carries two points for men and one point for women.

The type of home training (whether strict, firm but not harsh, usually or always had own way, or irregular) gives two points to men and one point to women for any one of the first three conditions.

The following have lower weights in estimating chance of happiness:

Amount of religious training, history of Sunday-school attendance, church membership, rated adequacy of sex instruction, source of sex information, premarital attitude toward sex, adolescent shyness, preferred parent, and dominance between parents.

Weights for Category 3. Background of the Marriage. Items in this category which showed little or no correlation with marital happiness for these subjects include number of years married, length of engagement, length of time over which the couple "kept company," number of persons with whom the subject "kept company" before marriage, rated resemblance of spouse to respondent's opposite-sex parent, husband's occupation at marriage, outside employment of wife after marriage, ownership of home, height of husband, height of wife (however, one point is given to the husband if he is not 12 or more inches taller than his wife, and one point to the wife if she is less tall than her husband), weight at marriage, change in weight of either spouse since marriage, weight deviation from the average person of the same height, number of social organizations in which the husband holds a membership, whether or not the subject wants children, the wife's present occupation, and the wife's last paid occupation.

Age differences between the spouses give the husband a score weight of one to three points; three if he is 12 or more years older than the wife, two points if he is 3 to 11 years older, and one if he is either 0 to 2 years older or 4 or more years younger. Age difference is less important for the happiness of wives, having a maximum weight of one point if the husband is of the same age, 1 to 8 years older, or younger by 4 years or more. That each spouse should get a score weight of one point if the husband is 4 or more years younger may be surprising, but it is in line with the data of my earlier study.

On age at marriage the husband gets one point for age 23 to 28 and two points for age 29 or over. The wife gets one point if the marriage occurred between the ages 23 to 28 inclusive.

The husband gets one point if the marriage did *not* take place in a civil office, but this item has no weight for wives. If the marriage ceremony was performed by a minister the husband gets one point, but again there is no weight for the wife. It appears that the very circumstances of the marriage ceremony about which brides traditionally are so much concerned are totally unrelated to the marital happiness of wives in this group.

On length of acquaintance before marriage the husband gets one point if the acquaintance was not less than one year; the wife one point if it was not less than six months. Apparently the woman can size up her future spouse more quickly than can the average man. This was also true in my earlier group.

On number of opposite-sex friends before marriage the wife gets one point for the response "many," the husband one point for the responses "few" or "several."

One of the most heavily weighted items in this section is the subject's report on whether his or her parents favored or disapproved the marriage. The weights here run to three points for the favorable judgment of each parent. Interesting in this connection is the fact that the father's judgment is as predictive as the mother's.

Another predictive item in this list is the respondent's rating of the relative mental ability of the spouses. The husband gets four points if he rates his own ability as equal to or somewhat less than his wife's, two points if he rates his own ability considerably less, and one point if he rates it somewhat greater. Contrary to common opinion, the least favorable condition for the husband is that he should consider himself "very superior" to his wife in mental ability. In the case of the wife it is most favorable for her to judge her own ability to be "considerably less" or "somewhat less than her husband's. The score weight is three points for each of these responses. The wife gets two points if she says they are "about equal," and one point if she says her own ability is "somewhat greater." The condition least favorable to her happiness is for her to consider her ability "very superior" to that of her husband's.

The story changes when we consider the difference between the two spouses in scores on an intelligence test given in 1940. Surprisingly enough, there was only a slight relationship between the happiness score of either spouse and the difference between them in tested intelligence. A score weight of only one point could be given to each, the most favorable condition being a score by the husband somewhat superior to that of his wife.

Unemployment of the husband after marriage is mildly associated with his unhappiness, justifying a score weight of one point if the amount of unemployment represented less than 20 per cent of the period since marriage. The wife, however, gets two points if her husband has experienced no unemployment. Similarly, the husband gets only one point if he has rarely or never changed his position without improving his condition, whereas this circumstance gives the wife two points.

Amount of husband's savings at marriage is relatively unimportant. The husband gets one point for any answer except "none," the wife one point if her husband's savings amounted to $500 or more. Regarding husband's income at marriage, he gets one point for any response except "none," the wife one point for any sum from $200 upward. The income of a couple at the time the test was taken is also of very low predictive value. The husband is given one point if the couple's income is not below $100 or above $500 per month; the wife one point if it is not below $100. This relative unimportance of income and savings is in line with the results of earlier studies.

Size of the community in which the subjects live is not very important, though the husband gets two points if they live in the country. The maximum score for the wife on this item is one point.

An item that shows higher correlation is the subject's rating of his own and his spouse's health. Three points to each spouse for either of the two ratings "perfect" or "superior," and two points to each for the rating "good."

On number of children the husband gets a weight of one point for the response "one" or "none"; the wife gets two points for "none" and one point for "one." Number in excess of one gets no weight for either sex. Both this and earlier studies indicate that in our present culture the relation of marital happiness to presence of offspring is less than it is commonly supposed to be.

Absolute amount of education has no predictive value, but the husband is given one point if his own education is about the same as or less than that of his wife. The wife gets one point if the husband's education is equal to or slightly less than her own, and two points if the husband's education is greater than her own.

Husband's present occupation shows no correlation with his own happiness, but the wife gets one point if her husband belongs to the professional class. This agrees with my data for 792 couples.

Many of the facts given will seem almost incredible to many readers, but the great majority of them are closely in line with results previously obtained for a less selected group. It seems that many of the current beliefs regarding the importance of this or that factor in the marriage background are based upon nothing more than tradition.

The maximum possible scores on the three parts of the test are as follows:

	MEN	WOMEN
(1) *Personality and temperament*	118	94
(2) *Childhood and family background*	37	23
(3) *Background of the marriage*	38	36

Excluding the third group of items, which can be used only with married subjects, the maximum total for the first two categories is 155 for men and 117 for women.

The reliability of the total marital aptitude score is .86 for men and .82 for women. Its validity is indicated (1) by the fact that it correlates with marital-happiness score to the extent of .62 for men and .55 for women, and (2) by the fact that it predicts later divorce almost as well as college aptitude tests predict college marks.

On the test of marital aptitude, as on the test of marital happiness, the gifted men averaged somewhat below husbands of gifted women, whereas the gifted women and the wives of gifted men had almost identical means. This suggests that if either sex is handicapped for marriage by very superior intelligence it is the man and not the woman (as popular opinion would have it).

IV. THE PREDICTION OF DIVORCE OR SEPARATION

Between 1940 and the end of 1949 there were 104 marriages of gifted subjects that ended in divorce or separation.§ For most of these subjects, scores as of 1940 were available on marital happiness, sex adjustment, and marital aptitude.[6]

The relative value of these three variables in predicting marital success or failure was estimated by comparing the mean scores of subjects who became divorced or separated by 1949 with the mean of subjects whose marriage remained intact to that date. The results showed that happiness scores and aptitude scores are both predictive of marital failure, and to about the same degree, but that the sex-adjustment scores have considerably less predictive value.

For husbands the happiness scores are somewhat more predictive than the aptitude scores. On two of the variables (happiness and aptitude) wives' scores are more predictive than husbands' scores. Only for one of the three variables (aptitude) is the average of husband-and-wife scores appreciably more predictive than the wife's score alone.

The low predictive value of the sex-adjustment scores suggests that the

---

§In the gifted group separation is almost always followed by divorce.

role of sex, per se, in marital happiness is secondary rather than primary. Couples who are psychologically well mated show a surprising tolerance for the things that are not entirely satisfactory in their sexual relationships. The psychologically ill-mated show no such tolerance, but on the contrary are prone to exaggerate any trifling amount of sexual incompatibility that may be present. Analysis of the sexual complaints expressed by my earlier group of 792 couples gave convincing evidence that such complaints are often just a convenient peg on which to hang psychological discontent.[3]

The Role of Temperament. Perhaps the most important conclusion suggested by the data reported in this chapter is that one's marital happiness is largely determined by one's all-round happiness of temperament. Happiness of temperament, in the sense here intended, is not to be confused either with Pollyannish or sugary attitudes or with the happy-go-lucky disposition. Its meaning is best defined in terms of the specific responses in the marital-aptitude test which correlate with scores on the marital-happiness test.

This conclusion regarding the role of temperament in marriage is supported not only by the present study but also by results obtained from a less selected group. It seems that there are persons who could live comfortably with any but the most disagreeable mate, and others who would find almost any marriage unbearable. The truth of the latter statement, at least, could be illustrated by the case histories of several of my subjects who in the course of a few years have gone through three or four marriages and as many divorces.

The role of temperament in marriage is further indicated by the low correlation between the happiness scores of husband and wife. As previously noted, this was only .52 for the present group and only .60 for the less selected group. The correlation could hardly be so low were there not a considerable tendency for each individual to go through life in his own happy or unhappy way. This, of course, is not to say that neither spouse is ever to blame for the unhappiness of the other; such an extreme view would be manifestly absurd.

If the theory here proposed is sound one would expect to find that marital-aptitude scores are correlated not only with later marital adjustment but also with the social and general adjustment in childhood and youth. A check of the aptitude scores against many case-history variables in the gifted group has revealed a number of significant relationships. For example, women who had been rated in 1928 as having "some" or "marked" nervous symptoms averaged 8.5 points lower in the marital-aptitude scores of 1940 than women who in 1928 had not shown such symptoms. The difference is quite reliable (CR=4.18). Both men and women who had shown "some" or "marked" social maladjustment in 1922 averaged, eighteen years later, 6 points lower in marital aptitude than women whose 1922 ratings on social adjustment were "satisfactory." Men with "satisfactory" social adjustment in 1928 averaged, a dozen years later, 12.6 points higher in marital aptitude than those with "some" or "marked" maladjustment (CR=4.53). The corresponding difference for women was 8.9 points (CR=3.00). Men rated "satisfactory" on general adjustment in 1940 averaged 15.8 points higher in the marital-aptitude test taken the same year than men with "some" or "serious" maladjustment (CR=9.62). The corresponding difference for women was approximately 10 points (CR=7.00). Checks of this kind were also made on the correlations of case-history data with scores on the marital-happiness test, and with similar results.

In conclusion, we have a fairly satisfactory measure of the marital happiness of a husband or wife at a given time, and we also have at least a rough measure of an individual's aptitude for marriage. The latter, when perfected, has greater potentialities for usefulness than the former because it taps more fundamental aspects of personality and temperament. Happiness in marriage is often ephemeral; aptitude for happiness is an abiding trait.

A shortcoming of the aptitude test is that it measures only the general aptitude of a given person. What we most need is a test that would predict the compatibility of a given couple. There has been a good deal of search for the magical combinations of likes and dislikes, agreements and disagreements, resemblances and differences, that are favorable or unfavorable to marital happiness; unfortunately, few have been found. Terman and Buttenweiser[4] computed tetrachoric correlations between marital happiness and agreement and disagreement of husbands and wives in their replies to some 500 questions relating chiefly to interests, habit patterns, likes, and dislikes. There were a good many items which appeared to be valid measures of compatibility within the group studied; however, when these promising items were tried out with another and larger group few showed much sign of being valid measures of compatibility, although many remained valid as indicators of happy or unhappy temperament in the individual spouse. The search for "good" and "bad" combinations should be continued, but much work will have to be done to carry us very far beyond the present general measure of happiness of temperament. We have seen that some combinations are better than others with regard to age, education, estimated intelligence, and a few other variables. The problem is to find enough predictive combinations to yield a reliable measure of compatibility.

Finally, there can be no universally valid test of marital happiness, marital aptitude, or marital compatibility. The things that go to make the "good" marriage vary from culture to culture. They are not the same for the Hindu and the Moslem, for the Samoan and the Scot, or for the peasant and the plutocrat of the same nationality and religion. They may differ as between California and South Carolina, Minnesota and Mississippi, Vermont and Virginia. Regional studies should be made for the purpose of analyzing and plotting such differences.

NOTES

[1]G. V. Hamilton, *A Research in Marriage,* New York: Boni, 1929.

[2]E. W. Burgess and L. S. Cottrell, *Predicting Success or Failure in Marriage,* New York, Prentice-Hall, 1939.

[3]L. M. Terman, *Psychological Factors in Marital Happiness,* New York, McGraw-Hill Book Co., 1938, pp. 309 ff.

[4]L. M. Terman, and P. Buttenweiser, "Personality Factors in Marital Compatibility," *J. Soc. Psychol.,* 1935, *6,* 143–71; 267–89.

[5]L. M. Terman and M. Oden, *The Gifted Child Grows Up; Twenty-five Years Follow-up of a Superior Group,* Stanford University Press, 1947.

[6]L. M. Terman, "Predicting Marriage Failure from Test Scores," *Marriage and Family Living,* Vol. XII, No. 2, May 1950.

Chapter 5

THE WEDDING, THE HONEYMOON, AND THE FIRST MARITAL ADJUSTMENTS

by Ada Hart Arlitt, Ph.D.

PROFESSOR EMERITUS OF CHILD CARE AND TRAINING AND PSYCHOLOGY, UNIVERSITY OF CINCINNATI

The couple are now ready to plan the wedding, since all the preliminaries of the engagement and the engagement adjustments are apparently successfully met. The wedding may be of six types: (1) the secret wedding, (2) the elopement, (3) a small home wedding to which only the family is invited, (4) a large home wedding, (5) a simple church wedding, (6) a large church wedding.

THE SECRET WEDDING

The secret wedding has only one advantage. It eliminates the cost of the simplest home wedding. Its disadvantages far outweigh the saving of time and money. In all other types of weddings except elopements there is a steadily heightened emotional tone leading up to and through the festivities which precede the wedding to the wedding itself. This is true of the family, their friends, and the engaged couple. The result is an emotional tone favorable to marital adjustments. After the ceremony the parents and friends are ready to release the couple from adolescence and to welcome them into the "young married group." For the couple the high tension of the parties and the final ceremony is ready to change over into the physiological and psychological states which accompany love, including sex. The bride has been the center of attention which she knows will terminate adolescence for her and for the groom. Having been the center of the stage, which is the desire of all normal adolescents, she should now be willing to relinquish this position.

All her social group and the surrounding social groups have been notified of the wedding. Both families have obviously approved to such an extent that the wedding has proceeded publicly. Society approves and, with the proper notices in the papers, the parties, and the ceremony, has given its final sanction.

The guests have had a part in setting the stage for a successful marriage, as most of them have contributed presents with which the couple will set up housekeeping. They have had a part in the entire procedure from the announcement of the engagement to the actual starting of the couple's home. Naturally, then, they will co-operate in making this marriage a success. Even if the wedding is a small one to which only the family is invited, these attitudes and adjustments are still present. In a secret wedding none of these things can appear. The relatives and friends who have been deceived and whose generosity has been frustrated may carry actual dislike for the couple and a conscious or unconscious desire to see the marriage fail. This is as true of the immediate family as it is of its friends. Socially the marriage is off to a poor start, even if it is announced within a few days after it occurs. If it is not announced for several months, only a few men of extraordinary good will can fail to suspect an element of "shotgun" technique in the marriage. If this is complicated by the birth of a child within a few months after the marriage is announced the child carries a definite stigma and society will accept the child and its parents only if the families on both sides stand back of them wholeheartedly.

Emotionally the situation may be even worse. The whole wedding procedure has been surreptitious and therefore associated in the minds of both with the fear which accompanies concealment. Fear inhibits love and produces throughout the entire physiological organism conditions which make normal sex adjustments impossible. The irritation which arises is likely to be directed by the couple against each other. The emotional pattern is one of fear and anger, not love. The first adjustments are the most important. Only in very rare instances indeed will these be good.

There is little excuse for a secret wedding and none whatsoever if it is announced immediately after it occurs.

ELOPEMENT

An elopement is also a poor method of starting married life. Frequently these elopements are not based on long engagements discussed with and approved by both families. They are a result of a sudden whim or an escape, by one or both of the couple, from something which should be faced before they marry. When the couple have decided that they prefer to save the cost of a simple home wedding they should nevertheless have the backing of the family on both sides and have the immediate family—that is, mother, father, sisters, and brothers on both sides—attend.

Elopements are not on the whole successful. Statistics show they result in many more divorces than do marriages entered into in the usual fashion with a church or home wedding.

THE SIMPLE HOME WEDDING

The simple home wedding comes next on the list. The ceremony may be performed by any legal authority who is a friend of the family or, more frequently, it is performed by a minister. Psychologically this latter is the wiser way to plan, as the church and the state are concerned with the adjustment of the couple. With the position of marriage as uncertain as it is today, the more social pressure that can be brought to bear to keep it together, the better.

For a simple home wedding without bridesmaids the cost should not be more than that shown in the following table.

EXPENSES INCURRED BY BRIDE'S FAMILY*

Item	Summer	Winter
Decorations	$ 25.00	$100.00
Dress and veil	50.00	75.00
Trousseau	300.00	300.00
Linens	200.00	200.00
Present (bride to groom)	10.00	10.00
	————	————
TOTAL	$585.00	$685.00

The major expenses of this type of wedding are the trousseau and linens which present-day custom states are to be the gifts of the bride's family. The refreshments, if they are supplied, should not cost more than fifteen dollars, since at a wedding of this sort champagne is not provided and a caterer is not employed. This type of wedding has every advantage and few disadvantages, since the expense for the groom is equally light.

An engagement ring	$200.00
A wedding ring	20.00
Present for the bride	20.00
Fee for the minister	15.00
	————
TOTAL	$255.00

The change from summer to winter makes no difference in the groom's expenses. Every psychological need except that for display has been met.

*For assistance in gathering these figures I am indebted to two members of my staff, Mrs. McDermott and Miss Dupps.

Both parents of bride and groom have come and shown their approval. The bride has appeared in the traditional bride's clothing, complete with veil, so that her husband can remember her at her loveliest for the rest of her life. The too great excitement of complicated church weddings has been avoided and the couple have saved sufficient funds to set up housekeeping in a more normal way.

The figures for an average wedding today with their expense to all concerned follow.

THE SIMPLE CHURCH WEDDING

Expenses incurred by the average family for a simple church wedding.

	Summer	Winter
Bridesmaids' flowers (3)	$ 30.00	$ 75.00
Decorations	100.00	150.00
Gifts to bridesmaids	30.00	30.00
Sexton	10.00	10.00
Invitations, etc.	85.00	85.00
Rehearsal dinner	50.00	50.00
Organist	25.00	25.00
Breakfast or reception	250.00	250.00
Dress and veil	70.00	150.00
Trousseau	400.00	400.00
Linens	200.00	200.00
Present (bride to groom)	30.00	30.00
TOTAL	$1280.00	$1455.00

Groom

	Summer	Winter
Brides bouquet	$ 15.00	$ 25.00
Bouquet for mother	10.00	10.00
Bouquet for bride's mother	10.00	10.00
License	2.00	2.00
Engagement ring	200.00	200.00
Wedding ring	25.00	25.00
Present for bride	100.00	100.00
Fee for minister	25.00	25.00
Flowers for ushers	10.00	20.00
Dinner for ushers	25.00	25.00
Presents for ushers	7.50	7.50
Suit—rented	10.00	10.00
Honeymoon	200.00	200.00
TOTAL	$639.50	$659.50

Bridesmaid's expenses (each)	Summer	Winter
Dress	$35.00	$ 50.00
Sandals	6.00	6.00
Hat or garland	4.00	15.00
Showers for bride	50.00	50.00
TOTAL	$95.00	$121.00

In the past seven years many stores have added special departments for prospective brides. The services which these offer should be approached with caution, since their cost, including photographs, may double the amount given here for a simple home wedding.

It is hardly necessary to point out the general effect of overexpenditure. The parents are left with so many bills to pay that they cannot easily help the couple in their normal plans. The groom has been put to an enormous expense. Unless he has saved a great deal he enters married life with a crippled financial status. The wife may have to work for several years in order to save enough to meet emergencies. Instead of entering married life relaxed, both are worried. Weddings of this type are the result of a general tendency in society today to increase possessions at the expense of spiritual growth. There can be little if any advantage in such increase in complications, except that they make the bride feel that she has had as good a wedding as any in her set and better than most.

For families of large incomes and grooms who are well on their way toward financial success, these expenditures present no problem, but very few couples are so well situated financially.

THE LARGE WEDDING

The large home wedding and the large church wedding are so far beyond the means of the average family that tables of expenses for these sorts are not included here.

THE PSYCHOLOGICAL ASPECTS

Whatever the kind of wedding, every superstition should have its inning, and there are many of these still present in modern society. The bride should wear traditional dress to give the husband the traditional impression. She should have something old, something new, something borrowed, and something blue. If throwing confetti is the custom, this procedure should be followed. Rice is dangerous, so confetti should be substituted. Because of the fact that rice is both indicative of fertility and is a part of many ancient wedding ceremonies in which the bride and groom eat from the same rice bowl, it seems a pity that its use has become so dangerous. If it were thrown after the couple it would be safe, but, thrown at them, it has injured a number. Wedding customs which have their origin in primitive societies, such as carrying the bride across the threshold, "Happy the bride the sun shines on," and "June brides are happier than other brides," may and should be conformed to if the couple feel strongly about them.

The psychological state which immediately precedes weddings other than sudden elopements should be kept in mind. For at least twenty-four hours before the actual wedding takes place there is a mounting tension in both men and women, but it appears to be higher in women. The girl begins to worry about the marriage and finally comes to the conclusion that the man is a stranger and that she does not wish the marriage to go on. This tension may be so strong that at the last minute she will elope with someone else as an escape. Such elopements are doomed to failure. Generally the groom is in the same state and at the dinner which occurs before the wedding he may drink too much and the ushers must see him home and put him to bed. He wakes up just about in time to dress and to rush to be married. The girl has no such easy way out and must fight her fears.

THE FEARS OF THE BRIDE

One hundred and fifty brides have described their fears, including the final one, in very much the same language. When they enter the church and look at the groom they feel that he is a complete stranger. This feeling increases as they go up the aisle. When the groom speaks the fear may be dispelled. For some it is dispelled only when at the end of the ceremony the groom kisses the bride.

Emotional disturbances of every kind are less for home weddings than they are for church weddings. They apparently increase with the size of the church, but in every one of the one hundred and fifty brides interviewed some fear did develop.

Other things being equal, the simpler the festivities, the better. The bride and the groom are already somewhat tired from the festivities preceding the wedding, and the longer they stay with their friends in a state of high emotional tension, the less they will have to give to the wedding night.

In many cases the number of parties given for the bride and groom and the complexities of the wedding itself, together with the reception which follows it, produce such fatigue in the bride and groom that the marriage may not be consummated for as much as forty-eight hours after the wedding. There are many instances in which twelve hours' sleep is necessary to relieve exhaustion before any emotion other than irritation can arise.

THE HONEYMOON

The choice of the place for the honeymoon should have been made in advance of the wedding and in the light of the financial position of the groom. He has not only to take care of all the expenses incurred during the honeymoon but also to have a sufficient reserve to meet the expenses incident to establishing a new home and supporting his family.

No one should accompany the bridal couple under any conditions. The presence of a third person, no matter how loving and considerate, is sufficient to bring about a state of frustration in both bride and groom. It may easily become a source of serious quarrels. Relatives and friends should not "surprise" the bride and groom with visits during the honeymoon for the same reason. To go where there are a number of friends who will entertain for the couple is equally unfortunate and again for the same reason. The purpose of the honeymoon is to provide a period of adjustment to marriage and not to provide an occasion for further entertainment and further follow-up by the family. The simpler the honeymoon, the more provision should be made for many activities of an interesting sort in which the couple may engage. Anyone who has had a long train trip—say, three days—with a good friend in the same compartment or space will remember that the first day was interesting enough but that by the end of the third day the friendship was strained or even terminated. No doubt married couples think they wish to see each other all day long without any special activities planned, but this is far from the case. No one is fascinating enough to provide a source of stimulation and interest for twenty-four hours a day for ten consecutive days.

Camping trips on which the couple constantly need to adjust to a changing environment, motor trips which are not too long and too wearing, places where there are sports in which the couple are mutually interested, or a city with motion pictures, theaters, museums, and parks, if the couple have sufficient funds to finance the expenses, are all good choices. Long train trips are not.

During the honeymoon certain psychological states will be present of which it is well to take account. They should be met before they produce lasting conflicts. Strain has pointed out that these are (1) the desire to tell the beloved everything about one's self, (2) a willingness to promise anything, (3) a desire to possess completely. Each of these must be watched carefully. It is always interesting to talk about one's self, and this is usually more common in brides than in grooms. Nothing is more boring than a person about whom one knows everything. While the bride and groom know each other very well, or they should not have been married, some things should be left for them to discover about each other for many years to come.

If the material talked about is in the nature of a too full confession, it is likely to produce shock effects from which they may not recover. If the couple are adult, and they should be, then each has fallen in love with some-one else before the final engagement and marriage. Unless what has occurred during the preceding experience is of so serious a nature that it should have been told before marriage, then to give names, places, dates, and "the blow-by-blow" description of what has gone on when one was previously involved is simply to make clear and vivid images in the mind of the confessee which may interfere with all later marital adjustments. If a couple who have been happily married fifteen years or more are asked if they had ever been in love with anyone other than the wife or husband, the answer will be that they fell in love only once and were never in the least interested in anyone other than the person to whom they are now married. All previous experiences are forgotten rapidly unless they are told in detail. If they are so told the partner in marriage will not let them be forgotten and they become inhibitory in their effects.

Plans of the bride and groom should not be so inflexible as to make an early pregnancy feared. The effect of fear on sex relations is too well known to need discussion here. Tension because of sex maladjustments during the honeymoon period may never be overcome. Many authorities tend to mini-mize the role played by sex in marriage, but it must be kept in mind that marriage is primarily a sex relationship.

The end of the honeymoon should find the couple physically and psycho-logically adjusted to such an extent that they are ready to undertake a life-time of living and working together.

If the honeymoon is not satisfactory to the bride a number of things may happen. All girls carry into marriage a species of imaginary playmate whom they bring out for their own satisfaction whenever life is not sufficiently interesting or rewarding. For brevity's sake this imaginary playmate may be called "the fantasy lover." The fantasy lover is usually someone whom the girl might have married but did not. She brings him out and tells herself that life would have been entirely different had he been her choice for a life mate. If the honeymoon is dull he may be brought out at once, and in the process of telling her husband everything she may make the imaginary playmate too real and too vivid to herself and to him. Even if he is never discussed with her husband she may make her adjustment to the imaginary lover rather than to her husband and never thereafter adjust to married life. Most marriages are made permanent or lost in the first two or three months. Many are lost through the failure of the honeymoon to satisfy psychological and physical needs.

Brides should recognize the presence of the imaginary lover as a fantasy. Husbands should never be made aware of the device which their wives are using for an escape from dullness and frustration.

The second attitude, a willingness to promise anything, should also be watched. No promise of any kind should be made during the engagement period or the honeymoon unless it can be kept completely and without reservation. At this point many married couples lose confidence in each other; for if promises are made and then not kept the marriage partner feels his mate to be untruthful and unreliable, two conditions on the basis of which no good marriage can be set up.

Complete possession is frustrating to both. All adults need a sense of freedom, but not too much freedom. They wished to be loved, cherished, and needed, but also to feel that they can function in the normal life pattern without being pulled back by strings. This is somewhat more true of men than of women. The young man who told his wife that she might bow to any man that she had known before her marriage but that she was not to stop to speak to him on the street or to let him buy her an ice-cream soda is a case in point.

The girl who continued to accept luncheon dates when her husband was busy and dinner dates when he was out of town was misusing any freedom which her husband had allowed her and should have been held to strict account for her behavior. Still worse was the girl who while still on her honeymoon insisted on having time to write to the men who had rushed her before marriage.

Finally the honeymoon may simply be dull. All marriages are characterized by periods which in a learning curve would be called plateaus; namely, periods which are somewhat dull and boring and in which the marriage seems to have come to a standstill. The first of these may occur during the honeymoon, which is much earlier than they tend to appear in an average marriage. A bride and groom who have some months of adjustment behind them do not find it difficult to pass through a plateau when it occurs. There is no such background of the habit patterns required in normal living to help the honeymooning bride and groom through a period of dullness and frustration.

If there is the least chance of a plateau occurring it is far better for the bride and groom not to take a trip but to move into their new home and spend their time together making it ready for pleasant living. Such work is never dull, and there is not time enough for a plateau to develop. Any disagreements which they might have as to where articles shall be placed and who shall plan what arrangement of which room are forgotten in the first rush of affection and in the joy of being together.

It should be made clear that large issues are not the ones which often cause the most serious difficulty. It is the sudden quarrel about unimportant matters, followed by a series of such quarrels, which make the marital adjustment poor.

A recent bride reported to me that the first quarrel with her husband was about picking wild flowers. After that he and she avoided all quarrels with excellent techniques. Every quarrel results in pain. Pain inhibits the setting up of habits which make being together enjoyable, just as it inhibits the setting up of all other habits. Every quarrel sets a brick in the wall between the people who engage in it. Every quarrel produces blocking and frustration. It also makes the person with whom one quarrels a stimulus to fighting rather than to the activity concerned with love-making. The age for quarreling is nine to eleven, not adulthood. It is to be hoped that such disagreements as exist will be met by other techniques, and the honeymoon is the time to establish these.

A busy, active, constructive honeymoon which results in joy in companionship and constructive work and thinking together sends the marriage more happily and more permanently on its way. The sooner the couple adjust to the circumstances which are to surround their first year or more of married life, the more stable the foundation for permanent adjustment.

BIBLIOGRAPHY

Arlitt, Ada Hart, *Family Relationships,* New York, McGraw-Hill Book Co., 1942.

Burgess, Ernest W., and Cottrell, L. S., *Predicting Success or Failure in Marriage,* New York, Prentice-Hall, 1939.

Strain, Francis B., *Love at the Threshold,* New York, D. Appleton-Century Co., 1939.

Chapter 6

HOME MANAGEMENT AND FINANCE

by Howard F. Bigelow, A.M.

PROFESSOR OF ECONOMICS, WESTERN MICHIGAN COLLEGE OF EDUCATION, KALAMAZOO, MICHIGAN

Most people marry today, not because they have to in order to live —for many single persons live rich and worth-while lives—but because they expect through marriage to be able to do more of what they want to do.

Marriage provides security in personal relations. It provides social status, a base from which to operate in activities outside the home, a place to go for care when sick, for rest and relaxation when well, and for love and companionship and affection. And it is also a place where a lot of necessary work gets done. On the economic side the family provides for the wants of its members.

While of necessity the members of a family group sacrifice some personal freedom for emotional and economic security, at the same time they gain a significant degree of independence of markets and money income by pooling their money and skills and personal possessions and doing for each other many things for which single persons must pay.

Everyone knows that it is impossible for two persons to live more cheaply than one. But it is entirely possible for two people to live together for a much smaller money outlay than they must spend if they live apart. How much better the members of a family will be able to live depends upon the effectiveness with which they manage the family's resources.

THE FAMILY'S RESOURCES

The resources of the family consist of the family's money income from employment and from investments, the skills, abilities, time and energy of its members, equipment and personal possessions which it has available for use in supplementing its purchases in the market, and the community resources available for the use of families of its type.

In taking stock of their resources, families think first of their money incomes. In 1953, personal income in the United States reached an all-time high of $284,500,000,000. The average family income was a little more than $6,000. Three quarters of the families had less than this average income. The median family income, of which half the families in the country have more and half have less, was about $4,000. Probably the middle 50 per cent of American families had incomes between $2,500 and $6,000. These estimates of family incomes are "before taxes." In the lower-income groups, income and social-security taxes take from 5 to 10 per cent, and in the upper-income levels a much larger proportion of the family incomes.

At the same time at least half the families in the United States own their own homes free and clear or have a substantial equity in them. Two thirds of the families in the United States own automobiles. There are more radios in use than there are families, though there may be a few families without one. Probably three quarters of the families own at least part of their furniture and a substantial amount of household equipment. Every family has some sort of clothing inventory. Every member of every family has a more or less extensive list of personal possessions.

A substantial proportion of families, even in the lower-income groups, have some small income from investments, if nothing more than a few war bonds. At least half, and perhaps more, of the gainfully employed are or are becoming eligible for some sort of social-security benefits.

There are few if any families that do not make some use of community resources—schools, churches, parks, highways, police and fire protection, health services of various sorts, or the variety of services provided for servicemen by the Veteran's Administration.

Thus resources of the family include much more than the family's money income, though in a market economy such as ours a minimum of money income is fundamental. There is plenty of evidence that successful and happy family living is possible at every income level, except possibly the very lowest, and that too much money, instead of making successful marriage easier, often makes it more difficult. The fundamental problem in family management and finance is to make the best possible use not only of the family's money income but of the time and energy and skills of the family members, of their possessions, and of available community resources. From the point of view of the individual family, the best possible use is that which will enable the members of the family to satisfy as many as possible of their most important wants.

THE FAMILY'S WANTS

The family's wants may be listed in general terms. Every family wants food, warmth, clothing and shelter, facilities for transportation and communication, and some provision for health, education, and recreation. In addition to these wants, which are satisfied for the most part with material goods, are a number of intangible but equally important wants: security, independence, companionship and affection, social position, the respect of others and self-respect, and even a bit of adventure now and then.

In the satisfaction of wants the material and the immaterial aspects cannot be separated. Some social prestige comes from being able to order an expensive steak in a crowded butcher shop. In a time of housing shortage homeownership gives a much-wanted sense of security. Ownership of an automobile gives freedom of movement. For some people the knowledge that they are well dressed gives a sense of personal security fully as important to them as the respect of others which their clothing commands. Even the affectional side of family living has its economic aspects. Personal relations within the family are often improved if the husband brings home a box of candy now and then or an extra pair of nylons. Flowers on anniversaries mean much to many people. Even husbands who are supposed to be primarily concerned with keeping down expenses appreciate a good-looking new shirt or a new cigarette lighter if it is purchased with money the wife has saved from her share of the family money.

There are three general ways in which families may provide the goods needed to satisfy the wants of their members. They may purchase what they want in the market, they may produce them for their own use,* or they may use the facilities, both governmental and non-governmental, which are available in their community. There is no one way in which all families satisfy any one want. Most families get their own meals, but many families buy their meals outside the home, and most families eat out at least occasionally. Men buy most of their clothing ready-made. Women buy much of theirs, though if they like to sew, or are hard to fit with the current styles, or want better

---

*At the present time, most families—urban families even more than farm families—spend more time in supplementing their purchases with goods and services which they produce for themselves than they spend in earning money income.

The apparent contradiction in the statement about rural and urban families is easily explained. Women in urban families have little opportunity to add to the family's money income by home production for sale in the market. They are limited in their home-production activities to production for family use.

The obvious exception to this statement is found in families in which both husband and wife have full-time jobs outside the home. (See H. Kyrk, *The Family in the American Economy*, University of Chicago Press, Chicago, 1953, tables, pp. 283, 289; and H. F. Bigelow, *Family Finance Revised*, J. B. Lippincott Co., Chicago and Philadelphia, 1953, tables, pp. 127, 129, 132, 140.

clothing than they can afford to buy ready-made, they may make a good deal of their own clothing. Some families buy the children's clothing as a matter of course, while others are equally matter-of-fact about doing most of the sewing for their children. Most families send their children to public schools, though some religious groups prefer parochial to public education; in some communities excellent private schools do a flourishing business. In metropolitan areas most families live in rented apartments. In smaller communities a substantial majority own their own homes. Similarly, in smaller communities probably four fifths of the families have at least one family car. In the larger metropolitan centers (with the possible exception of Detroit and Los Angeles) only from one third to one half have automobiles, and even the car-owning families depend to a large extent on public transportation.

The quality of living which a family enjoys depends in part on the number of wants satisfied, in part on the ways in which those wants are satisfied, and in part on the balance maintained between different types of wants. Because of the diversity in individual family situations there can be no one best way for all families to work out their problems of management and finance. Instead there are many right ways, and there are also many wrong ways. Each family, therefore, must work out its own problems in its own way, with due regard for the physical and social environment in which its members live, for the resources which the family has available, for the work which its members are called upon to do, and for the special needs and interests of all the family members.

WHO DOES WHAT

In managing family affairs there is no longer any traditional division of men's work and women's work. World War I, the depression of the 1930's, and more recently World War II have ended the tradition, so far as America is concerned, that the place of women is in the home. If a woman can contribute more to the family by working at home, that is her place. If she can contribute more by working outside and adding to the family's money income, that is what she should do.

However, if wives are to help by working outside for money, husbands can expect to help with the work of the family at home. The eight-hour day and the forty-hour week have left the husband with time to do many things about the house which his wife did of necessity when her husband was employed from seven in the morning till six at night every day in the week.

In the 1920's it was taken for granted that the husband would earn the money and his wife would spend most of it. Now he has time to help with the spending. Especially at the super-markets men go along to help carry home the week's groceries. During the war, when husbands were away in the service, wives took over the complete management of the family affairs, including such activities as the payment of taxes and insurance, the supervision of repairs to the house, and the upkeep of the family car.

The problem of management, therefore, is no longer a simple problem of automatic division into men's work and women's work. Instead each family is free to work out for itself the division of work and of management which makes most effective use of the abilities and connections of both the husband and the wife. As the children become old enough they can be given a share in family responsibilities.

There are a number of typical work-and-management patterns. A family can select the one best suited to its immediate situation and adapt it to its immediate needs, modifying it from time to time to suit changing conditions.

For example: If both husband and wife are employed, both will be helping to earn the money income, both will share in the spending, and both should share in the other work of the household. If the husband only is gainfully employed, the wife will assume a larger responsibility for the work of the household, for much more of the routine planning and management, but she will plan some work and some purchasing for him to do, selecting the sort of thing that he can do best. If the husband is a business executive or a professional man whose work makes heavy demands on his time or takes him often away from home, it may be wise for the wife to take over almost completely the management of family affairs, even if she has to hire some household help to give her the time she needs for purchasing and management. This will leave him only the responsibility of the family's investments and insurance and taxes, which he can handle along with his business or professional activities.

There are similarly a number of ways in which to divide the detailed work and management of the family. One frequently used is for the wife to plan the meals and purchase and prepare the food, shop for her own and the children's clothes, and take care of the details of day-to-day household operation, while her husband sees that the rent is paid, or that the payments are made on the house, and that taxes are paid and the home kept in repair. Usually the husband sees to the upkeep of the car and to the heavy work around the yard, though if his wife likes to work outdoors she may take over the care of the flowers and the kitchen garden. The husband usually manages the family's savings and investments, though if his wife has good business judgment he may consult her about individual investments. Usually the husband takes over the purchase of any articles in which his business connections give him special advantages. If his wife has better money sense than he does and is a good shopper, he may turn over most of the buying to her and put in his time doing more work around the house.

Many families find that it works better to change their division of work from time to time. When the children are small it may be wise for the husband to take over some of the buying and some of the heavier work which his wife did earlier in their married life. Or his wife may prefer to have him take over the care of the children when he is at home and leave her free to get out of the house and do the shopping.

In any case, it is important that each family work out either formally or informally a clearly understood and definite plan for the handling of family affairs. So far as possible it is desirable for each of the members of the family to do what he or she can do and likes to do best. Usually the plan works more smoothly if each member of the family keeps the other informed as to what he is doing and participates in current planning. Usually formal planning sessions are not necessary, though it often helps to sit down and talk over some particular problem. Members even of fairly large families usually know each other well enough so that in their planning they can take each other's preferences into account without formal votes or majority decisions. In fact, some formal family councils which are dominated by one or two strong personalities are actually less democratic in their processes than less formal planning procedures.

TECHNIQUES OF FINANCIAL PLANNING

Many families find that financial planning is one of their most difficult problems. The first step in working out a spending plan for a family is to make a rough plan in general terms, so much for food, so much for clothing, so much for shelter, so much for the family car, and so on, in order to get an idea of what can and what cannot be done with the family's money income. In making this preliminary estimate the family should plan in terms of take-home pay rather than in terms of income before taxes and other deductions. If the family has any considerable amount of business or investment income it must be sure to make adequate allowance for taxes.

Some families like to make a preliminary plan by setting aside a given percentage of the family's income for each of the major divisions of family expenditure. Others find they get a better idea of what they can do with their money if they make their preliminary estimates in dollars and then see what the available dollars will buy.

When the members of the family have a general idea of what can and what cannot be done with the family's income they should work out a detailed spending plan. Since there are a number of expenditures which must be made once a month, many families prefer to work out in detail each month's expenditures. Others prefer to plan the use of their money from payday to payday, as they expect to receive it, planning exactly how they are to spend each pay check.

In making a spending plan, a family must provide for both expenditures, like food and rent and utilities, which must be made each week or each month, and for expenditures which come at longer intervals, like insurance, taxes, vacations, the license for the car, and the winter's coal. Some families include these occasional expenditures as an integral part of their detailed spending plan, adding them in the months in which they must be met. Other families prefer to make a separate plan for these larger occasional expenditures, setting aside each payday in a special account enough to cover them.

Time is required to make a comprehensive, realistic, and workable spending plan. It cannot be done in an hour between the supper dishes and the evening movies. The things for which a family must spend its money are so many and varied that it seems almost impossible to make a plan without overlooking something. But by working out the plan a little at a time, first planning in detail for expenditures for food, for shelter, for clothing, and so on; then putting the parts of the plan together and finally checking to be sure that there will be money available to make each expenditure when it must be made, any family that can add and subtract can make a usable plan which will enable its members to get more for their money than would be possible with unplanned spending.

FOOD

For most families food is the largest single item of expenditure. The family's food should be nutritively adequate, though not necessarily elaborate or expensive. In the last few years information about nutrition has become available in simple graphic form. By observing a few simple, easy rules one can plan a nutritively adequate diet for a family and at the same time make plenty of allowance for reasonable food preferences. People can have a nutritively good diet at every income level except the very lowest, although there will always be a few families, even in the upper-income groups, who spend generously for elaborate but nutritively inadequate diets.

Although it is not necessary to spend large amounts of money for food, families with larger incomes ordinarily spend more for food than families of the same size with smaller incomes, but their food expenditures usually take a smaller percentage of the family income. Large families in any given income group usually spend more for food than do small families, but they spend less per person.

The best way to estimate the amount that a family should spend for food is to plan in terms of so many cents per person per day, rather than in terms of a given percentage of the family income. In 1935–36, 40 cents per person per day was the national average. In 1953, food costs were more than double what they were in 1935–36. On that basis a family of four persons in 1953 would be doing a good job of feeding the family if they are spending not more than 90 cents per person per day, or $25 a week, or $108 a month. A family of two may find it necessary to spend from 10 to 20 cents per person more than the four-person family, since it buys its food in smaller quantities. A larger family, of five or six or more, may be able to save from 10 to 20 per cent over a family of four.

Any family can cut its food costs materially by spending time to save money. It can cut from 10 to 20 per cent and sometimes more from the cash outlay required to provide the family with food by careful buying in self-service super-markets instead of full-service stores, by buying raw materials and preparing food, baking bread and cakes and pastries, by cooking potatoes, beans, turnips, and cabbage instead of opening cans, by buying low-cost stews and roasts instead of minute steaks and chops, and by growing a garden and doing the family's canning.

CLOTHING

The provision of clothing for the family involves the purchase of three types of items, those like shirts, ties, and hose, which must be purchased more or less regularly throughout the year, a group of seasonal items which must be purchased in the fall, winter, spring, and summer, and a few major articles —heavy coats, raincoats, and suits—which must be purchased only once in two or three years.

Studies of family expenditures indicate that for any group of families at almost any income level the proportion of the family income spent for clothing is surprisingly uniform. In the early 1950s, families have spent about 12 per cent of their income for clothing. Families in the larger cities spent slightly more. Families in the rural areas spent slightly less. These percentages held true for the most part regardless of the size of the family. But while the average expenditures were uniform, variation from the averages on the part of individual families was greater than in almost any other item of family expenditure. In any year in which a family must buy a number of expensive garments its expenditures for clothing will run much above the average. In years when the family is using garments bought a year or more before the current outlay for clothing will be less than the average.

How the family's clothing expenditures are divided among the different members of the family depends in part upon the income level, in part upon the occupation of the husband, in part on whether or not the wife is working outside the home, and in part on the number and age of the children. Usually when the children are small parents spend more money for their own clothes than they do for the children's, but when the boys and girls are in high school and college, usually the family spends more for the daughter than for her mother, and more for the son than for his father. For this is a time in the life of the young people when it is highly important for them to feel well dressed.

There are a number of ways in which to plan for clothing expenditures. Some families prefer to make the bulk of their clothing purchases at two or three times during the year, buying a complete outfit of spring clothing just before Easter, some summer things early in June, and their fall clothing in September or October. Other families plan to buy a few new things at the beginning of each season but postpone the purchase of many garments till the end-of-season sales. The family with a regular income frequently finds it easier to spread clothing expenditures along through the year. The family with irregular income may find it easier to outfit the family completely when they have the money available.

There are definite advantages to planning clothing expenditures for two or three years at a time. A family can even cut its clothing expenditures by planning to purchase expensive articles for the husband one year and for the wife the next. Except for the periods when the children are growing rapidly, it is also possible to do the same thing for them, selecting garments which are large enough and of good enough quality to last for two years.

Families purchase a number of garments with the intention of using them for several years. Most women buy street dresses with the idea of wearing them at least two years. Fully as many plan to use them for three years as plan to discard them at the end of one year. This does not mean that they do not buy a new dress every year. Rather they buy a new dress every spring or fall, and they also have a last year's dress to wear shopping and perhaps a dress two years old to wear to the market on rainy days. Similarly there are some indications that men average three quarters of a suit a year. That means they buy a suit every year for three years. The fourth year they buy an overcoat or a topcoat instead. Thus they usually have two or three wearable suits hanging in the closet.

There are a number of ways to keep down the outlay for clothing. Clothing should be bought with the length of time it is to be used definitely in mind. By spending a fifth or a quarter more for a better quality of garment it is possible to get one which will wear twice as long, but if the garment is needed only for a single season it is usually cheaper to buy a quality which will be worn out when it is to be discarded. Substantial savings are possible by buying out of season those articles in which fashion is not too important. It is possible to save by buying one article which can be put to a number of uses, or a few articles which can be combined in a number of ways, rather than by duplicating complete outfits. In families with children, clothing can be passed from one to another, redesigning the garments when necessary. The cost of clothing can be cut substantially by buying materials and making the garments, since materials usually cost only one third to one half as much as finished garments of similar quality.

HOUSING

The type of housing a family selects should depend largely on what the family wants to do at home. In the war years families had little choice. They had to take what was available in the community and adjust their manner of living to the kind of shelter they could obtain. In ordinary times, however, it is usually possible to choose both the type of shelter and the way to pay for it. If both the husband and wife are employed they may prefer a small, conveniently located apartment which can be kept in order with a minimum of work. If only the husband is employed the family may prefer a larger house in which the wife can do more for her family.

A young couple with small capital may start housekeeping in a couple of light-housekeeping rooms or in a small rented apartment. Then when they have had time to save a little money they can buy some furniture and move to a somewhat larger unfurnished apartment. If they plan to locate permanently in the community they may use part of their savings for furniture and part for a down payment on a house, and use the money they would otherwise save to complete the payments on their home.

The family's choice of a home determines not only the amount which must be paid for the house itself but a number of other expenses as well. If the family rents a completely furnished, heated apartment, the rent includes the payment for fuel, utilities, and the upkeep of the furniture. If it rents an unfurnished house, the type of house, its construction, exposure, and heating plant determine within rather close limits the amount the family must pay for fuel and utilities. The size, design, and construction of the house determine the amount of work necessary to keep it clean, in good order, and in good repair.† The location of the house determines the amount and type of transportation the family must use and the amount the family will have to pay for transportation to and from work, to stores, to church and school.

It is impossible to make any exact statement about the amount a family should spend for shelter. Usually in the income groups under $5,000 or $6,000, families with small incomes must spend a larger proportion of their income for shelter than do families with the larger incomes. Larger families usually spend a somewhat smaller proportion of their incomes for shelter than do smaller families, though frequently they get as much or more space per person by living in the older, larger houses. Families in large cities usually spend more for shelter and get less for their money than do families living in smaller communities.

It is usually unwise for a family to spend more than 20 or 25 per cent of its income for the rent of an unfurnished house. A family living in an apartment with everything furnished can expect to pay 35 or 40 per cent of its income for accommodations of similar quality. If the family plans to own a car it should keep payments for shelter to not more than one sixth of its income. A family ordinarily should not buy a house which costs more than twice its annual income, or three times its present income if it is sure of a steadily increasing income during the period it is planning to live in the house. If a family is paying for its home on the installment plan it must be sure that the payments on the house and provision for taxes, repairs, and insurance do not add up to more than the family is able to pay for rent and set aside regularly for savings.

In deciding whether to rent or buy a home a family must consider the advantages and disadvantages of each method of payment for shelter. Ordinarily, if, over a period of years, the family rents the same kind of shelter it would be willing to own, there is not much difference in the cost. For while the home-owning family does not have to pay rent every month, it must pay taxes, make needed repairs, and either invest substantial amounts from time to time in modernization and improvement or take a substantial loss in the value of its property from depreciation and obsolescence over a number of years. And it must count as part of the cost of owning its home the interest which the money it puts into the home would earn if invested in securities.

When it buys a home the family determines once for all the type, the size,

---

†A large house does not always require more housekeeping than a small one. For in a small house, if the space provided is not quite adequate for all the different things the members of the family do, frequent getting out and putting away of equipment is necessary, while in a large house, with separate space for different activities—a sewing room, a laundry, a rumpus room, and the like—it is possible to walk out and close the door for a time on partially finished tasks.

and the cost of its home. The type of shelter cannot be easily adjusted to changes in the family's shelter needs. The family is protected against increases in shelter costs which come with increases in property values, except in so far as these increases affect the cost of repairs and taxes. The cost of the family's housing can be reduced only by sale. Once its home is paid for, however, the family has more flexibility in making expenditures for shelter, for when it is necessary to keep expenditures to a minimum it can postpone improvements and reduce its current outlay to no more than the payment of taxes, insurance, and a minimum of absolutely necessary repairs.

The family that rents its home must make regular payments every month. By moving from time to time it can adapt its shelter to changing family needs and to changes in the family income. It must face the possibility of increases in rents during periods of rising prices and housing shortages. It can adjust its expenditures for shelter downward when prices or incomes decline.

The family that buys its home on the installment plan has some of the advantages of owning and some of the disadvantages of renting. There is no landlord to raise the rent, but the family must make the payments on the property regularly or lose not only a place to live but a substantial part of what it has already paid as well. And it must remember that it has no landlord to make repairs and pay the taxes. It must plan for larger cash outlays while paying for the home than when renting, for it must pay not only the current cost of its shelter but make payments on the principal as well.

THE FAMILY AUTOMOBILE

For the two thirds of the American families that own one, the family car represents a fourth major expenditure. Before the war car-owning families with incomes up to $5,000 or $6,000 spent on the average from 10 to 15 per cent of their incomes for automobile ownership and operation. Families that buy a new car every year usually spend from 12 to 15 per cent of their income each year. Families that buy a new car only once in four or five years spend as much as 20 or 25 per cent of their income for a car the year they purchase a new one, but as little as 5 per cent for upkeep and operation the years they "make the old car do."

When a family owns a car there are two types of costs to be met—costs of ownership and costs of operation. Ownership costs continue as long as a family owns a car, whether the family uses it or not. Ordinarily an automobile depreciates in value almost as much if it is not driven at all as if it is driven any reasonable amount. Garage and parking space must be provided. Insurance costs are based on the value of the car and where it is garaged, rather than on the miles it is driven. License and taxes must be paid each year. Operating expenses for gas and oil, for tires and battery, for repairs and servicing depend on how much the car is driven and under what sort of road and weather conditions. Ownership costs are determined when the family buys a car. Operating costs depend on how much the car is used. The more a family drives in a year, the larger will be its total expenditure for the automobile, but the lower will be the cost per mile.

In deciding whether to buy a car, the family must consider the total cost of owning and operating the car. In deciding whether or not to take a particular trip, it needs to consider only the additional cost of the particular use, since the overhead cost of ownership goes on whether the car is used or not.

It costs more to own a new car and more to operate an old one. When new cars are available at moderate prices it may cost less to trade in an old car for a new one every year or two than to buy new tires and pay for a motor overhaul for the old one. When new cars are high in price it may cost less to drive the old car another year or two and pay the extra operating costs. If some of the members of the family can do most of the work on the car the family can get satisfactory transportation at low cost by buying an older car and doing the repair work necessary to keep it in good running order. If the family must pay for all the servicing a newer car may in the course of a year or two actually cost less money.

In deciding whether or not to own a car, a family should consider not only what the car will cost, but what will be the effect of car ownership on other family expenditures. Owning a car may make it possible for the family to live in a less expensive neighborhood and to trade in low-service stores and super-markets. Sometimes the head of the family can get a better job than would be possible without the car. Owning a car may, however, make the family want to go about more and spend more for other things as well as for the automobile. The decision, therefore, should be based first on the relative cost of living with and without an automobile, and second, on whether the more expensive way of living is worth the extra cost.

HEALTH

Adequate provision for the health of the family involves two types of expenditure—more or less regularly recurring expenditures for minor illness and preventive medical and dental care, and occasional heavy expenses for incapacitating accidents and serious illness which may require hospitalization and surgery or long-continued medical treatment. These occasional heavy expenses are often accompanied by loss of income if the husband is incapacitated, or by extra expenses for additional service if the wife is unable for some time to do her usual work about the house.

The cost of routine care varies from family to family, depending on the size of the family, the ages of its members, their general level of health, any special physical handicaps which may be present, and the types and cost of medical care available in the community. On the basis of their own experience most families are able to estimate closely the cost of routine care, but it is impossible to anticipate either when there will be heavy expenditures for incapacitating accidents or serious illness, or how much the necessary medical and surgical care will cost.

The members of some families seem to have low resistance to disease. Some people work in occupations in which there is more exposure to accidents and illness. Other families seem to be lucky and avoid serious accidents, or have a higher level of health. Often, however, this higher health level is due at least in part to preventive measures. Many families save money in the long run by spending money for regular physical checkups, for the correction of minor difficulties before they become serious, and by the observance of reasonable rules of hygiene. Often the expenditures for medical care may be reduced materially by being sure to provide the family with proper food, comfortable clothing, adequate shelter, and suitable recreation.

Families find that their expenditures for health vary widely from year to year. In the nineteen-twenties, 40 per cent of the families in the United States incurred 90 per cent of the total cost of medical care, while the other 60 per cent made only 10 per cent of the expenditures.

A family can provide in advance for a substantial part of the cost of a serious illness or accident by carrying insurance to cover the cost of hospitalization and surgical care. Families can carry health and accident insurance which will provide them with a minimum of income during most of the disability of the wage earner. Insurance can, however, cover only part of the cost. An insurance company will not knowingly provide health and accident insurance paying more than 80 per cent of a person's regular income. Most policies provide for at least a seven-day waiting period before payments begin. In order to keep the cost of hospital insurance within what most families can pay, the number of days of hospital care provided in any one year is limited to what most families find adequate. Insurance for the cost of medical attention is still experimental. While families find that hospital insurance helps in meeting the cost of serious illness, they must expect to provide for a substantial part of the cost out of savings or, if their savings are inadequate, to arrange for credit, and adjust their other expenditures so that they can gradually pay the balance of the cost.

There are two types of hospital insurance now available. One type pays a stated amount per day for each day that an insured member of the family is confined to the hospital. The family pays the hospital bill and is reimbursed by the insurance company when it presents evidence of hospitalization. This type of insurance provides a given number of dollars to apply on the cost of hospital care. The insurance company pays a stated amount per day, regardless of how much the hospital facilities cost. If the patient uses a ward bed which costs less than the per diem payment, the family has the difference to apply on other costs. If the bed costs more, the family pays the difference.

The other type of insurance provides a stated amount of a given type of hospital care. The hospital deals directly with the insurance company, collects what is due under the provisions of the policy, and bills the patient for any services not covered by insurance.

The cost of hospital insurance usually varies with the amount of coverage it provides and whether the insurance is purchased on an individual or a group basis. Usually it is easier for the head of a family to qualify for hospital insurance as a member of a group. Under a group plan he can usually get a given amount of protection at substantially lower cost. A number of industrial group plans now written include provision for continuing the insurance on an individual basis at somewhat higher cost if the head of the family changes his employment. In any case, it is important to learn exactly what any given insurance plan does and does not cover and to observe the terms of the policy carefully so that you will be sure not to be left without insurance when protection is most needed.

RECREATION

Recreation is an item for which it is possible to spend almost any amount of money. Some recreational expenditures are expenditures for recreation as such—tickets to the theater, sports equipment, memberships in country clubs —while others take the form of additional expenditures for food, clothing, car operation, extra current for the radio or television set, or extras on the grocery bill, like candy and cigarettes.

Recreation is capable of greater elaboration than almost any other type of expenditure. At the same time, by care in planning, it is possible, by the expenditure of some time and energy and thought, to have a good time with little if any cash outlay. The family which must keep expenditures to the minimum may entertain simply at home instead of inviting friends to theater or restaurant or night club. If food is indicated they may select meals which do not call for much food, like Sunday-night suppers. In returning dinner invitations they may serve inexpensive but interesting meals, perhaps with a few extra trimmings, placing the emphasis on attractiveness rather than elaborateness of serving, and on the taste rather than the expensiveness of the food. Much can be added to the significance of anniversaries by such simple devices as candlelight and simple table decorations, with the gift of personal items that would be bought sooner or later but which give added pleasure because they are constant reminders of important days.

Even when a family must keep its money outlay at a minimum it must not neglect adequate provision for suitable recreation, for recreation is an important element in maintaining the family's physical and mental health. If the members of the family have plenty of time and energy at their disposal they can concentrate on the type of activities that require time and effort but little outlay of money. If the family is using all the energy it can safely spend on necessary work its recreation program should provide a maximum amount of relaxation with a minimum expenditure of time and energy, using whatever money the family can afford.

The family should plan its recreation with all its other activities in mind. If the husband is meeting people all day long his recreation may well take the form of quiet evenings reading or listening to the radio. If he is seated at a desk all day he may need physical exercise which he can get from golf, bowling, or tennis, or by working in his garden or at some physically releasing type of hobby. If the wife is kept rather closely at home most of the time her husband should take her out to dinner and the theater occasionally. If both husband and wife are employed and are often away from home they may get the variety they need by entertaining their friends at home. The family's recreation program should not use money which the family cannot afford. But it should provide the release from the current strains of daily living which is necessary to keep the members of the family in good physical and mental health.

PLANNING FOR THE LONG LIFE OF THE FAMILY

If a family is to use the resources at its disposal to provide the richest and most satisfying life for its members it should plan for each particular period in the life of the family with the whole life of the family clearly in mind. This is not so difficult a problem as at first it might seem, for every family passes through a life cycle with a series of clearly defined stages—marriage, the establishment of the family, the birth, schooling, adolescence, maturity, and departure of the children, a few quieter years in later middle life, old age, retirement, and death. Each of these stages brings with it characteristic needs and wants which make varying demands on the family's current money income.

The number of years an individual family spends in each of these stages varies somewhat with the age of the husband and wife at marriage, the number of their children, the intervals between the children's births, and the amount of education with which the children are provided. Even families without children pass through a somewhat similar cycle, which makes changing demands on their incomes as their interests grow and change with the passing years.‡

Similarly, the swing of the business cycle and other business changes bring changes in the family's income and other resources. Changing business conditions affect the prices a family must pay and the income it receives. They affect the kind, quantity, and quality of goods on sale in the market. They affect opportunities for employment of the family members and for the saving and investment of family funds. Changing business conditions affect the age at which marriage is economically feasible, the size of the family which it is wise to rear, the length of the effective earning period of the family members, and the age at which retirement is imperative or financially possible.

Every family will live through several complete swings of business cycles, each one just a little different from all the others. Most families will experience at least one period of pronounced inflation and probably will live part of their lives during periods in which the long-time trend of prices is up and part in periods in which the long-time trend of prices is down.

Because of these concurrent changes in the family life cycle and the business cycle, the family's current income will not necessarily vary proportionately or even directly with the family's changing needs. There may be a few families in which the husband's earnings increase more rapidly during the years that the family is bringing up its children than do the demands upon those earnings. But most families face years in which necessary expenses are larger than the family's current income, years in which the family's income is more than adequate for current needs, and years in which the family, by careful management, is able to live within its income with varying degrees of financial strain.

The establishment of the family involves the investment of considerable money in furniture and other household equipment. This usually is not too

‡For childless families the necessity of providing for their old age entirely from their own invested savings takes the place of expenditures which other families make on their children. And families without children, all through their lives, want to spend money for many interesting things with which to fill the time other families spend caring for and enjoying their children.

difficult to manage, especially if both the husband and the wife are employed. The years in which the children are born bring new expenses at a time when the family must get along without the wife's earnings. Usually the years when the children are in elementary school involve a minimum of financial strain. But during the peak of the life cycle, when the children are in high school and college, only a few families are able to provide everything the members of the family need out of the husband's earnings, or even out of the family's current income, unless several members of the family contribute from their earnings.

ADJUSTING TO CHANGING WANTS AND CHANGING INCOME

There are a number of ways by which a family may adjust to the changing demands on its income. Usually at one time or another every family uses all of them. A family may plan in advance for large expenditures, spreading them along over a considerable period, seeing to it that not more than one or two must be made at the same time. This is what a family with a weekly pay check does with its larger monthly bills, when it pays the rent out of one week's check, pays for the utilities out of another, stocks up with staple groceries with the third, and uses most of the fourth week's check for new clothes or for the payment on the family car.

The principle is the same when the family is planning for larger occasional expenditures which are made only once in several years. No family in the lower or middle income groups is able to make more than one or two major expenditures out of any one year's income. When the family buys a new car that is the one major expenditure for the year. Next year there will be money for a vacation trip. The year after that it will be possible to redecorate the living room and modernize the kitchen. And the next year the family will want to purchase another car.

A family may provide itself with expensive durable goods by purchasing them in advance of the time they will be needed, when there are not many other demands on the family income. Many families buy and complete the payments on their home early in the life of the family, or buy a new car which they drive for five or six years while the children are in high school or college.

A family may save money for specific expenditures which require a larger outlay than the family can make out of any one year's income. Most families find that several years' savings are necessary to provide for the children's college education. Some families prefer to save their vacation money for two or three years and take an extensive trip rather than to have two or three inexpensive vacations nearer home.

A family may want to make some large expenditure before it has had time to save all the necessary money. If it is sure that it can make the necessary payments it may decide to use its credit. Faced with the necessity of making extensive repairs on their car, a family may decide to turn in the old car and pay for a new one on the installment plan. If there is an acute shortage of furnished apartments a family may find it easier to get suitable shelter by renting an unfurnished house and using their credit to get the furniture they need.

In using credit it is important to distinguish between purchases which will add to the family's expenses and purchases which, once they are paid for, will reduce the family's current outlay. And since there is a great deal of difference in the terms on which credit is available, it is important to know what different kinds of credit cost and to use the type that will let the family buy on credit at the lowest additional cost. It is wise to use credit only when having something now rather than saving first and buying later is worth the additional cost of buying on credit.

A family can reduce the demands on its money income by having the members of the family do more for themselves and by making more use of community resources that do not cost money. A family can cut its food costs by doing more baking and canning. It can cut its clothing costs by making and by making over more garments. It can cut its recreation costs by having good times at home and by using public parks and playgrounds, attending municipal concerts, or getting new books to read from the public library.

And for the inevitable unforeseen and often unforeseeable emergencies and contingencies, like the loss of a job, the opportunity to move to a better job, a chance to make an unusually fortunate purchase or investment, accidents, or unexpected illness, a family can carry insurance of various kinds and can set up a cash reserve for contingencies.

Ordinarily a family finds that it pays to carry insurance against the contingencies in which there is a small chance of a large loss, and to set up cash reserves to cover the contingencies for which the total amount of expenditure varies little from year to year. A family should never neglect to insure its home and furnishings and personal possessions against loss by fire. Usually it is wise to add the additional protection against windstorm and other types of damage which are included in what the insurance man calls "extended coverage." Automobile insurance is a necessity. Coverage against loss from fire and theft is inexpensive. Property damage and public liability insurance is required in many states for the protection of others. Collision insurance is more expensive but usually worth having when the car is new.

Already some eighty-five million people have found it pays to carry hospitalization insurance; an increasing number of families are adding insurance to cover the cost of surgical care. But since bills for routine medical care do not vary much from year to year, most families prefer to pay their doctors' and dentists' bills direct, setting aside a little extra in savings in years when medical expenses are low to use in other years when the family has more than the usual amount of illness. Most families carry some life insurance on one member or more of the family, to provide funds for funeral expenses and something for the family to live on in case of the death of a family member.

Every family needs a substantial cash reserve to draw on in case of any one of a number of contingencies. If possible, the family should have about the equivalent of six months' income in a savings account or invested in government bonds or other easily marketable securities, where it can be got at on short notice. This contingent fund may be used for a number of purposes. If the head of the family loses his job, his unemployment insurance will help to defray some of the family's current expenses when he is not working, but savings are necessary to keep up payments on insurance, a home, the car, and other essential fixed charges. The fund may be drawn on to meet unusually heavy medical expenses. It may make it possible for the family to move to better employment, or to take advantage of an unusual opportunity to buy a new home, or new furniture. In case of serious damage to the automobile, it will provide funds with which to buy a new car. Contingent reserves are to be used. But when funds are withdrawn for these perfectly legitimate uses they should be replaced as soon as possible, so that they will be available for other contingencies.

A WORD OF ENCOURAGEMENT

The management and financing of a family is not an unimportant job to be carried on in spare time. For the way a family manages its affairs has a great deal to do with how well the family lives on the means at its disposal. Nor is it something to work too hard at. There is no value in management for its own sake. The test of success in family management is not the amount of money earned or saved or spent, nor the amount of work done by the members of the family, but rather the quality of living the family makes available for its members, not only this year, but every year throughout the whole long life of the family.

Chapter 7

EXTRAMARITAL RELATIONS

by Lester W. Dearborn

DIRECTOR, BOSTON MARRIAGE COUNSELING SERVICE AND FORMER CHAIRMAN, AMERICAN ASSOCIATION OF MARRIAGE COUNSELORS

Extramarital relations include any sexual relationship outside of marriage. Premarital relations may not necessarily involve the prospect of marriage; often they involve only the intended spouse. I believe that larger numbers of young people of this generation are more free in sexual expression than they were a generation ago. However, our present methods of obtaining knowledge concerning the sexual experiences of young people compared with the little knowledge obtainable twenty-five years ago make comparison largely a matter of guesswork. A number of statements by competent investigators[1] reveal that a relatively high percentage of engaged couples have had a complete sexual relationship before their wedding. Of the engaged couples coming to me in preparation for marriage I have found that between 65 and 70 per cent have been having intercourse, and in this I am not counting heavy petting or intimacies that fall just short of intercourse itself.

A few years ago I had an opportunity to interview eighteen married women out of a group of twenty, all of whom were over forty-five years of age. I took advantage of this opportunity to ask each whether or not she had had sexual intercourse with her husband before marriage; thirteen admitted that they had. This, together with a large number of older wives who during counseling have also made such an admission, makes one speculate as to the actual sex practices of the previous generation.

In a reply to sex questions during a psychiatric examination at Army induction centers two doctors[2] report that out of a study of 4,600 cases of unmarried males between the ages of twenty-one and twenty-eight, 79.4 per cent had had sexual experience. Some 56 per cent of these men had had relations with what they referred to as "nice girls," meaning by this a girl whom the man could introduce to his parents and would consider marrying.

Observations made by these psychiatrists indicated to them that "intercourse with future spouses before marriage will become universal." Were investigation possible, the results might reveal that having sexual intercourse with the intended spouse before marriage has been a practice for a much longer time and by much larger numbers than we have imagined.

What has happened to bring about such a change? It is reasonable to assume that there is no difference in the sexual natures of the young people today from those who preceded them. We will look at the changing customs for our reasons.

A type of knowledge fairly widespread among the young today has greatly minimized three controlling fears of the past, the fear of detection, fear of infection, and fear of conception. Last but not least as a definitely controlling factor is the change in our attitude toward supervision of the young. Modern education, which teaches that the young must be given independence and freedom of action, has pushed chaperonage to the background and to a large extent eliminated it as a social custom. Automobiles make it possible for young people to travel a great distance in a short time, and so the effectiveness of community supervision is eliminated. A great deal has already been said about drinking, trips to roadhouses and overnight cabins, and a lot of emphasis has been placed on the breakdown of religious controls. When considering promiscuous behavior or isolated episodes which have followed some drinking or party experience these are undoubtedly important factors, but this evidence is misleading in the total picture. For a large number of those who are intimate with their intended spouses their greatest protection against detection is their own impeccable behavior. Some admit to moderate drinking, many report that they do not drink at all, they do not visit roadhouses, they have never been in an overnight cabin, and seldom do they ever report the use of a hotel room. No, the locale more often reported than not is their own homes, with no greater protection needed than their own reputations and the present-day attitude that chaperonage or parental supervision is considered unnecessary.

Premarital relations are discussed in another chapter. The subject is introduced here only to show changing attitudes toward having sexual intercourse without legal or religious sanction.

The sex life of the unmarried adult has always posed a social problem. While celibacy has been the expressed ideal, it has been recognized that this is difficult for many and impossible for some. Together with this there is considerable evidence that in striving for such an ideal the resulting nervous tensions, the fears and worries which are caused by lonesomeness or feelings of insecurity that are the natural corollaries of singleness combined with sex hunger put such persons in a state of readiness for sexual intimacy when the closeness of companionship tends to bring the erotic factor clearly into focus and the time and the place make capitulation easy.

Most males beyond the age of thirty who are not married are single because they are the sole support of a dependent parent or have some form of family obligation or have been unreasonably long in becoming vocationally established. Also, they may be among those males who reject marriage; from 10 to 15 per cent of males prefer bachelorhood,[3] but preference for bachelorhood does not necessarily include a preference for celibacy. Whereas a few women may deliberately choose to remain unmarried (particularly those who select a professional career in preference to that of homemaking), many of them are single because of such factors as a prolongation of their educational program, overprotective parents, lack of prospective males in their circle, family responsibilities, and a lack of sex drive during those years when an interest in mate selection should be paramount. Some men and women are, because of conditioning or otherwise, homosexual and thus find heterosexual relationships unattractive. Others in practice are bisexual and because of this are not inclined to tie themselves to a permanent relationship. Here also we must consider the single woman who has fallen in love with a married man and, having developed a romantic attachment for a man who is conventionally unobtainable, she prefers to enter into a sexual liaison with him rather than to give him up.

The older a man gets beyond the age of thirty, the less concern he seems to have with the possibility of marriage. The woman never seems to give up hope. This may be accounted for in many ways. The need for emotional and physical security and the uncertainty concerning her vocational and social future concern her to a much greater degree than they do the man. Yearning as she does for a home and children and the love and protection of a mate, without them she pictures a dreary future and becomes increasingly anxious to avoid it. As her diminishing prospects of marriage are brought more sharply into focus she finds herself at the same time becoming more than ever conscious of her sexual needs. Personal counselors have for some time been aware of the fact that girls in their late adolescence and early twenties are apt to have much less desire for sexual intercourse than does the woman who is eight to ten years older. This fact is substantiated by the evidence that has been brought to our attention concerning the peak of male sexuality being reached somewhere between the sixteenth and twenty-second year and very slowly but steadily declining toward middle age; whereas the sex life of the female evolves slowly and so much so that many of them are not aware of any particular drive until they are in their late twenties and early thirties. We are told that they will reach the peak of desire somewhere between their thirty-fifth and fortieth year.[4] We can see from this that the man's desire for a permanent sexual relationship may be decreasing at the very time when the woman's is radically increased.

This, then, together with the breakdown of social controls, helps to explain why there may be a considerable increase in the number of unmarried people who lay no claim to celibacy. We have to recognize that sex is an appetite that man is predisposed to satisfy, and the stronger the drive, the more insistently he strives to find a means of circumventing a convention which would prevent it. In the male this has always been recognized. While in precept we have rather feebly denounced it, in practice there has been social acceptance. The man will be blamed only if he is caught *flagrante delicto*. The social change is largely in the matter of the woman's behavior. Here again we are faced with the changing mores. The fears concerning conception, infection, and detection have been greatly reduced. The woman no longer has a fear of being ostracized if a decent regard for the proprieties is being observed. It is quite common for friends to dismiss their suspicions of what is going on with a shrug of the shoulders and a "none of my business" attitude.

Security, a home of her own, children are much stronger motives in the woman than in the man. With all this she becomes acutely aware that, having passed her thirtieth year, her childbearing years are growing less; while at the same time, whatever a particular male's procreative ability may be and whether or not his chances of fathering children also diminish, certainly the average male does not think of this as a probability. All this, then, leads many a woman as she gets older to decide in desperation to get a man by hook or by crook. Undoubtedly, so far as the woman is concerned, many of such sexual relationships are looked on by her not only as a means of emotional release but as a device leading to a permanent union. I have talked with many refined and educated young women in their late twenties and in their thirties who in reporting a liaison are so forlornly clinging to this hope that they are placing reliance on tenuous promises despite their better judgment.

There will always be sexual activity among the unmarried, but encouraging all this by a laissez-faire attitude is certainly not conducive to a strengthening of marriage and the home.

STATISTICS

There are few published surveys that make any pretense at giving statistical information concerning postmarital relationships. While there have been a number of published reports concerning premarital relationships and other types of sexual activity, any account concerning illicit behavior of married people is largely conspicuous by its absence. One of the leading and competent studies, that by Terman,[5] frankly admits that there was no attempt to get at postmarital relationships because the author feared that in doing so he might lose rapport with his subjects. He did, however, make a study of their desire for such experience. Dr. Hamilton,[6] in his studies of a selected group of one hundred married men and one hundred married women, reports that "twenty-eight men and twenty-four women had had illicit sexual intercourse while married to their spouses." Dr. Katharine Davis[7] sought to correlate opinion with practice and found in the matter of opinion that while about one fifth of the women agreed there were occasions when the wife might be justified a somewhat larger number sought to justify such an experience on the part of the husband. Then when measuring opinion against practice she found that many who accepted some justification had had no such actual experience in their own marriages, while a number of those whose opinions were negative reported that such experience had taken place. Any critical opinion from the standpoint of available data would at this time be of little value. At the same time it can be easily understood that in any statistical study it is far easier to get people to commit themselves about other forms of behavior and about their sexual relationships before marriage and in marriage itself than it is to elicit information concerning their present unconventional behavior, especially where such behavior involves serious legal as well as social implications.

The recently published two volumes which have become popularly known as the Kinsey study are, without question, a report on the most comprehensive study of human sex behavior that has yet been made. In these volumes the authors point out that in the discussion of extramarital experiences there is undoubtedly more cover-up than in the disclosure of any other type of sexual activity. While the authors show some doubt as to the adequacy of their own figures in coming to any accurate conclusion concerning the number of unfaithful husbands or wives, they feel that on the basis of estimate they have enough information to support the conclusion that about half of the husbands will have intercourse with some woman other than their wives during their married lives. In the volume on the female, they report that about 7 per cent of the married females in their late teens and up to the age of 25 reported such behavior; that from the age of 26 to the age of 40 there was a definite increase in the number of such incidents, so that they estimate that about 26 per cent of those who had reached the age of 40 had had or were having such experience by that time. They discovered, however, that after the age of 40 "only a few females began, for the first time, to have extra-marital coitus." These figures in regard to the female have particular significance because of the already mentioned fact that the woman becomes increasingly aware of her sex needs after the age of 25 and with increasing intensity reaching a peak somewhere between the middle thirties and early forties. In my own marriage-counseling practice I find an increasing number of wives whose sexual needs are not being satisfied by their husbands, wherein they are becoming maritally discontented. This is a condition which is confirmed by a report by Dr. Albert Ellis concerning his New York practice.[9]

If current literature reflects the times, certainly a number of popular authors who deal with social subjects make statements inferring that adultery today is the rule rather than the exception. One writer[8] in particular, whose books have been widely read and much discussed, takes this viewpoint. A current best seller by Gibson is quite typical of the modern novelist's picturization of the misunderstood spouse seeking solace in the arms of his paramour.[10] Undoubtedly these authors intend to awaken our people to what is going on around them and hope for a recrudescence of social conscience and individual responsibility, but one can't help wondering if it may not have the opposite effect, that of encouraging a person to excuse his own conduct in the flippant words, "Everybody's doing it now."

In many of the question periods following my lectures, although this subject has not been a part of the discourse, I have had the question raised, "Isn't it true that a great many people have extramarital relations?" A common question is, "Isn't it true that most men have extramarital relations?" Another question is, "What attitude is the wife to take when she finds her husband has been having relations with another woman?" To consider, therefore, that this subject is of interest and of great concern to thousands of our population whose lives are definitely affected by this type of behavior is reasonable.

Here is an excerpt from a twenty-year report of our Service, 1934–54, covering 3,938 individuals. Males, 35 per cent; females, 65 per cent; education: below secondary, 6.6 per cent; having secondary, 31.9 per cent; above secondary, 57.6 per cent; not obtained, 3.9 per cent.

About 20 per cent of the married couples who come to me for counseling report infidelity on the part of one or both partners, generally one, and generally the husband. I have had a number of cases, however, in which the wife was the offending partner. In some of these instances there was reported but a single episode of unfaithfulness, and in many of the others the repeated unfaithfulness has been confined to one partner. Illicit experiences involving a married person incidentally revealed in a conversation on irrelevant matters—for instance, an unmarried woman with a personal problem who reveals a relationship with a married man—would not be included.

The term unfaithfulness refers to sexual intercourse and does not include reported behavior that falls short of intercourse, such as flirtations, petting, or group behavior, such as nude bathing parties or strip poker. Again for emphasis let me repeat that this statement cannot be used as a valid index for the general population. Most people who come to a counselor seek to preserve their marriages. Probably a far greater number of couples involved in infidelity are among those who want separation or divorce. Certainly records of divorce proceedings disclose infidelity as a major cause.

In a study of this kind one becomes overwhelmed with all of the possible avenues of exploration. The personalities of the man, the wife, the paramour, their personal maladjustments with all the contingent factors, similarities and differences in their education, philosophy, religion, together with depth of religious conviction, parental and sibling affections and hostilities, happy or unhappy home life, vocational and social adjustments, all make such a complicated mosaic as to defy any breakdown into simple patterns for group study. We cannot classify husbands and wives under specific reasons for illicit relations. No matter how hard we try we will always have to come back to a study of the individual case.

Dr. Groves, in his book,[11] differentiates between acute unfaithfulness and chronic unfaithfulness, defining the first as being an extramarital relationship which has happened but has not become a habit. To this I add a third classification, quondam unfaithfulness, referring to that situation where the illicit experience has been long past but recently disclosed. The marriages in which the problem is acute or quondam are the ones more likely to be seen by the marriage counselor. In conference that which could be classified as chronic occasionally comes to the attention of the counselor, although often the affair has been so discreetly carried on that the mate has no knowledge of it and consequently it has had little traumatic effect on the marriage itself. It is the single incident or occasionally repeated unfaithfulness or the discovery of an incident which has happened since marriage but now is long past that creates in the spouse a fear for the future, and as their love has not been entirely alienated they seek counsel in the hope that something may be done to save their marriage.

The following are a few of the sociosexual behavior patterns disclosed in cases of unfaithfulness:

Where the husband is the offending partner:

1. *He has marital as well as extramarital relations.*
2. *He has extramarital relations with no marital relations.*

3. He has been unfaithful and yet considers his marriage a success.

4. He complains that his wife's lack of orgasm has made intercourse with her uninteresting.

5. He reports interest in deviated methods of expression or in precoital preparation which are displeasing or uninteresting to the wife.

6. He defends himself on the basis that he has a greater sexual need and capacity and that it would be unfair to the wife to expect her to submit to his frequency.

7. He will complain that she fails to meet certain fetishistic needs of his: complete nudity, variety in coital positions, some sadomasochistic approach, oral stimulation; he seeks a woman who shows reciprocal interests.

Where the wife is the offending partner:

1. Neglect of her sexual needs on the part of the husband.

2. She complains of him as a lover—he doesn't show affection, doesn't compliment her, is abrupt and inconsiderate in his sexual approach—she complains of marriage monotony.

3. She complains of lack of orgasm but feels the husband does little to help her to a climax.

4. She is masochistic and longs for strong and aggressive action on the part of her husband; he fails to comply.

5. Occasionally the wife will report an illicit experience and yet report her marriage a success.

Of course the foregoing are inconclusive and of little value so far as classifying cases is concerned. They are merely excerpts from the original complaint and tend to show that adultery is usually but a symptom of a deeper and more basic problem. Because of this it is extremely difficult to isolate this problem as a subject and to discuss it constructively. One immediately finds oneself tempted to get into personality problems and is immediately conscious of all the neurotic psychiatric implications, the importance of background factors and family conflicts.

This chapter does not include consideration of sociopathological problems in which a married person is involved in rape or pedophilia, nor does it include resort to the prostitute, nor homosexuality.

Speculatively I shall now indulge in oversimplification and for this purpose make the following assumptions:

Assumption 1. That in most well-adjusted marriages neither partner is in a state of readiness for illicit experience.

Assumption 2. That where a state of readiness exists there are both positive and negative factors operating for or against such an experience.

Here is the age-old conflict between duty and desire. While duty sometimes wins, it often comes out second best. With the number of males who are not married and the number of unmarried females, most of whom would be if they could, plus a growing number of unhappy mates, one doesn't have to go far for the opportunity. In fact, opportunity often comes knocking at the door in the form of a little subtle seduction and some that is not so subtle. The seducer, by the way, is not always the married one nor always the older. All that has previously been said about the sex life of the unmarried (this includes the divorced and widowed) becomes a part and parcel of this whole problem.

One who is in a state of readiness for an illicit experience may find it difficult and may never surrender because of the conflict with his social and religious ideals,[12] but if in doing this he becomes a martyr to righteousness, heaven help the family! In justifying one's behavior the human being's ability to rationalize is so remarkable that there is no limit to the reasons given. Here are a few of the more common ones:

1. Sexual frustration—difference in intensity of desire, difference in ability to respond, difference in individual love requisites—impotence of husband, frigidity of wife, etc.

2. Lack of ego satisfaction—lack of prestige in the family, no build-up at home, being unfavorably compared to others, conflict with in-laws, inadequate income, etc.

3. Propinquity—there was the opportunity, the excuse; it just happened.

4. Pseudo-romantic love. Here I am not referring to the romantic idea on which the marriage may have been based and which has turned out to be a hoax, although this may be the case, but rather to the romantic idea which causes a man or woman to "fall in love with someone else" and thus implicitly out of love with the spouse.

I have selected three cases involving postmarital relations of the husband. Their composite statement would read something like this:

"I loved my wife when I married her. We have been getting along very nicely. We have two beautiful children whom I love dearly. My wife is a fine housekeeper and a wonderful mother, but I am in love with this other woman. I can't get her out of my mind."

All three of these husbands deny that their sexual relations with their wives have been satisfactory, but the three wives claim that for them the sex life was very satisfactory up to this time. The husbands are still living with their wives, and each reports that because of the counseling the wife has received she is a better sexual partner and that on the whole the domestic relations have improved, but the wife knows and I know that each is still carrying a torch for the paramour. How long the marriage can continue in this state is anybody's guess. At the beginning each husband talked about divorce and the wife was appalled at the idea, but a woman who has done everything to co-operate and has inventoried her personality traits and tried to make adjustments and has become more active and responsive sexually reaches the limit of her endurance when she finds her husband turning away from a kiss, ignoring the little pleasantries and attentions, and sitting around the house with a bored expression or finding every possible excuse to go out on business.

In these three cases each husband found something more than sexual satisfaction with the other woman, and it is this something to which he is tenaciously clinging. I refer to the many little things that are inflationary to his ego. She makes him feel important while his wife has taken him for granted. One thing all three of these men have in common is that each was brought up by a dominant and overprotective mother. In two of these cases the father was reported as lacking in aggressiveness; in the third the father was dominant but in conflict with the mother. In business all three men were successful, but the history of each showed that he tended to withdraw from reality and flee from responsibility in any emotional crisis.

If their marriages do not survive all three of these women are by now better prepared to meet the eventuality, and while their homes will become broken, the attitude of the parents toward the children and the children toward the parents and between the father and mother will be fraught with much less tension than would otherwise be so, for there is such a thing as education for divorce. Where by deed or word the partner's ego has been hurt it is much more difficult to effect a reconciliation than where the problem is merely that of a sexual experience outside of marriage.

Running concurrently with the effort to prepare young people for marriage by providing courses and counseling on successful marriage and family living, there is a similar effort in the direction of re-educating those who have been off to a poor start or have already run into difficulties.

This second effort, like the first, is already paying dividends. Hundreds of couples varying in ages from their early twenties to their late forties, but perhaps the largest group in the age range from twenty-five to thirty-five, are being helped every year by competent counselors to re-evaluate their problems in terms of a better understanding of each other's personalities and needs, of understanding and accepting sex in a more realistic way, in coming to realize that the more we put into a marriage the more we take out, and that spouses are, after all, only human beings with human frailties, and that marriage itself is no panacea for character defects or personality maladjustments. Where there is a will on the part of both there is a way to rebuild their marriage and make it a lasting and satisfactory experience.

Adultery, like poverty, we have with us always, but he who helps a couple to make or maintain a happy marriage makes a direct contribution to a reduction of extramarital relations.

NOTES

[1]Lewis Terman, *Psychological Factors in Marital Happiness,* 1938, Chap. 12; Clifford R. Adams, *How to Pick a Mate,* 1946, p. 46.
[2]Hohman and Schaffner, *American Journal of Sociology,* May 1947.
[3]Adams, op. cit., Chap. 10.
[4]Dr. A. C. Kinsey, Wardell B. Pomeroy, Clyde E. Martin, *Sexual Behavior in the Human Female,* 1953.
[5]Terman, op. cit., p. 338.
[6]G. V. Hamilton, *Research in Marriage,* p. 346.
[7]Dr. Katharine Davis, *Factors in the Sex Life of Twenty-Two Hundred Women.*
[8]Philip Wylie, *Generation of Vipers,* 1942.
[9]Dr. Albert Ellis, *Marriage and Family Living,* February 1953, Vol. 15.
[10]William Gibson, *The Cobweb.*
[11]Ernest R. Groves, *Conserving Marriage and the Family,* Chap. 3, 1944.
[12]A. C. Kinsey, Wardell B. Pomeroy, Clyde E. Martin, *Sexual Behavior in the Human Male,* 1948.

BIBLIOGRAPHY

Adams, Dr. Clifford R., *Preparing for Marriage,* New York, E. P. Dutton & Co., 1951.

Brink, Frederick W., *This Man and This Woman,* New York, Association Press, 1948.

Ellis, Albert, Ph.D., *The American Sexual Tragedy,* New York, Twayne Publishers, 1954.

Himes, Norman E., *Your Marriage, A Guide to Happiness,* New York, Farrar & Rinehart, Inc., 1940.

Leuba, Clarence, *Ethics in Sex Conduct,* New York, Association Press, 1948.

Levy, Dr. John; Munroe, Ruth, *The Happy Family,* New York, Alfred A. Knopf, 1938.

Mace, David R., *Marriage: The Art of Lasting Love,* New York, Doubleday & Co., 1952.

Chapter 8

PSYCHOLOGICAL FACTORS IN MARITAL MALADJUSTMENTS

by George J. Mohr, M.D.

The most simple difficulties in marital relationships may be those that reflect ignorance and inexperience on the part of otherwise wholesome and healthy personalities. Where this is so these difficulties are readily overcome by reasonable educational procedures. During the past decade and a half, very many marriages among very young people have occurred. In part, this has been a result of the pressures created by World War II and an inflated economy. Modifications in educational philosophy, with emphasis upon the early assumption of self-responsibility by youth, and encouragement of attitudes of independence have further contributed to this. The result has been that young and psychologically immature people contract marriage. Many of them are young people still in college or with some years ahead of them still to be spent in professional or technical training. For young people such as these, there is most particularly the necessity to understand the psychological considerations that make for marital success or maladjustment. A psychologically healthy person can learn about relationships in marriage as he can learn about anything else. At the other extreme are the more serious disturbances encountered in marital life. Impotence caused by psychological factors, premature ejaculation, frigidity, and other serious interferences are problems that cannot be discussed in general terms. Such conditions require patient diagnosis and treatment by skilled psychiatrists in each case.

Many marriages are difficult for one or both partners by virtue of certain lacks in personality development. These create problems that lie between the extremes that have been mentioned. The vicissitudes of these marriages are the subject of this section.

Sexual relationships within marriage reflect the adequacy or inadequacy of the personalities of the partners, as judged by the maturity they have developed. As in other adult life relationships, sexual conduct and association are expressions of one's understanding of his own role and of the meaning and role of his partner.

In the course of development from infancy to adulthood a continuous series of changes and readjustments in personal relationships is made by everyone. This series of changes is characterized by a process of separation from situations that have been secure and satisfying, and the entering into relationships in which some measure of the previous security must be relinquished. Thus, the secure, intra-uterine position of the unborn child is disrupted by birth. He is thrust into an environment that makes new demands upon him. In turn, the nursing infant is soon weaned from breast or bottle and must eat in a more mature fashion. The preschool child must go to school, get along with a bit less of his mother's protective care, and learn to take his place among a group. Similarly, eventually, the protection of a school environment must be relinquished for the more demanding world of active work in our society. Marriage can be regarded as the final step that brings one to the position of adult and parent, in which one is fully responsible for oneself and others.

Each step in this development implies a readiness to meet a new situation that makes greater demand upon the more mature capacities of an individual than did the previous life period. This readiness involves an understanding of the situation to be met and an acceptance of the role to be played in the new situation as desirable.

What has just been said places emphasis upon the necessity to emerge from attitudes of too great dependency in order to meet the demands of adult life. A corollary of the basic proposition involved is the necessity to achieve adult attitudes and capacity for relationships in the sexual field. Sexual reactions and the forms they evidence in adult life cannot be separated from the history of the child's emotional life and development. His sexual perspectives in adulthood reflect the history of his interpersonal relationships from infancy on.

EMOTIONAL ATTACHMENT TO THE PARENT

The initial emotional attachment of any child is to the mother, the source of all comfort and security in infancy. All physical and emotional gratifications stem from the experience the child has in being tenderly cared for by her. The training he undergoes, in cleanliness, in habits of eating, sleeping, will color his earliest expectations of what is and is not permissible in life. This initial exclusive attachment to the mother is soon modified by the fact that a father begins to play a role in the child's life, a complicating role.

While the major relationship between a child and father is that of affection and warm regard, there are many diverse aspects of feeling that color the relationship at various age levels. Children consider the father's presence, in some measure, as a threat to their own exclusive claims to the affection of the mother. Sometimes fathers feel the same way about the children. Fathers are commonly reacted to as threatening; they are big, overwhelming to a very small child, and at times punitive. Normally boys remain quite competitive toward their fathers and inwardly tend to question very much the possibility that they will ever be able to attain his adult, masculine qualities. This competitive attitude of boys later continues to be expressed in the highly competitive relationships between growing boys. The boy who can outdistance, outfight, outswim his mates is accorded the primary position among them.

When a father is able to relate himself to a small son in terms that mean to the boy that the father basically approves of him and accepts him, this tends to bring to the son the assurance that he is a potentially adequate and acceptable person. He can see the possibility that someday he may be a person like his father and expect to assume the responsibilities and prerogatives that go with masculine adulthood. Such a basic attitude is called identification with the father. This identification serves as a psychological platform on which the son may stand as he struggles through the various phases of his development through childhood and adolescence. On the basis of this identification he can project his interest outside himself and beyond the relationships of the family group alone in terms of eventual interests in a man's work, a man's social life, a man's sexual life.

A similar evolution occurs in the basic attitudes of girls. Girls must evolve through an even more complicated series of relationships, the normal end result of which is an identification with the role of the mother as a woman with a corresponding capacity to face a woman's familial, social, and sexual role in life.

The personalities and training attitudes of parents may facilitate the course of development or cause deviations or even serious disturbances in this development. A mother can be too protective, too possessive and encompassing, too directive and domineering to permit a son to develop the necessary certainty about his own masculine capacities. Or a father may be too intimidating, too unaccepting of the son's potential masculinity to permit the boy the development of masculine attitudes and outlook. The result sometimes is, in less serious situations, a young man without sufficient independence of spirit and normal aggression. In more extreme situations the boy may never achieve the capacity for independence in work, social life, sexual life. The alcoholic, the homosexual, the incompetent, all derive in appreciable measure from disturbances in development of this nature.

Here are some excerpts from actual case histories. The case histories are not to be approached in a spirit of pessimism. Most "successful" marriages, if scrutinized, would show some or many of the human situations here discussed. Such successful marriages are those in which the marital partners have learned to understand disturbing aspects of their relationship sufficiently to ensure the comfortable continuance of family life.

A frequent source of failure to achieve good adjustment in marriage is that seen in the life of a young man or woman who remains basically too dependent upon a mother or father. Some mothers refuse to give up their "prerogatives" as mothers—continue to feel their demands upon the affection and interest of a son or daughter come first, resent the intrusion of an "outsider" to replace them. In turn, a son or daughter may continue to feel that primarily loyalty is to parents rather than to spouse, may remain too convinced of the wisdom and power of the parent and too dependent to discover that he or she and the spouse constitute a family apart from the parents and are in a position to determine their own way of life, with or without parental sanction.

THE MOTHER ATTACHMENT

A young businessman, R. S., sought the advice of a psychiatrist because he had a tendency toward depressive periods that at times severely interfered with his ability to devote himself to his business affairs and periodically he drank to excess. Superficially R.'s marital situation seemed to be satisfactory. Interview with his wife, however, made it clear that he was infantile and demanding toward her. She said: "I have three children, not two." The family continued to live in the home of R.'s widowed mother. The mother presumably remained in the background, but actually all decision and program reflected her judgments and wishes.

R. was the younger of two children, an energetic older sister whom he had always considered an authority having married and moved elsewhere. As a child he was frail; his mother remained solicitous, overprotecting, and maintained a strong guiding hand. The young man grew up, convinced of the high idealism and great wisdom of the mother to whom he referred all life decisions. His father had been a rather successful and capable businessman but obviously played a secondary role in the family life.

The marital life developed by this man reflected a continuation of his role as a son who looked to women as protecting, maternal persons. His healthy ideas impelled him toward marriage and the establishment of a family. The childish and dependent aspects of his personality determined a great compromise, however—that his family continue to live with his mother.

He refused to adopt that independent, active attitude toward his own wife that would make it impossible for her to find in him a "third child."

A situation such as this usually is not well tolerated by either partner in a marriage. This capable young man inwardly rebelled against his position in life. He was surprised to find that his idealization of his mother masked an intense resentment toward her as the person who limited and restricted him. His sense of duty and loyalty to her did not permit him to be aware of this deeper hostility. This conflictful attitude served to make it impossible for him to function freely either as dutiful son or independent man. When he was able to win for himself the permissions his mother was unable or unwilling to grant him, he found it quite possible to arrange a healthier mode of living and a happier marital relationship.

THE FATHER ATTACHMENT

This familiar picture of persistence of attachment to a mother on the part of a son has its counterpart in attitudes some young women maintain toward their fathers.

An attractive young woman, H. S., mother of a son and daughter, complained of fatigue, a feeling of inadequacy and discomfort when among her friends. She had lost her previous capacity to work actively at her home tasks and among a group of young women friends who were interested in various club and welfare activities in the lively suburb in which the family lived. She had been married six years. Until recently she had considered her marriage successful, but now she questioned whether her discomforts might not be related to dissatisfactions in her marriage. She expressed affection for her husband. The sexual aspect of their marital life had always been on a wholesome and pleasant basis. Mrs. S., however, indicated a growing disinterest in her husband's physical approaches, and she was critical of him in many ways. She had concluded he was dull and uninspiring, too devoted to his business interests, not socially as active and as "interesting" to others as she thought he should be.

Actually Mr. S. was a personable, pleasant, and capable man. He was head of a small manufacturing firm, successful financially. During the war he devoted long hours to his work, showed much ingenuity and capacity in bringing the wartime production of his plant to a high degree of efficiency, and made a real contribution to the war effort. He was rather a reserved man, friendly with a small group of business associates. While not as socially inclined as his wife, he encouraged her own social activities and took part himself with good grace, but only at times with enthusiasm.

When Mrs. S. spoke of her father her voice kindled with enthusiasm. She described him as a dynamic, energetic, capable person, imaginative, resourceful, very successful in business affairs, inventive, and ingenious. Her father, she felt, was a much bigger personality than her husband. Somewhat pensively she commented on her father's great preoccupation with his affairs that kept him away from home much of the time. Actually she had had relatively little contact with him during her childhood. Her affection and esteem for him, however, were unlimited.

Mrs. S.'s dissatisfactions with her lot and her highly depreciatory attitude toward her husband reflect her appraisal of her father and her expectations and longing as a child toward him. By virtue of his very remoteness, her father could remain the highly idealized being he still represented in the fantasy of the daughter. The non-spectacular, though really adequate, agreeable, and affectionate husband was measured against the image of the ideal father and most certainly found wanting. No matter how effective he may be in reality, no flesh-and-blood husband, with the faults and weaknesses that usual husbands are bound to have, can stand the test of such a comparison.

The childish longings in relation to such an idealized father remained to obstruct the possibility of a realistic appraisal of a husband. For Mrs. S. recognition and acknowledgment of the overemphasized role of this ancient, childhood feeling toward her father permitted a more mature evaluation of her actual life situation and of her relationship to her husband. She found it possible to recapture normal enthusiasm about the everyday affairs of real family and social life and to go ahead effectively in her role as wife and as mother.

PERSISTENCE AS A CHILD

The basic persistence of the concept of oneself as son or daughter, rather than as adult man or woman in marriage, reflects itself in many ways.

A successful businessman, J. L. was anxious and uncertain about his work. His discomfort began at a time when he was advanced in his firm and placed in a position of authority over other men. Heretofore he had always been in a secondary position, with a boss over him to whom he could turn for advice and who had ultimate responsibility.

He made no complaints about his marital life, but his wife was somewhat unhappy about their childless state. When questioned about this childlessness J. L. indicated that there were no children because his wife "had not insisted upon it," that early in marriage it seemed quite a responsibility to have children, and now, relatively late, he thought himself and his wife a little too old to begin the rearing of a family. He knew of no physical obstacles to the having of children.

J. was the younger of two sons, reared by a strict and authoritative father. Both boys obeyed him implicitly without thought of ever questioning the father's authority, even when quite grown into manhood. When drafted into military service in World War I, J. L. was recommended for training in the Officers' Candidate School. He refused this training, saying he preferred the position of a private rather than that of an officer with responsibilities possibly involving lives of other men. He served through the period of enlistment in a very competent manner, evidenced considerable personal courage in action, but never got beyond non-commissioned officer rating. On return to civilian life he started in a subsidiary position in the firm in which eventually he was promoted to a managerial position.

Throughout life J. L. inwardly considered himself the son who should dutifully carry out the orders of a stronger and wiser father. He refused the authority that goes with the position of a father in rejecting training as an officer—and in avoiding fatherhood in his marriage. When life circumstances made it impossible for him to escape any longer the real responsibilities of a fatherlike person he became psychologically upset and was finally forced to recognize and evaluate the limitations he had imposed upon himself. On gaining an understanding of the nature of his discomfort, he was able to make a good adjustment to the demands of his work situation, but it was a bit too late in life to start the rearing of a family and the rounding out of an otherwise good marital life.

TIME REVEALS SOME MARITAL DIFFICULTIES

Time and experience serve to bring about modifications in attitudes toward life situations. This fact is at times overlooked by a partner in marriage.

A forty-three-year-old attorney, R. B., had concluded he wished a divorce, but he was concerned about the possible effects of family disruption on his only child, a thirteen-year-old daughter.

R. B. was an only son. His father, successful in law, tended to treat him much as "his boy." Only in recent years had R. decided to pursue an independent career. He severed his professional association with his father and established a new firm. He remained quite close to his own parents, however. He considered his childhood life a happy one, spoke of the great devotion his mother had to home and family, and of her capacity to understand and anticipate his needs and those of his father. R. said that there had been much quarreling and bickering throughout his marriage, but during the last two or three years this had been increasing. His wife was from a family of artistic and literary interests. She had achieved a modest success as a writer of short stories and radio scripts. R. was more impatient than pleased with her success, felt she neglected the home and her child in the service of her outside interests, and constantly compared her attitude toward home and family with that of his mother.

Actually the household was a well-conducted and well-regulated one in which, however, the wife made generous use of household help to relieve her of routines. R. told how he was "madly in love" with his wife at first. He showered her with gifts and affection and did everything to meet her wishes.

During their engagement they had a rather serious difference which led to a threat on the part of his fiancée to withdraw from the engagement. He "gave in" and never risked such a threat again for many years. During recent years, however, he had increasingly resented her "lack of co-operation." While establishing himself independently in his work there was a period of relative stringency; he felt his wife did not go along with him in necessary reduction of expenses. He worked harder and harder, grew short and impatient with his wife. He concluded he was not in love with her any longer, became critical of her person, of her manner, of everything about her. He withdrew from her sexually and felt there was nothing attractive about her in any sense. He toyed with the idea that maybe he would fall in love with someone else, essayed a mild flirtation or two, but soon realized that his dissatisfaction with his wife had nothing to do with the possible attractiveness of other women. Finally, embittered by the innumerable deficiencies he apparently found in his wife, he concluded a divorce was in order.

Mrs. B. was taken completely by surprise by the suggestion of divorce, as she had always considered herself fully devoted to her husband. She had been fully aware of his increasing irritability with her, attributed it to overwork and too great preoccupation with his professional affairs, and had been urging him to find time for a holiday away from the demands of his work. She had long been uncomfortable and unhappy but assumed the "fault" was entirely with her husband.

Here again two intelligent and well-intentioned people almost brought their marriage to dissolution because of inability to see their problem clearly. The initial equilibrium in this marriage was established by the somewhat too passive and too dependent attitudes of the young husband. Loving and affectionate by nature, he early adopted the attitude that security in love was dependent on conformity to all wishes and desires of his beloved. It was pretty much a matter of being a good boy so as to risk no rejection or anger, an attitude he held toward his parents as well. Relatively late in life, particularly under the stimulus of his successful independent activities in his profession, he achieved a basically more active attitude and reacted against his own earlier too-compliant tendencies. The wife, in the meantime, in all good faith, accepted the initial basis of their relationship and assumed a taken-for-granted attitude toward her husband, unaware of the fact that people can and do develop and change as they mature in years. The result was, finally, a "strike" on the part of the husband; after having taught his wife over years of time to expect certain reactions on his part, he rebelled against the very situation he had largely brought about.

It proved not too difficult for each of these people to gain perspective about their marriage and the nature of their difficulties. The real maturity the husband had achieved enabled him, albeit a bit painfully, to recognize the immature, dependent attitude that determined his earlier need to yield in all issues. The wife was truly surprised to discover that she had been much too complacent in her expectations of her husband. It was interesting to note that she was actually stimulated and challenged by the necessity to understand herself and her relationship with her husband.

Not infrequently failure on the part of a young woman to cope adequately with marital life is determined by disturbing and deeply implanted attitudes toward sexuality and toward the marital status. Two related pertinent concepts are (1) the idea that sexuality is vulgar or "bad" and hence forbidden, possibly dangerous, and (2) a woman's role, particularly in marriage, is considered by her to be a secondary and depreciated role.

This basic depreciation of a woman's role in marriage was a much more emphasized conscious theme in social attitudes toward women a generation ago than now. It was a heritage of the Victorian era, in which all sexual interests were considered, at best, bad taste; at worst, sinful. Today, under the emancipating influence of healthier attitudes toward women, toward femininity, and toward the womanly sexual role, the surface manifestations of this attitude have disappeared. In some measure, however, they have gone "underground" and are represented in the less conscious or unconscious attitudes of many women. Some mothers succeed in transmitting to their daughters attitudes toward sex that make it difficult, if not impossible, for the daughters to accept the sexual marital role as one consistent with self-respect and dignity. At times the sexual role is envisaged not merely as "bad," but as brutal, painful, dangerous to physical health; something to be suffered rather than experienced as part of a creative way of life.

Mrs. L., the mother of three daughters, was a conscientious, scrupulous mother. She concerned herself carefully with the rearing of her daughters, with emphasis upon personal cleanliness and strict morals. While her children were quite young the emphasis upon health was extreme; e.g., regularity in bowel movement occupied a position of first importance, with ready recourse to enemas or other means of internal "purification" at the slightest provocation. The father in this family was a mild-mannered, good-natured bookkeeper, who provided for the material security of his family but left the rearing of the daughters entirely to the energetic wife and mother.

As the girls matured the mother was insistent that marriage was something to be avoided, sexual behavior to be deplored, and the bearing of children an onerous and distasteful burden to which no daughter of hers should submit. She emphasized the dangers and discomforts of pregnancy and the trials and cares involved in the rearing of children. One devoted all one's time and energy to the rearing of a family with no prospect of thanks, reward, or satisfaction. In view of this, sexual relations had no justification.

The daughters in this family were intelligent and capable. All of them, nevertheless, were sufficiently impressed by the mother's attitudes that none was able to accept the prospect of marriage. Of the three, one, after a period of residence away from home, was able to question the desirability of a life without marriage and sought psychiatric advice. She came to an understanding of the distortions in the mother's attitudes and the effect of these on her own life relationships and eventually she married, armed with understanding which should prevent a repetition of the mistakes in her own rearing in relation to a daughter of her own. The two sisters remained victims of the great limitations imposed by the mother, unmarried, restricted in social outlook, both still preoccupied with problems of physical health in keeping with the mother's great concern in this field.

Without the specific depreciation of the sexual role as above discussed, many girls grow into womanhood with the deep conviction that women are cast in a secondary role in life, and that particularly in marriage a woman's position is a depreciated one. We cannot discuss those important cultural and social considerations that play a large role in the determination of such feeling on the part of women. It is a fact that in some societies women may be in the position of chattel rather than in equal partnership in life relations. But even in a society such as our own, where in some respects femininity carries with it special prerogatives, there is still a tendency on the part of some women to feel that the world is essentially a man's world— boys and men only can achieve full personal freedom and full expression of their potentialities, while women are thwarted and cannot do the same. The result is a tendency to regard homemaking, the bearing and rearing of children as routine, dull, and not a source of gratification as creative work.

Whether or not social attitudes provoke convictions as to presumable inferiority of women as compared with men, we can recognize very early a questioning by both boys and girls as to the significance of differences between the sexes. A not uncommon conclusion arrived at by very small children is that girls are in some measure deficient. To the small child the lack of an obvious genital organ seems to constitute a deficiency. This is not a theoretical assumption about children. It is something that quite a few children remark upon directly and openly and about which, at times, they need correct information. Often, however, because of anxiety on the part of a child or lack of awareness or prudery on the part of a parent, the whole questioning attitude is repressed. The uncertainty and depreciated evaluation of the little girl remain, however, to color the attitude of both boy and girl.

As might be expected, such attitudes toward the person or the functioning of women are likely to evolve in families in which little girls may be given reason to believe that their brothers are more highly valued by one of the parents. Some parents openly prefer sons to daughters. In such a family a girl may remain convinced that she can never amount to much, or she may possibly strive to become the sort of person the desired son would have been. A certain number of professional women soft-ball players are daughters of fathers who had really hoped to have a son rather than a daughter; a son who should be a fine figure on the baseball field. The daughter attempts to meet the father's hopes and expectations by pinch-hitting, as it were, for the desired son. It does not help them much in their development as girls and women.

A child's greatest need is to be loved and valued by parents as he *is;* this is the key to the possibility of developing self-dignity and a sense of personal worth-whileness. If this self-evaluation is disturbed by the concept that only boys are truly valued by parents, there ensues a never-ending struggle with the proposition that to accept femininity is to accept something inferior.

Many marriages are disturbed by this hidden repudiation of femininity. Resistance to acceptance of the sexual role in marriage, resentment at the demands of household and children, envy of the presumably freer and more rewarding or worth-while activity of the husband disturb the equanimity of many families.

Any realistic appraisal of the relative positions of man and woman in marriage would allow for the biological fact that men and women are different in their roles; that their differences cannot be gauged on a single scale of values but in terms of complementary functions and activities that make for successful joint living together in marriage. Whenever, by virtue of circumstances or because of pressures depending upon personality peculiarities, one partner is thrust unduly into the role usually carried by the other, a natural equilibrium is disturbed.

This equilibrium, in a healthy marriage, is one in which the wide range of basic needs and desires of both partners is adequately met. These include the need for love and affection, satisfaction of the more ideal expectations of a respected and beloved partner, material security, social prestige, parenthood, sexual expression of love. To be sure, the manner and degree to which these needs are met vary widely, and the nature of the equilibrium attained is highly individual for each couple. A marriage may sustain some degree of limitation in both degree and range of satisfactions in the several fields, but it is clear to see from the cases cited above that the possibility of a workable equilibrium can readily be disturbed. This is particularly true when the basic attitudes outlined earlier tend toward a denial of the validity of one's own or one's partner's needs in marriage.

Psychiatrists who have an opportunity to scrutinize the conflicting rational and non-rational attitudes of their patients are able to outline with considerable precision the nature of some of these situations of conflict. Referring back to the attitude on the part of some young women that their role in marriage is secondary, or a depreciated one, one finds with rather astonishing regularity a characteristic sequence of inner reaction and external behavior. Such a young woman, impelled by healthy impulses toward marriage and motherhood, nevertheless unconsciously tends to select as a mate a man who she instinctively feels will not overwhelm her sexually or otherwise, will not dominate or coerce her, and in relation to whom she will feel equal or superior. In actuality, however, such a woman to whom prestige and position mean so much will expect a great deal of her husband, real adequacy if not superiority in all fields, vocational, social, sexual. She will wish him to achieve for her all that she feels she is denied because she is a woman. Having selected as a mate a man whom she considers not too dangerous or threatening, she now senses and resents in him the very deficiencies that enabled her to accept him as a mate. She becomes depreciatory toward him, aggressive and hostile toward him for failing to meet her more unconscious concepts of what a husband should be like.

Many versions of this theme are encountered in real life. If a wife is able to see through the contradictory character of her own expectations she may be able to protect herself from the effects of such a vicious cycle, gain more assurance as to the valid aspects of her relationship with her husband, and achieve a workable association in marriage. Similarly, if a husband is able to understand the implications of such an attitude he, too, may be able to do much to promote a healthier equilibrium. It must be remembered that it takes two to create any given life situation. The husband, in the type of marriage we are discussing, certainly has made his initial contribution to the difficulty. Those attitudes of unaggressiveness and passivity that made him seem sufficiently non-dangerous to the neurotic part of his wife's feeling do exist in him; the question is whether they exist in such degree and operate so automatically as to play into the cycle of fear, depreciation, expectation, and disappointment to which we have referred. He may be able to see that, after all, his apparently domineering and aggressive wife is really dependent upon him and his life success for basic satisfaction as he is dependent upon her. If so, he may surmount his own reactions of resentment and hostility toward his wife, insist on fulfillment of standards of performance he sets up for himself, and in this manner tend to bring about stability in marriage.

A word must be said about the persistence of psychologically disturbed patterns of behavior in marriage. It is apparent from what has been said that deeply implanted attitudes inimical to successful adjustments in marriage disturb or disrupt many marriages in the ways described. It has been stated that these attitudes usually evolve during the course of development of the child toward maturity and are dependent in considerable measure upon the nature of the training and rearing. It should here be emphasized, however, that all too often the nature and the very existence of these disturbing attitudes are not recognized or are explicitly denied by the victims themselves. In personal relationships and in understanding of inner motivations, desires, and strivings, objectivity and rational understanding are achieved with much greater difficulty than in other fields of human inquiry. Many people are never able to approach rational understanding of their own behavior and motivations, although maturing life experience helps in the direction of such understandings.

Our medical experience shows, however, that precisely those people who are most disturbed in their marital relationships often fail to "learn" by their unhappy experiences. A trip to the divorce court is frequently followed by a marriage in which the same marital difficulties are again encountered. One has succeeded in separating oneself from an unhappy situation, but not from the basic attitudes and expectations that made the first marriage an unhappy one and that operate the same way in a second marriage. Perhaps there is little point in the termination of marriage unless there is basic clarity as to the nature of the deficiencies in the relationship. Nothing short of such understanding can offer much in the way of insurance against the possibility of a repeat act in a subsequent marriage. On the other hand, such understanding frequently makes possible the successful continuance of a threatened marriage.

Chapter 9

THE HEALTH AND HYGIENE OF MARRIAGE

by Thurman B. Rice, A.M., M.D.*

FORMERLY PROFESSOR OF PUBLIC HEALTH, INDIANA UNIVERSITY SCHOOL OF MEDICINE

Assume that the choice of the marriage mate has been such that there is a reasonable hope that the partners can carry through their respective roles with at least average success. The excitement of the wedding and the precarious decisions of the honeymoon are recently past, and the happy couple are back home, ready to begin the reality of homemaking.

There is a reasonably adequate income, the housing problem is passably well solved, and there is need to meet the perplexities of everyday life as married couples everywhere must meet them if they are to accomplish the purposes of marriage on an adult level. The health and hygiene of marriage must take the place which until now has been played almost wholly by starry-eyed romance. Actually, a state of health in the marriage relation will enable romance to persist, just as wholesome food will permit health in the usual sense to persist. Romance must be fed with solid food; it cannot long thrive on cake and kisses.

Assume that the couple have married at a time when each was hungry for sexual contact with the beloved one. If such is not the case they should have waited longer, or, failing this, should continue the courtship even though the marriage vows have been said. Healthy young people will find the new privileges extraordinarily pleasing in most cases; the problem is to keep them so. They must learn to use sexual gratification somewhat as they use food, to the end that they may grow in vigor and in appreciation, and thus to accomplish the purposes of sex.

PURPOSES OF SEX RELATIONS

The purposes of sex are three:

1. *Procreation.* If civilization, culture, race, and nation are to be pre-

---

*Dr. Rice died December 27, 1952. This chapter has been edited by Dr. Morris Fishbein.

served, persons of health, character, and ability must reproduce themselves and furnish heredity, environment, and the training so necessary to the continuation of the species on a high level. This is a duty of those who have good bodies and minds—even more, it is a privilege.

2. *Self-expression.* Something in the nature of men and women makes them desire intimate contact with a loved one of the opposite sex, and with that one to produce and enjoy his or her own offspring. A deep sentiment is involved and must be gratified if the individual is to reap a rich emotional family life. Just as the healthy person enjoys wholesome food, so does he or she enjoy this family relation and is the better for that enjoyment.

3. *Security.* Men and women are more secure when there is between them a rich sexual relation and their children share this security. The infancy of the human child is longer than that of any other species of young; he needs his parents until he is fully grown and even beyond that time. Anything, then, which will hold his parents together is a protection to him and to the entire family. The ability of the parents to use sex for such a purpose is of vast importance to all who comprise the family group.

A marriage starts then with a couple hungry for sexual contact. But the happy lovers must remember that it will not always be so. They will soon satiate themselves to some extent, at least. Is that, then, the end of love or the beginning of the end? It may well be the death of romance unless there is an understanding of the real purposes of marriage. It is not to be supposed that the institution of marriage was designed merely to furnish safe conditions for intercourse, though obviously that is one of the objectives. There will come a time when even the most ardent man or woman will desire something else—something more. Early in married life the couple must begin to develop other objectives than intercourse. As the years pass these will become more satisfying and precious and will come ultimately to replace the pleasures of sexual union. As a result happiness can continue indefinitely as a reward for wise and meritorious behavior.

An analogy may serve to illustrate this point. Assume that a man is building a new house in which he expects to live. In the beginning he is enormously interested in the digging of the foundation and visits the site twice a day to observe progress. This foundation seems most important— as indeed it is; it even seems most fascinating—as indeed it well may be. Later, as the house progresses, he transfers his interest to the other parts of the building; and finally, upon its completion, he moves into and lives in it with no further thought for the foundation. This is as it should be unless one strangely prefers to live one's whole life in the basement, as so many do—speaking sexually. I repeat that the basement of the house is important and that sexual intercourse, which is the foundation of happy married life, is important, but it is not the whole of the house or of the marriage. Let us hope that the foundation upon which the house or the home is built is utterly sound and secure, as carefully and scientifically constructed as able workmanship can provide, but remember that it is a means to an end rather than an end in itself. Intercourse between two persons deeply in love has many rewards in addition to and exceeding those of physical gratification.

The householder who comes home after an honest day's work has a right to expect an attractive, well-cooked, and nicely served dinner—provided, of course, that his wife is not ill or excessively worn by the day's work. If the food is on the table at six o'clock he will eat, enjoy the food, and then give no more thought to food during the remainder of the evening. If he is still waiting at seven he will be restless; by eight o'clock he will be angry if he is not served; by nine o'clock he will be furious, and probably long before ten he will have gone to the corner restaurant. Sex is much like food in this respect; persons who are not fed at home are tempted—at least—to go elsewhere. Or if the food is on the table at six but consists of a can of salmon, a bottle of milk, and a box of crackers—all of it nourishing but carelessly served —the man of the house is likely to think that it is a poor home that is his and may go elsewhere. The wife whose husband is too lazy or too stupid to try for a bit of glamour is likely to yearn for someone else with a bit more consideration for her feelings. I am not attempting to justify the implied misconduct associated with this analogy but only to show the attitudes of mind which lead to such misconduct.

CLEANLINESS ESSENTIAL

What are the actual factors which have a good or a bad effect upon marriage happiness? There is tidiness, for example. It is doubtful if there is anything more destructive to romance than soiled underwear or body odor. They must be guarded against with the utmost care, and yet one must have a smattering of good judgment too. If the housewife must do her own laundry she may not wish her husband to be overly free with the linen. She may prefer to have him wear his underwear until it is really soiled a bit than to be confronted with a mountain of washing and ironing each week. Possibly her husband would rather have her wear her dainties longer than to have her exhausted with the effort to keep herself "as sweet as when she stepped out of her bath two hours ago." A house, or a wife, or a husband may be so dainty that there is no comfort in living with it, or her, or him. One cannot relax well in a home or with a person who is too nice to get a bit messed up. After all, there is the work of the world to be done, and it is impossible for workers to avoid soil and perspiration entirely. All of this is a matter for adjustment.

Much the same may be said of the matter of personal cleanliness. Surely one cannot compromise with cleanliness, and yet cleanliness is a relative term. A home cannot be managed as would be the surgery operating room in a hospital. There are those who bathe twice or more times a day and others who follow the once-a-week pattern. Certain parts of the body require particular care—the genital area, the feet, the armpits, the hair, and the mouth. Genital odors—if they are not excessive—may be stimulating to some, but in general they are best avoided. Certainly they are objectionable when they can be detected in casual contacts or when one is in the same room with the person from whom they exude. External cleanliness is all that is necessary to prevent such objectionable odors. A cleansing douche is often refreshing, but it is not usually necessary for the prevention of odor. An antiseptic douche will tend to kill the useful bacteria found in the vaginal tract and is best not used. Such a douche is not an adequate contraceptive device and may lead to abnormal discharges which are more offensive than the natural odors of the vaginal tract. Bathing should be adjusted to the sensitivity of the conjugal partner and the convenience of the bathing facilities. Those persons who are so fortunate as to have hot water and a modern bathroom should remember that bathing may be a major operation in a crowded home without modern sanitary conveniences. Clearly in such a home frequent bathing could put a serious strain upon the one bathing and upon those who must live with him or her.

In any consideration of health an evaluation of costs and benefits must be made. It is entirely possible to make such a fuss about matters pertaining to health as to cause health to be lost rather than gained. Just as nothing can be so dangerous as the assurance that one is absolutely safe, so nothing can be so injurious to health as to give to health matters one's entire attention. The couple who work too hard and worry too much attempting to make the home perfection in these matters are likely to be too tired and harassed to enjoy the precious privileges when and if they are attained. Such is far from being a healthful state of affairs. The mother who spends so much time *working for* the children that she has no energy left to *play with* them is not being wise. The father who kills himself or injures himself in the effort to provide everything for his family is failing to provide them with what they need most—himself. His sacrifice is noble, perhaps, but strangely unappreciated in many instances.

It is wrong from the standpoint of the healthfulness of a marriage for the two most responsible persons in the family to be spendthrifts and to keep the economic status of the family in a perpetual state of jeopardy; it is equally wrong for them to make such a fetish of the economic stability that they keep the emotional status of the family in a perpetual state of jeopardy. It is possible to be a spendthrift in more ways than one. He who wastes love, the opportunity to play with his children, and to be *one* in a lovely family is of all spendthrifts the worst—the one most to be pitied—or despised.

HYGIENE OF THE BEDROOM

The bed and bedroom of a married couple hold an important place in their health and hygiene relations. Arguments are offered for and against the double bed. One sleeps better when he or she is alone, the cover can be better adjusted, there is less danger of transmitting respiratory infections, and there are several other advantages. There are definite disadvantages: the cost is greater, it requires more laundry and more bedroom space. The crux of the matter lies not in such practical considerations, however, but in those emotional and conjugal ones which are the heart and soul of marriage. There are many conveniences and enjoyments in the double bed which cannot be well set down on paper. They lead to a rich warm comradeship which is utterly priceless to many couples who would not wish to be labeled "old-fashioned." I recommend that young people give the double bed a try and that older couples make the transition from one twin bed to the other easy and frequent, and as often in one direction as the other. I can hardly imagine a more effective damper of romance than separate rooms for husband and wife, or the practice of having one or the other sleeping with a child. The practice of sleeping in separate rooms or beds so that the number of children can be held down may or may not have the desired results in this respect, and it may or may not lead to interest in another person who is less unattainable.

There are many differences in tastes and there are really good reasons for separation of the beds. Bad breath, body odor, snoring, restlessness, pulling of the covers, differences in sleeping habits, and other peculiarities may make it desirable for the couple to separate themselves in the interest of continued affection. Certainly the beds should be separated when one or the other has a transmissible disease. Sometimes the beds may be set so close together as barely to avoid touching and the advantages of both the single and the double bed pretty largely attained. Whatever the arrangement, it should be the one which gives the least cause for mutual dissatisfaction and the greatest possible opportunity for the unhampered enjoyment of marital rights and privileges.

There are persons who like to indulge in minor "vulgarities" when under sexual stimulation. They may wish to use words which they would not use at other times, and they may rightly feel that the technical words properly used in a scientific discussion seem stilted and quite out of place in the intimacy of sexual stimulation. All of this is a matter for adjustment. The relation should be neither stilted nor vulgar. It is an intimate contact which calls for words of endearment, for pet names and delicate shades of meaning —for anything, indeed, that will enhance the enjoyment and bring appreciation and happiness to both partners, but in particular to the *other* partner. Cave men may be desirable to cave women, but most women probably prefer to live and make love under more civilized surroundings. A man may wish his wife to be free in her affections, but he will rarely want her to be wanton.

NUDITY

Whether or not the nude body is to be exposed to view is another matter for individual taste. A great many women have been reared in such a way that nudity will inevitably seem vulgar to them. In such case the husband who seeks to indulge his wish to see his wife in that condition may spoil all chance of enjoyment on her part. Women with beautiful bodies may well wish to expose them when sexually stimulated and may derive much pleasure from such behavior, but a puritanical man may see in it an evidence of vulgarity which is highly repugnant to him. Women with less attractive forms may well wish to dim the lights or prefer darkness for their lovemaking, much to the disgust of the husband who feels that he needs stimulation of every sort to attain the degree of stimulation which his tardy responses require. Men should remember that the "human form divine" is usually feminine. Clearly the male body is less glamorous in itself than is that of the "pin-up girl" variety. This matter of degrees of exposure and light in the room when making love is something to be given careful consideration if success is to be expected. Each of the couple should be careful to avoid pressing the point. Obviously it is a matter of taste rather than morals, but there is no accounting for tastes in this regard.

FREQUENCY OF SEXUAL INTERCOURSE

The question as to how often intercourse may be "indulged" or enjoyed is one that is often asked. Amazingly, many books and pamphlets written to instruct in such matters attempt to answer this question by giving a definite number ("twice a week"). Nothing could be more absurd. Individual preference and ability will vary so widely that it is utterly impossible to give a categorical answer. Since the act is good and gives great pleasure; since it is perfectly legitimate in marriage and binds the couple closer together when performed properly, repetition as often as it can be satisfyingly performed should be encouraged. Even writers who profess to great beauty in the act will tend to warn against what they call excessive indulgence. Obviously the determining factor should be one closely related to the desires and the capacities of the couple. Without wishing to be arbitrary in such a personal matter, the following principles are sound:

1. Intercourse should be enjoyed as often as both *the husband and the wife desire it.*

2. It should be an invigorating experience leading to a state of relaxation, satisfaction, or exhilaration which is conducive to sound sleep or peace with the world as determined by the time of day.

3. Due consideration must be given to the matter of childbearing in the determination of frequency and methods to be used.

Within these limits satisfying intercourse in wedlock is of tremendous value to the couple, to the family, and to the stability of society at large. It is impossible to see how one can come to any other conclusion than that—within these restrictions—intercourse is an extremely practical art which should be studied, improved, and finally made perfect.

Nevertheless, it is doubtful if anything could be more disgusting or irritating than a husband—or a wife—who coaxes or demands sexual satisfaction at the most inopportune and embarrassing times, or who wishes to indulge himself or herself at the expense of the other partner. A young husband who observes his bride excessively languid or even exhausted as a result of his demands must surely feel a real sense of shame if he can feel at all. The wife who sees her husband going tired to his work need not be surprised if he is unable to earn the home and the security which they need. Excessive childbearing can make of the marriage bed a place of danger and fear; can make the home a place of chaos full of squalling babies and wet, smelly diapers. A wise couple knows how to steer a course between excessive indulgence on the one hand and sexual starvation on the other.

When the husband and wife are rather equally balanced in their sexuality the problem is obviously much easier than when one is hot and the other cold. In the latter instance great tact, patience, and forbearance are needed in the early months of marriage if a satisfactory arrangement is to be expected. Assume—for the sake of variety—that the wife is the more amorous; that she needs more and can enjoy more intercourse than her husband can give to make her thoroughly satisfied with her home and marriage. In such case the husband will do well to play with her as much as he can before beginning the act itself; as soon as she has attained an orgasm he will do well to withdraw and save his energy for the next time, which will come all too soon for his relatively weak powers. At once it will be pointed out by those who still believe in the old-time physiology that he will seriously injure his nervous system by indulging in an incomplete act. Actually the incomplete act is less injurious in such a case than would be overindulgence. If he does not permit himself to get too close to the orgasm it is not injurious at all. Such an arrangement allows many happy acts of love on the part of the husband and a corresponding number of highly satisfying experiences for the wife. The incomplete act—so far as the husband is concerned—is a sort of kiss of affection and endearment at a time when he is perfectly capable of enjoying such, though he would be exhausted by the complete act. The wife of such a considerate man should be grateful and appreciative and should be more than eager to make up to him for any inconvenience the séance may have caused him. By such an arrangement he will not need to wonder whether the eager wife is tempted to make a cuckold of him—a source of considerable additional satisfaction. He will be able to feel a great pride of accomplishment in being able to hold the love of an amorous woman—no small accomplishment! He will be insuring the safety of his home for himself and his children.

It is generally supposed that it is more likely to be the husband who is excessive in his demands. What can a conscientious wife do to take care of such a situation—other than make a martyr of herself? There is indeed much that she can do if she loves the man and wishes to make him happy. Sexual intercourse is exhausting to a wife only when she puts herself into it actively —either positively or negatively. By being utterly passive or nearly so, she can satisfy her husband without tiring herself. At such a time she may well ask him to get along with the project of attaining an ejaculation; she may ask that he cut short the amorous dallying which at other times would be welcome; she may likely need a lubricant; and she may properly ask him to take responsibility for the contraceptive used—if one is used. She should not pity herself and pout about it, but should co-operate to the extent that is necessary for the quick attainment of the relaxation that he may greatly need. How great must be the appreciation of a husband whose wife, observing his unrest, suggests or gladly acquiesces to a short act of intercourse which will ease his tension and permit him to get the sleep which he needs if he is to do the work of the morrow. It is of such things that happiness in marriage is made. Intercourse with a passive wife may not seem exciting, but when it makes a man love the good helpmate by his side and adds to his appreciation of the unselfishness and love she bears him, it serves a purpose which is precious indeed. It is far to be preferred to the arrangement which may make him too susceptible to the charms of the unsatisfied woman he may meet when he is away from home.

DISPARITY OF SEX ORGANS

While the genital organs of most couples are average size and therefore quite compatible, it is entirely possible that there will be some degree of physical disproportion. Such disparity will not necessarily present great difficulty if there is the desire on the part of the two partners to make the attempt to correct the situation by making adjustments. If, for example, the penis is too small to give full satisfaction compensation may be made if the wife will place under her buttocks a pillow or, even better, a few folds of firm, thick blanket which will have the effect of preventing her from sinking down too low in the bed. When the reverse relation is at fault a pillow under the small of the back will turn her pelvis away from her husband in such a way as to avoid too deep entrance. The use of a lubricant such as a surgical or a contraceptive jelly will be of assistance. Investigation by a physician of muscular spasm as the vaginal entrance or search for inflamed or tender areas may be required. By means of different positions of intercourse and other adaptive measures the organs will gradually become more yielding to disproportions.

TIMING IN SEXUAL INTERCOURSE

There may be difficulty in timing. Usually such differences can be overcome by the exercise of some effort on the part of the one partner, or restraint on the part of the other. As a rule it is the husband who tends to come to the climax first. In such case he is likely to ejaculate too early and leave the wife unsatisfied. This can sometimes be corrected by spending more time with sex play before the actual conjugation is attempted, or the husband may cease his movements but leave the penis in the vagina while he caresses the tardy wife. There is a belief that the two orgasms must be simultaneous if the best results are to be obtained. This is not necessary. There are indeed advantages in having the wife reach the climax first. Usually she will not object to a brief continuance after she has attained satisfaction. By this arrangement the one or the other is in full possession of control at all times and can more readily assist the partner in the climax of the act. This is a matter of personal preference and control as to whether the one or the other method shall be used.

The husband can usually attain satisfaction from the first though he may not be expert in the early months of marriage. The wife, however, may have to learn to relax and to induce the orgasm. Many brides are bitterly disappointed that they are not successful at first. It is not unusual to hear of a young wife who is relatively unsuccessful until after the birth of her first child. This does not mean that she is frigid but only that she is inexperienced. Rarely does the condition continue if the husband is co-operative and skillful and she is willing to relax and to learn. The matter of relaxation is quite important. Young women have been taught to restrain themselves; the muscles of the pelvic region (perineum) are tight and strong. The nervous type of girl may need more rest and sleep than she had been getting in the pre-marital period; she may need to sit in a warm bath for ten or twenty minutes before attempting intercourse; she must have great love for and reliance in her mate; she needs to have perfect confidence in her contraceptive protection or, even better, to be willing to accept a pregnancy as the natural outcome of the act of copulation. Quite naturally she probably will not wish to become pregnant immediately after marriage, nor will she wish to be submerged by a deluge of children. In such case she can relax only when she is reasonably sure that pregnancy will not ensue. It is rare indeed that a healthy woman with a proper attitude toward marriage will fail to attain success in intercourse if she has a husband whom she loves and respects and who is willing to put the attainment of her success before his own.

Sometimes we hear of women who are so eager to experience an orgasm that they try *too* hard and exhaust themselves in the effort. Hysterical tears and frenzied effort are hardly consistent with the reasonable hope of success in such case. They may be quite disastrous. Success in this important matter is something that may be requested but not commanded. Rarely is a frontal attack upon the objective successful. One may eagerly *invite* happiness of this sort, but one is not permitted to *demand* it at the cost of tears and sobs. It will not obey such a summons. Women of this sort are *not* frigid —the frigid woman just doesn't want anything to do with sexual intercourse. Frigidity is far too complex a phenomenon to discuss in detail here. The too-eager wife usually needs only to relax and let appreciation for the sexual act develop.

PREVENTION OF CONCEPTION

Methods of contraception relate themselves to the whole matter of marital hygiene. They may constitute an occasional hazard and so need to be discussed in this place. There are women and men who will feel a twinge of conscience in the use of them, as they have been taught that they are somewhat immoral or that they are dangerous in some way. There are couples who hold such a warranted fear of pregnancy that they can in no wise enjoy conjugal relations without them. There are some methods, like the intra-uterine stem, which are actually somewhat dangerous to health and should be avoided for that reason; others are ineffectual, like the douche, and by failure lead to a distrust of all such means; and still others are such a nuisance as to be quite disturbing, particularly to the less amorous member of the pair.

In the matter of conscience we have little to say. That is a matter for the individual couple and one which would best have been decided *before* marriage. Intercourse has three purposes, not merely the one purpose of procreation. It is argued by some that not even the beasts are so crass as to have intercourse for pleasure only. Well, maybe that is the reason they have remained beasts, while man has developed all of the lovely sentiments and emotions which cluster about the home and have made the human species superior to the cattle of the field. A husband and wife need to be much in each other's arms, while at the same time in this complex world they need to have some control over the number of children they may beget. To practice contraception or not to practice contraception is a matter for the individual couple to decide, and it is to be hoped that they can and do agree on the principle and the methods involved.

DANGEROUS DOUCHES

As a matter of *danger* there is little to be said except that the use of poisonous douches is obviously wrong. The vaginal mucous membrane will absorb bichloride of mercury, phenol, and other such products, as does the stomach. Irritating douches are a menace. For example, suppose a cresol douche is made up with hard water and the strength is gauged by the *color* of the mixture. The milky color is really due to the *hardness of the water*. When a wife uses soft water (away from home, perhaps) and the white color does not develop promptly, she is prone to add more cresol and to get a bad burn. Sometimes warm water is not available for a douche. Cold water may be a considerable shock to the organs flushed with blood as they are after intercourse. A stem pessary reaching into the cavity of the uterus obviously may carry infection upward from the vagina.

A method of contraception which is ineffectual may lead to a tremendous family fight if it fails at a crucial time, causing either the husband or wife or both to be much disturbed and possibly to be excessively outspoken on the subject. There is no contraceptive device which is absolutely foolproof. All of them require intelligent use and a certain amount of self-restraint at a time when restraint is not easy to attain. A failure at a crucial time may jeopardize the possibility of confidence in such methods at all subsequent attempts. Couples using contraceptives should remember that in all probability the product of a failure will at a later period be the most precious thing in their lives, and that an occasional failure is nearly always a good thing. It will be fortunate if they remember that he who dances must at least occasionally pay the piper.

By all means the method chosen must be one which puts the burden of bother and responsibility upon the one of the pair who is most anxious to have intercourse. The amorous man who requires his reluctant wife to take all the precautions so that he—the all-important male—may have his enjoyment and then get to sleep is certainly not being wise in looking only after his own pleasure. A more accurate way of destroying the last vestige of passion could hardly be devised. Early in marriage the use of the condom is safer in such a time of inexperience. The method has its many objections but is far preferable to diaphragms, douches, and contraceptive jellies, foams, suppositories, and the like, so long as the wife is relatively uninterested. Even after the wife has become more passionate it would be well if the husband would share with her the trouble, restraint, and annoyance that is inherent in all of these methods.

I am not urging the use of contraceptives but merely pointing out the various possibilities of physical injury or annoyance which may result in injury to the lovely relation which should exist between a husband and wife. Couples will be far happier as a rule and the marriages will be more stable if such a number of children are born as will satisfy the natural parental desires of the individuals concerned. Women with children live longer on the average than those without children. Marriages with children are less likely to end in divorce. Certainly it must be evident that couples with children get tremendous enjoyment out of them and that there is no place in the world so lonely as the old people's home for childless men and women. Men who have something to work for are more likely to succeed in business or in the professions and, in spite of the increased expense of children, amass more wealth on the average than do men without such expensive responsibilities. There is such a thing as being compelled to make good. A man with a family of four or five children has a far more definite incentive than does he who works alone.

When pregnancy occurs there is much for the wife and the husband— now prospective parents—to learn. They should first go—at once—to the family physician. If they have not made such a connection they should do so at once and stay close to such an adviser during this period—a period of some stress, but also one capable of high and most satisfying idealism. The emotions of two good persons loving each other, legally married, and conscious of the soul-stirring fact of pregnancy are so precious and so complicated that it is utterly impossible to give any conception of them on a printed page. The person who has missed this experience has missed the most exalted experience which life has to offer.

What about intercourse during pregnancy? This question has been answered negatively in a categorical way far too many times. One who understands the anatomy and physiology of pregnancy will see in the relation no danger whatever, provided two or three considerations are memembered.

1. Need a loving husband be reminded that he must be very careful and gentle at such a time and that he must under no possibility hurt his wife? It would seem that this is very evident.

2. Intercourse should not be undertaken if abortion or natural labor is evidently likely to happen within the next few weeks. The reason is to be found in the fact that infectious germs might be introduced into the birth canal.

3. If such an act would leave the wife nervous or restless it should be avoided because nothing *must be permitted to disturb the mother* and child at such a time if it possibly can be avoided.

It is significant that many wives are unusually passionate during pregnancy. Sometimes it is the only period in their married life when they can have intercourse without fear of pregnancy; sometimes the consciousness of the tremendous role which is being enacted makes the couple more than commonly precious to each other. Pregnancy is—and properly should be— a period of high purpose and unselfish dedication to a great function. Under such a stimulus the prospective parents may well draw nearer to each other in their resolve that, come what will, they will protect, develop, and cherish the child which is developing between them. If refraining from intercourse will enhance this emotion, they should refrain; if indulgence—within the limits mentioned above—has the effect of binding them together more permanently, their own welfare *and* that of the child is served.

INTERCOURSE AMONG THE ELDERLY

What about intercourse as one grows older? Quite naturally the hot fires of youth will abate as the years pass. There are other things in life than passionate love—other things which are even more precious and enduring. The appreciation of these other things should be developed as one becomes more and more mature. Then as the fires of passion grow dimmer there will be other sources of warmth and comfort in the days that would otherwise be cold and lonesome. How foolish is the man who says, "When I get too old to chase a blonde I shall be willing to begin chasing a golf ball!" Or the man who says, "When I grow too old to be interested in a pretty woman I shall be ready to die!" How foolish is the woman past the age of physical attraction in the erogenous sense who tries to look and act as if she were eighteen.

It is surprising sometimes that she should succeed so well with her skin and fail so badly with her understanding of life. She, of course, fools no one but herself—if we may suppose that she succeeds in fooling herself. Be your age, Grandma, and be happy!

It will surprise many readers to know that many old couples still are able to enjoy sexual relations—even ardent intercourse—when they are in their seventies and even occasionally beyond. Which ones are they? They are the ones who have been highly successful in such matters in their younger years, the ones who have saved their precious powers and protected them from disease, promiscuity, and abuse. They have not wasted or thrown away their heritage but have developed it and used it to make themselves strong and capable. Many such women greatly enjoy intercourse for long years after the menopause. By having "passed" in the early years of enjoyment they have earned the right to take a postgraduate course in the same subject. What a beautiful picture it is to see an elderly couple supremely happy with life as it is lived by a good old man and a sweet old lady. One can only envy the one who at eighty is able to enjoy the companionship or the memory of the one who has meant more to him or her than any other. Surely this is success in life! It would be better to fail in all else and succeed at home than to succeed in all else and fail at home.

Chapter 10

MISCARRIAGES AND ABORTIONS

by Alan F. Guttmacher, M.D.

CHIEF OF THE DEPARTMENT OF OBSTETRICS AND GYNECOLOGY, THE MOUNT SINAI
HOSPITAL, NEW YORK; CLINICAL PROFESSOR OF OBSTETRICS AND GYNECOLOGY,
COLUMBIA UNIVERSITY

Abortion is the ending of pregnancy at any time before the fetus or prospective child is large enough to have a fair chance for survival. In terms of length of pregnancy, viability is usually considered the beginning of the seventh month. In terms of size of the infant, the border line between viability and non-viability is 1,000 gms. (2 lbs. 3 oz.). This does not mean that all infants weighing less are foredoomed to death—an occasional infant weighing as little as a pound and three quarters has been known to survive —nor does it mean that all weighing more than 1,000 gms. are certain to be reared. It simply means that the 1,000-gm. fetus has more than an obscure chance for living. When the newborn weighs more than 1,000 gms. it is automatically forced out of the abortion class into the ranks of the premature infant; the delivery is no longer termed an abortion but now becomes a premature birth, irrespective of the pregnancy's duration.

The word "abortion" has an unwholesome, criminal content for the uninstructed person. He is accustomed to use the more euphemistic word, "miscarriage," for the spontaneous varieties of early pregnancy interruption, reserving abortion to describe the man-made type. Not so the physician; he uses abortion to designate any pre-viable pregnancy termination. The doctor does differentiate between spontaneous or unintentional and induced abortions, the former occurring from natural causes, the latter being brought about by instrumentation. He also divides induced abortions into therapeutic and illegal. The distinction between these is self-evident but perhaps made a little more pointed by an incident which happened at Johns Hopkins in the third-year obstetrics class of the late J. W. Williams two decades ago. Dr. Williams asked a student, "Mr. Meyers, what is the difference between therapeutic and illegal abortion?" The student pondered a long time and then pontifically replied, "A therapeutic abortion is done to save the life of the mother"; and Dr. Williams, quick as a flash, interjected, "Yes, and an illegal abortion is done to save the life of the father."

Spontaneous abortion is frequent. In a series of one thousand consecutive pregnancies among my private patients, spontaneous abortion occurred to 98, 9.8 per cent. The average frequency of spontaneous abortion among total pregnancies reported by several others was about the same. This figure should be slightly increased for the patient who aborts so early that she neither needs nor seeks medical assistance. Therefore, the good round figure 10 per cent is probably a more accurate statement of the frequency of spontaneous abortion. In the experience of most observers, this frequency is not affected by the number of pregnancies—it is as likely to happen in the first as the eighth. However, incidence of unintentional abortion is greatly increased when the woman is of relatively advanced reproductive age (thirty-five or more), when there is a history of previous abortion, and when more than six months were required for the conception to occur. In a series of patients less than twenty-five, who conceived in less than three months and who had never aborted, we found an unintentional abortion rate of 4 per cent. In a similar series of women over thirty-five, who took longer than six months to conceive and who had previously aborted, we noted a spontaneous abortion rate of 38 per cent.

The time of abortion has been found to be the second month in 30 per cent, the third in 42 per cent, the fourth in 17 per cent, the fifth in 8 per cent, and the sixth month in 3 per cent. Thus, 72 per cent of spontaneous abortions occur before the fourth month of pregnancy begins, the commonest time being 10.8 weeks after the onset of the last menstrual period.

Cases of spontaneous abortion may be divided into two main groups: a major, in which abortion is the result of random or fortuitous factors, unlikely to repeat in the next pregnancy except by cruel chance; and a much smaller group in which a recurrent factor appears to cause abortion with succeeding pregnancies. Speert, in a publication now in press, reports 121 instances among 17,490 obstetrical patients of the Presbyterian Hospital in New York who gave the history of three consecutive spontaneous abortions, one case in every 145 pregnancies. In this study, Speert demonstrated that in more than 70 per cent the pregnancy following such a series of consecutive abortions resulted in a term child. Despite the optimistic outlook for the group as a whole, there is the occasional case in which the uterus never seems able to carry a fetus to viability. The use of hormones and vitamins, despite their vogue, seems to exert no influence on a favorable outcome.

What causes spontaneous abortion? The causes are multiple, but by far the most frequent is defective germ plasm. I heard a learned professor explain the concept of defective germ plasm to a distinguished society of obstetricians and gynecologists in this homely fashion. He drew from his vest pockets several unopened pods of garden peas. "Now, gentlemen," he said, "I can present to you a visual example of defective germ plasm. I bought these on the way to this lecture and I dare say in almost every pod we shall find at least one runt placed among the full, large, normal peas." He cracked open two or three pods and, sure enough, in each pod there was a stunted pea among the seven or eight full-grown ones. "This, gentlemen," he said, "is a bad egg; this is defective germ plasm." Bad eggs occur throughout the whole vegetable and animal economy, from the dwarfed, shriveled, rotten plum among the green plums of the plum tree, to the fragmented, deteriorated fertilized egg washed from an oviduct attached to a freshly removed human uterus.

Defective germ plasm may be theoretically due to three different mechanisms; a serious chromosomal abnormality in the egg of the female or the sperm of the male; physicochemical mishap in the complicated reaction of fertilization, or finally some strictly environmental factor connected with the embedding and early development of the fertilized egg within the lining of the uterus. Perhaps in such a case a normal fertilized egg implants too superficially or too deeply, just like a seed or bulb planted too deeply or superficially in the soil. Or perhaps the maternal organism supplies inadequate food because of a deficient blood supply to the precise implantation site. Such causes of defective germ plasm are conjectural, and when we examine the result, the defective conceptus (fetus, egg membranes, and afterbirth), we have no way to determine which of the several mechanisms was actually involved.

The life history of a typical ten-to-eleven-week abortion caused by defective germ plasm progresses as follows: Pregnancy commences as usual ten to fourteen days after the onset of the menses, but it is likely to be peculiarly free of symptoms. There is the usual failure to menstruate when the missed menstrual period is due, but breast enlargement is inclined to be minimal. Nausea and vomiting are likely absent or, if present, they, too, are minimal. The pregnancy continues to progress for three to four weeks, then development ceases and the whole conceptus dies. The patient feels very non-pregnant. Her breasts may even become smaller again, and if there was nausea it is likely to disappear. The dead conceptus is carried without incident for four or five weeks longer, and then a brownish vaginal stain appears. Within twenty-four to seventy-two hours some fresh bleeding may commence, and soon lower abdominal cramps begin. Clots now pass from the vagina, and later a plum-sized, firm mass—the pregnancy—is expelled. If such is the case, the whole unpleasant episode is over. If bleeding and pain continue, hospital admission may be necessary to carry out curettage, loosening with a tiny hoe from the interior of the uterus the dead and partially fragmented conceptus.

When examined, defective-germ-plasm abortions show varying degrees of imperfection. The fetus or embryo may never have been present at all, and only a thin-walled sac filled with clear fluid is expelled. The English, with their fine sense for our common language, term this degree of imperfection a "blighted ovum." At the other end of the scale one may find a normal placenta with intact membranes containing fluid and a dead, well-formed, partially deteriorated embryo. The embryo, however, instead of being firm and slightly transparent, is soft, and opaque, with shreds of tissue peeling off.

In contrast to the defective-germ-plasm abortion is the abortion of a perfectly normal conceptus. Examination reveals a sac containing clear fluid attached at its base to a shaggy chestnut-bur-like placenta (afterbirth). That is, when the placenta is immersed in liquid the normal protrusions from the surface, called villi, stand forth like the spicules of a chestnut bur. Within the sac is a firm, semi-transparent, perfectly formed, smooth-skinned embryo.

On the basis of a series of aborted pregnancies examined by two authoritative laboratories, that of the Boston Lying In Hospital and the Carnegie Embryologic Institute of Johns Hopkins, approximately 70 per cent of all spontaneous abortions are due to defective germ plasm. This means that among spontaneous abortions three or four abnormal, dead ones are expelled to each normal, fresh one in a living or recently dead state.

The next problem is what causes the 30 per cent of abortions which result in the extrusion of completely normal membranes, placenta, and embryo. It is obvious that in such cases some factor within the uterus or without either causes it to contract prematurely and squeeze out its immature contents, or the sac of membrances which contains the embryo floating in its protective fluid to rupture. In such a case the fluid which is constantly being formed drains out continually and after a highly variable time—hours, days, or weeks —the uterus undergoes contractions and expels the whole contents. Many instances remain unexplained, while for others we know the causes. Many people think that physical violence is a common cause for abortion. This is not the case. I have been called to the hospital accident room more than once to examine a woman who had been "kicked in the stomach by a gentleman friend." The bruise was there, but the pregnancy remained undisturbed. I heard of a woman who jumped from a cliff to produce abortion. She fractured both legs but delivered a normal child at term. One of my patients, a ballerina at a night club, invited me to watch her perform when she was four months pregnant. All I can say is that watching her cavort reinforced my faith in the belief that you can't shake a good egg loose any more than a storm can shake unripe normal fruit from a tree. A careful study was recently reported from a naval hospital comparing the abortion rate among wives who remained at the base throughout pregnancy and those who traveled about in early pregnancy. There was an insignificantly lower abortion rate among those who traveled. It made no difference whether travel was by automobile, airplane, or train. The reader may question this because he knows someone who aborted while traveling. It is difficult to separate cause from coincidence in medical happenings. Violence or unusual physical exertion may occasionally precipitate the actual expulsive phase in the abortion of a defective, already dead conceptus, but it must be extremely rare for it to initiate the abortion of a normally developing embryo.

If physical activity does not cause the abortion of a normal conceptus, what does? Abnormalities of the reproductive organs may: certain cases of fibroid tumors of the uterus, deep tears of the cervix (mouth of the womb), or scarring from previous operations on the cervix, rarely an incorrect position of the uterus. Multiple pregnancies, twins or triplets, are prone to terminate in abortion. Excessive amnioic fluid within the uterus (hydramnios) is another cause. Severe maternal illness, especially infections such as pneumonia, may bring on abortion. Syphilis, however, does not cause abortion; untreated, it is likely to cause the birth of a dead, premature infant; properly treated, it results in a normal-term child. In addition to the causes enumerated there are many others we as yet know nothing about. We can find no explanation for a majority of normal-appearing abortions. Normal abortion in contrast to the defective-germ-plasm variety is commonly a late abortion, usually in the fourth or fifth month. Frequently the first inkling the patient has is the unexpected rupture of the bag of waters.

SUPERSTITIONS ABOUT ABORTIONS

There is an immense amount of misinformation regarding abortion. So far as doctors know, there is no proven tendency for abortion to occur particularly at the time of the missed menstrual period. Shock, grief, or fear rarely if ever causes abortion. Fresh paint has no selective action in disturbing an early pregnancy. Stretching, stooping, bending, or pedaling the sewing machine does not unhouse the embryo. Sexual intercourse, in the absence of any abnormality in the woman's reproductive tract, will not bring about abortion. Such iconoclastic statements are hard for many people to accept because they know of a case in which thus and so happened. Let me remind you again that it is difficult to separate cause from coincidence in medical happenings.

CARE OF ABORTION

As soon as a pregnant woman stains or bleeds she reports to her physician at once. In each one hundred women who commence pregnancy, thirty will stain or bleed at some time before the seventh month. Of the thirty who will stain or bleed, ten will abort and twenty will continue pregnant as though nothing ever happened. The doctor does not know to which group a patient belongs except by the actual outcome; however, he tries to guess from the history and the findings on examination. If the bleeding occurs about the time of the first missed period it may be an abbreviated menses during early pregnancy, a perfectly normal occurrence. Then, too, the bleeding may arise from some abnormality of the cervix, such as inflammation or perhaps a polyp, a small tassel-like growth protruding from the mouth of the womb. If, however, the bleeding is significant enough to stain a pad thoroughly in an hour, then abortion is probably threatening. Since the doctor can't be sure whether it is the 70 per cent germ-plasm variety which threatens or the 30 per cent regrettable termination of a normal pregnancy, he is truly on the horns of a dilemma. He really has two problems: first, he does not know whether it is incidental bleeding of little importance or whether abortion impends; then, too, he does not know whether the abortion is the variety he wants to try to save—the normal-pregnancy type—or whether it is the type he wants to aid in expelling—the defective-germ-plasm variety. Not knowing what to do, most doctors treat all types of pregnancy bleeding as though each patient were on the verge of aborting a normal conceptus. They argue that if it is insignificant bleeding it will stop anyway and treatment will do no harm. If it is faulty germ plasm no medicines will forestall abortion, but if it is the threatened abortion of a normal embryo treatment may do some good.

Treatment consists of bed rest, the administration of Vitamin E by mouth and several hormones, body chemicals, either by mouth or hypodermic. Vitamin E is the substance which is so important in the proper implantation of the rat embryo, though as yet necessity in human pregnancy remains more suspected than proved. Several hormones may be given: progesterone, estrone, and thyroid. Progesterone is a chemical manufactured by the ovary during the first few months and then by the placenta, the afterbirth. It has a soothing action in preventing the uterus from contracting. Estrone, another placenta chemical, is supposed to aid the uterus in the utilization of the progesterone, and it is also supposed to increase the blood supply to the decidua, the lining of the uterus. Thyroid medication stimulates general metabolism, and in so doing sort of tunes up the other glands of internal secretion. The old horse-and-buggy treatment of ice bag and morphine by injection has been displaced by vitamin and hormone combinations.

If the bleeding becomes intense, resulting in the passage of large clots, curettage, the cleaning out of the uterus, is considered mandatory. Sometimes abortion is incomplete—part of the pregnancy tissue is passed and part remains behind in the uterus. If this occurs, curettage must also be performed.

Spontaneous abortion has acquired an unjustifiably dangerous reputation because of its kinship and confusion with its nefarious cousin, illegal abortion. The spontaneous variety almost never invalids and rarely if ever kills, particularly today, with transfusion available to combat blood loss and antibiotics to combat infection.

The question of how soon the patient who aborts may attempt pregnancy again is answered differently by different doctors. Three thousand and forty-two physicians stated their views in reply to a recent questionnaire which I sent them. The average physician advised his patient to wait 6.6 months before trying again; some permitted immediate reimpregnation, while others required a year to elapse.

In my own practice I have two answers. If the abortion was of the defective-germ-plasm variety I allow immediate reimpregnation. At the same time a basal metabolism is taken and thyroid prescribed if indicated. On the other hand, if the abortion resulted in the expulsion of a normal conceptus the patient is gone over completely to try to elicit the cause. If one is found, correction is attempted and then the green light is flashed. If no cause is found, I advise that she wait six months before abandoning contraceptives, in the hope that during this interval the unknown factor will correct itself.

THERAPEUTIC ABORTION

Therapeutic abortion is the legal termination of pregnancy by artificial means before the baby is viable, because some serious health complication of the mother is sufficiently aggravated by continuation of pregnancy to threaten her life or further impair her health. In this country therapeutic abortion is sanctioned by all major religious groups except the Catholics. They will not sanction therapeutic abortion even in an attempt to save a mother's life, though refusal is certain to cause the death of the mother of several living children. The Roman Church does not recognize any exceptions.

In the United States laws regarding therapeutic abortion vary slightly from one state to the next but in essence are much alike, being patterned after the English Abortion Act of 1860. In substance, abortion can be legally produced only if two physicians who have been in practice for five years or longer and who are in good standing attest in writing that continuation of pregnancy would place in jeopardy the life of the mother. Previously the only conditions which were believed to merit therapeutic abortion were serious organic diseases of the heart, lungs, or kidneys, or incessant and life-threatening vomiting of early pregnancy. Several years ago the interpretation of jeopardy was broadened to include the mind, so that women who have true depressions, hallucinatory states, and other abnormal mental conditions are now frequently aborted. In many communities further liberalization has occurred so that eugenic indications are included. For example, a woman who produces hemophiliac sons (males with uncontrollable bleeding tendencies) or the pregnant woman who acquires German measles (rubella) during the first twelve weeks of pregnancy is considered a fit candidate for therapeutic abortion. In about 30 per cent of the latter cases the child is born with a very serious abnormality: congenital cataracts of the lens of the eye, a malformed heart, or microcephaly—a form of idiocy in which the head is tiny. The long list of eugenic indications is not well standardized, and the same conditions may be considered grounds for therapeutic abortion by one doctor and rejected by another.

It is difficult to state what proportion of total pregnancies necessitates therapeutic termination. The criteria for interruption are so different from one doctor to the next, or one hospital to the next. Most medical authors who have written on this subject feel that an incidence as high as one in every 150 pregnancies is probably justified for teaching institutions with referred problem cases, while in the strictly private hospital the incidence should probably be no higher than one in 250.

Abortion may not be done with the sanction of the law simply because a woman wishes it or because of economic or social factors, no matter how dire. I learned this early in my obstetrical career, when in charge of an obstetrical outpatient clinic. A social agency referred a little twelve-year-old who had been impregnated by her own father. The father had been arrested, tried, and sentenced to the penitentiary. I was young and naïve and greatly outraged at the thought that this little helpless girl must bear her own father's bastard. The Chief of Service agreed to allow abortion if I could get a letter from the state's attorney authorizing it. I tried, I failed, and she bore her father's child.

In England some progress has been made through the famous trial of the Crown versus Dr. Alec Bourne. A sixteen-year-old unmarried girl was seized and raped by three soldiers. Pregnancy resulted. Dr. Bourne aborted the victim on the public wards of a London hospital, notified the Crown's counsel, and asked to be arrested. A three-day trial followed. His lawyers contended that the law could be construed not only to protect the mother's physical life but her mental and emotional life as well. Courageous Dr. Bourne was acquitted by the jury.

One of the difficulties about the problem of therapeutic abortion is the inequable distribution of the procedure. In borderline cases—and all too frequently in cases which are not even borderline—the patient's prestige and money are very vocal in getting an undesired pregnancy terminated. I am loath to admit it, but far too often a minor difficulty is stretched into a major abnormality for the right person. In order to negate this factor of personal influence many hospitals have set up abortion boards to consider all requests for therapeutic abortion, private and ward. At the Mount Sinai Hospital in New York, where I work, the chiefs of the five major services—medicine, surgery, pediatrics, neuropsychiatry, and obstetrics-gynecology—make up the board and consider each request for termination of pregnancy very earnestly. The board is privileged to call experts from other departments to help them arrive at a proper decision. If any member of the committee of five opposes the abortion, interruption is disallowed.

Therapeutic abortion is carried out as a vaginal operation if pregnancy is thirteen weeks or less. It is either done in one stage under an anesthetic by dilating the mouth of the womb with instruments and then loosening and scraping out the pregnant contents, or in two stages. In this case the cervix and uterus are first packed tight with gauze, followed twenty-four hours later by curettage. The operation is done in a hospital under appropriate anesthesia. If the pregnancy is more than three months, most doctors prefer to empty the uterus via the abdominal route. A miniature Caesarean section is done—the abdomen is incised, the front of the uterus cut open, its pregnant contents removed, the womb sewn together again, and finally the abdominal incision repaired.

ILLEGAL ABORTION

Illegal abortion presents one of the most important and yet one of the least studied problems of modern medicine. There are many conjectures but few known facts. This is borne out by a consideration of its incidence. In 1936 the late Dr. Frederick Taussig, in his authoritative book, *Abortion*, concluded that there was one abortion to every 2.5 births in the urban communities of this country and one abortion in every five in the rural areas, yielding a total of 681,600 abortions annually, an abortion rate of 22 per

100 pregnancies. Since the spontaneous abortion rate is approximately 10 per 100, this means that 12 per cent of the total pregnancies in the United States, according to Taussig, are terminated by illegal interference. Stix, in her 1935 study of pregnancy wastage among patients living in the Bronx, reports an illegal abortion rate of 22 per cent, while two years later Wiehl and Berry, in a study of a population sample from the five boroughs of New York City, report a rate of only 4 per cent. Thus we have three competent studies with illegal abortion rates varying from 4 to 22 per cent of all pregnancies.

Illegal abortion not only presents medical problems of grave importance, but other problems of equal magnitude. Here are some of the high lights in the realm of medical sociology. Wiehl and Berry report a high induced-abortion rate for third and fourth pregnancies in women of the low-income group. Taussig writes: "The vast majority of all abortions, equaling 90 per cent, occur among married women, especially those between 25 and 35 years of age who have had several children. The recent increase in abortion has been primarily in this group." Other investigations conclude that 85 per cent of the women resorting to illegal abortion are married, 12 per cent single, and 3 per cent widowed. Both Stix and Taussig find that the rate among Protestants, Catholics, and Jews is approximately equal. According to the study by Stix, 75 per cent of illegal abortions are induced by persons designated as doctors by the patients, 19 per cent by midwives, and 6 per cent self-induced. Taussig states that more than 50 per cent are performed by doctors, 20 per cent by midwives, and less than 30 per cent by the patient herself. It is most important for American medicine to admit existence of the problem, a problem which cannot be cured by present prohibitory laws and halfhearted moral censure.

Fisher in 1954 arrived at the conservative estimate of at least 330,000 illegal abortions each year in the United States. He states that less than one thousand convictions occur annually for this offense. He points out that no other felonious act is as free from punishment as criminal abortion.

DANGERS OF ILLEGAL ABORTION

The dangers of illegal abortion are twofold, psychic and physical. It is a degrading, soul-searing experience for many women, partly because of the kind of people usually involved in its performance and also its clandestine nature. It is an experience which is slow to be forgotten. Then, too, the presence of loved children within a home are constant reminders of the child who could have been and is not. I know many a patient who has deep regrets for the impetuous step she took. In one instance the mother of three sons was persuaded by her husband to have an illegal abortion. The constant remorse and regret turned a physically happy marriage into virtually an asexual friendship. The physical dangers of illegal abortion are death or infection, the latter ending in sterility by sealing the oviducts closed.

The mathematical likelihood for either danger is in proportion to the skill of the abortionist. Dr. Frederick Taussig observed legalized abortion when he visited Russia before 1935. At this time the Russians claimed a death rate in their hospital abortions of five per 200,000, a much lower figure than in their non-hospitalized abortions. However, Dr. Taussig finally pares down the slightly optimistic appearing Russian claim to ten deaths per 100,000. This is the best possible figure extant for therapeutic abortions. Since they are done legally far less frequently in this country than they were in Russia, when abortion was within the law, the United States figure even in the hands of the best clinics would probably not equal this. The real death rate in the hands of ill-trained, illegal-abortion performing doctors, or the granny-type midwife, is probably extremely high though whatever figure one gives is a poor guess. The death rate is probably not high in the hands of the well-trained big-scale illegal medical abortionist. Many of them have the skill and the physical plant necessary to get good results. No unprejudiced, sound investigation has ever been made in this country or western Europe of the volume, methods, social implications, or results of the large-scale, expert illegal abortionist. Such unbiased research is in order.

Of course the most dangerous variety is the abortion performed by the patient on herself. All varieties of implements are used: hatpins, hairpins, slippery elm sticks, long feathers, etc. The most popular is the bougie, a tapered firm rubber tube which can be purchased by a woman in almost any drugstore. Tragically enough, some women die from self-induced abortions who are not even pregnant. I witnessed such an autopsy; the woman had poked a fatal hole in her uterus, but there wasn't the slightest evidence of pregnancy, recent or remote.

Emmenagogue or abortifacient drugs which are sold by the carload are perfectly useless. Both the legitimate and fly-by-night drug houses peddle pills which are supposed "to bring a woman around." They contain ergot and various vegetable compounds, but if the woman is really pregnant, with a normal well-implanted egg, she can swallow them to the point of self-poisoning without effect. If she has a bad egg and is on the verge of a spontaneous abortion the drugs may conceivably bring it about a few hours earlier. If she is not pregnant at all and swallows her twenty black pills with a teaspoonful of water and a glass full of faith it may bring on normal menstruation. The action is through the release of the inhibiting brain censor, fear of pregnancy rather than pregnancy having caused her to fail to menstruate in the first place. The federal government, by virtue of the Pure Food and Drug Act, has launched a campaign against the continued sale of such fake menstrual-producing prescriptions.

So far as is known, nothing by mouth or injection will cause a pregnant woman to abort. The only method yet found is the use of some mechanical agent, such as curettage, the dangerous injection into the uterus of an irritating chemical, or the temporary introduction into the uterus of some foreign body, such as a bougie or slippery elm stick.

Abortion is a chapter in medicine which still has many blank pages and other pages which social progress must and will rewrite.

PART THREE

Conception, Pregnancy and Childbirth

Chapter 1

ARE YOU GOING TO HAVE A BABY?

by Janet Fowler Nelson, Ph.D.
VICE-PRESIDENT, AMERICAN ASSOCIATION OF MARRIAGE COUNSELORS

One may equally well pose the question, "Are you going to have a family?" For there are no childless families; there are only childless marriages. Why are you going to have a baby? When are you going to have a baby?

There is no single time or place which is simply and exclusively reserved for consideration of "having a baby." From earliest childhood, by the very process of being reared in a family, growing up in a community of families, a young couple have been thoroughly conditioned to the idea of family life. Too often they accept the pattern without further intellectual or emotional examination. They expect to grow up, to get married, to have a baby. "It's the thing to do."

Perhaps there is no other single human experience more rewarding or richer in human values. But the full benefit is achieved only by thoughtful and responsible appreciation of these values. What should be one of the most thoughtful decisions of early married life is often, at best, casual acceptance of an established pattern—a pattern reinforced in today's culture by the oversentimentalization of the mother-baby stereotype. The unreality and sentimentality of much of our escape literature distorts the baby picture as surely as it does "love's young dream in a white cottage, complete with rambler roses and the newest in washing machines"! However, both editorially and advertising-wise, there is a hopeful tendency in some of our current women's publications to present a more responsible and realistic picture, as witness the increasing use of professional consultants on magazine staffs.

Ability to understand and weigh the economic and health aspects of childbearing and child rearing, and insight and appreciation of the emotional factors involved, are essential to really responsible parenthood. Dr. O. Spurgeon English, professor of psychiatry at the Temple University

Medical School, remarks: "Parenthood seems to make more demands upon the present-day adult than he is prepared to accept. A study of the needs of infants and children indicates that they must have interest, affection, and time spent with them, which, if given in adequate amounts, conflicts with the tempo of our busy world and the desire for adults to get more out of life for themselves." Baby bookkeeping, therefore, must be written in three columns: psychological, economic, and medical.

First, the psychological factors involved are vitally important. From the point of view of the baby, we recognize increasingly the importance of being wanted and loved, of being assured of that element of unearned love which parents give their children and which is such an essential element in their subsequent emotional development. From the parents' point of view, planning to have a baby is itself a measure of their marriage. It certainly requires a high degree of emotional maturity. It is an affirmation of faith. Lawrence K. Frank, writing in the *Journal of Heredity*, states it thus: ". . . planned parenthood is an affirmation—made deliberately and jointly by a man and a woman, who see in childbearing a way of affirming their personal and social values, signifying the importance of love, and courageously projecting those beliefs into the future."

Just as there is increasing emphasis on father participation in the "great event," during pregnancy and even in the delivery room itself, according to Dr. Earle Marsh in a recent talk before the American Association of Marriage Counselors, so too one cannot emphasize too strongly the imperative of beginning this sharing experience in the planning stage. It has been suggested that it would be highly advantageous for everybody concerned to talk, not about the pregnant woman, but the pregnant family. The relationship between husband and wife, lines of emotional sensitivity and appreciation and response, should be, not weakened by a new focus on a baby, but strengthened.

A period of initial marital adjustment then, prior to undertaking a first pregnancy, is almost always desirable. Current statistics indicate that childless marriages are most likely to end in divorce. Such figures have sometimes lent themselves to the argument that having children prevents divorce. Ergo—why worry about early marital adjustment? Just have a baby and all will be well. One can as easily argue, of course, that it's the happy couples who have babies. The others have divorces. There is no argument, however, among psychologists who are concerned with total personality integration and satisfying family relationships. They agree that cold-bloodedly having a baby to trick a recalcitrant husband or wife into a legally more permanent relationship is likely to be a boomerang to the integrity of the marriage relationship itself and downright cruel and devastating to the child. Having a baby is neither an escape from an untenable marriage relationship nor an insurance policy against divorce. It is a fulfillment of a couple's desire to have a home of their own. And it takes time to establish that "home." People must have time to work out their own personal adjustments, to establish firmly the Mr. and Mrs. relationship, to dig roots of emotional security sufficiently deep to withstand the many adjustments, many of them trivial, some of them more serious, and all of them significant, of pregnancy and early infancy.

Just as the marriage adjustment itself is related to the previous emotional experience of each person as well as to their premarital love relationship, so some of their appreciation and a beginning of their initial acceptance of parenthood go back to their days of courtship and engagement. Many research studies indicate that similarity of background and interest contributes to successful marriage adjustment. One of the most important of these factors is mutual acceptance of the normal family pattern. From an individual point of view, there must be acceptance of individual masculine and feminine roles.

HEALTH VALUES

Psychological values, however, are not the only ones to be explored prior to pregnancy, or to marriage itself. Health is essentially important. Elsewhere in this book the importance of the premarital examination has been noted. This medical examination of the young wife will have revealed any structural deviations or major organic weaknesses of the heart, lungs, kidneys, or blood. And both husband and wife should have a clear bill of health on venereal infection or such hereditary diseases as tuberculosis, for instance. All these factors should be rechecked before a pregnancy is actually embarked on, especially if any length of time has intervened. The chapters on pregnancy and childbirth and on the premarital examination itself indicate the medical implications of these factors; they are merely noted here to reinforce the suggestion that the health of the mother particularly must be recognized as of paramount importance and considered prior to pregnancy. Also discussed elsewhere is the whole problem of fertility.

Part of the general health picture is the question of age. It is increasingly troublesome in our country, which seems to put a premium on late rather than early marriage because of educational and economic factors. However, both psychological and undisputed medical authorities point to the advantage of having children while still young. Our best authority teaches that the decade between twenty and thirty in a woman's life is the optimum period for childbearing. This does not mean, however, that with wise and competent medical care women over thirty run undue risk. Dr. Mary Calderone, Medical Director of the Planned Parenthood Federation of America, says: ". . . women have safely borne children toward the end of the child-bearing cycle." Dr. Ashley Montague, in his recent book, *Adolescent Sterility,* points out the further fact that neither is too young childbearing to be desired, for it incurs increased risks for both mother and baby. The establishment of nubility, and not just menstruation, is the measure of physical readiness for childbearing.

ECONOMIC PROBLEMS

"It's not the original cost, it's the upkeep!" In income brackets from $5,000–$10,000 the total cost of bringing up a child to the age of eighteen averaged slightly more than $20,000 in 1947; in 1955 the figure will be substantially higher. (Of course cash in hand is no more essential here than prepayment of eighteen years' rent, but neither is it to be disregarded.) Proportionate to the total income, the cost is less in lower income brackets. However, this is offset by the fact that, statistically speaking, it's the low-income groups that have the largest families. Further, in terms of long-time planning, they are not only economic liabilities in themselves but constitute a hazard to other members of the family, in terms of availability of housing and similar factors. The advertisement currently much quoted isn't really awfully funny: "Wanted—a place to live by couple with five months' old baby of great sentimental value. Prefer to keep child if possible. Will drown if necessary to get roof over our heads."

The initial cost, however, is not to be lost sight of and is an immediate and practical consideration. Having a baby costs money, but not as much as you might think. Group hospital and medical insurance plans have helped to lower the cost of having a baby. Most private physicians are willing to base their fees on the earning capacity of the parents, charging in each case what they are able to pay. Many of them encourage a "pay-as-you-go" plan during the time before the baby is born, so that the cost is spread over a number of months instead of being paid in a lump sum. Also, during the past few years, excellent maternal health clinics have been established throughout the country, many operated at state or city expense. Ask your doctor, health department, or health agencies about the hospitals and other facilities in your community.

Costs for maternity care differ in various parts of the country. In some communities $40 or $50 may cover everything—in others it may cost several hundred dollars. Find out about physician and hospital fees in your community early so you can make whatever plans or arrangements are needed.

Careful planning for the necessary day-to-day budget increases—food, clothing, and transportation—as well as the cost of original equipment must be taken into account. Health and medical care for the new baby must be provided for. And don't forget the occasional "sitter" when the parents desire an evening out.

HER JOB?

One further important and very specific decision, inclusive of health, economic, and psychological values, which many young couples face at this time, is the question of the wife's job. An over-all philosophy of her relationship to the marriage partnership, in the home and/or on the job, will have been arrived at in many discussions during the engagement period and in the first months of marriage. However, this is the point where the question ceases to be philosophical and becomes intensely practical.

From an economic point of view, at the same time that initial expense is at its peak, day-to-day income, for a shorter or longer time, is reduced by the margin of the wife's earnings. Both these factors must be considered and provided for, budget-wise.

Even more important is the health of the working wife who is pregnant. Many job adjustments can and should be made. For instance, at the business or professional level, extensive travel is "out." In industrial occupations, pregnant women should be given lighter and more sedentary work whenever possible. Types of occupations which should be considered undesirable for them include those which require heavy lifting, continuous standing or moving about, reaching, or marked vibration. Hours of work are important too—no more than eight hours a day or forty-eight hours a week. A forty-hour week is preferable. And in terms of her domestic responsibilities, she needs very practical help. Cynical observers have remarked that working wives work not at one job, but at two. Never a desirable situation, during pregnancy it becomes imperative that strain and fatigue be guarded against. Happily this is a very practical area for husbandly co-operation.

The whole question of maternity leaves must also be considered. We are used to thinking of these in terms of the job security and economic advantage they offer. Important as these considerations are, an intelligent policy on maternity leaves is equally important to the health, the physical and psychological health, of the young mother. The minimum length of leave before delivery is two months. Many doctors are urging that this be increased. Similarly, the minimum leave after childbirth should be two months—or more.

The "or more" is particularly significant from a psychological point of view. The period of adjustment following childbirth is important physically. It is also a highly important period of emotional and marital adjustment. To achieve a sturdy and sound "family relationship" takes sensitiveness and insight, to be sure. It also takes time. Nor must the baby's psychological needs be neglected. The need and importance of a close mother-child relationship in early infancy is being increasingly recognized by the psychiatrists. Two years, three years, seven years, etc., have been variously noted in the literature as the critical, crucial years of a child's emotional development. To the extent this is related to a woman's job, the decision, mutually arrived at, as to just when the mother should resume her occupation, is one of the most important a young couple makes. It is quite true that the literal amount of time spent at home is not the single measure—quality of relationship, not quantity, is our concern. Again one suggests the three criteria, this time including the baby: psychological values, economic need, and health.

MULTIPLE CHILDREN

All these factors—health, economic, and psychological—are equally, perhaps even more, important the second or third or fourth time you are asked the question, "Are you going to have a baby?" They are important in terms of the same practical as well as psychological adjustments which the parents face. But something new has been added: the health, the economic well-being, and the emotional, psychological adjustment of the older child or children must be evaluated.

TIME BETWEEN PREGNANCIES

The important factor of time between pregnancies must be considered. Medical research indicates that adequate spacing is important not only to the mother's health or the new baby's, but, as measured by statistics, important also to the health of the preceding child. The mother who has a second baby too soon may diminish the adequacy of the health care that she can give the first baby.

In round figures, a two-year interval between births is usually suggested. Dr. Alan Guttmacher of Johns Hopkins University reported a poll of some three thousand physicians whose collective opinion is that "the average medically desirable interval from the termination of one pregnancy to the beginning of the next is 14.1 months, which means a medically desirable interval between babies of 23 months." His report further adds, "With the previous pregnancy terminating in miscarriage, the average physician advises patients to wait six months before trying again."

From an economic point of view—as in planning the first child—the same factors of initial cost as well as day-to-day budget increases have to be considered. There is, to be sure, some saving in equipment and clothing that can be "handed down," but this slight saving will probably be more than compensated for by the fact that parents will have become aware by this time of the general wear and tear of the "patter of little feet."

However, important as practical factors of baby budget making may be, the psychological values for both parents and children inherent in belonging to a large family are numerous. The emotional hazards of being an only child have been frequently discussed. Growing up with older and younger brothers and sisters provides one of the most fertile fields for practical and practicing democracy. The family is our first laboratory in which to develop skills in dealing with difference—difference in age and sex, difference in physical and mental aptitudes and interests, difference in responsibility. The challenge is to avoid developing attitudes of scorn for and exploitation of difference, or the dullness of mediocrity which results from insensitivity to difference. Especially, from the point of view of a democratic society, the importance of being one of a large family lies in learning to appreciate difference and in using it constructively. From the point of view of a child's personal emotional development, it is the original seat of the green-eyed monster—for jealousy of shared affection, of special privilege is universal and perfectly normal. Yet family life carries within its own framework the potential correctives of this particular expression of emotional insecurity. As Dorothy Baruch points out, "Love is the best antidote for jealousy. Where love is rich and plentiful, a person is fortified against pettiness, against envy, against smallness and uncalled-for hurt."

Preoccupied as we have been with the social and emotional development of the child, we often fail to note that the emotional strain on the (over) conscientious parent is considerable. In a day when some parents have become self-conscious and fearful of their personal responsibility for their children's development, it does not ease the situation to have all one's eggs in one basket. Families used to be able to afford at least one black sheep; we don't have even that doubtful privilege today. Parents are really less able to evaluate the progress and development of one child than if they have several. They have more time, to be sure, but exclusive preoccupation does not lend itself to objectivity, nor have they, within their own family group, any practical basis for comparison.

The relation of children to each other is another consideration. However, much of the strength of that relationship will depend on the extent to which they participate in the planning for the arrival of each new brother and sister.

For the very young child there is little in specific overt planning that can be done; the vocabulary range of a two-year-old is itself somewhat limited. However, development of attitudes and emotional sensitivity is not limited by verbal expression. The exposure method is helpful here. The very young child is not going to resent or question the addition of a baby brother or sister to nearly the same extent if he is used to seeing other people's babies, other people's preoccupation with them if you will, his own mother's pleasure in the arrival of the baby next door. Just as wise parents make a special effort after their own new baby arrives to make sure that their first little fellow feels especially loved and secure, so can the child learn, before the event, that sharing his mother's attention—for an afternoon, say, when together they take over Aunt Mary's youngest—is no fundamental threat to him. At best, however, this is a learning process and it takes time. It is a fortunate child whose parents are sufficiently wise to accept expression of the fear and uncertainty and even hostility that a little fellow feels when baby sister arrives.

Older children, to a degree corresponding to their own physical and emotional development, will actively participate in planning ahead for the new baby's arrival. Having a new baby in one's own family is one of the healthiest and happiest opportunities for sex education. Also, advance familiarity with the actual material adjustments that must be made—provision for sleeping and bathing, for example—removes much of the shock of displacement which is itself a contributory factor to emotional disturbance.

There is, too, for the older child who participates and shares in wanting and welcoming a new baby, sometimes a faint glimmering of giving—of not always being just on the receiving end of unearned love. Conflict and the rough-and-tumble of children growing up together are not eliminated, nor should one wish or expect it to be, but there is something soul-satisfying about viewing the turbulence of normal family life against the fleeting picture of the little girl who, sitting near her father as she uncertainly holds the new baby for the first time, looks up at him and says, "Daddy, now I know what it is to love someone."

Chapter 2

HEREDITY: FACTS AND FALLACIES

by Warren P. Spencer, Ph.D.
DEPARTMENT OF BIOLOGY, COLLEGE OF WOOSTER, WOOSTER, OHIO

Heredity is the study of the likenesses and differences between parents and children and the way in which these are transmitted. The bodies of all higher plants and animals, including man, are made up of many cells. In the average man there are about thirty million million red blood cells and in his brain about fourteen thousand million nerve cells. Yet each human being developed from a single fertilized egg cell formed by the union of one sperm and one egg cell. In each cell there is a small body, generally spherical or oval in shape, the nucleus, which contains the material known as chromatin. This substance is the physical basis of heredity. While the human egg cell is much larger than the sperm, this difference in size is due to the cytoplasm, the part of the cell not included in the nucleus. The bulk of the sperm cell is nuclear material. All of the sperm cells from which the approximately two and one half billion human beings now living on the world developed, if brought together, would form a mass not much larger than an aspirin tablet. Thus all of the physical hereditary material which went into the formation of the living members of the human race would form a mass of material approximately the size of two and one half aspirin tablets. This tiny physical bridge carries the total of the hereditary factors from one generation to the next.

The fertilized egg cell from which each of us developed contained within its nucleus forty-eight tiny rod-shaped bodies of chromatin: the chromosomes. The chromosomes occurred in pairs, one of each pair contributed by the sperm cell and the other by the egg cell. This cell underwent many successive divisions, eventually resulting in the myriad cells which make up the adult body. At every cell division each of the forty-eight chromosomes became duplicated; every resulting cell therefore contained a complete set of chromosomes identical to those in the fertilized egg. During development the cytoplasm outside the nucleus of the cells became differentiated, resulting in the several tissues and organs of the body. In the ovaries of the female and the testes of the male certain cells, the primary sex cells, undergo a special type of division, resulting in a reduction of the chromosome number to twenty-four. Each sperm or egg cell contains one chromosome of each pair. This is in preparation for the union of the gamete, egg or sperm, with another gamete of the opposite sex to give forty-eight chromosomes in the nucleus of the fertilized egg or zygote. About half of the hereditary material, therefore, comes from one parent and half from the other parent.

MECHANISM OF SEX INHERITANCE

Among the twenty-four pairs of chromosomes in the male, one pair is different because the two members of the pair are of different size. The larger one is termed an X-chromosome, the smaller one a Y-chromosome. Therefore, at reduction division, half of the sperm cells receive an X and the other half a Y. In the female the corresponding pair of chromosomes are both X-chromosomes. Thus every egg receives an X-chromosome. When a Y-bearing sperm fertilizes an egg, the resulting zygote is XY and therefore male; when an X-bearing sperm unites with an egg, an XX zygote, a female, is formed. The sex of any child is thus determined by the type of sperm cell received from the father. On the basis of this mechanism, about half of the children conceived should be male, the other half female. Of course the sex distribution among the children of a family will be subject to the usual chance fluctuations observed when small samples are involved. Even in large families a certain small proportion of these will be expected to be all of one sex purely by chance.

THE GENES

Both the sex chromosomes, the X and Y, and the other twenty-three pairs, the autosomes, contain the ultimate units of heredity, the genes. The genes are minute bodies arranged in linear order in the chromosomes. As the chromosomes become duplicated at cell division, each gene becomes duplicated. Each gene occupies a definite position, its locus, within the chromosome. As the chromosomes occur in pairs, the genes also occur in pairs. By various methods the number of genes in a single chromosome set, such as occurs in egg or sperm, has been calculated for the fruit fly, *Drosophila,* to be about five thousand to ten thousand. The number of genes in a chromosome set in man is probably of the same order of magnitude.

While little is known as yet of the ultimate physical and chemical nature of the gene, significant researches in this field are being carried on in many laboratories. In the light of our present knowledge the gene is a relatively stable unit, which undergoes self-duplication at each cell division. On rare occasions a sudden change occurs in a gene. Such a change is known as a gene mutation. The new form of the gene is known as an allele of the original gene, and generally is stable and capable of reduplicating itself in the new mutated form. A given gene may mutate to more than one type of allele, thus forming a multiple allelic series. As each gene and its alternative types can occupy only one place or locus in a chromosome, only two alleles of a multiple allelic series can be present in a given individual, since the chromosomes and chromosome or gene loci occur in pairs. Furthermore, only one allele of the series can be present in a germ cell where the chromosomes occur singly. However, populations of individuals can carry all the members of a highly complex multiple allelic series.

The genes condition the characteristics of an organism. A given gene interacts with the rest of the genetic constitution of the individual and with the environment in the development of a given character. A certain character is not necessarily produced solely by the action of a given gene; but unit character differences are due to the differing effects of a gene and its allele. The gene make-up of an organism is known as its genotype, the expressed characters as the phenotype. Where the two genes of a pair are identical, the individual is said to be homozygous for the gene in question; conversely, an individual containing two different alleles at a certain locus in a pair of chromosomes is termed heterozygous. Any mutant gene which, when present in heterozygous form along with the usual or normal allele, conditions a change from the normal character is known as a dominant. Any mutant allele which must be present in homozygous form to condition the character change from the normal is known as a recessive. Some dominants, however, have a more extreme effect in homozygous than in heterozygous form. Any gene carried on the X- or Y-chromosome is termed sex-linked. The effects of such sex-linked genes may have nothing to do with primary or secondary sexual characters, but their distribution will be correlated with the distribution of the sex-determining chromosomes.

Only when a gene is present in alternative forms or alleles in a population or species can its existence be known. The rarer allele or the one which conditions a deviation from normal in character expression is considered the mutant gene. In some cases in which alternative alleles are both present in high frequency it is difficult or impossible to say which is the mutant and which the original gene from which it arose. Where a gene is located on an autosome, a chromosome other than the sex chromosomes, and must be present in homozygous form to have any observable effect, the gene is known as an autosomal recessive. In man autosomal recessives range in effect from those in which the phenotype is an extreme abnormality, lethal at or soon after birth, as infantile amaurotic idiocy, to those in which the phenotype is probably fully as viable and normal, though different, in quality or quantity, from that produced by the original dominant gene allele. The recessive, blue eyes, and the inability to taste the chemical phenyl-thio-carbamide are examples of such non-deleterious mutant types.

A few other recessives may be mentioned to illustrate the range of expression of such factors. Ichthyosis fetalis is a disease characterized by greatly thickened and deeply furrowed skin and abnormally shortened neck. The infant dies a few hours after birth. Such genes as this and infantile amaurotic idiocy are recessive lethals and always tranmitted by heterozygotes, parents who carry the lethal gene along with the normal dominant gene allele and are themselves normal. Fortunately mutant genes of this type are relatively rare, and there are few matings in which both parents are heterozygous, the necessary condition for the production of an affected infant. Phenylketonuria is inherited as a recessive. Affected persons are idiots or imbeciles, and quantities of phenylpyruvic acid are excreted in the urine. Deaf-mutism is a less serious condition sometimes inherited as a recessive. Alkaptonuria, another recessive, results in a failure to oxidize homogentisic acid, an intermediate product formed in normal protein metabolism. The urine of those with alkaptonuria darkens on standing. Arthritis sometimes develops as a by-product of this recessive. To complete this series of examples is albinism, in which affected persons lack normal pigment of skin, eyes, and hair and are somewhat less vigorous than normal individuals. Blue eyes and taste deficiency, mentioned above, are clear-cut but innocuous recessives, probably equal in vigor to normal or rather alternative types. This is a representative sample of human autosomal recessives. Many others grading from serious abnormalities to slight effects are known. A still larger series are thought to be recessives, although more data are required to make certain of their manner of inheritance.

An autosomal dominant gene may produce its effect in heterozygous condition. If the gene is fully penetrant—that is, always expressed in heterozygous condition—then it follows that in any family pedigree the phenotypic character never skips a generation. This is in definite contrast to recessives, which usually appear sporadically in pedigrees. The list of known autosomal dominants in man is larger than that of recessives, for any dominant mutant, however rare in the population, will be expressed in those persons who carry it. Here also a series of cases might be arranged according to the degree of abnormality produced. However, this series will not extend as far toward extremely gross abnormal, semi-lethal, and lethal types as the recessive series for the obvious reason that such mutants, if they occurred, would immediately be lost. The affected person carrying the mutant gene would be killed off before transmitting it to the next generation.

An example of an autosomal dominant apparently without deleterious effect is white forelock or "blaze," in which a streak or patch of white hair occurs on the head, sharply demarcated from the normal hair. Several dominants are known which affect the skeleton. Examples of these are brachydactyly, short fingers; polydactyly, extra fingers or toes, lobster-claw or split hand; and achondroplastic dwarfism. In the latter condition the trunk is of normal length, but arms and legs are short.

INHERITED NERVOUS DISEASES

Several serious diseases of the nervous system are inherited as dominants, in which the abnormal symptoms develop late in life. Such a dominant may appear to skip a generation in its transmission, as some persons carrying the gene may pass it on to the next generation and then die before the onset of the disease. Had these people lived long enough, the dominant abnormality would probably have developed. Creeping paralysis is an example. This condition generally manifests itself in the late fifties or the sixties, long after the normal reproductive period. Such genes, which have their abnormal phenotypic effects late in life, are not selected against in the population, as they are transmitted to the next generation by an individual before they have any lethal or deleterious effect on the individual carrier himself. Huntington's chorea, characterized by progressive mental deterioration, is another such dominant which has its onset in middle age.

The inherited nature of most dominants is relatively easy to determine from their high incidence in family pedigrees and the fact that they do not skip a generation in their manifestation. Where the dominant produces an extreme abnormal effect, either physical or mental, particularly if the effect is present at birth or develops early in life, it would seem preferable for anyone with the condition not to have children and risk passing the gene to them. The chance of any child of such an individual developing the same abnormality is one in two. For a well-expressed dominant with full penetrance, the chance of a normal individual who has a parent showing the abnormality passing this condition on to offspring is practically nil.

SEX-LINKED RECESSIVE CHARACTERS

In the human X-chromosome there is a region which has no homologue in the Y-chromosome. For gene loci in this part of the X there are no corresponding loci in the Y. Certain genes present in this part of the X are known as sex-linked recessives. The gene must be present in both X-chromosomes of the female to produce its characteristic phenotypic expression. However, in the male with only one X-chromosome, the gene, if present in this X, manifests itself, as the Y-chromosome carries no allele at this locus. Thus many more males than females in the population will show such sex-linked recessive characters. Red-green color blindness is an example. With a frequency of about 10 per cent color-blind to 90 per cent normal genes, roughly 10 per cent males and 1 per cent females are color-blind. For other sex-linked recessives the gene frequencies differ and the proportions of affected males and females consequently differ; but there are always more males than females showing the character. The gene for color blindness can be transmitted by a father only to his daughters, while a mother may transmit the gene to either sons or daughters. A color-blind boy always gets the gene from his mother, never from his father. This follows from the fact that his X-chromosome comes from the mother.

Hemophilia, hereditary bleeding, is a sex-linked recessive gene with a low frequency. Only affected males have been identified. Possibly the gene is so rare that homozygous females have not been produced. Possibly the homozygous condition is lethal in females.

Progressive muscular dystrophy of a certain type is inherited as a sex-linked recessive. The affected person shows a progressive degeneration of muscles beginning in the first decade of life. These hopeless cripples die at an early age. There is one chance in two that a normal sister of such an affected male carries this gene. If she marries and has a child there is one chance in eight that the child will be a male with this disease.

SEX-LINKED DOMINANTS

A few sex-linked dominants occur in man. The known sex-linked recessives in man are much more numerous than the sex-linked dominants. These recessives are easily discovered even though a particular recessive is rare, as they show up in any male carrying them. Probably mutant autosomal recessives in man are also more frequent than dominants, but are less often discovered because of their mode of inheritance. One example of a sex-linked dominant is a brownish discoloration of the enamel of the teeth. All the daughters, but none of the sons, of an affected man show the condition, as he passes his X-chromosome to daughters but not to sons.

The Y-chromosome carries a segment which is not represented by a homologous segment in the X. Genes in this segment are passed directly from father to son, and all sons of an affected father will be expected to show the character. One such gene conditions webbed toes. In the pedigree males alone are affected. These exclusively Y-borne genes are much fewer than the sex-linked genes carried in the X-chromosomes.

INHERITED BLOOD FACTORS

Several inherited blood factors are of practical interest. The blood groups A, AB, B, and O are inherited as a system of triple alleles. In the presence of the gene A in either heterozygous or homozygous condition human red blood cells contain the antigen A. The gene A^B in heterozygous or homozygous condition results in the red-cell antigen B. The gene a is recessive to the other two, and when this gene is homozygous, neither antigen A nor B is present. Thus the blood group O, absence of both antigens, has the genotype aa; blood group AB has the genotype AA^B; blood group A, the genotype AA or Aa; and blood group B, the genotype A^BA^B or A^Ba. These antigens react with the antibodies in blood plasma to cause clumping or agglutination of the red cells. It so happens that those antibodies are always present in blood which can be present without causing red-cell agglutination. When blood transfusions are given, the antigen-antibody reactions of donor and recipient blood must be guarded against by proper matching of blood groups. For some years an additional allele has been known in this series which results in a weaker A antigen antibody reaction.

THE RH FACTOR

Some year ago Karl Landsteiner and A. S. Wiener discovered an important pair of alleles in human bloods, the dominant rhesus factor, Rh, and its recessive, rh. When an rh-negative woman, rh rh genotype, carries an Rh-positive fetus, Rh rh genotype, an antibody is often produced in her blood in response to the presence of the Rh antigen in the blood of the fetus. This antibody accumulates slowly, but in certain cases, particularly second or third pregnancies of this type, enough of the antibody from the mother's blood passes over into the fetal blood to set up a violent reaction, involving destruction and agglutination of fetal red cells. The baby is born with a complex of symptoms, including severe anemia. The condition is known as erythroblastosis fetalis and is frequently fatal unless a transfusion of rh-negative blood is given soon after birth. J. B. S. Haldane has stated that the Rh gene is perhaps responsible for more infant mortality than all other known hereditary factors combined. The white population of the U.S.A. shows a frequency of about 60 per cent Rh genes to 40 per cent of alternative alleles. The critical type of mating is of an rh-negative woman, rh rh, and an Rh-positive man, Rh Rh or Rh rh. In the last few years a large series of multiple alleles has been demonstrated at the Rh-locus, or more accurately at three closely linked loci.

MEDITERRANEAN FEVER AND SICKLE-CELL ANEMIA

J. V. Neel and W. N. Valentine have shown that a gene in heterozygous condition produces a mild blood condition which they designate thalassemia minor. The same gene in homozygous form produces thalassemia major, characterized by severe anemia and generally fatal soon after birth unless multiple transfusions are given. The gene in question has a relatively high frequency in southern Italian and Greek populations. Sickle-cell anemia, often fatal in childhood, is produced by a gene in homozygous condition. This same gene in heterozygotes is characterized by the production of some sickle-shaped red corpuscles in the blood, but apparently no serious effects. Heterozygous carriers of both of these serious blood diseases can be recognized by the proper clinical tests. One of the goals of modern human genetics is to develop reliable tests for the recognition of carriers of other inherited mutant genes, which in homozygous form produce serious diseases and abnormalities.

NORMAL HEREDITARY DIFFERENCES

One might gather from the facts presented that most mutant genes in man are highly deleterious. Certainly many of them are, but these severe hereditary abnormalities have naturally been the first to draw the attention of medical men and those interested in human heredity. Many mutant genes in man condition relatively minor characteristics, some of which should be classed as differences rather than abnormalities. The discovery of more of these character differences, particularly where the mutant gene frequency is high, is one of the major current aims of human geneticists. Such characters will be important in advancing our knowledge of human heredity and eventually will have practical applications in linkage studies involving the more serious inherited human abnormalities.

Many conditions are known to have a hereditary basis, although the exact mode of inheritance is not yet known. Such problems could readily be solved if one were working with plants or other animals, but obviously man is not an experimental animal, at least in so far as the analysis of hereditary differences is concerned. Difficulties of analysis include the fact that some conditions are the resultant of multiple genetic factors, several mutant genes at different loci reacting to induce the condition, and to the fact that some apparently identical effects are induced by different genes or even by environmental factors. Genes which modify the action of the principal mutant gene, resulting in irregular expression or even complete suppression of the character, complicate the picture.

One should not lose sight that the normal alleles are inherited by the same mechanism as the abnormal mutant genes. Fortunately, when the "dice of destiny," as Dr. D. C. Rife has termed the genes, were cast, human beings received at least one normal allele at most gene loci. Genetics studies on many organisms, both plant and animal, where controlled breeding experiments were possible over a long period of time, have shown that characters such as bodily vigor, high disease resistance, long life, or excellence in performance of some function useful to man are inherited. Most of these favorable characters have been shown to be the product of the united action of many different gene pairs, so-called quantitative characters. It is reasonable to conclude that favorable characters in man, including many mental, artistic, and creative traits, have a basis in heredity. However, the analysis of the inheritance of such characters lies in the distant future. The uncritical methods and naïve conclusions in studies such as those of the Jukes and Kallikaks are regarded with suspicion by modern students of human genetics. No doubt good and bad heredity were involved, but much more critical methods must be used to establish the mode of inheritance of quantitative mental and physical human characters.

MODERN METHODS OF STUDYING HUMAN INHERITANCE

As man is not an experimental animal, at least so far as studies on heredity are concerned, the accumulation of data is often difficult and sometimes impossible. Three main methods of study supply most of the information. The first of these to be employed was the careful compilation of family pedigrees involving the transmission of alternative alleles. A second method, developed in recent years, has been the statistical study of gene frequencies in populations. This method has been remarkably successful, as it does not rely upon following gene differences through several generations. For many genetic factors it furnishes valuable and accurate data which could not be compiled by the family-pedigree method. Finally, studies on identical twins have added much valuable information on the relative roles of heredity and environment. Identical twins arise by the separation of the product of a single fertilized egg into two units, either at the two-cell or some later stage. Such twins carry identical chromosome and gene complexes, and consequently differences between members of a pair are due entirely to the environment.

Haldane has reported mutation rates for several human genes. His figures are found in Table 1. Most of these studies have been made on the population of Denmark. The highest mutation rate he reports is for achondroplastic dwarfism. Apparently about one normal human gene in twenty-five thousand at this locus mutates to a dominant allele which conditions this phenotype. In a study of the inherited blood disease, thalassemia, J. V. Neel has calculated a mutation rate of about one normal gene in two thousand to the mutant type in an Italian population. These recent studies indicate that even if a human stock could be obtained which carried no deleterious mutant genes these would soon arise by mutation. The eugenic hope of a race entirely free of defective germ plasm seems to be impossible of attainment.

TABLE I.   MUTATION RATES IN SOME HUMAN GENES
(*From J. B. S. Haldane*)

MUTATION	RATE
achondroplasia	*1 per 25,000 genes*
hemophilia	*1 per 31,250 genes*
retinoblastoma	*1 per 71,500 genes*
aniridia	*1 per 100,000 to 200,000 genes*
epiloia	*1 per 125,000 to 250,000 genes*

FALLACIES: INHERITANCE OF ACQUIRED CHARACTERS

Jean Baptiste Lamarck, a French biologist who lived and wrote in the late eighteenth and early nineteenth centuries, proposed a theory of organic evolution based on the idea that changes which took place in the body of a person through use or disuse of organs or through the effect of various environmental factors would be inherited by the offspring. This idea came to be known as the "inheritance of acquired characters." The concept was accepted by Darwin at least to some extent and by most biologists of the late nineteenth century. Remnants of this theory are still adhered to by many people not conversant with the studies of modern biology. Many critical laboratory experiments have been conducted. The evidence is uniformly negative. Changes which take place in the body of a person through environmental influences do not have an effect on the heredity of the offspring. Birthmarks, deformities, mental or physical traits, whether good or bad, are not induced in the child during pregnancy by the experiences of the mother in that period. Alleged effects of this kind are mere coincidences. However, the development, health, and well-being of the fetus may be influenced by the intra-uterine environment. The Rh antibody developed in the blood of the mother and acting on the blood of the fetus is a case in point. Presumably the general condition of the expectant mother may influence to some extent the development of the fetus. Such changes have nothing to do with the hereditary mechanism. Syphilis may be transmitted from mother to unborn child, but it is not inherited. To state that it is inherited is a misuse of terms.

RADIATION INDUCED MUTATIONS

In quite a different category, however, are the changes which may be induced in the germ plasm by radiations from radium, X rays, and the various radioactive by-products of atomic fission. In 1927 Dr. H. J. Muller demonstrated that X rays induced germinal mutations in the fruit fly, *Drosophila,* when these flies were subjected to radiation. These observations have been abundantly confirmed by extensive experiments on many other organisms, including mice. Furthermore, it has been shown that the number of mutations induced by radiation is proportional to the dosage, even for extremely low dosages. A current fallacy in this connection is that there is a low tolerance dosage, below which mutations of the germ plasm will not occur. This fallacy ignores the mechanism of mutation. It is of course true that the chance of a mutation being induced in a given germ cell following low dosage exposure is relatively low. In this new atomic age every precaution should be taken to keep exposure of individuals and of populations to a minimum. Persons of reproductive age should not have their sex glands subjected even to light dosages of X rays, radium, or other radioactive agents if this can possibly be avoided. Most mutations induced by these agents are deleterious.

HEREDITY AND ENVIRONMENT

A common and widespread fallacy is the idea that nothing can be done if a disease or condition is inherited. This idea arises from a misconception of the roles of heredity and environment in the development and control of characters. Throughout life there is a constant interplay of hereditary and environmental factors in the development, growth, and health of the individual. Many characters and conditions having a hereditary basis may be changed, suppressed, or magnified by the manipulation of the environment. The disease diabetes, which at least in many cases has a hereditary basis, may be controlled by the proper use of insulin. Diabetics may lead relatively normal lives and live to a ripe old age. A chief aim of modern medicine is the discovery of environmental factors, including drug treatment and even surgery, which will compensate for hereditary defects. However, the treatment of the individual does not alter the germ plasm. Acquired characters are not inherited.

PREDETERMINATION OF SEX

Several methods have been proposed whereby the sex of the human offspring could be predetermined. Experimental studies on rabbits and other laboratory animals have shown that at present these proposed methods are invalid. True, there are a few more human males than females born. When the records for stillbirths are included there are on the average about one hundred and twenty male conceptions to one hundred female conceptions. The explanation suggested for this fact is that the Y-bearing sperm, possibly because of the smaller size of the Y-chromosome, has a slight advantage over the X-bearing sperm in the fertilization race in which these two types of sperm engage. The time may come, but is not yet here, when some sort of mass sorting of these two types of human sperm, followed by artificial insemination, may make it possible to predetermine the sex of a child.

STERILIZATION OF THE UNFIT

It has often been suggested that sterilization of the unfit would solve the hereditary problems of mankind. In the case of a well-defined hereditary dominant, marked by gross abnormalities, either mental or physical, sterilization, segregation, or efficient contraception should be advocated. However, some of these dominants tend to be self-eliminating through early death of the afflicted persons. Furthermore, Haldane's work on human mutation rates indicates that a eugenic program can never eliminate all defective dominants, although their incidence could be brought down to that determined by mutation rates. At present the chance of transmitting a defective dominant, which is generally one in two, and the seriousness of the abnormality should determine the reproductive behavior of the individual involved.

When the elimination of defective recessive genes is concerned, sterilization or other methods of preventing reproduction of afflicted individuals has relatively little effect on the frequency of the recessive genes in the population and, therefore, on the number of individuals showing the defect in the next generation. This is due to the fact that most of the deleterious genes are carried in heterozygous form, and most such heterozygous carriers cannot now be detected. However, from the purely personal point of view—and in such matters few people place racial welfare above personal happiness—persons in family lines in which recessive abnormalities have appeared would do well by their prospective offspring not to marry blood relations.

DISTRIBUTION OF GENES IN FAMILIES AND POPULATIONS

A fallacy sometimes held by those who have heard a little about Mendelian heredity is that where two parents are heterozygous for a recessive one fourth of their children will show the character. Actually, in individual families any ratio might be found between the dominant and recessive characters among the children of two heterozygous parents. In fact, all of the children or none of them may show the recessive character. Likewise, when one parent is heterozygous for a dominant and the other parent does not carry it, there is no assurance that half of the children will show the dominant. All or none of them may show it. Such fluctuations from expected ratios may occur when small samples are taken, and the children in any one family constitute a small sample. Furthermore, it is incorrect to conclude that because two alternative characters appear in a human population in approximately a three-to-one ratio the more frequently occurring character is the dominant, the other the recessive. It may well be that the frequently occurring character is the recessive. The incidence of the alternative characters in the population depends upon the gene frequencies.

A commonly held fallacy is to suppose that characters due to alternative alleles are always invariable in expression. There are many examples known in the heredity of plants and animals where the character expression fluctuates widely under the influence of genetic or environmental modifiers. Many persons carrying the genes conditioning the character may be normal or show the character to only a slight degree. Such persons may, however, transmit the mutant gene.

HEREDITARY EFFECTS OF RACE CROSSING

Hereditary differences in races and the hereditary effects of race crossing raise difficult questions. Here fact and fallacy intermingle even in the writings of some otherwise competent scientific investigators. Isolated and exceptional cases are used to prove the rule. Prejudice supersedes reason. In spite of many factors operating to bring about miscegenation, there still remain on the world large and more or less contiguous populations which differ from others in a number of obviously inherited traits. To state that one such group differs from another by a few superficial and unimportant hereditary traits would seem to be begging the question. Actually recent studies, which could be carried on objectively on several of the inherited blood factors, have shown definite differences in gene frequencies of the various alleles from racial group to racial group. These studies indicate that probably racial groups do differ widely in the frequencies of many genes.

The factors over which most of the controversy rages—mental ability, physical stamina, emotional balance, and the constituent traits which make up these complexes—are determined intraracially by multiple genetic factors interacting with a large number of environmental variables. Only gross departures from the norm, conditioned by one or a few gene substitutions, have been genetically analyzed. It seems futile, then, in our present state of knowledge to attempt to establish either the thesis of racial superiority or of racial

equality. It is no answer to the questions raised to repeat the cliché that fluctuations within a race are greater than fluctuations between races. For the
major races of mankind the curves of variation for most physical and mental
characters are broadly overlapping. In spite of many published studies pur-
porting to deal with racial comparisons, the data are fragmentary and inconclusive. Where race crossing on a wide scale has occurred, obvious biological
disharmonies in the hybrids have not been demonstrated. This does not mean
that a careful analysis on a large scale might not demonstrate statistically
some disharmony.

In individual cases, in considering marriage between members of two
racial groups, the social implications of such matings are likely to far outweigh the biological factors involved. Where no serious social consequences
are likely to accrue, racial intermarriage can hardly be condemned on biological grounds. Where social stigmas are still prevalent, two individuals of
different races need to consider the security and happiness of offspring in
addition to their own inclinations. There seems little doubt that miscegenation will increase in this fast-shrinking world. In any case, the intelligent
choice of a mate, sound in mind and body, is the best insurance of success in
undertaking the greatest of all biological adventures, marriage and the rearing of a family.

ON BOOKS AND CLINICS

For the convenience of readers whose interest may have been stimulated
by this brief chapter on human heredity, a short bibliography or reading list
has been appended. Perhaps some further guidance may be helpful. For those
who wish a brief résumé, in clear and easily understood terms, well illustrated, Dr. Rife's *Dice of Destiny* is recommended. For those who prefer a
more lengthy presentation, scientifically accurate but written in popular
style, Amram Scheinfeld's *The New You and Heredity* is suggested. A more
advanced treatment of the subject will be found in Dr. Curt Stern's *Principles of Human Genetics.*

In recent years a number of Human Heredity Clinics have been established, where professional advice by competent medical geneticists may be
secured.

BIBLIOGRAPHY

Dunn, L. C., and Dobzhansky, T., *Heredity, Race and Society,* New York,
Penguin Books, Inc., 1946.

Glass, Bentley, *Genes and the Man,* New York, Bureau of Publications, Teachers College, Columbia University, 1943.

Haldane, J. B. S., *New Paths in Genetics,* New York, Harper & Bros., 1942.

Rife, D. C., *The Dice of Destiny,* 2nd edition, Columbus, O., Long's College Book Co., 1947.

Scheinfeld, Amram, *The New You and Heredity,* Philadelphia and New York, J. B. Lippincott, 1950.

Snyder, L. H., *Medical Genetics,* Durham, N.C., Duke University Press, 1941.

Stern, Curt, *Principles of Human Genetics,* San Francisco, W. H. Freeman and Co., 1949.

Chapter 3

FACTORS FAVORING FERTILITY

by *M. Edward Davis, M.D.*

PROFESSOR OF OBSTETRICS AND GYNECOLOGY, UNIVERSITY OF CHICAGO MEDICAL
SCHOOL

The survival of any species depends as much on its ability to reproduce as on an adequate supply of food and a favorable environment. Reproduction may be a simple process such as we see in the one-celled animal Cothurnia, in which the daughter cell, by the simple expedient of fission, separates from the mother cell and floats away to begin life as a new individual; or as in some worms which split in two or more segments, each segment forming a separate worm. Fission is a fundamental biologic phenomenon as well as a physical attribute of the atom.

Such simple reproductive processes without sex, suitable for single-celled animals and lower forms of life, are obviously not adapted to the more complicated species. Human reproduction involves a carefully synchronized mechanism to allow for the blending of the male and female genetic qualities into an offspring resembling its parents. Male and female germ cells must meet and unite. The resultant fertilized ovum is transported safely to the nesting place where it can continue its development to completion. Human fertility necessitates normal organs, co-ordinated glandular function, and a sound regulatory nervous mechanism.

THE RHYTHM OF REPRODUCTIVE FUNCTION

Periodically in the ovaries of all sexually mature animals follicles containing the ova or eggs begin to ripen. When one or more of these germ cells have become mature their follicles rupture and release them. This periodic event is associated with an intense mating desire in the female. The lowly sow remains quiet and peaceful during the two and one half weeks of each three-week cycle, interested only in eating and sleeping. For a period of three days, estrus, when ripe follicles are present in the ovary, she becomes restless and excitable, seeking out the male and accepting him promptly. The cycles in some animals are short—four or five days in rats and mice—or exceedingly long. The shortest cycle is seen in the hen, which lays an egg once a day, and the longest in the locust, where reproduction occurs once in seventeen years. In the human the reproductive cycles recur at about four-week intervals.

In most of the animals the female will accept the male only during those periods when an egg is ripe and ready for rupture. In fact, in a few, such as the cat and the ferret, the sexual act induces the rupture of ripe follicles and the discharge of their eggs. Most women usually are not aware that ovulation is taking place or that a ripe follicle is present in the ovary. Probably it makes itself known by certain changes, but these are imperceptible to most people. Rarely, some women will have a twinge of pain in one or the other of the groins or an indefinite sensation of discomfort at the time of rupture of the follicle. This has been known as *Mittelschmerz,* the German for pain in the middle of the cycle. Sexual activity is not confined to the short period in the cycle when a ripe follicle is ready to rupture. No unusual sex urge increases the likelihood of fertilization of the mature ovum. Periods of fertility and infertility must be established in each person from physiologic data available.

CYCLICAL EVENTS IN THE HUMAN OVARY

The human ovary or the female sex gland has a duel function—to produce ova or eggs for reproduction and as a gland of internal secretion. Reproduction is dependent on both of these roles, for it would be impossible for a fertilized egg to continue its development in the absence of the ovarian hormones.

The activity of the ovary which produces the ova is cyclical in character. Each month in the mature woman a number of primary follicles containing these ova begin to grow in size under the influence of an internal secretion from the pituitary gland. This growth period lasts about two weeks and is culminated by the rapid enlargement of a single follicle, rarely two, for a period of seventy-two hours. This follicle finally ruptures, catapulting the egg in the direction of the oviduct, or the Fallopian tube. This process of follicle rupture and the discharge of the ripe egg is designated as ovulation.

Theoretically the egg escapes free into the abdomen, but by an ingenious mechanism it is almost invariably directed to the funnel-shaped entrance of the Fallopian tube, which serves as a passageway from the neighborhood of the ovary to the interior of the uterus. This quill-like structure has a special lining consisting of delicate folds and a muscular wall adapted to the transportation of the egg toward the interior of the uterus. At the time of ovulation the Fallopian tubes undergo wavelike contractions, such as are seen in the intestines, designed to move anything within their lumina toward the uterus.

The life of the human ovum is short, probably less than twenty-four hours if fertilization does not take place. However, if intercourse occurs immediately before or soon after the egg escapes from the follicle, fertilization can take place. Spermatozoa, the male germ cells, are deposited about the cervix or they are forced into the mucus of the cervical canal at the time of copulation. Spermatozoa are equipped with tails which they use for locomotion. They penetrate through the cervical mucus, travel across the lining of the uterus, and seek out the ovum within the Fallopian tube. If it is still alive one spermatozoon penetrates the outer covering, and its nuclear portion or center unites with that of the egg to accomplish fertilization. The egg can now begin to grow, to divide and subdivide, to produce a normal baby 267 days later. The act of fertilization thus connotes the beginning of a new life.

The fertilized egg is moved slowly down the Fallopian tube, entering the cavity of the uterus at the end of about three days. If its stay in the tube is prolonged beyond this period, its rapid growth will interfere with its movement and it may become attached to the wall of the tube. It may continue to grow in this locality ultimately, giving rise to a condition known as a tubal pregnancy. Normally it enters the uterine cavity, where it remains unattached for three or four days more. At the end of day six or seven, the fertilized egg, now a globular mass of dividing cells, no larger than the head of a pin, attaches itself to the succulent lining of the uterus. It burrows rapidly beneath the surface, producing a minute amount of bleeding, and is covered over by the broken-down, partially digested cells. From this period of implantation its growth will be rapid and spectacular.

THE OVARY AS A DUCTLESS GLAND

The ovary is a gland of internal secretion also. This knowledge is quite recent. In 1929 Doisy, a St. Louis investigator, isolated the first of the ovarian secretions, the estrogenic hormone.

The estrogenic hormone is present in the growing follicle of the ovary and all the cells of the follicle produce it. This hormone has been found in many body tissues and fluids in different chemical forms and varying concentrations. It is abundant in the placenta or afterbirth during pregnancy, and the placenta probably serves as the chief source of supply. More recently Dodds and a group of co-workers in England discovered that certain synthetic chemical substances have estrogenic properties. Many estrogenic preparations now in use in medicine have been created artificially.

The estrogenic hormone has been known as the female sex hormone because all the feminine attributes depend upon it. Yet it is present in many organs, tissues, and fluids in the male as well as the female. In fact, the urine of the stallion is a rich source of estrogens. Masculinity and femininity are relative terms; male and female sex hormones are present in both. In the female the estrogens predominate, whereas in the male, the male sex hormone or testosterone is in greater concentration normally.

The estrogenic hormone brings about the developmental changes in the little girl which begin at puberty and culminate at maturity. Under its influence the feminine figure evolves, the breasts develop, the feminine hair pattern emerges, the external and internal genital organs grow to normal size and shape, and the young girl begins to menstruate. Even the feminine pitch of the voice is dependent on estrogenic hormones.

The menstrual function begins irregularly at first. Then as follicle growth and development in the ovary become cyclical in character it assumes an adult pattern, typical for the individual. The average interval between menstrual periods is twenty-eight to thirty-one days, but some women have short cycles recurring every twenty-one to twenty-four days, and a few have long cycles of thirty-one to thirty-five days. Menstrual bleeding at irregular intervals is abnormal in character, and it is usually the result of some hormonal or organic disorder.

It is customary to date the beginning of the typical cycle with the onset of menstruation because the woman is aware of this cataclysmic event. The first day of bleeding is designated as day one of the cycle. In reality the bleeding period belongs to the previous cycle; it represents the destructive phase of what has already taken place. Under the influence of the estrogenic hormone in the growing follicles the endometrium, or the lining of the uterus, begins to grow in thickness. Maximum growth is reached sometime in the middle of the cycle, at which time a follicle in the ovary has reached complete development. Follicle rupture and the discharge of the ovum usually occur somewhere between days twelve and sixteen in the average cycle of twenty-eight to thirty-one days. Ovulation is the result of stimulation of the ovary by another hormone from the pituitary gland. The follicle wall collapses with the escape of the egg, but the cells that make up the wall undergo a sudden spurt in growth, rapidly developing a thick, wavy border of yellow-colored cells about an ever-diminishing central cavity. This structure is known as the corpus luteum, or the yellow body. The lutein or pigment cells which make up the corpus luteum produce the second of the ovarian hormones, progesterone. Willard Allen and George W. Corner in this country and several investigators in Europe isolated this hormone in pure form in 1932.

The elaboration of progesterone by the yellow body in the ovary is the signal for a rapid change in the development of the lining of the uterus. Under its influence the endometrium now becomes velvety and succulent. The individual glands and cells which comprise it fill up with secretion rich in those nutriments necessary for the early development of the fertilized egg. The interior of the uterine cavity becomes a real nesting place for the reception, attachment, and growth of the developing embryo.

In the event that the egg does not become fertilized, the life of the corpus luteum is fourteen or fifteen days. As this structure ceases to function progesterone disappears from the circulation, changes in the blood supply of the uterine lining occur, menstruation starts, and the endometrium of the uterus begins to disintegrate. Menstruation is a destructive phenomenon, for it is the outward expression of a process aimed at removing the beautifully developed uterine lining no longer necessary for the fertilized ovum. Each month Nature makes elaborate preparations for the reception of a fertilized egg, but with the exception of one or several times in the woman's lifetime it is doomed to disappointment.

THE FERTILE PERIOD

Fertility is limited to a very short span in the average cycle. It is possible for a normal, healthy couple to fail to conceive after several years of married life. The egg can be fertilized for a very short period after it leaves the follicle, probably a matter of hours and certainly no longer than a day. Spermatozoa survive a relatively short time in the reproductive tract, although they live for a much longer period under ideal conditions. Spermatozoa in the vagina live no longer than three or four hours, usually less, for the acid secretion is inimical to them. However, the cervical mucus is a favorable environment and they may remain alive in this region for as long as twenty-four to thirty-six hours, perhaps longer. In all likelihood the cervical mucus acts as a reservoir for their protection, and groups of germ cells penetrate through the mucus and travel upward toward the Fallopian tubes. If pregnancy is to occur, coitus must take place within twenty-four hours of ovulation. The fertile period in each cycle when conception can take place can be narrowed down to one or two days.

It is important to determine the time of ovulation. Women who are anxious to conceive must know whether ovulation occurs and the time of its occurrence. Several methods have been devised to determine whether ovulation has taken place in any given cycle, but they have not been practical in detecting the ovulatory period. The physician in the study of the sterile couple may remove a tiny fragment of the uterine lining at the end of the cycle or at the onset of bleeding. The characteristic picture of this tissue will reveal whether progesterone was available in the cycle. Obviously progesterone is indicative of ovulation and the conversion of the ruptured follicle wall into the corpus luteum. He may examine the urine for the presence of pregnandiol, a substance derived from progesterone. However, the most practical method of following the changes in the ovary is by means of a body basal temperature graph.

BODY TEMPERATURE AND OVARIAN FUNCTION

Body temperature variations in healthy individuals have been known for years. They are sensitive indicators of physical as well as mental activity, metabolic activity, and other physiologic functions. Muscular work, food taking, or mental excitement tend to raise the level of the temperature. Rest and sound sleep lower it. Typical curves have been set up demonstrating these fluctuations during a twenty-four-hour period under varying conditions. They follow what is known as a diurnal pattern, for the temperatures at night are lower than those recorded during the day, the nights being devoted to rest and the days to activity.

In the healthy male there is no variation in this pattern day after day. In the female, on the other hand, the normal function of the ovaries alters this basic curve. During that period when the follicle is growing in the ovary the daily temperature remains at a rather low level. The rupture of the follicle, the discharge of the ripe egg, and the rapid conversion of the follicle wall into the corpus luteum are associated with a rise in the level of the temperature, following which it reaches a plateau where it remains until the end of the cycle. Twenty-four to thirty-six hours prior to the onset of menstruation the temperature drops to the level existing prior to ovulation. The author has demonstrated experimentally that the rise in temperature is due to the elaboration of progesterone by the corpus luteum. In the event that pregnancy ensues there will be no drop in body temperature, for this hormone of gestation will continue to be supplied by the corpus luteum, and later, by the placenta.

A body basal temperature graph can be set up according to the illustration or suitable graphs can be obtained from physicians (Fig. 6). The simplest procedure is the following: Immediately on awakening in the morning the oral temperature is taken. The thermometer should be one that can be read easily and it should be left in the mouth for five minutes. The reading should be recorded promptly. It is important that the temperature be taken immediately on awakening so that it represents a basal reading. Each graph should begin with day one, the first day of menstruation, and end with the onset of the following period. Coitus and any unusual event should be recorded on the appropriate day, for such information may be valuable to the physician. It is well to remember that the temperature is a sensitive barometer and that any unusual excitement, nervousness, or unusual occurrences may influence an otherwise normal curve. At least four out of every five women will find that the body basal temperature graph is an accurate guide to cyclical changes in the ovary. The graph should be kept for at least two or three menstrual cycles in order that it reveal the pattern for the individual.

The temperature graph can be used as an aid to conception. Usually there is a slight drop of the temperature prior to the rise which may indicate follicle rupture. Intercourse should take place at the time of the drop as well as at the time of the rise. Coitus on two or three occasions during this ovulatory period may result in pregnancy. Married couples in which the husband is of low fertility should refrain from intercourse prior to the drop and after the rise in temperature has leveled off for thirty-six to forty-eight hours. Concentrating on a short period during the cycle may increase the fertility of the male who, because of a low spermatozoa content, is of low fertility. In the event the premenstrual temperature drop does not occur, the temperature remaining at the elevated level, pregnancy can be suspected.

The body basal temperature graph can be used by women who do not wish to become pregnant, especially Catholic women who cannot avail themselves of the usual contraceptive measures. The safest procedure in women who have cycles of average length is to avoid coitus from day ten until forty-eight hours after the rise in temperature has reached a plateau. Intercourse can take place from the end of the menses until day ten and from forty-eight hours after the rise until the next menstrual period. The rise in temperature is rarely more than 0.6 or 0.8 of a degree Fahrenheit, so that great care must be taken to obtain reliable curves (Fig. 7). The author has written a small book entitled *Natural Child Spacing* (Hanover House, Doubleday) in which the simple rules for mothers who wish to space their children are described and illustrated.

Body basal temperature graphs are a great aid to the physician in the study of sterility, menstrual difficulties, and many problems concerning the reproductive organs, so that they are invaluable as a part of a good medical history.

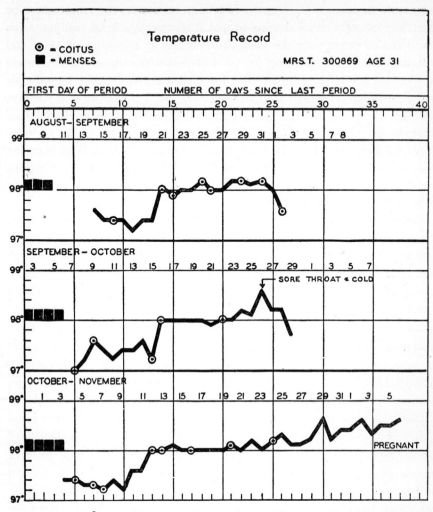

FIGURE 6.   BASAL TEMPERATURE RECORD FOR THREE MONTHS

The basal temperature record of a patient who consulted us because she could not become pregnant. The graph covers three monthly cycles. The dark blocks indicate the menstrual days. Note that in August the temperature remained under 97.6° until the twelfth day after the beginning of menstruation, when it suddenly began to rise, reaching the plateau on the thirteenth day. It remained elevated until the twenty-fifth, when it began to drop, followed by menstruation thirty-six hours later. The rise in temperature is indicative of the rupture of a mature follicle in the ovary, the discharge of the ripe egg, and the formation of a corpus luteum. In October no drop in temperature occurred. The continued elevation indicated that the egg had become fertilized and that the patient was pregnant.

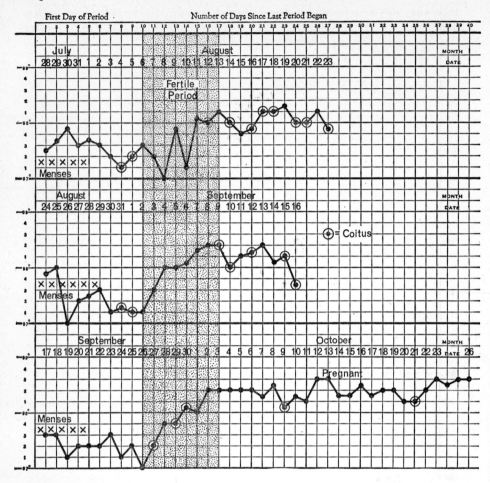

FIGURE 7.   BASAL TEMPERATURE RECORD FOR FOUR MONTHS

Body basal temperature record of a patient during a four-month period. She did not wish to become pregnant during July and August, so she refrained from intercourse from the tenth day of the cycle until the eighteenth day. These periods showed the typical rise in temperature associated with ovulation. In September she decided to try for a pregnancy, so she had intercourse on days 11, 13, and 14, during which time the rise in temperature occurred. The subsequent failure of the temperature to drop indicated that she conceived on one of these days. The basal temperature curve is an excellent index of fertility and can be used to prevent pregnancy as well as to favor its occurrence.

One simple method of determining the time of ovulation is by means of temperature graphs. Theoretically the normal temperature of a healthy individual is 98.6 degrees. Actually, there are always slight variations from this figure. It has been found that woman's temperature is lower during the first part of the menstrual cycle than it is during the last two weeks of the same cycle, and further, that the shift from the lower level of temperature to the higher occurs about the time of ovulation. Therefore, in many cases it is possible to determine the time of ovulation by keeping a graphic record of each day's temperature. The variation in temperature is slight, only a few fifths of a degree, so it is essential that the temperature be taken with the utmost practical accuracy.

The temperature is to be taken precisely according to your physician's instruction; some doctors wish the temperature taken in the morning, some in the evening; some prefer mouth temperatures, some rectal temperatures. No matter what technique is used, the results will be about the same. One of the best plans is as follows:

(1) Take the temperature as instructed by your physician for five minutes by the clock immediately after waking in the morning and before arising, eating, drinking, or smoking.

(2) Note the temperature immediately by a dot on the graph. If the temperature so recorded differs markedly from previous readings, and particularly if it is lower than previous readings, the thermometer should be shaken down and reinserted for an additional five minutes by the clock and the reading verified before it is recorded permanently.

(3) If the temperature rises two or three fifths of a degree above the previous level and if the rise is not due to a sore throat or some other ailment, it is probable that ovulation is taking place. This is particularly likely if the temperature rise occurs about fourteen days before the next period is expected, or if the rise corresponds with a similar rise in the graph of the previous menstrual cycle. In many instances the temperature drops one or two fifths of a degree the day before it rises.

(4) If the temperature is taken according to directions and is accurately read, the time of ovulation will be indicated. Intercourse during the twenty-four hours following the temperature drop, or during the twenty-four hours following the temperature rise offers the best chance for conception.

(5) It is necessary to continue keeping the graph for at least three menstrual cycles before it is of much value. With a graph of two cycles at hand to provide the pattern of your own temperature curve it is usually possible to predict when the temperature will shift (ovulation). Sexual abstinence for several days before ovulation allows time for the male to store up matured sperm, and this probably increases the chance of fertilization. Intercourse more than once in twenty-four hours is unnecessary.

(6) In order to assist your physician in interpreting the graph, it is important to make the following notations:

Encircle the temperature dot on the days when intercourse occurs and write "A.M." or "P.M." as the case may be above the circle.

Some women can recognize ovulation by a twinge of pain low on one side of the abdomen, or by a slight drop of vaginal bleeding. If either of these signs appear, make a note of it on the graph.

Any recognized cause for fever should be noted on the chart; for example, a cold, grippe, marked indigestion, or even following use of alcohol.

Mark the days of menstruation by an "X." It is not necessary to take the temperature during the flow.

Commence a new graph for each cycle, beginning by placing an "X" at the left of the graph sheet on the line marked (at the top of the graph) "1st day of period."

A sample graph is shown on page 240. Note that in the first graph there was no chance for conception because intercourse did not occur at the time of ovulation. During the next cycle the timing was better and pregnancy followed.

(References to the medical literature will be found in the *J.A.M.A.*, 124: 698–700, March 11, 1944; *J. of Ob. & Gyn. Brit. Emp.* 52: 241–52, June 1945; *Med. Clinics of North America*, 1425–34, November 1945.)

MENOPAUSE

The end of the reproductive period, the menopause, or the "change of life," comes on in the fifth decade in most women. It may occur as early as forty or as late as fifty-five, but the average is forty-seven years. The menstrual periods may stop altogether, come at increasingly longer intervals, or become completely irregular. The menstrual irregularity must be carefully evaluated by a physician, for this is the decade when cancer of the uterus occurs most often and menstrual change may mask a developing growth. Fertility of the individual decreases rapidly and ceases entirely with the end of the menstrual function. Many of the irregular bleeding periods are not associated with ovulation. When the menstrual periods have not recurred for six months or longer pregnancy is no longer possible.

It is common gossip that pregnancies can occur during the menopause. Many women have heard about these so-called "menopausal babies." They have been ascribed to a sudden spurt of fertility during this period. There is no scientific evidence that such is the case. These pregnancies in the menopausal decade probably occur in spite of rapidly waning fertility. Women are likely to drop the usual birth-control safeguards when they reach the forties and particularly when menstrual periods come at more and more infrequent intervals. Some of these irregular cycles are associated with ovulation, and if coitus is timed so that the ovum becomes fertilized the couple may have a baby to brighten their middle age.

The menopause is associated with a decrease in the ovarian hormones which leads to many physical and functional changes. In most women readjustments take place rapidly so that no serious complications result. In a few, mental and emotional strains may become sufficiently severe to warrant medical treatment.

Chapter 4

PREGNANCY

by Edith L. Potter, M.D., Ph.D.

DEPARTMENT OF OBSTETRICS AND GYNECOLOGY, UNIVERSITY OF CHICAGO, AND
CHICAGO LYING-IN HOSPITAL

Pregnancy constitutes one of the most important events in the married life of any couple. The selection of a mate, the creation of a home, the establishment of a position in the community are most often consciously or unconsciously directed toward the preparation of a suitable environment in which to bear and rear children.

The average couple are anxious to have children and await the knowledge that pregnancy has begun with great eagerness. Most men and women are well aware at the time of marriage of the physiologic processes involved in the conception and bearing of a child. The woman is particularly conscious of and often more keenly looks forward to the possibility of pregnancy than her husband. Within her body cyclic changes are constantly taking place which indicate that she is ready to become a mother.

The reproductive organs of the girl child are undeveloped at the time of birth and in the early years grow somewhat more slowly than the rest of the body. In the early teens their growth is accelerated, and during the middle and late teens they assume a size and maturity which are compatible with having a baby.

Puberty is indicated in the girl by the first appearance of the constantly recurring evidence that her body is making a monthly preparation for pregnancy. Puberty is ordinarily defined as the period at which sexual maturity is attained and the girl becomes capable of reproduction. This is not quite true in most girls, for generally many months or even years elapse between the onset of the menstrual function and the time of the first pregnancy, even though they are exposed to the possibility of pregnancy earlier.

Beginning with puberty and continuing for thirty or more years, the uterus prepares every four to five weeks for the reception of a fertilized egg.

It makes ready an environment in which the egg can grow and develop until such time as the infant which comes from it is capable of maintaining an independent existence.

At birth the ovaries of the girl infant contain hundreds of thousands of ova—eggs—the majority of which remain in their original state until the time of puberty. Then, because of the stimulating effect which is exercised on the ovaries by hormones or glandular secretions coming from the pituitary gland, many ova begin to enlarge each month. The pituitary gland is a small pea-sized structure located near the center of the head. It produces many different hormones that act on many different parts of the body, but the one that stimulates ova to grow is one of the most important. When the ova do begin to grow a special group of cells surrounding them grow, too, and within this area fluid appears. The cavity filled with fluid becomes larger and the ovum lies in the wall. The ovum, the fluid, and the surrounding cells are called a Graafian follicle. The fluid contains a hormone called estrogen, the female sex hormone.

For some unknown reason, in spite of the fact that many ova each month grow and become surrounded by fluid, only one reaches complete maturity. After approximately two weeks of growth the cavity surrounding this one ovum attains a diameter of about one half inch and bulges up toward the surface of the ovary. The wall then gradually gives way and the fluid escapes, carrying with it the ovum that has been held in place in one part of the lining of the cavity. The ovum is received into the Fallopian tube, the outer open end of which lies in close proximity to the ovary.

As soon as the fluid escapes, the cavity collapses, and its lining grows thicker and becomes yellow in color. The follicle is then known as a "yellow body," or corpus luteum, and the production of a new type of hormone is commenced.

The hormone, estrogen, which is present in the fluid surrounding all the ova in the Graafian follicles, stimulates the lining of the uterus to begin growing. The second hormone, which comes from the follicle that has been converted into a corpus luteum, is known as progesterone. It acts on the uterine lining to bring about the final preparation for pregnancy. The lining becomes a thick soft cushion and secrets material which the ovum, if it is fertilized, can use as a first source of nourishment.

The life of the ovum after it leaves the ovary is short—probably not more than 24 hours. The lives of the sperm cells after they are deposited by the male organ in the vagina or female organ are also short; they, too, are believed not to survive for more than 24 hours. When spermatozoa enter the vagina they move rapidly upward into the uterus or womb and out into both Fallopian tubes. If they reach the outer end of the tube which contains an ovum while the ovum is still alive, many approach it from all sides. If one is successful in penetrating the ovum a change occurs in the outer surface which makes it impossible for others to enter. When the ovum and sperm cell are thus united, fertilization, or conception, is said to have occurred. The first step in the development of the baby has been accomplished.

If spermatozoa do not reach the ovum in time, it dies and quickly disintegrates. Then, since the possibility of an immediate pregnancy no longer exists, the corpus luteum degenerates and ceases the production of progesterone. The uterus no longer needs to be ready to receive the growing ovum. The lining gradually grows thinner, it is gradually shed, and blood leaks out of small blood vessels. This loss of blood is known as menstruation. Menstruation is an indication that an ovum was liberated from the ovary, that the uterus was prepared to receive it, and that the ovum failed to become fertilized and lodged in the uterine lining.

Nature is persistent! As soon as menstruation commences, a new set of ova begin to mature and the entire process is repeated. If pregnancy does not interrupt, menstruation occurs in the majority of women at 26- to 32-day intervals from puberty to the menopause.

The ovum generally escapes from the follicle near the mid-interval between menstrual periods; this is ordinarily the only time during which pregnancy can be started. It is consequently called the fertile period. The time when the ovum is liberated may occasionally be altered, and conception has been known to have occurred on every day from the beginning to the end of the cycle. For this reason the avoidance of sexual intercourse only during the "fertile period" is not a certain means of preventing conception.

SIGNS OF PREGNANCY

In a healthy young woman who has been menstruating regularly, the first indication that pregnancy has been initiated is ordinarily a failure to menstruate at the expected time. Soon afterward the breasts begin to grow larger and firmer. Occasionally some disinclination for food and a feeling of nausea on first arising in the morning are experienced.

The physician cannot ordinarily make a diagnosis of pregnancy by examination of the uterus until about two months have elapsed after the last menstrual period. Sooner than this, and usually after about five weeks, one of the pregnancy tests, known as an Aschheim-Zondek or a Friedman test, will indicate the presence of pregnancy. These tests are based on the fact that parts of the developing ovum produce a hormone which is excreted in the maternal urine. If a small amount of urine containing this hormone is injected into a mouse, a rabbit, or a frog, these animals undergo certain changes which can be easily recognized.

An entirely positive diagnosis cannot be made until pregnancy is sufficiently advanced for the beating of the infant's heart to be audible through the mother's abdominal wall or until X-ray examination discloses the bones of the fetal skeleton. This is generally near the middle of pregnancy.

FALSE PREGNANCY

On rare occasions the development of a uterine or ovarian tumor may simulate pregnancy, and still more infrequently women desirous of bearing children may have all of the symptoms of early pregnancy, even to the abdominal enlargement, without actually being pregnant. This latter condition is known as pseudocyesis and may persist until such time as it is possible to convince the woman that she is not pregnant.

CHOOSING A DOCTOR

When any woman suspects that she may be pregnant she should immediately consult a physician. The choice of a doctor is sometimes hard to make, for the average patient has little way of knowing the qualifications of any particular physician. Obstetrics—the branch of medicine dealing with the care of the mother during pregnancy and delivery—is a specialized field and one to which many physicians devote an entire lifetime. Since such persons are specially trained, often having spent many years in a hospital concerned only with this kind of work, they are better equipped to handle emergencies which may arise than is the physician who has not spent time in special training. If the expectant mother lives in a community large enough to support one or more obstetrical specialists she should by all means consult one of them. The family doctor can often recommend such a person, or the names of such doctors can be obtained from the local health department, medical society, or hospital.

There are many reasons why the bearing of children is a much safer process now than it was in the days of our mothers and grandmothers. One of the most important of these is the improvement in the care available to women during pregnancy. A patient who consults a physician as soon as she realizes she may be pregnant and remains under his observation until the baby is born will have a much greater chance of having a normal living baby than one who does not see a doctor until late in pregnancy or only when the baby is ready to be born.

TOXEMIA OF PREGNANCY

One of the three principal reasons why some women lose their lives during pregnancy is the development of a condition known as pregnancy toxemia. This disease, if it develops, will be discovered by the physician during the course of his examinations when a woman is being observed regularly. If all women received adequate prenatal care this condition should practically disappear as a cause of death, for only when it progresses unrecognized does it become a serious danger.

When an expectant mother visits the doctor during pregnancy he takes her blood pressure and examines her urine on each occasion. He watches her weight and follows her diet. On her first examination he ordinarily makes a blood test for syphilis. This is required by law in many states, and even in those where it is not mandatory it is a generally accepted procedure. Some women unknowingly acquire this disease and some who believe themselves cured can still transmit it to their unborn children. If the condition is discovered in the first half of pregnancy and treatment is then begun the child will be protected and will almost never be affected.

THE RH FACTOR

In most places the blood of all pregnant women is examined for its Rh status. About one out of every seven women is Rh-negative. If the husband of such a woman is Rh-positive it is possible for the infant to inherit the Rh-positive type of blood possessed by its father. Normally the circulation of the mother and that of the infant never communicate, but in a few instances some of the infant's blood may leak into the mother's blood stream. If this happens the mother may react to the infant's blood cells as she would to bacteria or any other foreign material. Antibodies are produced which can combine with Rh-positive cells and destroy them. This is a protective mechanism which is normal in all people. When such antibodies are formed, however, the infant may be harmed; these antibodies may pass through the placenta into its circulation and may combine with its blood cells and destroy them. Such blood destruction causes anemia and jaundice in the infant. The condition is known as erythroblastosis fetalis, or congenital hemolytic disease. Fortunately it is relatively rare and is found in the children of only one out of every 25 or 30 Rh-negative women. The treatment of the disease is directed toward curing the infant's anemia and relieving its jaundice by means of blood transfusions. The Rh status of the mother's blood is determined before or during pregnancy so that if she is found to be Rh-negative the infant may be carefully watched after birth and the earliest signs of the disease detected. With modern methods of treatment about 90 per cent of all children with this disease who are born alive will live and will be entirely well in a few weeks.

HOSPITAL OR HOME DELIVERY

If hospital facilities are available no woman should consider giving birth to her baby at home. As we no longer consider it justifiable to remove an appendix in the farmhouse kitchen, so it is unwise to consider home delivery. In most instances difficulties are not encountered during delivery and both mother and child do well, but one can never be sure in advance that sudden emergencies may not arise. Hemorrhage and infection, the two most important causes of maternal death in addition to toxemia, are much better controlled or prevented in a hospital than they can ever be in a home environment. The infant, too, may be greatly benefited immediately after birth by the facilities available in a well-equipped hospital.

DIET IN PREGNANCY

Few women need to make any drastic changes in their ordinary mode of life when they become pregnant. At this time it is especially important that the diet be adequate in the basic food materials, especially those that are rich in proteins, vitamins, and minerals. Large amounts of starches and sugars should be avoided, for it is important that the gain in weight be not excessive. Many women when they realize they are "eating for two" indulge in immoderate amounts of food. This is unfortunate not only because overeating may be one of the factors leading to the development of toxemia, but also because the weight put on at this time may be difficult to lose after the termination of pregnancy, and the excessive fat may persist for many years. Many a husband has been sadly disillusioned to find that the slim, graceful girl he married has become the fat, ungainly mother of his children.

The weight gain attributable directly to a pregnancy is only about fifteen pounds. The average infant at the time of birth weighs about seven and one half pounds; the bag of waters, the placenta, and the uterus weigh about an equal amount. Any gain in excess of this is ordinarily the result of the deposit of fat in the maternal tissues.

Exhausting physical exercise should be avoided, although this is true at all times and not only during pregnancy. Moderate exercise, whether in work or play, is of help in keeping the body in good physical condition.

SEXUAL INTERCOURSE DURING PREGNANCY

There is ordinarily no reason why sexual intercourse may not be continued during the early part of pregnancy if the pregnancy is progressing normally. If there have been previous miscarriages avoidance of intercourse during the second and third months, especially near the time when menstruation would have occurred if a pregnancy had not been established, is generally recommended. During the last two months before the expected date of delivery intercourse should be discontinued to avoid the risk of introducing bacteria into the vagina and to avoid the possibility of stimulating the uterus to deliver the baby prematurely. Immediately following the birth of the baby the uterus is susceptible to infection, and bacteria which are present in any part of the birth canal may constitute a possible source of such infection. For this reason nothing, including douches, should be introduced into the vagina during the last few weeks before the expected date of delivery or in the first few weeks after delivery.

NO MENTAL EFFECTS ON BABY

Young mothers are sometimes afraid that they may mark their babies by having unpleasant experiences or by witnessing unusual or distressing events. Such fears are without foundation; there are no nerves connecting the baby to the mother, and no emotion from which the mother suffers can be transmitted to her child. So-called birthmarks are caused by abnormalities in the development of localized parts of the skin and are not related to the mental or emotional state of the mother.

HOW THE BABY IS FORMED

When a woman becomes pregnant a marvelous series of events is initiated. The changes that take place in the nine months that elapse between the time the ovum is fertilized by a sperm cell until a fully developed infant is ready to be born are more wonderful and awe-inspiring than any other phenomenon in nature. Two individual cells unite to become one; by growth and division new cells are formed that divide and redivide countless numbers of times in order to produce the gradual differentiation into organs and body forms that results in the creation of a living human being. Each human being is the replica of its thousands of ancestors. Each fertilized egg possesses all the potential qualities with which the father and mother can endow their child; already are determined the infant's sex, the color of its eyes, the shape of its nose, and all of the other characteristics that will become visible only months or years later.

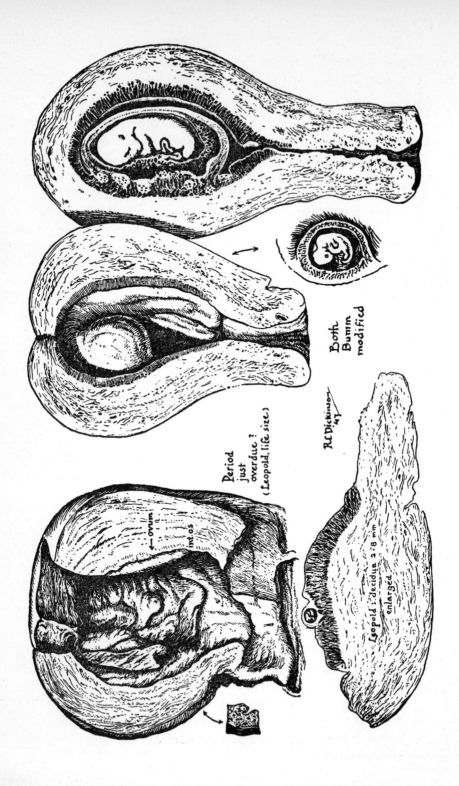

Period
just
overdue ?
(Leopold, life size)

RL Dickinson
47

Both
Bumm
modified

ovum
int. os

Leopold : decidua 2·8 mm
enlarged

FIGURE 8. EARLY PREGNANCIES AND EMBRYO DEVELOPMENT

The Start of Life. In the uterus on the left the ovum has come to rest in the lining. Early as it is, with a menstrual period just skipped, the urine test proves conception. The center figures show a fortnight's swift growth. Next there is seen, on the rear wall, the beginning of the placenta. The series below depicts two months' progress, watching the top line of figures for actual age since fertilization and along the dark line for weeks since the last menstruation. Thus at one month the growing ovum is the size of a big pea; and this curled-up little embryo carries along into the next week a real tail, when it is as bulky as a finger tip. Then buds appear which will develop into arms and legs. Later a not-too-happy face fronts a large bulge of head. All the time it is suspended in fluid. The vessels in the umbilical cord carry blood to and from the placenta; they provide the nourishment and eliminate waste products from the infant while it is in the uterus.

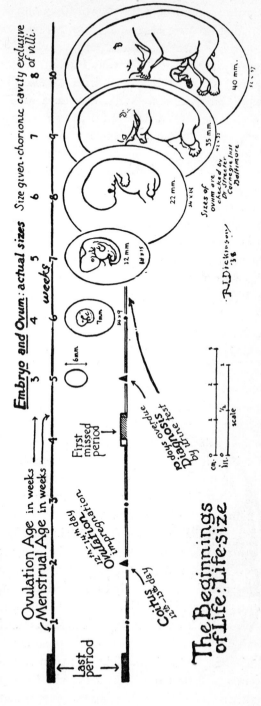

The Beginnings of Life: Life-size

R. L. Dickinson '36

For three or four days the growing ovum moves slowly downward through the Fallopian tube and for another three or four days passes over part of the uterine wall. About the seventh or eighth day it settles near the upper center of the front or back wall of the uterus. During the time of its downward passage it has developed first into a small solid mass of cells and then through rearrangement it has become a single layer of cells surrounding a hollow cavity filled with fluid. In one portion of the wall a small group of cells known as the inner cell mass has remained; in this area the infant will develop; the rest of the wall will grow into the elaborate structure which is known as the afterbirth or placenta. By means of the placenta the infant obtains its food, water, and oxygen and eliminates waste material before birth. See Figure 8.

As soon as the hollow ball of cells comes to rest it gradually sinks down into the uterine lining. The wall of the hollow sphere thickens, and on the outer surface small buds appear which rapidly elongate and branch. Quickly the surface of the sphere is covered with small treelike structures. As they grow they penetrate the maternal tissues dissolving away the uterine cells with which they come in contact. They also dissolve parts of the walls of the blood vessels in their immediate vicinity so that maternal blood leaks out and surrounds all of the branches of these treelike structures.

Inside of the branches small blood vessels containing blood cells begin to appear. The ends of the various blood vessels unite and also unite with similar vessels which have been forming on the inner surface of the hollow sphere and in the region of the inner cell mass. When this system is complete a circulation of blood is established which flows from the region where the embryo is forming in the inner cell mass outward over the inner surface of the large cavity and into all of the branching structures growing from the outer surface. A similar set of vessels carries the blood in the reverse direction back to the embryo.

These treelike structures that contain the blood vessels are known as villi; for several weeks they cover all of the outer surface. Gradually part fail to grow and soon become degenerated so that by the middle of pregnancy villi are found attached only to a round area making up about one fifth of the total surface. The villi in this region continue to become more and more branched; the branches intertwine to form a fairly solid-looking mass shaped something like a pie. By the end of pregnancy this mass has grown to be about an inch thick and eight to ten inches in diameter. It is called the placenta. The part from which the villi have degenerated remains and it, together with the placenta, forms the outer wall of the sac holding the watery fluid by which the infant is surrounded while it is in the uterus. It breaks and the fluid escapes before the baby is born.

Even though the placenta seems a firm, compact structure, enough room is present between the villi to make it possible for maternal blood continuously to bathe their outer surfaces. Blood flows out into the placenta from the arteries of the uterus, circulates between the villi, and returns to the uterine veins. The oxygen and food material that are present in the maternal blood filter through the walls of the villi and enter the infant's blood which is in the vessels contained within the villi. These substances are then transported to the body of the infant and provide the materials required for growth and development. The infant's waste products are removed by a reversal of the process which supplies it with food. They are carried in the blood of the infant out through the umbilical cord into the villi and from there filter through into the mother's blood and are removed by her organs of excretion. The blood vessels connecting the infant with the placenta are united into a single ropelike structure called the umbilical cord.

Almost all of the organs are produced in a preliminary form in less than four weeks from the time cell division commences. Growth progresses so rapidly that by the end of the first eight weeks practically all organs and all parts of the body can be distinguished. Even the fingers and toes can be made out. From this time until the end of pregnancy the principal change is an increase in size.

After the infant has attained an age of about 38 weeks counting from the time of conception, or about 40 weeks counting from the first day of the last menstrual period, it is sufficiently mature to be capable of maintaining a normal existence outside of the mother's body. From 5 to 10 per cent of infants are born between the twenty-eighth and thirty-eighth week of pregnancy. These are premature infants, and in order to survive they must have special care. This is particularly true of the smaller ones.

BIRTH OF THE BABY

By the end of pregnancy all of the structures in the lowermost part of the mother's body have become softened and relaxed and are prepared to dilate and permit the passage of the infant. When everything is in readiness the muscles in the uterus begin to contract, and the cervix, which is the lowermost portion of the uterus, gradually grows thinner and the opening enlarges. The muscular contractions generally cause acute discomfort, the amount of pain, however, being variable in different women. The time required for the cervix to open sufficiently to allow the infant's head to pass through is somewhat longer in a first pregnancy than in subsequent pregnancies. Even in a first pregnancy it rarely takes more than 12 to 18 hours.

As soon as the cervix is completely dilated the uterine contractions become stronger and the infant is pushed downward through the cervix and vagina and is expelled from the birth canal. The infant is born! Immediately it opens its mouth and begins to cry. Respiration is established, never to stop as long as life lasts.

Within a few minutes of the birth of the infant the placenta and the membrane making up the wall of the sac within which the infant developed are also expelled from the uterus. These structures are essential to the infant during intra-uterine life, but when it is born their function ceases. Since they are expelled after the infant, they are commonly called the afterbirth.

Many women approach the time of delivery with great fear. There is little reason for this in the present day because the great advances that have been made by medical scientists in the knowledge of how to care for women before and during childbirth and the better facilities which are available during the time of birth have greatly diminished the dangers associated with childbearing.

Some doctors believe that fear is at the basis of most of the unpleasant sensations women experience during pregnancy and that it is responsible for most of the pain associated with delivery. To the extent that this is actually true, the expenditure of time and energy in attempting to allay those fears is well justified.

After the birth of the baby and the delivery of the placenta, the uterus contracts down into a firm solid mass that is only a fraction of its size just before the delivery of the infant. The muscles and tissues of the floor of the pelvis also contract and help to hold the uterus up in place. It takes approximately six weeks for the uterus to return to pre-pregnancy size and for the muscles of the pelvic floor to regain their strength. At the end of that time the processes associated with pregnancy have been terminated and the body starts again on its unceasing cycle of preparing for a new pregnancy.

Chapter 5

THE BIRTH OF THE BABY

by J. P. Greenhill, M.D.

Since bearing a child is one of the most momentous events in a woman's life, she naturally, and rightly so, is anxious to have the probable date of this event designated.

PREDICTING THE DATE OF BIRTH

It is impossible to predict accurately the day when a baby is to arrive. We can, however, determine the approximate date in a number of ways. These are:

1. Add seven days to the first day of the last monthly flow and subtract three months. Thus if the last menstrual period began on July 10, by adding seven days, getting July 17, and then subtracting three months, the date April 17 is arrived at as the approximate day labor may be expected. In most cases the confinement will take place within a few days before or after this calculated date. Confinement, termed labor medically, is the period during which a child is born.

2. A woman having her first baby may add twenty-two weeks to the day she first feels the baby move. A woman who has already borne children should add twenty-four weeks because the second or subsequent babies are felt to move earlier by her than by one who never has had a baby.

3. If the exact day of conception is known, 266 days added to this will give the approximate date of confinement. For example, if conception took place on January 1, counting 266 days from this date will make the approximate date of delivery September 24. Conception is the impregnation or fertilization of the ovum with the male cell or spermatozoon. Delivery is the expulsion of the child.

4. By repeated examinations a physician can often determine the day of the baby's birth within a few days of its arrival.

PREPARATIONS FOR CONFINEMENT

Since premature delivery—that is, delivery before the expected date of confinement—is not uncommon, it is a good plan to have certain articles ready a few weeks before this time. For women who plan to have their baby in a hospital, these articles should consist of two nightgowns, a robe, two pairs of stockings, a pair of slippers, a few handkerchiefs, a toothbrush and tooth paste or powder, a hand mirror, a comb, and a hairbrush. Most hospitals supply the baby's clothes until it is ready to leave. Therefore, the day before the patient expects to depart from the hospital the husband or someone else should bring some clothes for the baby to wear when it leaves the hospital. These should be a shirt, a nightgown or robe, a few diapers, a sweater, a cap, and two blankets. Of course these are only a few of the things which the expectant mother should buy a few weeks before the baby is expected to arrive.

As newborn babies quickly outgrow their clothes, not much is needed at the time of birth. Nowadays clothes for the baby are made to be comfortable for the child and easy to put on and to take off. They should be of light texture, for in steam-heated apartments babies are generally burdened with too many clothes. The clothes that a newborn baby requires are shirts, dresses, robes, nightgowns, diapers, booties, blankets, sweaters, and a cap.

WHEN TO CALL THE PHYSICIAN FOR CONFINEMENT

Labor is the term applied to the process of giving birth. Its onset is usually distinguished by three signs:

1. Rhythmic contractions of the womb, which are felt or defined by the mother as abdominal cramps. These may be felt by placing the hand on the abdomen, since the latter hardens during a contraction and relaxes when the cramp subsides. At the beginning these cramps or labor pains are irregular in frequency and intensity; they begin in the back and spread or radiate to the front. At first they occur at infrequent and irregular intervals, but later they become more frequent and more regular in time, also stronger and localized in the abdomen. "False pains" are weak contractions which occur a few days to a few weeks before actual confinement. They may be distinguished from true labor pains by the fact that they do not increase in frequency, intensity, or duration; that is, they soon subside.

2. The escape of fluid from the vagina. This is not urine. It results from rupture of the bag of waters in which the baby is enveloped. Labor pains usually do not begin until a few hours after this flow or dripping starts, but

it is advisable for the patient to go to the hospital after notifying the physician.

3. A thick, mucous, bloody discharge from the vagina, known as the "show."

Only one of these signs is usually present at first, but it is sufficient to warrant notifying the physician. Then the hospital should be informed that the patient is on the way. Sometimes abnormal symptoms may arise at about the time of confinement, and the physician must be told about them without delay. These symptoms include bleeding from the vagina, a sudden fainting attack, severe and persistent cramps in the abdomen, vomiting, disturbances in vision, and twitching of the muscles. It is a good thing to keep the telephone numbers of the physician, his assistant, and the hospital in a place where they are available without delay.

Ordinarily a number of hours elapses between the beginning of labor and the delivery or birth of the baby, so there is no need of excitement or haste. Women having their first baby are known as primigravidas. After a woman has delivered her first baby she is a primipara. For them the average duration of labor lasts about thirteen hours. Women who have previously borne a child or children are called multigravidas or multiparas. For them the average labor generally lasts about eight hours.

STAGES OF LABOR

Labor is divided into three stages known simply as the first, second, and third stages. The first stage is the period of preparation and extends from the beginning of labor until the neck of the uterus is opened up completely. The duration of this stage is generally about twelve hours in primigravidas and about seven and a half hours in multiparas. The second stage is the period of expulsion of the baby from the uterus to the outer world. This stage lasts about one hour in primigravidas and from fifteen to thirty minutes in multiparas. The third stage is the period during which the afterbirth separates from the uterus and is expelled from the genital tract; its duration averages about ten minutes. It is difficult to decide on the exact moment when the first stage ends and the second begins, but this is of little consequence. The beginning of the third stage is, of course, easy to determine because it starts immediately after the baby is born. The figures given for the length of each stage are average ones, but there are wide variations. Many labors are much shorter than the average and some last considerably longer. Furthermore, the experienced physician can often shorten the second stage of labor without harm to either the mother or the child.

THE POSITION OF THE BABY IN THE UTERUS

As soon as possible after labor begins the physician or his assistant sees the patient. In many hospitals an intern greets the patient when she arrives. Regardless of which physician sees the patient early in labor, certain examinations will be made. The patient's temperature and pulse are first taken, generally by a nurse. Then the abdomen is examined by a physician to determine the position in which the baby lies. In about 96 per cent of all cases the baby lies in the uterus with its head in the mother's pelvic cavity and its buttocks up near the mother's ribs. These cases are known as head presentations. In about 3 per cent the baby's buttocks, and not its head, lie in the mother's pelvis. These cases are known as breech presentations. In about one half of 1 per cent the baby's body lies crosswise to that of the mother, and such a presentation is termed transverse.

When we speak of normal presentations we refer to head presentations, but not all of these are normal. The most favorable presentation for a baby is that in which the head is in the pelvic cavity in such a way that the face is pointed downward toward the mother's back, and the top of the baby's head, known as the occiput, is directed upward toward the mother's abdomen. This type of head presentation is known as an occiput anterior (front) position, because the occiput is in the front half of the mother's body. The vast majority of babies are born as occiput anterior presentations, but in many instances the baby's face is pointed upward toward the mother's abdomen at the beginning of labor. Generally the face is turned around spontaneously so that its direction is toward the mother's back, and the baby is delivered normally as an occiput anterior presentation. In some instances, however, the face persists in its upward attitude. This condition is known as persistent occiput posterior, because the occiput remains in the posterior (back) part of the mother's body. These cases sometimes present a great deal of difficulty, but experienced physicians can easily deal with them.

Face and brow presentations are uncommon. With the former delivery is usually spontaneous, but brow presentations must be corrected before delivery can be effected.

A breech presentation is abnormal because sometimes it is hazardous for the baby, especially in primigravidas; in multiparas it is seldom troublesome. It can nearly always be detected during the last few weeks of pregnancy and by manipulation can be converted into occiput presentations in many instances. Therefore, the incidence of breech presentations can be reduced by manipulation near the end of pregnancy. This is advantageous because occiput presentations are much less likely to lead to difficulty in labor.

A transverse presentation during labor is always abnormal. Whereas the vast majority of babies presenting by the head and also a large proportion of those presenting by the breech can be delivered spontaneously by the mothers or with a little aid, a spontaneous delivery of a full-term child presenting transversely is practically impossible. Therefore, when a transverse presentation is detected, the baby is nearly always delivered by the physician through the vagina as soon as the neck of the uterus is open completely. In cases of transverse presentation the physician delivers the baby's feet first by a procedure known as version (turning) and extraction.

An abdominal examination will not only reveal the position of the baby but also whether twins are present. Generally two distinct heads can be felt, especially if one is down low and the other is up high. The most certain way of detecting twins is when two sets of heart tones are heard. If one discovers two sets of heart tones which are different from each other and are different from the mother's pulse, twins are present. Of course an X-ray picture will readily reveal twins or verify an abnormal presentation. An abdominal examination will also reveal the frequency and strength of the labor pains.

INTERNAL EXAMINATION

An internal examination is made after the abdominal one. Nearly always this is done through the rectum and not through the vagina to avoid any risk of infection to the mother. Examinations through the rectum require no special aseptic preparations and carry no danger. An experienced physician can obtain practically as much information from a rectal as from a vaginal exploration in most cases. Such an examination will disclose whether the presenting part of the baby is a head (and which type), breech, or other part, how far down the head or other presenting part is, the thickness and size of the opening in the neck of the uterus, whether the bag of waters is intact or ruptured, and other conditions. Following this examination, the blood pressure is taken, and a specimen of urine is obtained for examination. If a patient had no prenatal care, the physician will examine the heart and lungs to be certain that they are normal.

Following the examination by the physician, the patient is "prepared" by a nurse. First the hairs on the external genital organs are clipped or shaved for cleanliness. Then, if labor is not too far advanced, the patient is given an enema. This is to clean out the lower bowel in order to avoid the expulsion of feces (bowel contents) and contamination during the birth of the baby. In most instances a shower is given the mother-to-be on admission to the hospital.

The progress of labor is followed by abdominal and rectal examinations and also by the strength, frequency, and character of the labor pains. Only a few examinations are necessary for the conduct of labor.

In a hospital the first stage of labor is spent in a labor room, not in the delivery room. In the labor room an attempt is made to keep the patient comfortable. When the pains become fairly strong and regular one or more drugs are given to relieve them. Numerous drugs are used for this purpose, but all must be employed with caution, since large doses of nearly all of them have a serious effect on the baby. Furthermore, the injudicious use of narcotic (sleep-producing) drugs may interfere with labor by prolonging it, by making operative intervention necessary, and by disturbing the third stage of labor, causing hemorrhage. Their unwise use is particularly hazardous because of the definite likelihood that the baby will be born narcotized and will require resuscitation (procedure to restore consciousness). Therefore, drugs must not be given too close to the end of the first stage of labor.

The use of drugs in the first stage is known as analgesia (relief of pain without loss of consciousness). When a general anesthetic is used, such as ether, nitrous oxide, or ethylene, the patient loses consciousness. We call this anesthesia. Most women are given an analgesic in the first stage of labor and a large proportion of women, especially those delivered in hospitals, receive some anesthetic during the actual birth of the baby. Furthermore, in most hospital cases an inhalation anesthetic is administered in the second stage; a few whiffs during each uterine contraction. This is really analgesia because pain is relieved but consciousness is seldom lost. However, in many normal cases and in nearly all operative deliveries, complete anesthesia is given so that the patient is unconscious for a few minutes to more than an hour. The time varies with the situation presented. During the time of unconsciousness the baby is delivered and lacerations (tears) or incisions are sutured (sewed up).

Some drugs are given during labor not only to relieve the suffering but also to produce a loss of memory. When these drugs are used the women usually have no recollection from the time they take them until a few hours after the birth. Drugs producing amnesia (loss of memory) must be used with great caution. Patients must be watched constantly while they are under the influence of these drugs because some become unruly. Such drugs should not be used if a baby is to be delivered at home.

Spinal anesthesia has become popular. However, because of the definite though slight risk and the chance of producing a minor or a major complication, spinal anesthesia has a limited field of usefulness. It is definitely a hospital procedure. Because of the possible dangers and complications, the trained personnel and apparatus required, there is no need to use it for the average woman in labor. Most of the pains of labor, which are quickly forgotten in any event, can be relieved by properly selected drugs and anesthetics.

Experienced physicians do not rely entirely on drugs to quiet their patients. Many women, frightened by stories they have heard or read, go into labor fearing the outcome more than the pain involved. It is the physician's duty to try to allay these fears, preferably before the onset of labor. Words of encouragement during labor often help as much as, if not more than, drugs. Some women will benefit by the Grantly Dick Read technique of preparation for childbirth by means of which fear and tension are removed through discussions and exercises. Since the morale of the husband has a distinct effect on the wife, the physician keeps him informed of the progress of labor, cheers him up, and sees to it that he and the patient secure rest. The husband is permitted to remain with his wife while she is in the labor room but not in the delivery room. The husband's presence is distinctly helpful in the labor room. On the other hand, the patient's mother is usually kept away from the patient until after the baby is born. This is wise because most mothers are usually abnormally apprehensive about their daughters and not infrequently instill rather than dispel fear.

TECHNIC OF DELIVERY

A woman in labor is kept in the labor room until shortly before the baby is to be born. Then she is moved into the delivery room. In primigravidas this is done soon after the second stage has begun. Multiparas are moved before the end of the first stage because the second stage—that is, the actual birth of the baby—may last only a few minutes. In this room every precaution is taken to maintain as strict asepsis and antisepsis as possible in order to avoid infection.

THE DELIVERY

Nearly all women who have normal deliveries are placed on a narrow bed. The physician stands to one side of the bed, usually on the patient's right side. As the baby's head emerges the physician guides it so as to avoid undue damage to the mother's tissues between the external genital organs and the outer or external part of the rectum. This area is known as the perineum. In most hospital deliveries women are given an anesthetic at this time because the emergence of the baby's head is a painful process.

IMMEDIATE CARE OF THE BABY

Very soon after the baby is born the umbilical cord (navel cord), by which the baby is connected with the afterbirth or placenta, is compressed with two clamps and cut between the clamps. When the baby is very small or appears anemic, the cord is not severed until it stops pulsating, which indicates that the baby has received all the blood it can from the afterbirth. One portion of the cord remains attached to the baby and the other to the placenta, which is still in the uterus. The clamp on the baby's end of the cord is replaced by a metal clip or a short piece of tape to compress the blood vessels in the cord and thus to avoid bleeding. Then a 1-per-cent solution of silver nitrate or a similar medicament is instilled into the baby's eyes to prevent blindness from gonorrhea. This excellent procedure is an almost universal law.

IMMEDIATE CARE OF THE MOTHER

After birth the painful contractions of the uterus cease suddenly; if the woman is awake she is greatly relieved. However, mild contractions continue until the afterbirth separates. Within a few minutes the afterbirth is separated from its attachment to the inside of the womb and it is forced into the vagina by the uterine contractions. When the physician detects this he pushes down gently on the contracted uterus and the placenta is expelled. If there has been any laceration the wound is repaired. During this procedure, and for at least one hour after the delivery of the placenta, someone must watch the uterus to be certain that it remains contracted and that there is no bleeding from it.

Since 95 per cent of all confinements are normal, women go through labor in most instances with a minimum of pain and damage. About 5 per cent of labors are abnormal. Only some of these abnormalities are definitely preventable; others are not. An experienced physician can deal not only with complications to the complete satisfaction of both mother and child, but, more important, he possesses the knowledge to prevent trouble and to recognize it early.

THE PUERPERIUM

The puerperium (pū-ĕr-pē′rĭ-ŭm) is the time interval that extends from the birth of the baby until the organs of reproduction return to their normal condition. This interval usually lasts from six to eight weeks.

After the birth of a baby the mother is generally kept in the delivery room or a recovery room for at least thirty minutes to be certain that there is no bleeding from the uterus. Then she is taken to her room. Here also the patient must be watched carefully for a while. If a narcotic is given shortly after the baby is born, it will ensure physical and mental rest and perhaps a few hours of sleep. During the first few hours after delivery it is best to pull down the window shades and to keep everyone out of the room except the nurse. Of course the husband is permitted to see his wife and to talk to her if she is awake on her arrival in her room. However, he should stay only a short time, but he may return a few hours later.

For the first three days after the delivery it is a good policy to disconnect the telephone and to have only the husband, the patient's parents, and the husband's parents as visitors. After this only two visitors a day, other than the husband, are sufficient and best. The fewer visitors and telephone conversations the patient has during the first week, the stronger and more rested she will be. If a baby is born at home it is difficult to restrict visitors, but someone should be delegated to act the firm and stern policeman. Certainly no one who has a cold or infection of any kind should be permitted to visit the mother of a newborn child or be allowed in the baby's room. In hospitals there is an excellent rule which forbids children less than fourteen years of age from visiting the mother of a newborn baby. Young children are prone to carry infections, and of course the sight of her other children will usually upset the mother and make her homesick.

The discomfort that most women feel passes a few hours after the baby is born. The multiparas may have "afterpains," or painful contractions of the uterus, for twenty-four to forty-eight hours, but these are relieved easily by mild drugs. Primiparas seldom have afterpains. On the third or fourth day most women complain of pain and swelling of the breasts. This is caused by the onset of the flow of milk. The discomfort is seldom troublesome and generally disappears after twenty-four to forty-eight hours when the baby, by its sucking action, has regulated the amount of milk in the breasts. Babies are generally put to the breast only twice during the first twenty-four hours, and after this they nurse every four hours, except during the night. Breast nursing is beneficial to the mother as well as to the newborn baby.

During the first week the decrease in the size of the uterus is remarkable. Immediately after the baby is born and the afterbirth is expelled, the uterus contracts to a ball-shaped mass the size of a large grapefruit. By the end of the first week this organ has become so small that it can hardly be felt on abdominal examination.

Today patients are permitted much more freedom in bed than was the custom in previous years. We permit the patients to get out of bed the day after the baby is born unless there have been complications. They return to their homes when the baby is six to ten days old.

During the first ten days after a baby is born mothers lose about five pounds. The weight loss during delivery is about twelve pounds and consists chiefly of the baby, the afterbirth, and the amniotic fluid, water, that surrounded the baby.

If a patient had some disturbance during pregnancy she will need special aftercare. Thus, if a woman had high blood pressure she will have to have repeated blood-pressure readings. If she had a kidney infection her urine will have to be examined every day. These women must be watched not only during their hospital stay but for months and perhaps years afterward. Such follow-up care is important for the patient's future health and certainly for a decision about having more children.

POSTPARTUM CARE

Postpartum means after delivery. When a patient leaves the hospital she may walk up to her apartment, but she should walk slowly and rest frequently. If there are a number of flights for her to go up it may help to have a chair carried from landing to landing so that she may sit while she is resting or she may sit on the steps. Since there is considerable excitement incident to dressing the baby, packing suitcases, saying good-by to the nurses, riding home, meeting neighbors, and so on, in the process of getting home, it is advisable that the patient go to bed as soon as she reaches home and remain there until the following morning. It is best for her to leave the hospital in the afternoon because of the advantage of traveling during the day and because by the time home is reached there are not many waking hours left. Once in the home, the patient should not go into the street until the baby is almost three weeks old.

Probably the most important factor necessary to safeguard a happy household with a newborn baby is a mentally calm and unperturbed mother. This is determined to the largest extent by the health of the baby. As was previously said, the day of departure from the hospital is one of excitement. As a result the baby not infrequently loses weight on that day. After the first day at home the mother must learn to be more or less callous to disturbing influences. Certainly petty inconveniences should not be permitted to interfere with her peace of mind. If there is a nurse at home she, of course, assumes much of the responsibility in the care of the child. Tranquillity of mind and absolute regularity in feeding the infant will usually guarantee a thriving baby.

During the puerperium the mother should have an abundance of sleep and, in addition, should rest in a reclining position for definite periods of time in the morning and in the afternoon. While resting it is advisable for her to lie on her abdomen for fifteen to twenty minutes just as we ask our patients to do when they are in the hospital.

During the first week at home visitors should be restricted to two a day besides the immediate family. Tact is necessary to avoid talkative visitors or to limit their stay. Likewise telephone calls should be limited in number and length, especially if at the other end of the wire there is a garrulous individual or one who wants to impart information concerning dreadful occurrences. Visitors who have colds or infections should not be seen and definitely must not be admitted to the baby's room.

If the mother herself has a cold she should cover her mouth and nose with a handkerchief or a mouthpiece when nursing or bathing the baby. No medicine should be taken by the mother or given to the baby without the sanction of a physician. Some drugs reach the baby through the breast milk.

If there are three- or four-year-old children in the home the development of jealousy in them should be looked for and averted. Sometimes they resent the attention showered on a new arrival. Showing the baby off before relatives and friends may aggravate such a tendency.

For the first few weeks after childbirth a nursing mother should consider herself a convalescent invalid. This does not mean, however, that she should fear doing any kind of housework or lack confidence in her ability to take care of her baby. More consideration must be given to general rules of health than is customary, and the diet should be abundant, varied, and balanced.

When nursing the baby one may sit up or recline. An extremely important thing to avoid is constant observation of the baby while it is at the breast, for this not only strains the mother's eyes and produces headaches but strains the muscles of the neck and back, which likewise become the seat of pain.

For the woman with a lax abdominal wall a supporting garment is most helpful. Tub baths are best not taken until after the third week, but showers and sponge baths should be taken daily during this time. Walking is helpful, but strenuous exercise, such as playing golf or tennis, swimming, skating, or even driving a car, should be avoided during the puerperal period. Social functions during these weeks should likewise be reduced to a minimum.

RETURN OF MENSTRUATION

The return of menstruation varies in different individuals. In those who do not nurse their babies the flow usually returns at the end of six weeks, while in those who do breast-feed their babies the first menstrual period appears any time after the third month. In some, however, the menses do not return until the baby is weaned. The first period is usually profuse, sometimes enough to cause alarm. At the time of the first period it is best for the woman to keep off her feet as much as possible, but if the flow is too profuse the advice of a physician should be sought. In fact, if the mother has any doubt concerning herself or the baby she should consult her physician rather than take the advice offered by well-meaning but often misinformed friends and relatives. Cracked or bleeding nipples or painful breasts particularly call for immediate notification of the physician.

It is customary for a patient to return to her physician at the end of the puerperal period; namely, six to eight weeks after the birth of the baby. At this time the physician will determine, by an abdominal and vaginal examination, whether the reproductive organs have returned to their normal state. Generally this checkup is designated as the "final" examination. This is unfortunate, because the patient regards it as the final contact with her physician until a new pregnancy begins or some disturbance arises. Since some women have complications or abnormalities or they develop after childbirth, it is advisable for women to see their obstetrician when the baby is six months old and again when it is a year old. All women should be examined at least once a year, even if they feel entirely well.

Chapter 6

THE PREVENTION OF CONCEPTION

by Abraham Stone, M.D.

ASSOCIATE CLINICAL PROFESSOR OF PREVENTIVE MEDICINE, NEW YORK UNI-
VERSITY COLLEGE OF MEDICINE; DIRECTOR, MARGARET SANGER RESEARCH
BUREAU, NEW YORK CITY; CO-AUTHOR OF "A MARRIAGE MANUAL" AND "PLANNED
PARENTHOOD"

Family planning has become a widely accepted practice in this
country. Present-day social, economic, and cultural conditions make child
spacing and family regulation desirable. Families in all strata of society are
increasingly resorting to measures for the voluntary control of procreation.

From time immemorial man has attempted to control the size of the
family. Among primitive peoples unwanted babies were often left exposed
or were destroyed, and infanticide was a widespread measure for limiting
the number of children. Later man learned that instead of destroying the
child after birth it was possible to destroy the products of conception before
birth. Thus abortion came into wide practice.

With the growth of knowledge, however, and with the increase in the
understanding of the physiology of reproduction, man learned that it was
not necessary to destroy the child either before or after birth, since it is
possible to control parenthood by preventing conception.

The principles of control of conception are based on the principles of the
physiology of conception. The origin of a new life depends on the meeting
and the union of a sperm cell and an egg cell, and the prevention of conception depends on preventing this meeting. Basically, the principle of most
contraceptive methods is to prevent the sperm cells from gaining access into
the uterus and tubes.

The Ideal Method. The requirements for an ideal contraceptive are:
First, harmlessness: there should not be any likelihood of any harm either
to the husband or wife or future offspring resulting from its use. Secondly,
reliability: it should provide certain protection in nearly every instance.
Thirdly, acceptability: it should satisfy the individual needs of those who

are to use it, which in turn depends on the method being simple and practical, inexpensive, aesthetically satisfactory, without interference with the spontaneity of the sexual act.

While the ideal contraceptive has not yet been attained, methods are known today that are entirely harmless, that give a maximum of protection, and are generally satisfactory. Further research is still needed, however, to develop even more completely acceptable methods—methods that will be simple and inexpensive enough to meet the needs of the great masses of peoples the world over, that will preferably provide long-term protection, and that will meet all aesthetic requirements.

The contraceptive methods available today may be divided into those used by the husband and those used by the wife.

MALE METHODS

The male methods of contraception depend upon the prevention of the entrance of the man's seminal fluid into the genital tract of the woman. For this purpose the husband can resort either to coitus interruptus, generally known as withdrawal or "taking care," or he can use a rubber sheath called a condom.

Coitus Interruptus refers to the withdrawal of the male organ just prior to the ejaculation, so that the seminal fluid is deposited outside of the genital canal. This practice is referred to in the Bible in connection with the story of Onan, whose duty it was to marry the widow of his older brother, who had died childless, and to beget offspring with her so as "to raise up seed" to his brother. Onan, however, did not want to raise children in his brother's name and so, the story continues, it "came to pass whenever he went in unto his brother's wife that he used to spill it on the ground." In other words, he resorted to withdrawal.

From the medical point of view this method is neither reliable nor desirable. It frequently fails to prevent conception as a result of inadequate control or of carelessness on the part of the husband, or because the precoital secretion sometimes contains spermatozoa; and the constant anxiety lest the withdrawal be delayed too long interferes with the spontaneity of the sex relation. Continuous resort to this method may lead to emotional and possibly also to organic disturbances in both partners.

The Condom is the other method that the man can employ for contraceptive purposes. It is designed to be applied to the male organ just before the sex relation and to prevent any of the seminal fluid from being deposited in the female genital tract. Devised some 400 years ago by an Italian physician to be used as a preventive against infection, it later began to be employed extensively as a method for the prevention of conception. The advantages of the condom are that it is harmless, reliable, and easily procurable. Its dependability is lessened to some degree by the possibility of breakage during use, as well as by the occasional slipping off after use and the spilling of the contents into the vagina. These mishaps can be obviated by testing for defects before use, by adequate lubrication, and by holding onto the sheath before removal of the organ. The condom can also be inspected after use, and if a tear is discovered a vaginal douche can be taken for additional protection.

Breakage of the condom has, furthermore, become less frequent in recent years since the Federal Food and Drug Administration has classified condoms as "drugs" and placed them under its control. The Administration has been confiscating and destroying sheaths sent in interstate commerce found to be defective or not up to the desirable standards. This has led to considerable improvement in the product, as well as to testing of the sheaths by the manufacturers prior to distribution.

The chief drawback to the use of the condom is the likelihood of its interference with the normal sexual response. It dulls sensation and if applied, as it often is, at the height of sexual excitation it interrupts the spontaneity of the sexual act. For these reasons many men as well as women object to its use. Furthermore, when the husband's potency is inadequate, the use of the sheath adds to the difficulty.

Aside from the fact that neither coitus interruptus nor the condom is entirely satisfactory, there is an additional objection to male methods; they make the woman dependent upon the man for contraceptive protection. Should he be indifferent, or careless, or in an irresponsible condition, he may subject her to the hazard of an unwanted conception. Contraceptive methods which can be used by the woman are therefore preferred.

FEMALE METHODS

If the husband does not use any protection and deposits the seminal fluid in the vagina conception may still be avoided if measures are used to prevent the entry of spermatozoa into the uterus. The methods available for this purpose may be divided into three groups: chemical, mechanical, and biological.

Chemical Methods. A number of chemical methods have been developed for contraceptive use—douches, suppositories, jellies, creams, foam tablets, and powders. All depend in part on their chemical properties, to paralyze or destroy the spermatozoa, and in part on their mechanical action, to wash out the seminal fluid or to provide a barrier to the entrance of the sperm cells into the uterus.

Douches. The vaginal douche, taken after intercourse, is perhaps the most popular female method for the prevention of conception. This method was first described and advocated by an American physician, Dr. Charles Knowlton, in a book on conception control published more than a century ago under the quaint title of *The Fruits of Philosophy*. "My method," wrote Dr. Knowlton, "operates in a two-fold manner, either of which may perhaps be effectual. It consists in syringing the vagina soon after the male emission into it, with some liquid, which will not merely dislodge nearly all the semen . . . but which will destroy the fecundating property of any portion of semen that will remain."

This method, therefore, depends for its effectiveness upon the mechanical removal of the seminal fluid and upon the destruction of the remaining sperm cells by the chemical ingredients in the solution. A variety of chemicals have been suggested for this purpose, and many manufacturing concerns have widely exploited their particular products for use in so-called "feminine hygiene."

While the vaginal douche may be useful for medical purposes when indicated, it is neither a reliable nor a satisfactory contraceptive method. It often fails no matter what type of solution is used. This is probably due to the fact that the spermatozoa may enter into the uterus directly after the ejaculation and thus pass beyond the reach of the douche. The need, furthermore, for arising immediately after intercourse is psychologically disturbing to many women, for the sexual relation should be followed by a period of relaxation and rest. The chief value of the douche, then, is for use either as an auxiliary to other contraceptive methods or as an emergency method when indicated.

Chemical methods, to be effective, should be applied prior to, rather than after, the sex act. A variety of products have been made available for this purpose. Those most frequently used are suppositories, jellies, and creams.

Suppositories have been popular largely because they are simple to use, are easily procurable, and do not require a medical prescription. Usually suppositories consist of a small solid cone or capsule containing some sperm-destroying chemical ingredient in a base of cocoa butter, gelatine, or other readily soluble substance. They are designed to be inserted into the vaginal canal a few minutes before intercourse and are supposed to melt at slightly below body temperature. When melted, the gelatinous or greasy base lodges near the opening into the uterus, acting as a physical barrier to the entrance of spermatozoa, while the chemical ingredients either paralyze or destroy the sperm cells. Thus they act on both mechanical and chemical principles.

None of the suppositories available at present, however, has proven to be sufficiently reliable. Sometimes they fail to melt rapidly enough, or they may be so placed that the entrance to the uterus remains exposed. A reliable, non-greasy suppository would provide a practical and simple method against conception. Future research may help to develop a contraceptive of this kind.

Jellies and Creams. A more adequate chemical contraceptive is provided by the jelly or cream, which consists of a semi-fluid, gelatinous, creamy or soapy base into which certain sperm-destroying chemicals are incorporated. Jellies and creams are introduced into the vagina by means of a special applicator and, like the suppository, their effect depends both on their mechanical and chemical properties—they block the opening into the uterus and at the same time immobilize the sperm cells. As the jellies and creams are already in a semi-liquid state, they do not have to melt in the vagina like the suppository and are therefore more apt to spread easily into the vaginal folds and cover the entrance into the womb.

The use of a jelly or cream alone as a contraceptive measure has several advantages. Its application is simple, it is readily available and its use does not require a preliminary individual examination. The disadvantages are the aesthetic drawbacks of overlubrication and leakage, and the fact that no jelly or cream available today is completely reliable. This may be due largely to the failure of the jelly to form an effective mechanical barrier, and in part also to its failure to immobilize all the spermatozoa in time.

Foam Tablets. Small vaginal tablets are also employed for contraceptive purposes. The tablet is inserted into the vagina shortly before intercourse and is supposed to dissolve in the presence of the normal vaginal moisture. The interaction of the chemical ingredients of the tablet produces a fairly copious foam, and the effectiveness of the tablet is supposed to depend partly on the physical action of the foam which enmeshes the spermatozoa and partly on the spermicidal properties of the ingredients. Tablets have the advantage of simplicity of use, but their reliability has not yet been sufficiently established.

There is, then, no chemical contraceptive available at present which meets the requirements of sufficient reliability and acceptability. Perhaps with further research new formulas may be developed which will make chemical contraceptives more certain and more acceptable.

Mechanical Methods. Mechanical methods generally consist of devices which are introduced into the vagina, such as diaphragms and caps, and which are designed to cover the entrance into the uterus. To a greater degree than any of the other methods mentioned they meet the requirements of harmlessness, reliability, and acceptability. They have no injurious effect, they provide more certain protection, and they interfere little with sensation or with the spontaneity of the sex relations.

Diaphragms, also called pessaries, are designed to lie diagonally across the vaginal canal. They are made of soft rubber with a flexible metal spring around the circumference and come in a variety of sizes and shapes. *Caps* are generally cup-shaped and are intended to be placed directly over the cervix, or neck of the uterus. They are made either of soft rubber or of firm materials such as metal or plastic. (Figure 9.)

The required size and type of diaphragm or cap can be determined only after an individual examination by a physician trained in this field of medical practice. As a rule they are used in conjunction with a contraceptive jelly which serves both as a lubricant and as an additional safeguard. The diaphragm may be inserted either before retiring or before the sexual relation and removed the following morning or immediately after use if preferred. Usually it is advisable to douche before and after the removal of the diaphragm, but if it has remained in place for eight hours after use a douche is not essential. The firm cervical caps are sometimes left in place for many days at a time and thus provide more prolonged protection.

The objections to the use of the diaphragm or cap are the need for individualization and the need for preparation before each sex relation. Some women are reluctant to take the trouble to insert the diaphragm or to use any method which requires vaginal manipulation. Greater skill in prescription, more careful instructions, and simplification in technique have, however, made the method increasingly more acceptable.

In addition to the methods mentioned there are mechanical devices which are introduced by the physician into the uterus and allowed to remain there for several months at a time. These are called intra-uterine methods and are known as "stems," "buttons," and "rings." They are made either of metal, plastic, hard rubber, or soft rubber. Their chief advantage is the fact that they provide prolonged protection without the need of preparation for each sex relation. Their use, however, is not recommended because of the possibility of harmful effects. A number of serious complications have been reported following the insertion of these devices. They open an avenue by which infection may ascend from the vagina into the uterus and tubes.

Contraception and Sterility. The statement is sometimes made that the use of contraceptive precautions may eventually lead to sterility. This statement has no basis in actual experience. Planned Parenthood Centers provide the records of tens of thousands of women who have employed contraceptive measures for varying lengths of time, sometimes for many years, and who

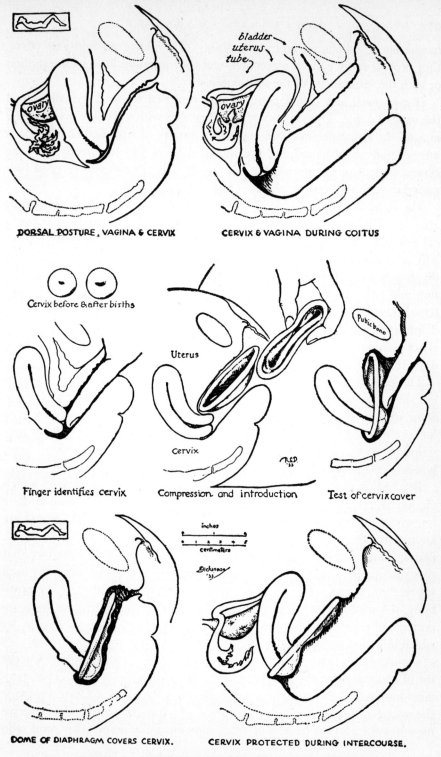

DORSAL POSTURE, VAGINA & CERVIX — CERVIX & VAGINA DURING COITUS

bladder
uterus
tube

ovary

Cervix before & after births

Uterus

Cervix

Pubic bone

Finger identifies cervix — Compression and introduction — Test of cervix cover

inches
centimeters

Dickinson '33

DOME OF DIAPHRAGM COVERS CERVIX. — CERVIX PROTECTED DURING INTERCOURSE.

FIGURE 9.   CONTROL OF CONCEPTION BY DIAPHRAGM

readily conceived when they discontinued preventive precautions and planned a pregnancy. There is no reason to suppose that the use of medically approved contraceptive measures will lead to a diminution in reproductive capacity.

However, since it is easier for a woman to conceive at younger ages, childbearing should not be postponed too long. Youth is the best ally of fertility.

Biological Methods. Future progress in contraception seems to lie in the field of biological methods. Some of these hold forth the promise of providing long-term protection combined with simplicity of use.

The "Safe Period." The simplest biological method is reliance on the so-called "safe period." While the man is always fecund and capable of impregnating the woman, the latter is fertile only during certain days of her menstrual month, at the time of ovulation; that is, at the time when the egg is released from the ovary. During other days she is presumably infertile. Conception can therefore be prevented by avoiding intercourse during the few fertile days.

According to present-day medical opinion, the human female produces only one egg cell during a menstrual cycle, usually about two weeks before the onset of the next menses. The egg cell retains its vitality for probably not more than twenty-four hours. As yet, however, we do not possess any sufficiently accurate method to establish with certainty the day of ovulation for the individual woman. For the present we depend upon studying the record of a woman's menstrual cycles over a period of about a year, as well as on a record of her daily temperature, taken immediately on awakening, over several months. The menstrual chart and temperature chart make it possible to estimate with a fair degree of accuracy the fertile and infertile days in women whose menstrual cycles are fairly regular.

A woman with a regular twenty-eight-day cycle ovulates presumably around the fourteenth day, counting from the first day of menstruation. Allowing two or three days for the life of the spermatozoa and two or three days for the life of the egg and possible variations, it is fairly safe to assume that the fertile period extends from the eleventh to the nineteenth day. Before the eleventh day and from the eighteenth or nineteenth day onward she will no longer be capable of conception because there will be no egg present to be fertilized. If the cycles are irregular, then the sterile and fertile days will vary accordingly. In general, the last ten days of the month, the ten days prior to the onset of the next menstrual period, can be considered to be fairly safe from the likelihood of conception. It is assumed that the first nine days of the cycle are also sterile, but this is much less certain because we do not know with certainty how long the sperm cells of the male can remain alive within the genital tract of the woman.

The objections to the reliance on the safe period are, first, the fact that it limits sexual relations to only a part of the month; second, that unexpected physical and emotional changes may suddenly disturb the regularity of the cycle and thus invalidate the previous calculations.

Hormones. Considerable research is now under way to develop biological methods for the control of conception, which would prevent either egg or sperm formation, the union of sperm and egg, or the implantation of the fertilized egg in the uterus. Recent experiments have shown that such effects can be achieved by the use of hormones or other chemical substances. Thus far, however, practically all the research in this field has been carried out on animals and the value of biological contraceptives for human use still remains to be determined. The reproductive mechanism is a delicate apparatus, and great care must naturally be exercised not to disturb any of the normal physiological processes. Nevertheless, it is not at all unlikely that it may become possible to render a man or a woman infertile for a very definite length of time by an occasional hypodermic injection or even by the oral administration of a few tablets.

Sterilization. In conditions in which a pregnancy should never occur, permanent control of conception may be advised by the physician. When childbearing or childbirth, for example, may jeopardize the life of the mother because of serious involvement of vital organs, when delivery by Caesarean section occurs for the second or third time, or when serious incurable mental defects or other hereditary conditions are present, sterilization may be the method of choice.

Sterilization operations may be performed on the husband or the wife. Sterilization of the male is a comparatively simple procedure. A small incision is made in the skin of the scrotum above the testicle, and the duct, called the vas deferens, is tied off and cut. The incision is then closed with a single suture, and the same procedure is repeated on the other side. Complete recovery generally takes place within a few days.

In the woman, an abdominal incision is required. The Fallopian tubes which lead from the ovary to the uterus are lifted and tied on both sides. This implies hospitalization for a few days. Simplified surgical techniques are at present under investigation. Sterilization can also be accomplished by means of X rays to the sex glands, but in women this produces artificial menopause and is indicated only in selected cases.

Sterilization does not involve the removal of any sex gland, nor does it affect sex desire or satisfaction. It is, however, a permanent and irreversible procedure. Fertility can rarely be restored to a man or woman who has been surgically sterilized. (Figure 10.)

In recent years considerable progress has been made in the investigation of contraceptive techniques and materials. The Council on Pharmacy and Chemistry and the Council on Physical Therapy of the American Medical Association have formulated minimum standards for contraceptive materials and now investigate products recommended for contraceptive purposes. The published reports of the Council investigations serve to provide the physician with a suitable guide in the prescription and choice of contraceptive products. Indirectly they also stimulate more intensive research in the entire field of human fertility and its control.

FEMALE FERTILITY AND STERILIZATION:

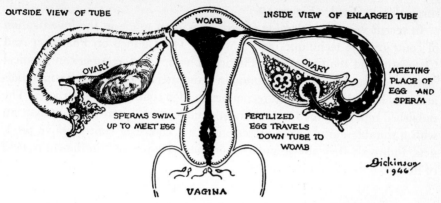

OUTSIDE VIEW OF TUBE

INSIDE VIEW OF ENLARGED TUBE

WOMB

OVARY

OVARY

MEETING PLACE OF EGG AND SPERM

SPERMS SWIM UP TO MEET EGG

FERTILIZED EGG TRAVELS DOWN TUBE TO WOMB

Dickinson 1946

VAGINA

FROM VAGINA SPERMS MOUNT THROUGH UTERUS FOR ONE TO ENTER OVUM BEFORE IT GOES TO UTERUS

TUBES BOTH TIED TO STERILIZE

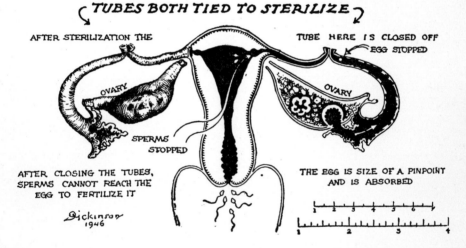

AFTER STERILIZATION THE

TUBE HERE IS CLOSED OFF
EGG STOPPED

OVARY

OVARY

SPERMS STOPPED

AFTER CLOSING THE TUBES, SPERMS CANNOT REACH THE EGG TO FERTILIZE IT

THE EGG IS SIZE OF A PINPOINT AND IS ABSORBED

Dickinson 1946

NOTHING IS DONE TO OVARIES : NO NERVES
ARE CUT: TWO BRISTLE SIZE PASSAGES
ARE SHUT OFF BY LIGATURE AND SECTION
TO PREVENT THE SPERMATOZOA FROM
REACHING THE OVUM: THIS OPERATION
CALLED SALPINGECTOMY MAY BE
COMPARED WITH A SIMPLE APPENDECTOMY
(POMEROY METHOD)

FIGURE 10.   STERILIZATION

PART FOUR

The Child in the Family

Chapter 1

THE PHYSICAL GROWTH OF THE CHILD

by Wilton M. Krogman, Ph.D.

PROFESSOR OF PHYSICAL ANTHROPOLOGY, GRADUATE SCHOOL OF MEDICINE, UNIVERSITY OF PENNSYLVANIA, AND DIRECTOR, PHILADELPHIA CENTER FOR RESEARCH IN CHILD GROWTH

FOREWORD

After your baby is born it continues to grow. You may react to this statement by saying, "How silly! Of course all babies grow." You are right! But I want to tell you how they grow, when they grow, how they increase in size, change in proportions, and mature. You'll agree that an adult is more than a baby just grown bigger.

You have a right to ask: "Why should I bother with physical growth? How will a knowledge of physical growth help me bring up my child?"

WHY STUDY HUMAN GROWTH?

1. We study the physical growth of the child as a measure of health progress and nutritional (or dietetic) balance. A child whose physical growth shows a uniform, even progress is a healthy and well-nourished child.

2. We study the physical growth of the child by observation and measurement at regular intervals. This gives us a check on health condition and an assessment of nutritional status. (You will note that these first two reasons are really phases of each other: the first refers more to progress, the second more to status at any given time.)

3. We study the physical growth of the child in order to ascertain its progress with reference to the group averages which constitute "norms" of progress. Let us say that Johnny is three years old, or seven, or thirteen. At each of these ages he is growing at a different rate. (We say he is in a different "stage" of physical growth.) How does he compare with other three-year boys, or seven-year, or thirteen-year?

4. We study the physical growth of the child to learn as much as we can about hereditary pattern. To do this it is necessary to know something

about the family background. We recognize that some children are from small family lines, others from average, others from tall or large family lines.

5. We study the physical growth of the child, finally, to establish each child as an individual. Children do not grow precisely alike; they follow a general pattern, to be sure, but their own growth progress is the measure of their own individuality.

Those of us who have measured thousands of growing boys and girls use an elaborate system of measurements. We measure the head, the face, the trunk, the arms, the legs, in precise detail—some forty or fifty measurements in all. This gives us an idea of *increase in size*. From these measurements we calculate about fifteen to twenty indices; i.e., the ratio or proportion of one dimension to another (e.g., trunk length divided by total body length). This gives us some idea of *change in proportion*. Our measurements, then, enable us to be accurate in our analysis of progress in physical growth.

MEASUREMENT OF HEIGHT AND WEIGHT

I am going to tell you about growth in only two dimensions: *height* and *weight*. These are not only two useful measurements but are also the ones about which we have the most information. But they are only two of many. We use them against the background of a detailed analysis of physical growth in every area of the body.

Technically speaking, height and weight are not really simple measurements. Height is made up of head height (from chin to crown), neck length, trunk length, and leg length; it involves, therefore, linear growth in the head, backbone, and leg bones. Weight is made up of bone, muscle, fat, and organs.

The measurement of height should be done as carefully as possible. Until the child stands well you will take *recumbent* (or lying-down) *length*. Place the baby on the back, see that the legs are straight (the knees not bent), and then measure the maximum distance from the top of the head to the sole of the feet, usually at the heels. It is best to do this, in the home, with the baby lying on a flat, hard surface (a table top or dresser top) so that the body will not sag or curve (as on a soft mattress or couch). A yardstick, placed alongside, is preferable; if a cloth tape is used see that it is stretched or tightened to the same degree each time it is used. (If you can use a steel tape, so much the better.) After the child stands you will take *vertical* (or standing-up) *height*. In the home it is easiest to stand the child against a wall and then mark where a level rule placed on the top of the head intersects the wall. (Put the ruler on the child's head, holding it parallel with the floor, and mark where the ruler touches the wall.) The distance from floor to mark should be measured with a yardstick, preferably, or with a tape, carefully used.

The measurement of weight is not difficult. The use of the ordinary basket scales for small babies and platform scales for standing on is quite acceptable. Note the readings (usually in pounds and ounces)* as precisely as you can. Remember, the younger the child, the more careful the reading should be. A few ounces or a fraction of an inch are much more important to a baby than to a ten-year-old.

I recommend measuring and weighing as often as the doctor suggests during the first year. After that, every six months until five or six years. Thereafter, annually should be enough. (If your family doctor wants more frequent weighings, then obviously you will observe the schedule he wishes.)

HEIGHT-WEIGHT TABLES AND GRAPHS

Tables 1 and 2 give heights and weights for boys and girls from birth to 18 years.† In these tables there are two columns, labeled Av. (*average*) and *range*. I have given stature (length and/or height) in inches and weight in pounds. For each age I have given the average height and weight typical of a boy or girl at birth and at one to eighteen years. In addition, I have calculated the *normal range of variation* for each dimension at each age. This is the range within which two of every three boys or girls at a given age will fall. Thus, these Tables tell two things: (1) the average, or mean, height and weight at each age; (2) the normal "spread" or variation around each mean value.

Now let me say a word about the use and interpretation of the *average* column. In the first place, an average is not much more than a statement of the mid-point of a range of variation. I mean by this that we *expect* some children to be below, some above, the average. That is perfectly normal. There are big children, small children, heavy children, light children—just as there are tall and short, heavy and light parents. The problem confronting

---

*This is as good a place as any to tell you about pounds and ounces, kilograms and millimeters. (We generally use the latter or metric system.)

$$2.20 \text{ pounds} = \text{one kilogram}$$
$$1.0 \text{ inch} = 25.4 \text{ millimeters}$$

For example, the baby weighs 5 kgs. This is 11.0 lbs. (5 × 2.2 = 11.0). Or the baby weighs 25 lbs. This is 11.36 kgs. (25 ÷ 2.2 = 11.36).

Or, for stature, the baby is 648 mm. long. This is 25.5 in. (648 ÷ 25.4 = 25.5). Or the baby is 33 in. long. This is 838.2 mm. (33 × 25.4 = 838.2).

†These are composite Tables. The birth measures are averages from my book, *The Growth of Man* (1941). The 3, 6 and 9 months figures are from Simmons and Todd (1938) on Cleveland children enrolled in the Brush Foundation. The 1–18 year data are basically from Gray and Ayres (1931) mainly on Chicago private-school children. I am grateful to Dr. Horace Gray for permission to use his data. I have converted his metric data to inches and pounds.

TABLE 1

Height (inches)

AGE	GIRLS		BOYS	
	Av.	Range	Av.	Range
Birth	22.0	21.0–23.0	22.5	21.5–23.5
1 yr.	29.5	28.0–31.0	30.0	28.5–31.5
2 yrs.	34.0	32.5–35.5	34.5	33.0–36.0
3 "	38.0	36.5–39.5	38.5	37.0–40.0
4 "	41.0	39.5–43.5	41.5	40.0–43.0
5 "	43.5	41.5–45.5	44.0	42.0–46.0
6 "	46.5	44.5–48.5	46.5	44.5–48.5
7 "	49.0	47.0–51.0	49.0	47.0–51.0
8 "	51.0	49.0–53.0	51.0	49.0–53.0
9 "	53.5	51.5–55.5	53.5	51.5–55.5
10 "	55.5	53.5–57.5	55.5	53.5–57.5
11 "	58.0	56.0–60.0	57.5	55.5–59.5
12 "	61.0	58.5–63.5	60.0	58.0–62.0
13 "	63.0	60.5–65.5	62.0	60.0–64.0
14 "	64.0	61.5–66.5	65.0	63.0–67.0
15 "	65.0	62.5–67.5	67.5	65.5–69.5
16 "	65.5	63.5–67.5	69.0	67.5–70.5
17 "	65.5	63.5–67.5	69.5	68.0–71.0
18 "	66.0	64.0–68.0	69.5	68.0–71.0

us, therefore, is, "When is a growing child too short or too tall, too light or too heavy?"

The birth length increases itself by about one half in the first year of life. Boys at birth weigh 3.60 kgs. (or 7.92 lbs.) and girls 3.50 kgs. (or 7.70 lbs.). At one year they are 10.89 kgs. and 10.25 kgs., respectively. Birth weight is almost tripled in the first year of life.

Let me, in Table 3, give you an idea how boys and girls grow in a percentage manner. This percentage is figured as the *amount* of growth in a given period (e.g., birth to one year) divided by the *size* of the dimension at the *beginning* of the period.

Let us look at the data of Tables 1 and 2 in more graphic form, as shown in Figures 11–14. In Figure 11 the average height (in millimeters) for boys and girls is plotted; in Figure 12 the average weight (in kilograms) for boys and girls is plotted; in Figure 13 the increments in height for boys and girls are plotted; in Figure 14 the increments in weight for boys and girls are plotted. These graphs are *curves* of growth in height and weight; Figures 11 and 12 are called *additive* or *cumulative* curves; i.e., the curve is

TABLE 2

Weight (pounds)

AGE	GIRLS		BOYS	
	Av.	Range	Av.	Range
Birth	7.0	6.0– 8.0	7.5	6.5– 8.5
1 yr.	22.0	19.5– 24.5	24.0	21.5– 26.5
2 yrs.	28.0	25.0– 31.0	30.0	27.0– 33.0
3 "	33.0	29.0– 37.0	34.0	30.5– 37.5
4 "	37.5	31.5– 43.5	38.0	34.0– 42.0
5 "	42.5	36.5– 48.5	43.0	38.0– 48.0
6 "	48.5	40.5– 56.5	49.0	43.0– 55.0
7 "	55.0	47.0– 63.0	55.0	48.0– 62.0
8 "	62.0	52.0– 72.0	62.0	53.0– 71.0
9 "	70.0	57.0– 83.0	68.5	57.5– 79.5
10 "	78.0	63.0– 93.0	77.0	64.0– 90.0
11 "	88.5	72.5–104.5	85.5	69.5–101.5
12 "	100.5	80.5–120.5	96.0	77.0–115.0
13 "	111.0	91.0–131.0	106.0	84.0–128.0
14 "	120.0	100.0–140.0	120.0	98.0–142.0
15 "	126.5	106.5–146.5	133.0	113.0–153.0
16 "	131.0	115.0–147.0	142.0	122.0–162.0
17 "	134.0	118.0–150.0	148.0	128.0–168.0
18 "	135.0	120.0–150.0	152.0	133.0–171.0

TABLE 3

PERCENTAGE GROWTH IN HEIGHT AND WEIGHT

HEIGHT		WEIGHT	
Age	Rate in Per Cent	Age	Rate in Per Cent
Birth– 1 yr.	50	Birth– 1 yr.	200
1– 2 yrs.	20	1– 2 yrs.	25–30
3– 4 "	8	3– 6 "	12
5– 8 "	5	7–10 "	10–11
9–12 "	3–4*	11–12 "	8*
12–14 "	4–6	13–15 "	10–12
14–adult	1–2 until cessation	15–adult	4 until curve levels off

*Girls are about 2 years earlier here; rate may be 1–2 per cent lower for height, 1–2 per cent higher for weight.

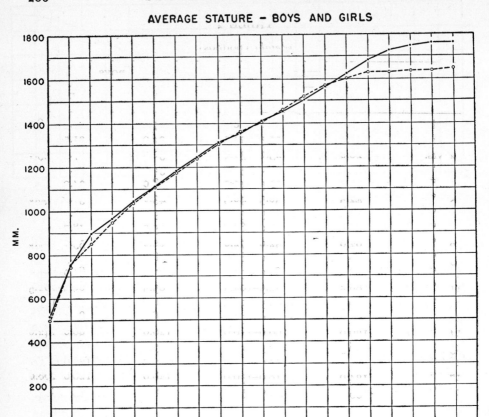

AVERAGE STATURE – BOYS AND GIRLS

YEARS

BOYS —·—
GIRLS --o--

FIGURE II.   AVERAGE STATURE: BOYS AND GIRLS

progressive since each average contains all gains or increments previously made; Figures 13 and 14 are *incremental* curves; i.e., the curve merely indicates the total amount of gain during a given period of time, usually from birthday to birthday; i.e., year to year.

Figures 11 and 12 show that in general boys and girls grow in height and weight pretty much alike up until about ten to eleven years of age. Then the girls are, on the average, taller and heavier than boys of the same age. This is true from about ten and a half to thirteen and a half years for height and nine to fourteen and a half years for weight. It is worthy of note that the weight superiority of the girls begins earlier and lasts longer than their height superiority.

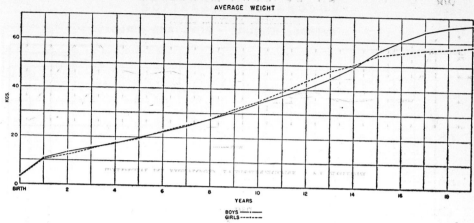

FIGURE 12. AVERAGE WEIGHT: BOYS AND GIRLS

In Figures 13 and 14 this is clearly emphasized. First, observe Figure 13. The early increments in height are great, as is shown by the fact that the curve *slopes downward* from the left. This means that, except during the first year, children grow more rapidly in height than in weight. Now, observe Figure 14. Here, after an early marked increment in weight, there is a gradual *upward slope* of the curve from the left. This means that, except during the first year, children grow more slowly in weight than in height. To put it into a simple rule: children grow tall before they grow heavy.

Figures 13 and 14 tell us other facts. Note in Figure 13 how the curve, after sloping downward, suddenly rises. Moreover, it rises *sooner in girls* than in boys. Again in Figure 14 note how the curve, rising gradually, suddenly shows a more marked upward slope. Again, *girls are sooner*. In both height and weight girls have a sudden increase (a "spurt") about two years, on the average, earlier than boys. The curves in Figures 13 and 14 tell us, therefore, that height and weight suddenly increase in the very early teens and that

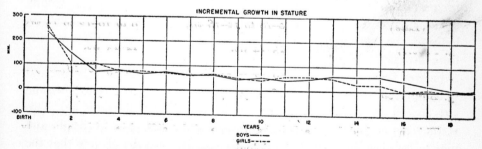

FIGURE 13. INCREMENTAL GROWTH IN STATURE

INCREMENTAL GROWTH IN WEIGHT

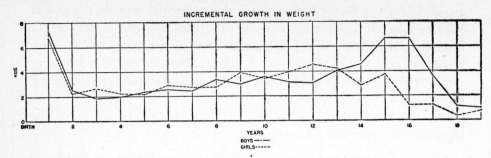

FIGURE 14.   INCREMENTAL GROWTH IN WEIGHT

girls are ahead of the boys in the onset of this sudden increase to the extent of about two years. This is evidence of the biological acceleration (or precocity) of the girls over the boys. We speak of this change in the slope (or degree of slope) of the incremental curve as evidence of the *pubertal phase* of growth. It is a time of very profound physiological change, associated with the development of secondary sex characters and the mature functioning of the sex glands (testes in boys, ovaries in girls).

AGE PERIODS IN PHYSICAL GROWTH

It is time now for us to set up some sort of time schedule for the *periods* or *phases* of physical growth. The following age schedule of postnatal growth is a reasonable acceptable average:

AGE PERIOD	BOYS	GIRLS
1. *Infancy*	*B—1 yr.*	*B—1 yr.*
(*Newborn*)	*B—2 wks.*	*B—2 wks.*
(*Infancy, proper*)	*2 wks.–1 yr.*	*2 wks.–1 yr.*
2. *Childhood*	*1–16 yrs.*	*1–15 yrs.*
(*Early*)	*1–6 yrs.*	*1–6 yrs.*
(*Mid*)	*6 to 9–10 yrs.*	*6 to 9–10 yrs.*
(*Late*)	*9–10 to 13–16 yrs.*	*9 to 10–12 to 15 yrs.*
3. *Puberty*	*13–14 yrs.*	*12–13 yrs.*
4. *Adolescence*	*13–14 to 18–20 yrs.*	*12–13 to 18–20 yrs.*
5. *Adulthood*	*18–20 yrs.+*	*18–20 yrs.+*

This time schedule reveals in itself some of the difficulties of being overly precise about physical and physiological growth changes. It will be noted that 2, 3, and 4 overlap in time. That is because the duration of childhood is established largely on the basis of physical (i.e., bodily) growth; the time of puberty is largely a physiological (functional) process; whereas adolescence is really a mixed term—it is part physical growth, part postpubertal adjustment, not only to the physiology of puberty, but (of equal importance) adjustment to the social consequences of heightened sexual functioning and awareness.

GROWTH AND RACE OR NATIONALITY

Stratz, a German, and Harris, an Englishman, emphasize the alternation of gain in height (spring-up) and gain in weight (fill-out). This is borne out by an inspection of the curves (Figures 11–14) of growth in height and weight. The child does not just grow bigger—it grows *proportionally*. This, of course, is true not of height and weight alone but of all the other many measurements that we take in our precise researches.

A single height-weight table cannot be used for all children. There are family-line factors; i.e., the inherited size. There are also racial factors. (See Tables 3 and 4.) As a rule, children born in America of first- and second-generation immigrants are taller, generation by generation. Also, there are racial differences in size (stature) which must be considered; e.g., North Europeans are taller, on the average, than South Europeans.

It is high time now to focus upon the physical growth of Johnny and Mary *as individuals*. We may leave "averages" and "norms" and concentrate upon the progress of *your* baby boy or baby girl. After all, that is what *you* are interested in.

THE "GRID" METHOD OF RECORDING
GROWTH IN HEIGHT AND WEIGHT

After you have measured and weighed your baby you will soon accumulate a table of heights and weights for ages. You can compare these to tables, of course, but you can do much more: you can easily plot the data on a record card that is the baby's very own. This record card is called "The Grid for Evaluating Physical Fitness."‡ Subject to the limitations of considering height and weight as simple measurements, the Grid is a very convenient method of graphing height-weight (and their age relationships). The Grid is a record of progress in physical growth as determined by increase in body length (height) and gain in body volume (weight). It does not pretend to analyze beyond these two factors.

‡Copyright by N. C. Wetzel, M.D. Published by, and available at, the NEA Service, Inc., 1200 W. 3rd St., Cleveland, Ohio.

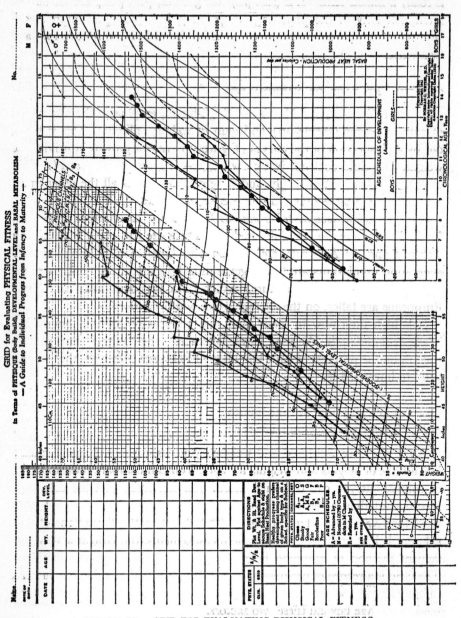

FIGURE 15. GRID FOR EVALUATING PHYSICAL FITNESS

In Figure 15 I present a Grid upon which I have plotted the height-weight curves§ of three grade and junior-high boys studied by me.

First of all, let us look at the Grid itself for a moment.|| There are two sets of ruled lines, one set to the left, the other to the right. The *left* set of lines are straight-ruled and are for *weight* (scaled up and down) and for *height* (scaled across the card). There are a series of "physique channels," with a central M (for "mid"), several A channels (for "above"), and several B channels (for "below"). The channels give an idea of body build: The A children tend to be heavier for height, the M are more balanced, the B tend to be lighter for height. Or, put it this way: The A are more "roly-poly," the M more sturdily "muscular," the B are more "string-bean." Wetzel rates A_4 as heavy, A_3 and A_2 as stocky, A_1, M B_1 as good, B_2 as fair, B_3 as borderline, B_4 as poor.

The generally accepted rule on the Grid is that *a channel is the path of growth for the child*. The channel, or physique (body build) indicator, is established by grade-school age, or perhaps even earlier. A child who follows his own channel is pursuing his own inherited growth pattern. A child who deviates—i.e., who "loses" his channel—is, for some reason, departing from his own pattern. The physician is the one to determine why, especially if the child "skids" markedly to the right; i.e., goes toward the B side of the channel system. As a rule, a child may zigzag in adjacent channels during growth.

There is one more item to note in the left-side channels; viz., the cross-lines numbered 30, 40, 50, and so on. These are called "isodevelopmental lines"—they are, in principle, our old friends, incremental lines. The general rule is 10 units' progress per year in healthy growth and balanced nutrition. The child who fails to gain the "10 per year" should be referred to a physician, just as surely as the one who deviates markedly crosswise in his channel progress.

Thus, on height and weight plotted against one another, the Grid acts as a screen to point out the youngsters who aren't "doing as well as they should." I repeat, the Grid does not diagnose, it does not tell why; it merely says, in effect, "Mother, I [*your* Mary or Susie, *your* Jimmie or Johnny] am not growing quite as I should—I think Dr. Smith should check my health and diet."

---

§It will be noted that the "curves" are more or less straight lines. This is due to the special ruling of the Grid and does not affect the interpretation of progress in physical growth.

||It is obviously impossible, in a general chapter, to give a detailed analysis of the Grid. For this I refer you to Wetzel (1941). There is also a "Baby Grid" not demonstrated in this chapter at all. (Wetzel, 1946.)

Now let's look at the *right* side of the Grid; i.e., the curved lines marked 98%, 82%, and so on. Here *age* enters in for the first time. This side of the Grid utilizes the isodevelopmental level of the left side, as we shall see when we examine Figure 15. This side is called "age schedules of development," or "auxodromes." It assesses the progress of the child in terms of above the 67 per cent (the normal) or below it; those above tend to be "accelerated," those below to be "retarded" in general physical growth. Or, again, those above probably represent a *large* family line, those below a *small* or *slender* family line. Thus the Grid offers an idea of height-weight progress against age and an insight into the family-line pattern of size and physical growth.¶

PUBERTAL GROWTH

We may turn now from considerations of height and weight to a brief discussion of puberty and its role in physical growth.** In general this is a phase of rapid physical growth; as a rule the "spurt" in stature precedes that in weight. Apart from this, however, there are other important physical changes. In boys the voice changes and facial hair becomes prominent. In both boys and girls body hair becomes prominent, first in the pubic region, above and to the sides of the external genitalia, and then under the arms. Also in both sexes the sweat glands in the armpits increase in activity just before hair appears there. In girls there is a marked increase in the size and a change in the configuration of the breast. Very often in boys there is a slight, temporary enlargement.

The most dramatic—perhaps because the most obvious—change in girls is the onset of the menarche (first menstruation). Formerly it was held to be racial; i.e., earlier among tropic-dwelling peoples. We know now that the onset of puberty, generally, is rather closely related to the socio-economic environment, to health, to diet, and possibly other factors. As a rule, girls in a good physical environment, with proper hygiene and health, good food, tend to mature earlier. There is no hard-and-fast average. One group of New York girls was found to have the menarche at an average of 13.5 years; another group of Cleveland girls, an average of 12.5 years. An average between 12–13–14 years is probably about right.

There are, however, in both boys and girls, "early maturers," "average maturers," and "late maturers," and these maturation patterns seem to run in family lines. Early maturers have an intense period of rapid growth and attain adult size and proportions very early. Late maturers, on the other

¶I shall not, in this chapter, discuss the columns labeled "basal heat production—calories per day." Your physician can help you with this.

**The ensuing discussion is based largely on Greulich (1944) and on Bayley and Tuddenham (1944).

hand, continue to grow much longer—they not only start later but have a slower pace.†† Late-maturing individuals are usually longer-legged (compared with sitting height) than early maturers.

I cannot end this chapter without some mention of two growth changes dear to the heart of every mother: (1) the eruption of the teeth; (2) the development of the motor behavior pattern of the baby, especially in the first year of life. I must also say a word about diet.

THE ERUPTION OF THE TEETH

All humans have two sets of teeth, a "baby set," or a "milk set," and a "permanent set." The dental formula of the first set is written as 2-1-2. This means, in order, two cutting teeth (incisors), one eyetooth (canine or cuspid), and two grinding teeth (molars). The dental formula of the second set is written as 2-1-2-3. This means, in order, two cutting teeth, one eyetooth, two chopping teeth (premolars or bicuspids), and three grinding teeth. The baby molars are succeeded by the permanent premolars. The three permanent molars have no predecessors in the milk teeth.

The baby teeth erupt ("cut the gum") in the following order and at the following times:

First incisor	*6– 8 mos.*
Second "	*8–10 "*
Canine	*16–20 "*
First molar	*12–16 "*
Second "	*20–30 "*

This holds for upper and lower, right and left, teeth, though lower teeth tend to be a bit earlier.

The permanent teeth erupt in the following order and at the following times:

TOOTH	UPPER	LOWER
First incisor	*7– 8 yrs.*	*6– 7 yrs.*
Second "	*8– 9 "*	*7– 8 "*
Canine	*11–12 "*	*9–10 "*
First premolar	*10–11 "*	*10–12 "*
Second "	*10–12 "*	*11–12 "*
First molar	*6– 7 "*	*6– 7 "*
Second "	*12–13 "*	*11–13 "*
Third "	*18+ "*	*18+ "*

††As I have already pointed out, boys are, on the average, two years behind the girls in attaining puberty. This holds for each group, "slow," "mid," "late." Obviously, in boys we do not have the same graphic moment, so to speak (i.e., the menarche), but we do have *identical changes in the curves of growth in height and weight*. That is how we compare the "rhythm" of growth in the sexes.

TABLE 4   WEIGHT IN VARIOUS PEOPLES

MALES

AGE (in yrs.)	CLEVELAND (in lbs.)	CHICAGO (in kgs.)	IOWA (in kgs.)	ENGLISH (in lbs. and oz.)	FRENCH (in kgs.)	GERMAN (in kgs.)	ITALIAN (in kgs.)	JAPANESE (in kgs.)	AGE (in yrs.)
1	23.85	10.89	10.84	20:0	——	9.7	9.0	10.8	1
2	29.05	13.43	13.58	28:0	——	12.0	11.3	12.4	2
3	33.54	15.29	15.63	32:0	——	14.1	13.7	13.7	3
4	38.39	17.27	17.47	32:1	——	16.3	15.3	15.2	4
5	43.16	19.64	19.48	36:8	18.44	18.6	17.0	16.5	5
6	48.53	22.22	21.50	40:8	20.40	20.8	19.2	17.7	6
7	54.65	24.64	26.34*	46:4	22.23	22.2	21.5	19.2	7
8	62.24	27.92	28.98	50:0	24.26	24.2	23.6	20.8	8
9	69.53	30.89	32.53	53:0	27.03	26.7	25.7	22.8	9
10	78.54	34.45	35.29	56:0	29.68	29.1	28.3	24.6	10
11	86.49	37.62	38.66	62:1	32.61	31.5	33.0	26.8	11
12	92.69	40.68	43.64	73:0	35.97	33.9	36.3	29.1	12
13	102.80	44.77	48.62	72:0	——	37.5	39.5	33.0	13
14	——	49.35	54.94	——	——	42.4	47.0	38.3	14
15	——	56.01	58.36	——	——	48.1	52.0	41.5	15
16	——	60.64	62.42	——	——	54.5	57.0	45.5	16
17	——	64.27	64.67	——	——	59.8	59.4	49.4	17
18	——	66.14	——	——	——	62.8	——	49.2	18
19	——	67.15	——	——	——	64.5	64.0	50.9	19
20	——	——	——	——	——	65.5		50.9	20

*From here on Iowa weights are one half year more.

TABLE 5   WEIGHT IN VARIOUS PEOPLES

FEMALES

AGE (in yrs.)	CLEVELAND (in lbs.)	CHICAGO (in kgs.)	IOWA (in kgs.)	ENGLISH (in lbs. and oz.)	FRENCH (in kgs.)	GERMAN (in kgs.)	JAPANESE (in kgs.)	AGE (in yrs.)
1	21.91	10.25	9.60	20:0	——	9.5	9.9	1
2	27.51	12.48	12.32	26:0	——	11.7	11.5	2
3	32.49	15.13	14.46	31:0	——	13.7	12.9	3
4	37.12	17.35	16.63	33:0	——	15.6	14.5	4
5	42.34	19.53	18.19	36:8	17.81	17.8	16.0	5
6	48.55	22.41	20.56	40:8	19.52	19.9	17.2	6
7	53.99	25.14	22.90	46:4	21.20	21.6	18.6	7
8	61.45	27.90	25.65	50:0	23.99	23.6	20.4	8
9	70.92	31.76	28.47	53:0	26.76	25.9	22.1	9
10	77.60	35.17	31.63	56:0	30.24	28.4	24.3	10
11	87.04	39.12	35.83	62:1	33.88	31.4	27.2	11
12	102.66	43.69	40.70	73:0	39.02	35.4	30.7	12
13	114.58	47.92	45.52	72:0	——	40.2	35.1	13
14	——	50.74	50.32	——	——	45.5	37.7	14
15	——	54.48	53.62	——	——	49.5	40.6	15
16	——	55.71	54.42	——	——	53.3	43.7	16
17	——	56.98	54.31	——	——	56.3	45.3	17
18	——	57.36	54.59	——	——	58.2	45.8	18
19	——	58.15	——	——	——	59.0	45.2	19
20	——	——	——	——	——	59.0	46.1	20

It is obvious that the lower permanent teeth erupt earlier than the upper. There is no difference, right and left.

I'd like to remind you that the foregoing eruption time schedules are subject to a certain amount of variability. Order may differ a bit, as the upper permanent first (or central) incisor—due to erupt at 7–8 years—may erupt before the upper first permanent molar—due at 6–7 years. A shift in order or a delay of several months is not cause for alarm. Of course if delay is too long your physician should consult with your dentist.

DEVELOPMENT OF MOTOR BEHAVIOR

For the development of the motor pattern of behavior we may note the observations of Aldrich and Norval (1946). They studied 215 normal babies in their first year of life. They observed the following twelve traits:

1. Smile: *response to an adult or adult voice.*
2. Vocal: *spontaneous sounds, as "ah."*
3. Head control: *when child is raised from the lying-down position by his hands the head does not loll.*
4. Hand: *when toy or other object is grasped.*
5. Roll: *when baby rolls from back over onto his abdomen.*
6. Sit: *when baby sits alone for a few minutes.*
7. Crawl: *when baby moves, by any method, across the floor or in the pen.*
8. Prehension: *when child uses thumb and forefinger in grasping.*
9. Pull up: *when baby pulls himself to a standing position.*
10. Walk with support: *when baby walks, holding onto hand, furniture, or play pen.*
11. Stand alone: *when baby stands alone for a short while without support.*
12. Walk alone: *when the baby takes several steps alone.*

Not all babies do all these things precisely in the same sequence or at the same time rates, but the following tabulation is substantially correct (the figures are in *months,* or tenths thereof).

	EARLY	AVERAGE	LATE
1. Smile	0.3	0.9	1.8
2. Vocal	0.8	1.7	2.5
3. Head control	1.8	2.9	4.0
4. Hand	2.7	4.0	5.2
5. Roll	3.4	5.0	6.4
6. Sit	4.2	6.1	7.9
7. Crawl	5.0	7.3	9.3
8. Prehension	5.8	8.0	10.1
9. Pull up	6.3	8.7	10.8
10. Walk with support	6.8	9.5	12.0
11. Stand alone	8.0	10.7	13.0
12. Walk alone	10.0	12.0	13.8

DIETARY NEEDS

I am here going to refer briefly only to the daily caloric needs of growing children. The data are from Houssay (1951). From birth to six months, feed 100 calories per kilogram of body weight, and from six months to one year 90 calories per kilogram of body weight. From one year on, as follows:

AGE	CALORIES PER DAY	AGE	CALORIES PER DAY
1–2 yrs.	840	7– 9 yrs.	1680
2–3 "	1000	9–11 "	1920
3–5 "	1200	11–12 "	2160
5–7 "	1440	12 " and up	2400

It is suggested that a "buffer" of about 10 per cent be added to cover the energy loss of the very active growing child up to about five years and after ten years.

CONCLUDING REMARKS

In this chapter we have told you just a little of what we know about the physical growth of the child—*your* child. The process of growth is as marvelous as it is complex, and it is a wonderful privilege to behold it. The general principles outlined in this chapter will aid you in understanding the unfolding developmental progress of your child. Together with your pediatrician or family doctor you can watch the child's healthy growth step by step.

BIBLIOGRAPHY

Aldrich, C. A., and Norval, Mildred, "A Developmental Graph for the First Year of Life," *J. Pediat.*, 1946, 29:304–08.

Bayley, N., and Tuddenham, R. D., "Adolescent Changes in Body Build," *43rd Yearbook, Nat. Soc. for Study Educ.*, 1944, pp. 33–35.

Breckenridge, M. E., and Vincent, E. L., *Child Development*, Philadelphia, Saunders, 1943.

Gray, H., and Ayres, J. G., *Growth in Private School Children*, University of Chicago Press, 1931.

Greulich, W. W., "Physical Changes in Adolescence," *43rd Yearbook, Nat. Soc. for Study Educ.*, 1944, pp. 8–32.

Houssay, B. A. (ed.), "Human Physiology," New York, McGraw-Hill, 1951, pp. 524–34.

Krogman, W. M., "Growth of Man," *Tab. Biol.,* 1941, 20:1–967.

Pryor, H. B., *As the Child Grows,* New York, Silver Burdett Co., 1943.

Simmons, K., and Todd, T. W., "Growth of Well Children: Analysis of Stature and Weight, Three Months to Thirteen Years," *Growth,* 1938, 2(2):93–134.

Wetzel, N. W., "Physical Fitness in Terms of Physical Development and Basal Metabolism," *J. Amer. Med. Assoc.,* 1941, 110(12):1187–95.

Wetzel, N. W., "The Baby Grid. An Application of the Grid Technique to Growth and Development of Infants," *J. Pediat.,* 1946, 29(4): 439–54.

Chapter 2

CHILD PSYCHOLOGY

by Elizabeth B. Hurlock, Ph.D.

THE GRADUATE SCHOOL, UNIVERSITY OF PENNSYLVANIA

I. THE CHILD IS NOT A MINIATURE ADULT

Throughout history it has been a generally accepted fact that children are miniature adults. For that reason attempts were not made to study them or to learn whether or not they might, in one way or another, differ from adults. They were presumed to have thoughts, feelings, emotions, and desires similar to those of adults, only on a more limited scale. These mental states were studied in adults and the results applied without revision to children. Children were treated as adults; they were dressed like their elders and they were expected to behave in accordance with adult standards.

A glance at a young child should be adequate to convince anyone—scientist, parent, or teacher—that the child is not a miniature adult so far as his physical make-up is concerned. His head is proportionally too big for his body, just as his arms and legs are proportionally too small. His shoulders are narrow and his abdomen bulges, while the shoulders of an adult are broad and his abdomen is flat. The eyes of a young child are set in the middle of his face, a position which, if found in an adult face, would produce a grotesque appearance.

The realization that physically the child is not a miniature adult should have raised the question in someone's mind as to the possibility of the child's differing from the adult in his mental make-up. In 1633 a Slavic educator, Comenius, published *The School of Infancy,* the first book to help parents in the guidance of their children. This suggested that children were mentally different from adults and, consequently, should not be treated as adults.

With this as an eye-opener, psychologists have investigated and have concluded that children are even more unlike adults in their mental make-up than in physical appearance. The effect of this realization has been a complete revision of the old methods of handling children. Of even greater importance is a reconsideration of what we expect of children. We now expect them to behave like children and not like adults.

II. ALL CHILDREN ARE DIFFERENT

No two children are alike, not even identical twins. True, all normal children have two arms, two legs, a trunk, and a head with two eyes, two ears, a nose, and a mouth. But the shape, size, and color of these different features will vary in one respect or another in all children. Johnny may be a blond, while his brother Tommy is a brunet. Mary is short and stocky in build while her sister Alice is tall and willowy.

Even identical twins, who can confuse most people, cannot fool their parents or others who know them well. Robert has a small brown mole on his left ear which his twin, Robin, does not have. Jane's eyes are set farther apart than Janice's, and her right eye has a slight brown area in its otherwise blue iris.

In mental abilities, differences in identical twins are greater than their physical differences, just as is true of ordinary brothers and sisters. Moreover, children who do not have any blood ties have even greater mental and emotional differences. In a class of thirty pupils the teacher will find thirty different types of mental make-up and thirty different personality patterns. True, some of her pupils will fall into general classifications, such as "the "bright," "the dull," "the excitable," or "the shy," but within each of her general classifications every child will be a separate and distinct individual.

Differences in children are partly the result of varied environmental influences, but they are largely the outcome of differences in heredity. Although brothers and sisters have the same parents, the germ cells from their parents which have united to produce them have not been identical. Within the *ovum,* or female egg, at the time of conception, are twenty-four tiny carriers of heredity, the *chromosomes.* Within the chromosomes are microscopically small carriers of unit traits, the *genes.*

The father's germ cell, the *sperm,* likewise has its twenty-four chromosomes with its own genes. The combination of genes from both parents determines the different physical and mental traits of the new baby. No two eggs or two sperms are alike in their chromosome make-up. For that reason the ovum fertilized by the sperm cell that resulted in Mary produced a different child from that produced by the ovum and sperm which united to produce her sister Jane.

The significance is that you cannot expect all children to think and act in the same way, nor can you hope to get good results if you treat all children as if they were cut from the same pattern. The disciplinary policy that brings good results when applied to one child may likely build up a sullen, resentful attitude on the part of another.

It is unquestionably much easier to formulate a set of rules for the guidance of children that could be applied to all children with anticipation of equal success. But it simply will not work! Each child must be studied in order to know the characteristics of his individual make-up. Only then will it be possible to direct and guide him in such a manner as to bring out his latent potentialities.

III. DEVELOPMENT RESULTS FROM MATURATION AND LEARNING

"Maturation" means the natural unfolding of traits potentially present in the child. It is Nature's method of growth. Plants or animals do not grow overnight, nor does a child. Day after day, and week after week, throughout the growth period, maturation brings about changes in the individual without any effort on his part. These changes appear at a fairly predictable time for every member of the species.

Everyone who has had anything to do with babies knows that teeth develop as a result of maturation. Rubbing the baby's gums may ease the pain that frequently accompanies teething, but it will not encourage the teeth to grow. Similarly, there is not any known way to delay the cutting of teeth until a time when teething will be more convenient for the baby or the members of his family.

To a boy or girl, sexual maturation, or "growing up," is a matter of great concern, especially when it is delayed. It is embarrassing to remain childish in appearance when one's classmates look like young men or young women. But what can the child do about it? Nothing, absolutely nothing. True, the use of certain hormones may hasten or alter development, but most doctors hesitate to use this artificial method until it is apparent that nature's work has been completed. Nature will usually take her own time and will not allow for interference in her plan for the child's growing up, regardless of any social problems which delay may cause.

"Learning," by contrast to maturation, means development which takes place as a result of the effort put forth by the learner. From experience we know how difficult it is to learn a poem, to learn to skate, dance, or play a piano, without putting forth effort in continuous practice. The more correct effort we put into learning, the more quickly we learn. We cannot count on the aid of Nature as we do in maturation. Learning is entirely up to us.

From a common-sense point of view it is unquestionably necessary to discover how much of the child's development we can count on from Nature and how much remains for the child to acquire through its own efforts. This is not as easy as it may first appear. You cannot dogmatically say, "I will do this and let Nature do the rest," any more than you can assume that Nature will take over the job if it requires more effort to learn something than the child is willing to put forth.

There has never been an instance in which a child has acquired the ability to play the piano through shirking his practice in the hopes that the skill would develop of its own accord. A child will, like Topsy, just grow up without learning, but in the absence of learning many abilities and skills needed for successful living will be completely lacking.

From careful and intensive research on this problem the psychologist has formulated two criteria which may be applied to any physical or mental trait to determine whether its development results from maturation or whether it will have to be learned. The first criterion is *universality*. If all babies start to creep on their hands and knees at approximately the same age and in a similar fashion, in spite of the fact that they come from different home environments where there is little similarity in the methods used by parents in rearing their children, then creeping is obviously not the product of learning but results from maturation.

The second criterion is *suddenness of appearance*. Just before puberty boys and girls are in the "gang conscious" stage of development. Their interests are centered in the activities of their friends, the approval and disapproval of their friends are powerful forces in determining their own behavior, and they feel lonely and unhappy when isolated from the gang.

Quite suddenly, sometimes over a week end, they lose interest in gang activities and begin to prefer isolation to the companionship they formerly craved. This sudden change, with the appearance of a new type of behavior, is characteristic of all behavior that is natural in its development.

Development, of course, depends upon the interaction of maturation and learning, not upon one alone. The child cannot learn unless the native foundation for learning is present. Nor will maturation alone produce a state of development which is adequate to meet the child's needs as he grows older. Through learning he will have to finish the work started by Nature and polish off the rough edges so that his behavior will better conform to present-day standards.

There are two significant conclusions to be drawn from the fact that the child's development results partly from maturation and partly from learning. The first is that you can control the development resulting from learning, but not the development that comes from maturation. In walking, for example, the sequence of steps leading up to walking consists of crawling, creeping, standing, and then walking. It is impossible to eliminate these preliminary stages or even to shift their order. The pattern is set by Nature and is unalterable.

The child's gait, or the way he walks, on the other hand, results from learning. Too small shoes or a too heavy body, for example, may encourage him to "toe in" to gain better balance. If permitted to walk in that fashion the habit of toeing in will develop. Similarly, timidity may cause the child to walk with short, mincing steps. If unchecked it will develop into a habit.

Gait is controllable. It is possible—in fact, it is easy—to develop a gait of one sort or another with directed practice. The longer an unsatisfactory mode of walking is permitted to persist, the harder it will be to change it. But it can be done even as late as the adult years if the individual wants to change his style of walking and is willing to practice until a new habit is learned to replace the old one.

The second significant fact about development is that learning must wait upon maturation. This means that a child cannot learn until he is ready to learn, or until the necessary foundation has been laid. The old saying, "You cannot run until you have learned to walk," illustrates this. The child must have the necessary body balance, plus the ability to move by the alternate use of his legs, before he can speed up his walking into a running pace.

There is no known way to speed up maturation so as to produce the necessary state of readiness for learning. Nature's unfolding of the pattern of development for the human being comes about in an orderly fashion and at a pace characteristic of each individual child. In one child, for example, readiness to read may appear at the age of three years, while in another child in the same family readiness to read may be delayed until the age of seven years. And there is nothing that anyone can do to change these speeds of maturation, to slow down one or to accelerate the other.

Trying to interfere with the natural speed of maturation only brings trouble to the child. Any attempt to force a child to learn before he is ready will build up a dislike, on the child's part, for the activity which he finds too difficult for him. Furthermore, it may result in fear of failure, which will militate against successful learning when the state of readiness finally occurs.

Many a child has literally been forced to stand on his feet and walk before his bones, muscles, and nerves have developed to the point where this is possible. No amount of practice in walking will speed up his learning to walk. His frequent falls will intimidate him and will build up so pronounced a feeling of self-inadequacy that it will actually interfere with his progress in learning to walk when the time comes for him to be ready to walk. Many cases of delayed walking have been definitely traced to attempts on the part of well-meaning parents to speed up their child's walking because Mrs. Jones's or Mrs. Brown's baby was walking at the age of their child.

Putting up barriers to the child's learning when he is ready to learn is also bad. These barriers may result from ignorance on the parents' part concerning the child's readiness, or they may be traceable to parental fear that some harm might come to the child should he attempt to learn. Whatever the cause, the effect on the child is the same. It stifles the child's interest in learning so that, should he be given an opportunity to learn at a later time, he will have little interest in doing so. The result will be slow and halfhearted learning.

IV. DEVELOPMENT FOLLOWS A DEFINITE PATTERN

The child's development, from conception to maturity, is not haphazard, nor is it a matter of chance. Rather it follows a definite, predictable pattern which is similar for all children, regardless of the nationality or socioeconomic status of the family to which they belong. In this pattern of development there is a close interrelationship between physical and mental growth. There is a reciprocal effect of these two, with physical growth in some instances influencing mental, while in other instances the reverse is true.

According to popular belief, the child who develops slowly during the early years of life in some mysterious manner will catch up to the pace of other children of the same age. As a matter of fact, just the reverse is true. The slow-developing child not only continues to develop slowly, but as the years of childhood pass the pace becomes increasingly slower until it is practically at a standstill. Children whose developmental pace is accelerated, on the other hand, continue to grow at a rapid rate throughout the entire developmental period. In other words, development proceeds at the pace at which it started.

Not all aspects of development occur simultaneously, nor is growth at a regular rate. When the child is growing in height, for example, his growth in weight is slowed down. Then, when he begins to take on weight, his height is at a temporary standstill. Similarly, growth in memory ability occurs at one age, growth in imagination at another, and growth in reasoning at still another. Development is thus rhythmic, not regular.

The rate of development differs for different children. It depends upon such factors as the child's level of intelligence, whether the child is a boy or girl, the state of health during the periods when development is normally rapid, his racial heritage, and the presence or absence of environmental barriers. Girls, for example, develop more rapidly than boys and reach their mature level sooner than do boys of the same age. Similarly, bright children are ahead of dull children at every age and in every aspect of their development.

Finally, in the normal pattern of growth, not all physical or mental features reach maturity at the same age. The child's brain is mature in size before the internal growth has been completed. The nose is the first facial feature to complete its growth, while the hands and feet come next. Unless this is known to the child it will be a source of great concern. Many boys and girls are seriously disturbed about their big noses, hands, and feet, only to discover that in time the rest of their bodies enlarge and thus eliminate the disproportions which temporarily existed.

Because growth follows a predictable pattern, with only minor variations from child to child, it is possible to anticipate what a child will be able to do at a given age and to plan accordingly. For centuries, educators have planned the curriculum of the school with this knowledge to guide them. They know that most children will be ready to learn to read at a certain age, to do higher mathematics at another age, and to grasp the meaning of historical facts at still another age.

As recent scientific studies have covered almost every aspect of the child's development, it is now possible to furnish parents and teachers with a guide for training children in the form of "developmental tasks." A developmental task is, according to R. J. Havighurst of the University of Chicago, "a task which arises at or about a certain period in the life of the individual." If a child is to make good adjustments and be happy, he must master the developmental tasks for his age. Otherwise, he will lag behind his age-mates, be out of step with what they are doing, and then will have to try to catch up while they are going ahead to master other developmental tasks.

A few of the important developmental tasks of babyhood are learning to take solid foods, to walk, to control the elimination of body wastes, and to talk. The child must learn the physical skills necessary for ordinary games, learn how to get along with his age-mates, develop the skills of reading, writing, and calculating, learn an appropriate sex role, develop a conscience and learn a scale of moral values. By adolescence, children in America have the developmental tasks of making adjustments to their newly developed bodies, of achieving emotional independence of parents and other adults, of selecting and preparing for a life career, and of preparing for marriage and family life.

V. ALL CHILDREN ARE "PROBLEM CHILDREN"

At each age, studies of children have revealed, there are certain types of behavior which are characteristic of that level of development. When judged by adult standards, they fall far short and are then regarded as "problem behavior." Had they been judged by standards for that particular age level, they would appear to be perfectly normal. An example or two will illustrate this point.

Spitting out food that does not taste good is a natural, protective reaction among animals and human beings. Babies and young children react to disliked food by spitting it out, regardless of where they are and regardless of the fact that, according to our present standards of good taste, this is considered to be "bad form." The food spitter is behaving in a normal way for his age level. But if he continues to spit out food until he is six, ten, or sixteen years old, long past the ages when other children have learned that such behavior is socially unacceptable, then food spitting may be regarded as "problem behavior."

In late childhood boys and girls, but especially the former, delight in dressing in clothes of sturdy, coarse materials. They shy away from dressy clothes. They are rather bored with cleanliness and revolt against the use of soap and water, with the excuse that they will "only get dirty again."

They are careless and slovenly in their dressing and even more slipshod in the care of their clothing. All of this is traceable to their interest in strenuous play, their desire to be regarded as "regular fellers" by their friends, and their desire to cut away from the parental restraints of early childhood.

The careless, slovenly age is a real problem for many parents who do not understand that this is merely a phase of growing up and is in no way permanent. The most careless boy, in late childhood, will probably turn into a dandy of the most extreme sort when he becomes adolescent. As the shift in interest is from boys to girls the desire to win their approval will motivate him to be as careful about his appearance now as formerly his desire to be regarded as a "good feller" drove him into his careless ways.

Only if behavior that is characteristic of one age level persists into older ages, when in most children it has long since been replaced by behavior of a more mature type, can it be regarded as "problem behavior." It is problem behavior because it is infantile in form. The child clings to infantile behavior when he has difficulty in adjusting to more mature levels, or when he discovers that he receives more attention from infantile than from mature behavior.

VI. CHILDHOOD FALLS INTO DEVELOPMENTAL PERIODS

Studies of very large groups of children have revealed that, while development is a continuous process, there are phases or periods when there is a shift in emphasis on the type of development that is taking place. This is pronounced enough to justify dividing the childhood span, from conception to maturity, into developmental periods, each with its characteristic form of development.

All children pass through all the developmental stages, but at different rates. Bright children, for example, develop more rapidly than do children of average or below-average intelligence. They therefore are accelerated in their development, while dull children are retarded. Because more children fall in the classification of "average" than above average or below average, the ages given here will refer only to the so-called "average child."

The subdivisions of the growth span are as follows:

A. *The Prenatal Period.* The prenatal period extends from the time of conception, when the ovum of the mother is fertilized by the sperm cell of the father, until the moment of birth. The usual span of time is 280 days or, roughly, nine calendar months.

During the prenatal period, there is rapid growth and development. From a miscroscopically small cell to an individual weighing seven or more pounds and measuring approximately twenty inches in length is tremendous growth in such a short period of time. The development is even more astounding. All parts of the body are differentiated and ready to function several weeks or months before birth, should the infant arrive in the world ahead of schedule.

B. *The Period of the Newborn.* The period of the newborn begins at birth, when the umbilical cord is cut, and lasts for approximately two weeks. This is a time of adjustment in which the infant must get used to breathing, to taking nourishment through his mouth instead of through a cord connecting his body with that of his mother, and to changes in temperature. Like all adjustments, the infant needs time to make them satisfactorily.

During the first week after birth it is not at all unusual for the infant to lose weight and to appear less healthy than he was at birth. Then, during the second week of life, the infant gradually adjusts himself to the new environment outside of the mother's body. By the end of the period of infancy adjustments should be completed. The infant then is ready to begin his postnatal growth.

Infancy is characterized by extreme helplessness. Without constant care the infant would not be able to survive. Nourishment must be put into his mouth and care taken to prevent his choking when he swallows it. Changes in temperature frequently cause colds which may be fatal. Having become accustomed to an even temperature in the mother's body, it is difficult for the infant to adjust to temperature changes.

The cause of his extreme helplessness is traceable to the fact that the muscles of the infant are so weak that he cannot move his body from the position in which he is placed. The only sounds he can make, should he want help, are cries which sound alike regardless of what is the matter with him.

While to the casual observer the infant's eyes are fully developed, they do not co-ordinate because of the weakness of the muscles that attach the eyes to the sockets. The result is that everything is seen as a blur. Similarly, the well-developed ear is temporarily clogged by mucus from the prenatal sac. Until this is drained out the infant is practically deaf. Hence, the two most important sense organs, the eyes and ears, are of little value to the infant in adjusting himself to his new environment.

C. *Babyhood*. Babyhood, the first two years of life, following the two weeks of adjustment after birth, is a period of decreasing helplessness. This is made possible by a gradual control over the body. The helpless baby, in time, partly through maturation and partly through learning, gains control over his muscles. By the end of babyhood the individual is remarkably independent when one considers the helpless state that existed just two short years before.

Physical growth is extremely rapid during the first year of life. Its pace then slows down during the second year. An average infant weighs 7 pounds at birth and measures 20 inches in length. At the end of the first year the weight is trebled, or 21 pounds, and the average height is 28 inches. Slowing down of growth in the second year is apparent in the fact that an average 2-year-old weighs 25 pounds and measures 32 inches.

During the middle part of the first year the first tooth erupts. From then until the age of approximately $2\frac{1}{2}$ years baby teeth come in, one at a time, but at a fairly rapid rate, until all 20 have erupted. This makes it possible for the baby to abandon infantile sucking and to substitute chewing and biting. By the end of babyhood the baby can eat much the same food as an adult eats. It is no longer necessary to reduce his food to a sieved or finely chopped form.

Control of the body muscles develops rapidly during the first year. But the development does not affect all muscles throughout the body simultaneously. Rather it spreads over the body in an orderly pattern from head to foot. This means that the baby can co-ordinate his eyes before he can grasp with his hands, he can hold up his head before he can sit, and he can sit before he can stand or walk.

By the end of babyhood muscle control throughout the entire body is normally so well developed that the baby can be a relatively independent creature. He can take off and put on his clothes, he can feed himself, he can get out the toys he wants and play with them, and he can even run errands or assume simple duties in the home. All of these skills, of course, will not occur spontaneously. They must be learned. But they can be learned only if the baby is given an opportunity to do so.

Speech is one aspect of muscle control. The words used in speech and the combination of words into sentences must, however, be learned. During the second year the baby learns words very rapidly. He thoroughly enjoys talking. He even goes so far as to try to combine his words into sentences. At this age, however, his sentences are usually incomplete and are supplemented by gestures. Being able to talk, even in the limited fashion of a baby, does much to decrease the helplessness that is characteristic of this age.

D. *Early Childhood.* Early childhood is, roughly, the preschool age. It extends from the end of babyhood, at the age of two years, to the beginning of school, at the age of six. Physical growth at this time is slow and steady, with a slight growth spurt just before the child's sixth birthday. Because growth is slow the child quickly learns to control his body. It is no longer necessary to make constant adjustments in this control, as was true when growth was more rapid.

Having gained control of his body, the young child now turns his attention to his environment. He is into everything and explores endlessly. What he cannot understand through his own exploratory efforts he asks questions about. This is the "questioning age," when every child is normally a "living question mark."

Because of his endless exploring, combined with poor judgment that is a logical accompaniment of limited intelligence and even more limited experience, the child needs constant supervision to protect him against harm. His desire to discover what is happening on the street, for example, may cause him to lean dangerously far out of the window. To discover how matches work he may strike a match without taking the necessary precaution of shutting the matchbox first.

Toward the latter part of this developmental stage all normal children begin to crave the companionship of other children. They lose interest in playing alone or in being with adults. But their first social experiences with their contemporaries are not always too satisfactory. Frequently they stand on the side lines and watch other children play or, when they actually try to play with the other children, the usual outcome is a quarrel. In time, and with practice, learning to get along with others will take place.

E. *Late Childhood.* Late childhood, which extends from the sixth year until the beginning of sexual maturity, around the age of 12 or 13 years, is often called "The Gang Age." At this time the desire for companionship, which first appeared several years earlier, reaches its peak of intensity. No longer is solitary play satisfactory to the child, nor does he derive the enjoyment he formerly did from the companionship of adults. He wants to be with his "friends," and his friends are contemporaries of his own sex.

This is the age when antagonism between the sexes is very strong. Boys are contemptuous of girls and girls feel the same way about boys. The influence of the child's gang upon his behavior, his outlook on life, and even upon his morals is very strong. Children think, act, and feel as their friends do. To them, being different is synonymous with being inferior. And this is the source of great emotional tension.

F. *Adolescence*. Adolescence, which means to "grow to maturity," is a period extending from the beginning of sexual maturing until the age of legal maturity, at 21 years of age. The average American child matures sexually at some time between the ages of 12 and 15 years, with girls slightly ahead of boys. During this developmental period the characteristic behavior is so different at different times that it has become customary to subdivide adolescence into three subperiods: preadolescence, early adolescence, and late adolescence.

(1) *Preadolescence* is the shortest of the three periods and lasts only for a year or two, during which time the sex organs are growing in size and becoming mature in function. There is also rapid increase in height and weight, the "adolescent growth spurt"; changes in body proportions; and the development of the secondary sex characteristics or physical features which distinguish men from women, such as the growth of hair on the face and body, change of voice, and growth of heavy muscles in boys, and the development of the breasts and hips, the growth of hair over the sex organs and in the armpits, and the development of subcutaneous fat which produces "feminine curves" in girls. In girls, preadolescence comes, on the average, between the ages of 12 and 13½ years, and in boys, about a year later. Sexual maturity is generally accompanied by loss of appetite, more or less constant fatigue, indigestion, headaches, skin eruptions, and a tendency to insomnia. While these conditions vary not only in intensity but also in frequency of occurrence, few boys or girls escape their impact.

Marked changes in behavior appear in preadolescence. The childish desire for constant social contacts gives way to a longing for isolation. Boredom, especially in play activities of all sorts, disinclination to work, general restlessness and irritability, moodiness, a critical attitude toward members of the family and former friends, quarrelsomeness, a tendency to be easily offended, sulkiness, lack of self-confidence, excessive daydreaming, and a marked interest in religion and sex are all common at this age. This has been called the "Negative-Phase," indicating that it is a period of short duration during which there is an almost complete reversal of behavior.

(2) *Early adolescence,* which begins with sexual maturity as judged by the first menstruation in girls and by the appearance of pubic hairs and nocturnal emissions in boys, lasts for about three years, from approximately the ages of 13 to 16 years. This is an awkward, shy, self-conscious age, in which the transformation from child to adult has not yet been completed. Owing to the rapid growth that takes place in pre- and early adolescence, the youth temporarily loses control over his body. This results in clumsy, awkward movements which merely serve to increase the self-consciousness that has come from the body changes brought about by sexual maturing.

As a defense against self-consciousness the youth tries to submerge his individuality by dressing and behaving like all his gang. Being different in any way is a source of much mental anguish. The youth feels that it focuses too much attention upon him. Gradually, as he learns to control his newly enlarged body, his self-consciousness decreases. With this comes a new feeling of self-confidence and a recognition of self as a personality.

(3) *Late Adolescence.* By the age of 16 years for girls and a year or two later for boys, the youth has gained his mental equilibrium. Instead of trying to submerge his personality into that of the group, the youth now wants to assert himself as an individual. No longer is he willing to be treated as a child. A stubborn, rebellious attitude toward adult authority develops. This grows in intensity until the age of legal maturity is reached and the adolescent is now recognized by society as "grown-up."

Some of the most common forms of self-assertiveness found in late adolescence are interest in clothes of extreme styles, rebellion against the religious doctrines accepted during childhood, revolt against rules and regulations of the home, the school, and the community, attempts to reform others, with special emphasis on members of the family, radical ideas regarding political matters, constant bickering and arguing with members of the family and friends, and show-off tendencies in dancing, driving cars, and sports.

Late adolescence is the age of romance. Both boys and girls are seriously preoccupied with sex in its every aspect. They are curious about sex matters. This curiosity leads them to talk about, read about, and experiment with sex. They fall in and out of love many times annually. Each romance is accompanied by intense emotions and with a preoccupation that interferes with their other interests and activities. At first the love affairs are more in the form of hero worship of an older individual than of real romance. But after a year or two of hero worship the adolescent falls in love with a contemporary.

Because of idealism fostered by reading romantic stories and seeing romantic movies, the adolescent frequently expects the loved one to have all the attributes, both physical and mental, of a fictitious hero or heroine. With the realization that the loved one is an ordinary mortal, disillusionment follows, and the romance ends in a bitter quarrel. After a few experiences of this sort, which are extremely disturbing emotional experiences to an adolescent, he gradually adjusts his attitudes to a more realistic level. Then romances become more stable and frequently lead to marriage.

The choice of a life vocation for many adolescents proves to be as great a source of emotional disturbance as are their love affairs. What courses they should take in high school, whether or not they should go to college, what line of work they should train for, what openings will there be for them when they are ready to go to work, how can they go into a line of work that will appeal to them without disappointing their parents who have already planned their future careers for them are all problems which confront adolescents as they approach adulthood.

Today girls as well as boys find the choice of a vocation a disturbing problem. No longer do they assume that their only role will be that of a homemaker. Like their brothers, they plan to have a career, but for them the career must be such that they can combine it with matrimony. Parental opposition to a costly education to fit the girl for the career of her choice, based on the argument that she will abandon her career when she marries, adds a complicating factor to the girl's vocational problems which is rarely present for a boy.

Adolescence, because it is a period of adjustment, is far from the happy, carefree age that most people believe it to be. There is always something to upset and disturb the individual who is passing through this transition from childhood to maturity. If it is not feeling up to par, then it is fear of being laughed at because of a cracking voice or clumsy movements, or, even worse, it is the feeling of utter despair that comes when an all-absorbing love affair has ended in a bitter quarrel.

Much of the moodiness, the rudeness, the lack of interest in members of the family, and the daydreaming of the adolescent may be traced to the fact that he is confused and unhappy. To cover up some of this feeling of insecurity he develops a cocksure attitude of confidence which too often gives others the false impression that all is well. In time the adolescent will, in most instances, make satisfactory adjustments to life, but it will not be until adolescence has passed and adulthood has been reached.

Chapter 3

ADOPTING A CHILD

by Lee M. Brooks and Evelyn C. Brooks
DEPARTMENT OF SOCIOLOGY, UNIVERSITY OF NORTH CAROLINA

I. SOME IMPERATIVE VALUES

Central in today's American family life are companionship and affection. These represent a transition from the old institutional rigidities and authoritarian pressures. More than ever the "good" family is seen as shared experience, freedom and discipline, rights and responsibilities, love and loyalties. Uniquely the adoptive family is this sort of shared experience, one that can rate high because its members have purposefully set about securing the values inherent in the warmth of affectionate companionship.[1]

Many a couple, after waiting and hoping for the birth of a child, have refused to be defeated by their actual or assumed biological incapacity. Others, because of impaired health or questionable heredity, marry with no expectation of having a child of their own blood. Still others, already parents, adopt one or more children. Through adoption such people often move into happier marital and family fulfillment.[2]

Adoption is the voluntary acceptance, the transplanting and nurturing of a child of other parents into one's own family circle and kinship. It is not altruism; it is a permanent and complete filial relationship distinct from guardianship or custody, each of these being a temporary legal arrangement for the protection of a child's person or property. Adoption is also different from foster care, which is a social device whereby, with or without pay, a household provides family life for a homeless child. These provisions may, and often do, lead to adoption. There is also adoption of children by relatives, by stepparents, and by fathers of offspring born out of wedlock. In such homes the motives and adjustments are likely to be different from those of the adoptive family where unknown infants or young children are eagerly sought by a husband and wife who have no blood kinship to the child adopted.

Bound by legal ties after adequate examinations and investigations have been made, the adopted child's position in the family is rightly as irrevocable as though he had been decreed through biological birth for that particular family. He becomes an own child with all filial rights, privileges, and obligations, provided the adoptive parents exercise scrupulous care about rights of inheritance, a matter to be emphasized later. Whenever a child is adopted, parents are adopted too. But for the child adoption is a social type of birth the moment the final decree is granted by the court.

As to the stability of the adoptive family, several widely different investigations emphasize the affection and loyalty, the mutual satisfaction of adopters and children in the family relationship, not only as estimated in subjective testimony, but more particularly as observed by disinterested persons outside the family circle. Most prospective adopters are disappointed, perhaps even frustrated, people. The child also has been disturbed by one or more major separations and he may have had other traumatic experiences along with improper physical care. Social workers who have supervised the placement and watched the developing relationship at close range, as well as researchers with rating scales and other objective measurements, believe that the adoptive family ranks favorably with comparable biological families. Even if this were not so, those who magnify the risks of adoption would do well to compare the adoptive family, not with superior biological families, but with the alternatives open to adopters and adopted children: childless homes and parentless children. Out of mutual need and purposeful effort can arise a stable and satisfying relationship.[3]

Benefits of Adoption. The family is the effective environment for bringing out plus or minus potentialities that are hereditary but which have not developed. The results may be likened to the interaction of soil and seed. Several interesting experiments have been made in the last decade which have shown an increase of intelligence-test scores in children after their adoption or foster placement in homes of superior opportunity.[4] These favorable results reinforce the belief that the "good" family promotes all-round growth among its members. These results, however, should not mislead anyone into expecting adoption to work a miracle. No investigation yet made has shown a sufficient increase in capacity to allow a child to rise from the bottom to the top of his class in school. That there should be improvement is not surprising. After adoption there may be greater attention to nutrition and other health factors, more stimulating contacts and perhaps better schools, and also such imponderables as added security, responsiveness, and new motivations. Most children fall short of what they might be because the environment fails to call out their full possibilities.

Chances of Adoption. Not all people who wish to adopt can expect to do so. Nor should all childless couples be encouraged to adopt. There is the conviction, for instance, that emotional balance and steady affection should outweigh material factors. For sterile couples, if the sterility has a definite psychic basis, its implications and the attitude toward it must be carefully considered.[5] In weighing the matter of age and resources it is to be expected that people in their thirties or early forties who are youthful in spirit, who possess physical and mental health, and the indispensable emotional maturity can satisfy the "golden mean" requirements. The imperatives of a self-inventory for prospective adopters involving motives, attitudes, and habits would be somewhat as follows:

Is the desire but an impulse or is it rooted in earnest purpose?

Will the result be mere ego satisfaction or continuous purposeful investment?

Do we have a genuine interest in children and youth as humanity's richest heritage?

Is our love for each other so sure that a child will bind us even closer without jealousy?

Are we willing to undertake twenty years or more of responsibility with many of our former interests displaced by or tributary to the child's welfare?

For better or for worse—since adoptions, like other family relationships, carry no guarantee of perfection—will we stand by our adopted child in all circumstances as though he had been our physical offspring?

Have we the ability to love the child for himself, whatever his background; to guard ourselves resolutely against the projection of our ambitions on to him; and to guide rather than to mold him—thus encouraging his growth power?

Can we grow with him, and share our best with him, without expecting gratitude?

Are we developing tolerance, habitual patience, emotional maturity, and the mental flexibility that ensures against rut-bound middle age?

When our adopted child grows beyond the early need for dependence will we be ready to let him go, confident that our family life has given him the security indispensable to independence?

The values in adoption, some of them implied above, are many for both parent and child, too many to list. As for all parents, they may include: heightened affection and loyalty between mates; the shared joy of guiding growth; a feeling of fraternity with all parents; a deepened concern for all children; an awakening of civic responsibility and a broadening of interests. For the adopted child, as in horticultural grafting, there is a chance for growth and fruitage such as no other experience can assure, especially as one considers the alternatives, the hazards of grudging shelter with relatives or institutional placement.

Children should be in families wherein flows a responsive and wholesome affection that nourishes happy development. However superior physically the provisions of an institution may be for the child, it is lacking with respect to his emotional and social needs. Collective handling does not reach the deeper core of child life to bring out the potentialities. Neither the institution nor boarding home can give the security of spirit that comes from the continuing and concentrated interest of parents with whom the child shares the feeling of identity in a family.[6]

The adoptive home is often a one-child situation, and this it must remain to a large extent so long as there is a scarcity of adoptable children, though there are many good homes with own and adopted children and still others where two or more children have been adopted. Some child-welfare agencies do, however, encourage multiple placements. The "only" child has been found to rate high in emotional and social development where parents are alert to the need of child companionship and where they provide for the development of skills and sportsmanship through plentiful contacts with playmates and visitors. The presence of brothers and sisters makes for more complete family life but carries no magic for social development. The home with both adopted and own children calls for particularly careful thought and planning to keep sensitive situations at a minimum. Childhood adjustment in any family and community depends upon effortful and planwise parenthood.[7]

If the answer "yes" can be given to the ten questions already set forth, the prospective parents will be well prepared for what is ahead in parent-child relationships. However, for the rearing of the adoptive child there are some aspects that invite special emphasis. In brief they are as follows:

Study and Guidance. *The waiting period after application has been filed can be likened to pregnancy. This is the preparatory period for study—through books, articles, and possibly child-study groups—on physical care, habit training, the mental growth of children, and mental hygiene itself. Thoughtful study and planning are a continuing need for effective parenthood. If they have had no previous experience with children the prospective parents can make an effort to get acquainted with their friends' children, perhaps borrowing them for short periods. They will want to observe receptively a nursery school or play group, for children cannot be understood or managed solely through books.*

The actual techniques of physiological baby care are relatively easy to learn. But psychological adjustment, involving emotions, attitudes, and habits in and between parent and child, comes by no formula. It comes only through patient, intelligent, and continuous effort.

Adaptation and adjustment embrace such practical questions as these: Should a fragile piece of furniture be replaced with something sturdier? Are the colors too delicate for rough use? Can a meal hour or a social custom be changed cheerfully? The readiness of the new parents may be partially gauged by their attitude toward necessary changes in terms of joyful anticipation or, on the other hand, of sacrifice.

Guidance and advice concerning problems of child nurture are part of the program of authorized child-placing agencies which usually continue supervisory contacts with the adoptive home for six months or a year before the final decree is granted.

The Child's Security. *The child has undergone one or more separations and changes. Especially he needs the maximum of that which gives self-security. This comes from well-ordered parental care and affection wherein the main ingredients are a steadiness of head and heart, a gentleness of hand and voice. Thus the child grows happily with a strong sense of belonging: his parents, his home, and his possessions; not "smother-loved" into selfishness but guided into socialized selfhood.*

As with the physiological needs of the child, household equipment ordinarily is not a great problem. Adoptive parents can, without much difficulty, learn to accommodate house to child: room and toilet facilities; child-size furniture; toys and play space, and other such matters. But adopters, often a little older than other parents, may have to make effortful changes in habit patterns before they are ready to welcome the child they want. HIS PSYCHOLOGICAL SECURITY IS PARAMOUNT.

From the first day he should be thought of as "one of us." If he is thus closely identified with his adoptive family and is told of his adoption as soon as he understands speech, as matter-of-factly as he learns the color of his eyes, he is no more likely than other children to develop mental or social aberrations.[8] The adopted child should not be shielded completely from knowledge of his past but be given strength to face it, to assimilate it through the warmth of constant affection and security. Otherwise there may be unsettling insecurity, even shock and estrangement from his family if unfortunate facts are discovered accidentally.

Growth is the "highest good" for the individual; mutual growth and trust in the parent-child relationship are the "highest good" for any family in the universal quest for security.*

As to the effect of adoption, not enough reliable studies of grown people adopted in infancy or early childhood are available. No one can rightly speak with dogmatic assurance. Selection of children and of families for adoption has changed so much in recent years that comparisons are difficult. Many of the changes have taken place because specialists, notably child-welfare workers, have profited from experience in this field. The press may emphasize the fact of adoption in spectacular cases of delinquency or crime, but as any thoughtful person must realize, equally notorious cases occur among people brought up by blood kin or among those reared in orphanages or in those families where there is a breakup in the bases of security. There is no proof or even indication that adoption affects adversely the emotional or

---

*For fuller discussion, see Brooks and Brooks, op. cit., Chaps. 5 and 6.

social development of adopted persons. The really wanted child, whatever his origin, will have full acceptance, equality, love, and security from those parents who are willing to study, who will accept guidance, and who strive to grow in those mental and spiritual qualities which are commensurate with life's most important privilege.

II. SOME LEGAL AND SOCIAL SAFEGUARDS

The remaining discussion will be devoted mainly to some of the legal and social fundamentals.[9]

Law and social work are requisites in approved adoption procedures. The courts and social agencies tend to emphasize the interests of the child, and rightly, because he is helpless in the hands of those who are deciding his destiny. He is entitled to all the protecting services available. This discussion, however, will focus attention on the adoptive family as a whole: the relationship within the family triangle with awareness of the interactions of the larger kinship.

Legal action is the unique factor in the adoptive family. Adoption should not be thought of as substitute parenthood, for it *is* parenthood of a distinctive type which requires judicial decision. It must be safeguarded by strict compliance with every detail of the law. Legal records are of special importance. When the child comes to the full understanding of his adoption —and he should be told in the simplest words when he is so young that he grows up with the knowledge—he will be secure in the realization that legal papers prove his family membership. Birth certificates and wills, very specific testamentary directions, are among the "musts." Many details that seem to the individual adopter unimportant, or even an interference by the state in a private matter, are based on real need when viewed from the perspective of the rights of all the people involved. Whatever his personal opinion, the wise adopter will follow the letter of the law and will make use of all the social aids put at his disposal. The lags in the law, as viewed against social needs, are numerous and even irritating, but advances are being made, especially in recent years. Judicial practices have not always kept pace with the modernizing of the law, but perhaps because of the increasing number of adoptions and the consequent necessity for improvement in procedures, decisions are tending toward more progressive social interpretation.

An increasing number of states require that every adoption shall have the supervision of the Department of Public Welfare, which means that all placements are made either by staff members or by agencies approved by them. In any state the advice of a local welfare official may be sought, or application may be made to a licensed private placing agency or children's home. Proper child placement demands expertness; there are sound reasons why adopters should use the services of a well-qualified nearby agency, preferably one in their own state. Much time and expense may be used up in tracing distant records, gaining consent, or clearing out irregularities that may greatly magnify the risks. Too often adopters who travel some distance for a child are tempted to accept a seemingly promising one without going fully into records and matters of legal procedure. They may hasten the final steps, minimize or circumvent the trial period, or fail to return to procure the final decree without which the adoption is not a fact. The distant agency, however good, is handicapped in its dealings with adopters whom it sees briefly. An agency gives its best services when there is time and opportunity for frequent consultation and full acquaintance with the adopting home.

The social investigation, covering both child and prospective parents, includes interviews, written application, visits to the adopting home, health assurances, and requests for financial and moral references. This is for the protection of the child and is to the advantage of the adopters. The more contacts the agency has with an adopting household, the better its picture of the expectations of the adopters and the fewer the chances for misfits. Because the adopter has a right to know pertinent facts, the careful agency will try to find out as much as possible about the ancestry of the prospective adoptee. The eugenically minded adopted person, when he approaches marriage in later years, will want to compare his questions on heredity with those of his mate-to-be. The results of mental tests and reports as to physical condition should not be overlooked. Many agencies have a policy of withholding the identity of a child's natural parents. Some children available for adoption are shadowed by earlier misfortune. Agencies often are willing for the adopters to know general facts about a child's original family even though names are not revealed.

Both the adopting father and mother should have a voice in the decision; acquiescence is not enough. It is the right of the child to be actively wanted, not just accepted, by both parents. Particularly if his early days have been insecure will he need the assurance of steady affection. The small child is more sensitive to the emotional states of his elders than most adults realize. It is unlikely that marriage partners are ready for parenthood if they are not able to agree on the essentials of the choice. They should be prepared for the emergence of unsuspected qualities in themselves and each other. They need not fear, however, that the new experience will detract from their relationship to each other if the decision to adopt and the choice of their child have been reached jointly. Parenthood is invigorating when mature people give themselves freely to it; the adoptive parent misses few of the emotional values. As the personalities of the adopters become enriched and more vital, they not only have more to give in all their relationships, but also their responsiveness to each other is peculiarly heightened by their mutual sharing of emotion as well as by their shared interest in the child.

The Trial Period. A trial period of six months or a year is required by law in many states. During this time the child lives in the adopting family whose name he takes. He is treated as an own child but not yet is the adoption irrevocable, as it is after the final decree. It is always within the province of the judge to require or extend the months of probation, but courts are not always aware of the social implications, for sometimes they can inadvisedly be persuaded to omit or shorten the trial period. From the point of view of court procedure the probation period is an unnecessary prolongation of a case; it means that the decree cannot be granted in the same term of court in which the petition is made, often involving a review of the case by a different judge. The study and experience of child welfare generally point to no less than a year's probation period, whatever the legal minimum.

Many adopters insist that they were as sure at the end of the first week as at the end of the year: This was *the* child for them. For others impatience has meant regrets, even grief. The emotions need intellectual brakes. Like an engagement to marry, the trial period gives the feelings time to get into more normal control. In a year's time the adopters will have begun to have some idea of the labor, expense, and self-control connected with parenthood. Twelve months is a long time in the life of a small child during which his physical growth and mental development can be far more accurately gauged than in pre-placement tests. It occasionally happens that even though both child and parents individually are ready for the experience of adoption, they are not suited to each other, are not psychologically fitted to each other's needs. Sometimes, in spite of every precaution, legal difficulties arise which must be cleared, difficulties that would have invalidated the decree had it been granted too early.

Court Proceedings. The laws of every state require court proceedings for adoption. Five requirements or aspects must be emphasized for the welfare of child and family: (a) consent of the child's natural parent or parents; (b) petition by the adopters; (c) decree granted by the proper Court; (d) records that are complete, clear, and confidential; (e) inheritance provisions. The first three have to do with effective implementation in the adoptive process; the last two point particularly to safeguarding the child's future.

CONSENT. One of the most valuable services of the placing agency is its guidance in legal steps. The agency knows the laws as well as the practices and problems of local administration; it will make the necessary contacts with the child's natural parents or other authorized person to secure consent to the adoption. Consent of the proper person in the required form is a fundamental of sound adoption procedure; its importance cannot be over-emphasized. When the agency secures consent, a meeting of the adopters and the natural kin is avoided unless the law requires their joint appearance in court. The consent required of natural parents protects their rights by allow-ing them to express their wishes, but it also terminates their rights and interest in the child. If the natural parents are dead, have forfeited civil rights, are insane or incompetent, or for some other reason are not qualified, another person or agency may be authorized to give consent. A few states permit formal relinquishment of the child to an agency or to the Department of Public Welfare, with the right to consent to adoption as well as for guardian-ship and custody.

PETITION. The adoption statutes of most states are fairly explicit on the matter of petition, both as to form and court jurisdiction. Here again the assistance of the placing agency is valuable because it is important to make the petition in the proper court, lest the validity of the adoption be ques-tioned later on jurisdictional grounds. Ideally adoption cases are handled in a children's court or family court by a judge experienced in work with children, at a private hearing from which reporters and the public are ex-cluded. More often the petition must be made in a probate or general court before a judge who may not be qualified by training or experience for this highly specialized work and who is under too great pressure of routine cases to give the time that is sometimes needed to authenticate every legal de-tail. Petition is usually made in the county or district where the petitioners have legal residence, though a few states make the child's residence the de-termining factor of jurisdiction or allow the latter as an alternative choice. Petition should be made in the manner prescribed and in the court specified, as a protection against any later question.

DECREE. The final decree is granted after the court has filed and acted upon the petition. This is done preferably, as required in the majority of our states, at the end of a six-month or a one-year trial period. A few states grant an interlocutory decree. The decree may be a simple confirmation of the petition or an elaborate court order expressing conditions and requiring the adopters to give the child proper care and treatment. Some decrees are in the form of a contract of which a certified copy is given to the adopters. Com-monly decrees specify the name by which the child is to be known.

RECORDS. Records deserve more emphasis than the statutes and courts have given them. Since adoption is an artificial relationship from the legal standpoint—as contrasted with the "natural" or blood ties which are stubbornly entangled in common and statutory law, and also in judicial usage far beyond the social claims of kinship—it is often necessary to have incontrovertible proof of adoption in order to protect the status and inheritance rights of the adopted person. An increasing number of states require notification by the court to the Bureau of Vital Statistics of every adoption. The child's birth registration is then altered or rewritten, the original record filed and often sealed, and a copy of the new certificate with the adoptive name of the child issued to the adopters. For further protection more and more of our states require that the new birth certificate shall not indicate that the child is adopted or whether he was born outside of marriage. A few states now issue a short form of birth certificate for *all* children in order to avoid singling out those of irregular birth. The adopter has a right to a birth certificate for his child and should request one if it is not provided at the time the adoption takes place. It may be needed for securing admission to school, for working papers, for securing a passport, or even for proof of citizenship. The birth certificate should be in hand as early as possible; there is unnecessary risk in waiting until some specific need arises. Some states require that all records and reports pertaining to an adoption be sealed and subsequently opened only on court order to "parties in action"; other statutes are permissive on this point. Adopters should request this protection in any case.

Inheritance rights constitute a most vital consideration. While there are fairly adequate statutes in most of the states to control the mechanics of adoption, there is a lag in the laws and court practices concerning inheritance in some states. Many of the laws dispose of status and inheritance rights by affirming that the adopted child has all the rights of the natural child, and some of the statutes add that these rights shall include inheritance. Yet in the face of such apparently clear statutory protection, court decisions have gone against the adopted child on some technicality which was construed as a flaw in the adoption, even though parents and child had lived together in fullest affection, all measuring up to every filial-parental obligation. In other cases there was no suggestion that the adoption was unsound; only the opinion that when a new statute clashes with an old established precedent, distant blood kin ("call of the blood") may come before the adopted son or daughter. Most litigation involving adopted persons is caused by disputes over inheritance of property.

New social laws must reckon with traditional attachments to the beliefs and practices of a former day. Until laws become more explicit and court decisions can be depended upon to back them up—as they will do when public opinion makes its mind more vigorously felt—the adopter needs to be particularly watchful. Even though courts are occasionally lenient, showing a fine social understanding, the adopter should see to it that there are no legal loopholes, no flaws in the adoption through failure to comply with some procedural detail. Also, he must specify the child by *name* as his *adopted* child if he wishes the child to be the certain beneficiary of life insurance or the recipient of property through a will or trust fund.

Black Markets in Babies. Even though increasingly the participation of the Department of Public Welfare is legally required in adoptions, "black markets" in babies are a continuing problem. Most of them operate solely for profit, with fees that may exceed a thousand dollars for a child who is usually an unknown newborn infant for whom records, reports, and birth certificate are lacking. The prospective adopter should use the services of a licensed, state-controlled organization that is adequately staffed. Never should such an important, far-reaching step as adoption be undertaken under any auspices that countenance a hasty, hush-hush procedure.[10]

Sometimes procedurally questionable, even extralegal placements ("Gray Market," so called) are made without profit by doctors, lawyers, social workers, and others genuinely disturbed over the present adoption situation. These professional people feel, with justification in some instances, that desirable adoptions are being needlessly blocked by inefficiency, understaffing, unrealistically high standards, failure of functionaries to work harmoniously, political preferences that give unfair precedence to applicants with wealth or prestige over better-qualified but less prominent families. A reputable agency or a whole state department may have an obsolete policy or too small a budget for an enlarged job. On the whole, however, Child Welfare Divisions of Public Welfare Departments are expanding their services because of the impetus of the Federal laws and financial aid for children since the middle 1930s. In response to public interest, agencies are showing an increasing sensitiveness to the need for a closer study of bottlenecks in adoptive services.

III. SOME RECENT TRENDS

Because of the unprecedented increase in the number of children to be cared for and the great demand for adoptable children, some agencies are experimenting with certain innovations and short cuts in an effort to meet the problem squarely and expedite a rather slow process. While exploitive fees have been among the objectionable marks of the bootleg adoption, in order to share the costs with the adopting family reliable agencies increasingly are charging a small fee, a step that seems justified both by financial need and by matter-of-fact public acceptance of a reasonable charge for professional services.[11]

Another experiment, one that considerably increases the number of potential adoptions, has to do with placement age. Some babies are now being taken directly from the hospital to the adopting home, where they are supervised during the study period, with the understanding that if the child proves unsuitable another one will be supplied, and perhaps with a prolonged probation before the final decree. This earlier placement has possibilities of considerable success because it gives to the child the security of attachment to a single home and thus the relationship at an early age more closely approximates that of the biological family. On the other hand, older children are sometimes being placed with families that do not insist on a baby, with especially good results for older adopters. Older children must be chosen and placed with particular skill, since prolonged institutional residence sometimes unfits them for the emotional give and take of family life. A child from a good foster home or from an own home recently broken by divorce or death often makes a good adjustment.

Adoptions are taking place where both the adoptive home and the child are considerably less than superior. This does not mean a deliberate lowering of placement standards but a recognition of the differences in mental capacity and social status that may be satisfied by a careful matching of qualities. Economic condition has proved to be a less reliable criterion for parenthood than emotional factors. Occasionally a child with a slight handicap or an ambiguous legal status is now being offered to a family willing to take the risk.

From war-ravaged countries, "transplanted children" have been adopted with success comparable to "all-American" adoptions. The legal, procedural details need further clarifying through international agreements if the adoption of foreign children is to be satisfactorily effective for all concerned.[12]

IV. CONCLUDING SUMMARY

We have tried to show in this chapter that in adopting a child from proper motives and through approved procedures marriage and family life can be enriched. We have emphasized particularly the importance of emotional maturity on the part of adopters, that adopting a child amounts to giving it social birth into full and complete family membership, and that there are values as vital and lasting in the adoptive family as are those in the usual biological family. The trend is clear that children thrive more fully in families than in institutions, for it is family life that nourishes and brings out the flowering of personality. The social and legal aspects, the imperatives of the law with respect to protecting the rights of the adoptive child have been given special prominence. Only the limitations of a necessarily little chapter on a big subject prevented the inclusion and development of manifold details.

The adoptive family, uniquely democratic, is in keeping with Nature's plan for the continuity of the species. Particularly for the childless couple does it have a cosmic as well as a personal meaning. To achieve maximum satisfaction for itself and constructive worth as a democratic function, adoption must be supplied with every safeguard of science and law. The adoptive family has needs which can be met only by community interest and concern for wise placement and the utmost legal security.[13] The success of the adoptive, as well as the biological, family rests squarely on the parents. Plan, decision, choice—these are the basic steps. Once the child is in the home, whether his advent has been biological or legal, parental functioning is a matter of social and spiritual dedication.

> *Thou child of all humanity—*
> *Thy birth, no choosing didst thou have*
> *Of time or place or circumstance;*
> *In darksome cave or atom's dawn,*
> *By whom or where, or even how.*
> *Yet in the endless flow thou com'st*
> *Like others in the cosmic stream.*
> *Thy home and life are ours in trust,*
> *God's promise of community.*

NOTES

[1]Ernest W. Burgess and Harvey J. Locke, *The Family from Institution to Companionship*, New York, American Book Co., 1953, 2nd edition, pp. 18–25, Chaps. 15–16.

[2]Margaret Kornitzer, *Child Adoption*, New York, Philosophical Library, 1952, Chaps. 1–5; Lee M. and Evelyn C. Brooks, *Adventuring in Adoption*, Chapel Hill, University of North Carolina Press, 1939, Chaps. 2, 3.

[3]Leontine Young, *Out of Wedlock*, New York, McGraw-Hill, 1954, Chap. 9; Barbara Kohlsaat and Adelaide M. Johnson, "Some Suggestions for Practice in Infant Adoptions," *Social Case Work*, Vol. 35, March 1954, pp. 91–99; Carol S. Prentice, *An Adopted Child Looks at Adoption*, New York, D. Appleton-Century, 1940, Chaps. 15–19; Brooks and Brooks, op. cit., Chaps. 2, 3.

[4]Margarete Zur Nieden, "The Influence of Constitution and Environment upon the Development of Adopted Children," *Journal of Psychology*, Vol. 31, January 1951, pp. 91–95; Marie Skodak and Harold M. Skeels, "A Final Follow-up of 100 Adopted Children," *Journal of Genetic Psychology*, Vol. 75, 1949, pp. 85–125.

[5]Paul Popenoe, "The Childless Marriage," *Fertility and Sterility*, Vol. 5, March–April 1954, pp. 168–72; Helene Deutsch, *Psychology of Women*, New York, Grune and Stratton, 1945, Vol. II, pp. 393–433 *passim*.

[6]Frank M. Howard, "Institution or Foster Home?" *Mental Hygiene*, January 1946, pp. 92–104; R. Spitz, "Hospitalism, An Inquiry into the Genesis of Psychiatric Conditions in Early Childhood," *The Psychoanalytic Study of the Child*, Vol. 1, 1945, pp. 53–74.

[7]Ernest Cady, *We Adopted Three,* New York, Sloane, 1952, entire book; Edith G. Neisser, *Brothers and Sisters,* New York, Harper's, 1951, Chap. 7.

[8]Florence Rondell and Ruth Michaels, *The Adopted Family,* New York, Crown Publishers, 1951, in two little volumes; Book I, "You and Your Child," a guide for adoptive parents; Book II, "The Family That Grew," a picture book for children. Frances Lockridge, *Adopting a Child,* New York, Greenberg, 1947, Chap. 10; Valentina P. Wasson, *The Chosen Baby,* New York, Oxford University Press, 1941, also a picture book for children; Brooks and Brooks, op. cit., pp. 10–11, 66–67, 183–87.

[9]*Final Report of Citizens Committee on Adoption of Children in California,* Rosenberg Foundation, Los Angeles (742 S. Hill St.), 1953, pp. 10–26; Marilyn Nott, "Breaking Adoption Bottlenecks," *The Survey,* Vol. 86, October 1950, pp. 443–47; Lockridge, op. cit., Chaps. 2–3; Prentice, op. cit., entire book; Brooks and Brooks, op. cit., see index and bibliography.

[10]Unsigned article, "Moppets on the Market: The Problem of Unregulated Adoptions," *Yale Law Journal,* Vol. 59, March 1950, pp. 715–36; "When You Adopt a Child," U. S. Children's Bureau, Washington, 1947, Folder 13, entire booklet of 24 pp.

[11]Eilene F. Crosier, "Fee Charging for Adoption Service," Child Welfare League of America, New York, November 1949, entire booklet of 16 pp.; *Final Report . . . California,* op. cit. p. 25.

[12]Kathryn Close, *Transplanted Children,* U. S. Committee for the Care of European Children, New York (215 Fourth Ave.), 1953, entire booklet of 79 pp.; Hugo Löhning, "Adoption under English and German Law," *International Law Quarterly,* Vol. 3, April 1950, pp. 267–78; Arthur K. Kuhn, "Adoption of a French Child by American Citizens," *American Journal of International Law,* Vol. 44, January 1950, pp. 150–52.

[13]Henry David Kirk, *Community Sentiments in Relation to Child Adoption,* Cornell University Library, Ithaca, 1953. This scholarly work, as yet unpublished, focuses on the place of the adoptive family in modern American society.

Chapter 4

REMARRIAGE AND THE STEPCHILD

by William Carlson Smith, Ph.D.

PROFESSOR OF SOCIOLOGY, LINFIELD COLLEGE, MCMINNVILLE, OREGON

The impersonality of our American life tends to place undue strains on marital ties; consequently, a considerable percentage of marriages prove to be unsuccessful. A stepchild in the picture is an additional hazard, and a remarriage becomes an even greater risk than a first marriage.

EXTENT OF REMARRIAGE

Remarriage in the United States is assuming large proportions. Several recent studies make this evident. A study of fourteen states by the Metropolitan Life Insurance Company[1] indicates that one fifth of those wed in 1950 were being married for the second time. Of all grooms who entered wedlock in 1950, 20.1 per cent had been previously married, 14.4 per cent of these were divorced, and 5.7 per cent were widowed. For brides the figures were 21 per cent remarried, and of these 15 per cent had been divorced and 6 per cent widowed.

A sample survey by the Bureau of the Census in April 1948[2] indicated that 21.3 per cent of the husbands who had been in their marriages less than two years at the time of the survey were remarried. For wives the percentage was 21.8.

In the remarriages, second marriages rank first, but some take the third, fourth, fifth, and even more trips to the altar; some tend to become chronically addicted to divorce and remarriage. A recent dispatch from California informed us one person was divorcing his sixth wife.

On the basis of a sample study, Bossard concluded that "of persons marrying more than once, approximately one out of sixteen is marrying a third or additional time."[3]

The relative importance of first and subsequent marriages varies considerably according to age. In April 1948, among men 14 to 34 years of age,

8 per cent had been married more than once; of those 35 to 54 years, 54 per cent; and for men 55 years and above it was 92 per cent. The corresponding figures for women were, 14 to 34 years of age, 14 per cent; 35 to 54 years, 66 per cent; and for 55 years and over, 96 per cent.[4]

INCREASE IN REMARRIAGE

In recent decades there has been a marked increase in the frequency of remarriage. Wives with more than one marriage to their credit are at present relatively more frequent than at any time in the past fifty years. Among the previously divorced and widowed, the remarried women increased about 17 per cent from 1910 to 1940. Persons in their second or subsequent marriages now constitute a higher percentage of the total of married couples, even though widowhood has actually declined in the younger age groups.[5] While the relative importance of family disruption because of the death of either mate has been decreasing, the increasing frequency of legal dissolutions has more than offset this decline. In the third year of marriage, three and one half times as many unions are dissolved by divorce as by death, and it is only after the fifteenth year of marriage has been reached that the mortality rate outstrips the divorce rate in marital dissolution.[6]

A survey of Allegheny County, Pennsylvania, covering the years 1912–30, showed a gradual increase in remarriages of the divorced, and this was more rapid than among the widowed.[7] The Census Bureau Survey of 1948 showed that three fourths of those divorced in the five-year period prior to the survey had remarried, while only about three eighths of those widowed in this same period had remarried. Glick concluded that widowed or divorced women with children tended to remarry more promptly, or not at all, than those who were childless.[8]

That the remarriage rate among divorced persons has reached a high point in recent years may be inferred from the fact that approximately 5,500,000 married persons obtained divorces in the 1940–46 period, while during these seven years the number of divorced persons who had not remarried increased only by some 500,000.[9] This depicts a trend in which approximately 90 per cent of the divorces end in remarriage. According to Glick and Landau, about three fourths of those remarried in 1940 had been divorced.[10]

The recent upswing in the divorce rate has had a decided effect on remarriage. Divorce makes room for more remarriages than death. In widowhood only one of the mates survives to remarry, but in divorce two persons become eligible for remarriage. Since divorce comes earlier than widowhood, divorced persons, especially women, have good prospects in the matrimonial market.

The chances of remarriage have increased in every age group, but particularly in the range from 25 to 34 years. Since women marry at a younger age than men, most of the divorcees who become eligible for remarriage belong to this young age group. The increase, however, is not restricted merely to these young women, but there has been a striking upswing among the divorced women in all age groups.

Age for age, the divorced have greater chances for remarriage than the widowed, and even greater than the single. In fact, the divorcee of age 30 is the most marrying of all women in her age group. At age 30 she has 94 chances in 100 of eventual marriage, the widow of the same age has 60 chances in 100, while the spinster of 30 has only 48 chances in 100 of entering a marital venture.[11] It is only in the late teens and twenties that the single person has a higher marriage rate than the divorced.[12]

The chances of remarriage grow less with advancing age. The rates for both marriage and remarriage decrease more rapidly for women than for men, but the divorced person has a brighter prospect of marriage throughout the whole life span than either the widowed or the single.[13]

MATE SELECTION IN REMARRIAGE

When previously married persons remarry, they tend to show preferences for mates in the same previous conjugal categories as their own. The widowed more often choose the widowed; their next preference is single mates, while they seem to avoid divorcees. The divorced most frequently select single persons, but from the previously married available mates they prefer the divorced persons. Even those who have been both divorced and widowed seem to single out those who, like themselves, have had double experiences.[14]

In a first marriage a man usually chooses a woman who is slightly younger but close to his own age. When he remarries, after the death of his wife or divorce, he tends to select a woman who is considerably younger, particularly if she is single. If he is remarried to a divorcee or widow, she is usually close to his own age group. Frequently single men marry widows or divorcees who are older than themselves. Bossard comments on this situation: "One seems to sense, in both the men and the women who had been married previously and chose single mates, an effort to turn back the hand of time, and to start again with a young mate."[15]

This tendency of men to select young women, both single and divorcees, works to the disadvantage of women in the same age bracket as the men. Many women in these upper age brackets are left unmarried as their desirability in courtship bargaining declines. For many it is a choice between remaining unmarried or accepting husbands who do not measure up to their standards.

CHILDREN AFFECTED BY REMARRIAGE

The presence of young children frequently provides an incentive to remarriage. A widowed or divorced father needs a woman's help in caring for his children. Widows and divorcees with children often need breadwinners, but the need is less urgent than in the case of a man, because of the rather common provisions made by widows' pension systems. If several young children are concerned, the need for early remarriage may be urgent.

Children are more likely to be involved in remarriages of the widowed than of the divorced. Widowers are more often left with children than are divorced men, the percentages being 40.1 and 22.6. In divorces, children are more often awarded to their mothers than to their fathers, the percentages being 54.9 to women and 22.6 to men.[16] This high percentage of widowers left with children probably is an important factor in their remarriage because of the need for homemakers.

The bulk of the divorces comes in the early years of marriage, when there are few or no children, while the widowed have, on the average, been married longer and have more children. Hence divorce more often than death separates childless couples in the early years of married life. According to the Census Bureau Survey[17] young children were found more often in homes of persons newly remarried than in those of persons who had recently married for the first time. Only about 25 per cent of those married for the first time within two years before the survey had children in their homes under 18 years old, as compared with some 56 per cent for the remarried. This difference is due to the fact that a considerable proportion of the children of remarried persons were the offspring of previous marriages.[18]

There is no accurate measure available of the number of children affected by remarriage. According to Spiegelman, in 1940 a total of 360,100 wives became widowed, and among them were 136,600 women left with 305,600 children under 18 years of age. Of these women, 65,100 had become widows before the age of 45 and were left with 167,500 children in their care; 7,600 wives were bereft of their mates under the age of 25. In the same year, 204,300 husbands became widowers and, of these, 75,100 men were left with 168,400 children under 18 in their care.[19] Davis estimated that there were 307,000 children affected by divorce in 1946, and in 1940 the number of children whose parents had ever been divorced was 1,533,000.[20] Marshall and May found only 15.4 per cent of Maryland couples to be childless in their study of divorce records in which were included non-support and desertion cases.[21]

According to Jacobson, the 421,000 divorces and annulments granted in 1948 involved about 313,000 children. About two fifths of the divorced couples had children. In that same year, children were related to more than 50 per cent of the divorces granted to couples married seven to 23 years. The heavy concentration of annulments and divorces in the early years of married life is responsible for the comparatively low percentage of decrees that involve children. In 1948, more than one half of the decrees were granted to couples married less than seven years.[22] In another connection, Jacobson concludes that there has been a more rapid increase in divorces in families with children than among the childless, and consequently an increasing percentage of children will be affected.[23]

These figures, however, do not indicate the number of children involved in remarriages; they give us only some indication of the number made available for such involvement. The available evidence seems to indicate that the remarried widowed have a larger proportion of dependent children than the remarried divorced.

SUCCESS OF REMARRIAGE

Are subsequent marriages more or less successful than first marriages? To that question we have no definite answer. There are several opinions with a considerable amount of disagreement. Sample studies have made available some data, but even here there is no definite agreement.

On the basis of a study of persons married at least five years in 1933, Popenoe concluded that 62 per cent of all marriages after divorce were happy, while in the general population about 70 per cent of first marriages of more than five years' duration were happy. This indicates that the success of first marriages is only slightly above that of the divorced who remarry.[24] A study at the University of Utah in 1949–50 found that the majority of second marriages turned out to be happy.[25] Locke reached the conclusion that bereaved persons in subsequent unions were no worse risks than persons in their first marriages, and only slightly better than remarried divorced persons. Divorced men, however, fared a trifle less well than divorced women in repeat marriages.[26]

Landis concludes that there is convincing evidence that first marriages are more successful than remarriages. The second marriage is about 50 per cent more hazardous than the first attempt, and a woman wed to some other than her first consort is a 10 per cent poorer risk than the remarried man.[27]

In a study of Iowa data, Monahan found that remarriages were less enduring and successful than first marriages. Among divorced persons who remarried, there was a greater risk of dissolution than for those in their first marriages. Data from Missouri also supported the Iowa findings. The Iowa figures also indicated that with each successive marriage the divorce rate increased.[28]

Hart and Hart report a study of one hundred applications for divorce in Cincinnati in which remarried divorcees furnished two to three times their quota of applicants as compared with the widowed. There was no comparison made with those in first marriages.[29]

The Census Bureau Survey of 1948[30] supports this position by showing that 20 per cent of the divorced had been married more than once while only 13 per cent of the widowed belonged in this category. But we must not forget that the divorced are younger than the widowed and consequently have a longer period in which to remarry and join the ranks of the divorced again. According to the available evidence, divorced persons, and particularly the young women, remarry sooner and in a higher percentage than the widowed. When due allowance is made for these facts, the difference between the two groups becomes considerably less. While the evidence is not overwhelming, it seems to indicate that remarriages are somewhat more hazardous than first marriages. Any conclusions, however, must be drawn with caution.

We cannot state with certainty what is responsible for any greater success of first marriages as compared with remarriages. Undoubtedly the stepchild is a factor in this differential rate. We do not know what percentage of the remarried brought dependent children into their new homes, but with the many thousand children made available for the steprelationship through divorce and bereavement and with the high remarriage rate, particularly among the divorced, a sizable number of children are involved. We may reasonably assume that these children played a part in wrecking a considerable number of remarriages. Jacobson concludes that "the ratio of 1.3 children per family with children in the first year of marriage appears to indicate that the divorce rate was relatively high among the remarried with stepchildren" in 1948.[31]

Undoubtedly the divorcee group contains more than its quota of persons unfitted for married life; thus we may expect a higher than average rate of failures in their second or subsequent marital ventures. Since there has been considerable sifting, we may assume that a high percentage of the poorest marital risks do not remarry. Probably many have learned from the first bitter experience and may bring to the second marriage much more understanding and a greater determination to make a success of the new venture. They are more likely to have passed through the "puppy love" stage, are less blinded by romanticism, and may be better able to appreciate genuine values. Some remarriages, to be sure, come "on the rebound" and are based on tenuous bonds. One or the other will remarry hastily in order to show the other that he is not a discard in the matrimonial market. He may impute to a comparative stranger all the qualities he desired in his first mate. Then, when the new spouse cannot measure up to all of these expectations, disillusionment brings him again to the divorce court.

Reliable statistics on the success of remarriage by widows and widowers are not available, but there is some evidence that they have a slightly higher incidence of success than divorcees. In a high percentage of the homes broken by death, the mates were happily adjusted and fewer "twisted" personalities are found in this group. Hence they are more marriageable.

There should be more successful remarriages among the widowed than among the divorced because the latter are usually disappointed, disillusioned, embittered. Happiness, however, in a previous marriage may be at times a disadvantage in a subsequent marriage, because there may be a tendency to idealize the deceased spouse. If the new mate cannot measure up to this idealization there may be unfavorable reactions and disillusionment. A young woman stated that she would prefer to marry a divorced man rather than a widower, because the former would not be comparing her with the "most perfect" woman.

In the remarriage of widows and widowers with children, the stepchild problem must be taken into consideration, but probably it will be less troublesome than in the case of the divorced, because many of the children lived in happy homes and were not warped in their development by the dissensions which resulted in divorce. There is, however, the problem of idealization of the departed parent and refusal to accept the substitute parent, who is considered inferior to the real parent.

A remarriage, when a stepchild enters into the situation, usually has an unequal chance of being as good as the first marriage. This holds true, particularly in the case of the widowed, because death invades all homes, good, bad, and indifferent. Many of these were well integrated and happy homes.

If a mother dies and leaves one or more children, the father needs a housekeeper, but his range of choice is more limited than at the time of his first marriage[32]—prospective wives hesitate about assuming responsibility for someone else's children. Because of this the second wife often comes from a lower social stratum than the first one. This cultural divergence makes it more difficult for husband and wife to adjust to each other. Furthermore, this new mother, who is noticeably inferior to the children's own mother, is not readily accepted by them. A college girl wrote of her home:

At our house we calmly ignored my stepmother. Humble and then defensively antagonistic all at one time, she kept us in hot water with foolish threats of suicide and desertion. I always prayed she'd go ahead and jump in the bayou. Father married her in self-defense to get a housekeeper. Her role was most difficult in a family so self-esteemed. My older sisters treated her "kindly," not "lovingly." We were clannish and she revolted occasionally with loud oaths and much talk of "sassy little angels." We forgot about her in public—few people knew she was in existence. Guests never paid her much attention—she just cooked.[33]

Such a situation was not conducive to harmony between the two spouses. Without the stepchildren the marriage might have been a satisfying one, but with them there was only a slight chance for success.[34]

Widows are more limited in remarriage choices than widowers. Glick found that approximately one half of the men and one fourth of the women who had been widowed in the five-year period before 1948 had remarried.[35] For a widow aged 25, her chances for remarriage are best during the second year of her widowhood, but the opportunities decline quite rapidly after the fourth year. After her thirty-fourth year, the widow's chances to remarry are not at all reassuring, while a man has a good chance even after his forty-fourth year.[36] If the middle-aged widow is to win another mate, she must possess unusual qualifications, such as charm, wealth, or social status.

Undoubtedly the economic factor plays an important part in connection with remarriage. Men have greater earning power and a woman may be willing to assume the responsibilities of stepmotherhood in return for economic security. Widows and divorcees, however, find that children are hindrances to remarriage. According to Spiegelman,[37] there is observable a slight tendency for the remarriage rate of widows to vary inversely with the number of children.

The success of a remarriage usually depends more upon the stepmother than upon the stepfather. She makes closer contacts with the children and consequently is more involved. Her situation, however, is usually the more difficult one. The stereotype of the cruel stepmother sets the stage against her. For a long time the older schoolbooks regaled the children with the Cinderella story and its variations in which the stepmother was always a cruel ogress. The child has heard stories about cruel stepmothers from his elders and even from his playmates. The imprint of this stereotype has been deepened by popular usage of the term stepchild. Anything that seems to be neglected is called a stepchild that is being mistreated by a cruel stepmother.

For example, residents on the Pacific Coast have been treated as redheaded stepchildren since they were given no good naval bases. Alaska is repeatedly referred to as our stepchild outpost. For many years arthritis and rheumatism have been stepchildren of that callous parent, neglect. As this was being written we heard over the radio that the thirty women incarcerated in the Oregon penitentiary are the stepchildren of our prison system. Reiteration of this idea does much to maintain the stereotype and hangs more millstones about the neck of the stepmother.

In order to be considered good, a stepmother must really be exceptional. Because so many children, and adults also, have the idea that the stepmother is usually mean and cruel, her role is a difficult one. Foster mothers do not have to share the undeserved onus that is attached to stepmothers. The stepmother has been given such a bad name that it requires a first-rate diplomat to succeed at the job of "stepmothering" and being a wife in a reconstituted home.

PROBLEMS DUE TO STEPCHILDREN

Stepchildren are often responsible for the development of tensions which wreck homes. A father wrote to a newspaper asking someone to take his nine-year-old boy, who could not live harmoniously with his stepmother, "otherwise we may have our home broken up again."

A widower with a son married a widow with two children. Seven times in seven years the couple separated, largely because of the stepchildren. The boy and his stepmother were at swords' points.

A widower with a daughter remarried, but soon he was granted a divorce because the stepmother was unkind to his daughter. He remarried again and almost immediately the girl began to annoy her new mother. The situation became increasingly tense until the stepmother declared that either she or the girl would have to leave home.

When one wife had difficulties with the stepchildren she left and refused to return to her husband. She stated that one of the stepchildren gave evidence of jealousy whenever she and the father manifested any affection for each other. Consequently they no longer displayed any affection in his presence. This restriction, in her opinion, tended to "pull her husband and herself apart." She realized that the father loved his children and that if she stayed she might disturb their relationship, for which she would then be blamed. She would not consent to remain and try to keep the children, but, on the other hand, she would not demand that they be sent away and thus be separated from their father. She determined to eliminate herself from the volcanic situation.

In some instances, while conflicts over stepchildren do not actually drive anyone out of the home, there may be definite breaks so that a family may live as two separate units under the same roof. In one household the friction between a boy and his stepfather would frequently become so severe that the husband would eat and sleep with his children in one part of the house while the wife and her children would withdraw to themselves.

Sometimes a stepchild resents the presence of a stepparent and sets about deliberately to drive the newcomer out. When a close relationship exists between child and real parent, the situation may be serious. A boy with a father fixation set about to get rid of his stepmother. There was a harmonious relationship between husband and wife, and the stepmother tried to be a good mother to the boy, but he would not accept her. He admitted that she was friendly toward him, but he resented her presence and would not respond. The boy, abetted by his aunt, told falsehoods about his stepmother. He was at least partially successful in his plan, for he was able to develop some strained relationships between his father and his stepmother.

One boy, who was involved in many difficulties, justified his lying, stealing, absconding, insolency, and truancy on the basis of his hatred for his stepmother. He had been greatly attached to his mother, but from the very moment his stepmother entered the house he could not bear the thought of her and deliberately carried out his many acts of misbehavior for the purpose of annoying her and driving her out. He discerned that the more difficulties he created for her the more tense the situation became. He was fond of his father and pleaded with him to have the stepmother go away, never to return.

In one home sharp disagreements developed between the father and stepmother because of the behavior of the boy. At times the father would defend the stepmother when the paternal grandmother would criticize her, but for the most part he was critical of the way she tried to manage his son. The boy became aware of his father's ambivalence toward the stepmother and deliberately created many situations in an attempt to make his father choose between himself and his stepmother. He stated that he would do anything to get rid of her. He complained that she favored her own child but was harsh and demanding with him. The father believed that the stepmother was jealous because the children were fonder of him than of her. The situation became so tense because of the boy that the father said he was a "sucker" for getting married again.

The reconstituted family is often the source of vexatious mental conflicts. One woman who seemingly made a happy remarriage came to be greatly disturbed. Open conflict had not developed between her son and his stepfather, yet since the establishment of her new home the boy had become a delinquent. Should she send the boy away to his own father and thus lose him completely? Should she go on living with the stepfather with whom she was contented, or should she leave her husband and live with the boy? She feared the boy was headed for a life of crime, and if she could be certain that it would be for the boy's own good, she would be willing to leave her husband. But she could not be certain—and the conflict raged within her.

A divorcee with two sons remarried and for some time all went well with the boys and their stepfather. Suddenly, however, one of the boys became rude toward his mother and quarrelsome toward his stepfather. The mother, who was doing all in her power to make a good home, was greatly disappointed when the boy and his stepfather quarreled like two boys. She was torn between her husband and her two sons. She was fond of her husband, and, were it not for the children, he would be all that she could ask. Since this difficulty had arisen, certain disagreements relative to the boys developed. There had been discussion about sending the boys to their own father, but the mother strenuously opposed that proposal because of the father's instability. She also disapproved the idea of having the boys spend much time with their paternal grandmother because of her overindulgence of them. The boy realized that the conflict with his stepfather was endangering his mother's marriage. He felt guilty about this and said that he would leave home in order to forestall a break.

One woman married a widower because she loved him and was determined to be a good stepmother to his two children. In a comparatively short time, however, the older child became such a disturbing factor that her marriage and family life were in danger of failure. Because of him there was so much dissension that, in her opinion, they had no home—only a house. She became irritable in her relations with her husband. This distressed her greatly, since she had entered the marriage with a keen desire to make it a success. The boy stated that he hated his stepmother and always would hate her because she had taken him away from his grandmother. This attitude on the part of the boy was a disturbing factor in an otherwise happy marriage.

FACTORS IN THE PROBLEMATICAL SITUATION[38]

How may we account for the highly hazardous nature of remarriage where stepchildren come into the picture?

Because of the complicating factors connected with remarriage, particularly where there are children, there can rarely be any prolonged period of dating, followed by deliberate courtship and moderately long-time engagement. A remarriage tends to approach the "hasty marriage" type which is correlated with a high divorce rate.

The second marriage is oftentimes a business proposition—a man needs a caretaker for his children while a woman needs a breadwinner.[39] Frequently a widower with children in need of a mother finds a widow with several children in need of a father. This merging of two or more sets of children often jeopardizes family tranquillity. Irritations, tension, and conflict are highly probable when such children are brought together in the intimacy of home life after they have spent several years in widely divergent circumstances. The situation becomes even more complex when there are *her* children, *his* children, and *their* children.

Repeating the words of a marriage ceremony will not all at once fuse two personalities together—they must adjust and grow together. In first marriages the two persons have to make adjustments only to each other and they have almost a full, undisturbed year to themselves for doing so. If a baby arrives in due course of time they have the opportunity to grow up with the child. Unconsciously the child adopts the codes and the values of the home and develops an integrated personality which fits that particular situation. When a widowed or divorced person with a child remarries, the situation is far different. The real parent has had opportunity to become accustomed to the child and has had something to do with training him in accord with his own ideas. The substitute parent, however, usually has had nothing to do with the training and only rarely does he or she know the habits or peculiarities of the child. The new parent must make adjustments not only to the new mate but to the stepchild as well. This second personality cannot be ignored and often is the cause of conflicts which wreck the marital venture. In first marriages the two mates may have some constructive conflicts which help in working out satisfactory relationships, but with a stepchild the situation becomes far more complicated and accommodations are less easily made.

In our society, where persons contemplating marriage must choose their own mates, courtship is highly important; it affords opportunity for mutual acquaintance and for making adjustments which may have an important bearing on marital happiness. A prospective stepparent and the child, however, all too often have no opportunity for becoming mutually acquainted and come together in a home as total strangers.[40] Serious conflicts may arise because the new parent may have a standard of values far different from those to which the child has been accustomed. In the period since the child lost his parent he may have played a certain rather satisfying role which is disturbed by the coming of the substitute parent who has an entirely different conception of the part that the child should play. These conflicts develop readily when strangers meet in the intimacy of family life, and they teem with possibilities for dissension between husband and wife and may ruin the marriage.

It is no surprise to learn that dissension developed in a home where a man addressed his two stepsons with the words:

"Had I known you two when I married your mother, I would have thrown you both into the river. You'd be better off now and not be causing me any worry. You'll never amount to anything, and I'd be doing you a favor now if I had dumped you into the river."[41]

Some or many of the habits of a child may be annoying to the new parent, even though there may be no intention of causing difficulty. Furthermore, the real parent may be utterly unaware of the strain thrown on the new parent.

There are many problems to face when a person knows there will be stepchildren, but the hazards are far greater when a person remarries and fails to tell the new spouse about the previous marriage and children. A girl wrote about her home:

Friction in the new marriage began the very first year. My father did not tell his second wife about his previous marriage. Two weeks after the wedding he brought home his daughter by his first marriage. This was a most trying situation for the new wife. The girl showed lack of care and the stepmother made clothes for her and tried to help her, but the response was one of disrespect, distrust, jealousy, and sometimes definite hatred.

Five children were born to this second union, and it was not long before they became aware of the difficulties caused by their half sister. They realized that the tension between their parents was due largely to her and, since she was their father's daughter, they tended to blame him for all the family troubles. When the stepdaughter left home the mother thought all would be well, but things had gone too far. The children disliked their father and never forgot the conflicts which had been caused by their half sister.

On several occasions the mother considered separation or divorce but did not carry through because she did not know how she might support the children.[42]

Oftentimes the influence of intermediate caretakers between the breakup of the first home and the establishment of the second one is important. When a wife and mother dies or leaves the home through divorce, the father, who usually must work away from home, makes some provision for care of the children. A housekeeper may be hired. In the lower economic brackets this person is often more or less inadequate. She knows little about children and often cares less; a stepmother who tries to bring order out of chaos encounters difficulties great enough to wreck the marriage upon which she entered hopefully.

If the intermediate caretaker is a grandparent, particularly a grandmother, the situation becomes precarious. The grandmother tends to exercise a pernicious influence over her grandchildren[43] even in so-called normal situations, but where a step-relationship enters the picture, then there is a probability that the perniciousness may be multiplied manyfold. The grandmother is usually overprotective and overindulgent, yielding to every whim of the child. In order to hold the child the grandmother will often use wiles and shower favors on him and will even poison the child's mind against his own parents. In this process the grandmother may develop a feeling of dislike, or even hatred, against the child's mother (her own daughter), a stronger feeling of resentment against her daughter-in-law, but a far stronger feeling against a stepmother who has come in to mother the child in the place of her own deceased daughter. A child who has been pampered by his grandmother is ill prepared for life in a reconstituted home with a stepmother and is a likely source of conflict and disorganization.

When a divorced parent who has custody of the children remarries, the other parent frequently schemes to turn the children against both the step-parent and the ex-mate and thus spoil the new marriage. In one case two divorcees with children had married and the ex-mates of both kept in contact with their children. Such a situation was not conducive to a high degree of harmony in the home.

Within any family there tends to be favoritism when one child receives slightly more attention than the others. In the step-family the setting is ideal for favoritism, be it actual or imputed, to become highly disruptive. A parent is usually more or less partial to his or her own children.[44] The parent may compare his or her own child with the mate's own child, to the disadvantage of the latter. One woman attempted to make her stepson feel inferior to her own son. For instance, she told a visitor that her stepson mispronounced certain words. Then she told her own son to tell the lady how to say the words and then show how the stepson said them.

Particularly serious difficulties may arise in the event the stepchild is defective or has characteristics which make him unattractive. One man accepted two stepsons but was greatly displeased when his wife made plans to bring her blind and mentally retarded daughter home from a state school. The woman was greatly disturbed by the conflict between her desire to allow her husband peace of mind and her duty to help her daughter. The husband contended that his income was insufficient to take on the additional support of the girl. If it were done the other children would suffer. If a stepchild has characteristics superior to those of one's own child, there may also be breakers ahead. One stepmother became jealous of her pretty stepdaughter when she realized that the girl was superior to her own child.

Frequently a stepmother is devoted to her stepchildren until she has a child of her own. Then, apparently, she gives herself completely to her own child and neglects her husband's children. In a situation like this the step-mother is in a precarious position. Even in an unbroken family the first child tends to resent the arrival of a new baby—he can no longer be the center of attention. Even though the parents continue to treat the first child in the customary manner, he will consider that he has been crowded out and is being neglected. What the child believes in such a situation is true for him, and on that basis he reacts. In the split home it is easy for the stepchild to charge his stepmother with neglect. The father, then, may note the pained expression on the face of his child, pity him, and feel resentful toward the inconsiderate stepmother.[45]

Failure to see eye to eye on matters of discipline is a fruitful source of conflict. To be sure, this is found in first marriages but is more likely to develop into bitterness over a stepchild. Often a father will accuse the step-mother of being too severe with his children and overindulgent with her own. Because of favoritism it is difficult to establish a biparental control over a stepchild. A foster child, since he belongs to neither parent, is on a basis of equality and can be controlled more rationally. Frequently a step-child resents control by the stepparent. He soon becomes aware of the anomalous situation and plays one parent off against the other, a procedure not in the interest of marital harmony.

The age of the stepchild must be taken into consideration. When children are young and helpless enough to feel the need of a mother to love them, pet them, and help them with their little troubles, it is comparatively easy for a stepmother to take a real mother's place in their lives. Oftentimes a child at the age of five, particularly if he has spent some time with an overindulgent grandmother, is difficult for a substitute parent to manage. When children advance in age, and particularly when in their early teens, they tend to become trials to stepparents. When a stepparent comes into the home after the children have grown up and left there is little contact and few opportunities for conflict to arise, except at times over property matters. At times an elderly widower with some property may marry a young "gold digger," and then trouble may come. In many instances the children are glad to have the widowed parent remarry because that provides companionship for the otherwise lonely person. Furthermore, that may avoid the complication of keeping the lonely and restless parent in the home with grandchildren.

Youthfulness of the stepmother is also a factor to be considered. Widowed and divorced men tend to select second wives who are considerably younger than themselves. Oftentimes they are not much older than the stepchildren they are to mother. Sometimes when the stepmother is only a little older than the children she becomes irritable and domineering in an attempt to control the children who are not awed by her youthfulness. In such a situation friction and even intense hostility can readily develop. The lot of the youthful stepmother is often hard.

STEPCHILDREN AND SUCCESSFUL MARRIAGES

Not all marriages that involve stepchildren are necessarily failures; many of them are far better than first marriages. Many enter remarriages carefully and thoughtfully. One stepfather said:

"Your own children are sent to you naturally, but for that boy I consciously assumed responsibility and he means a great deal to me."[46]

Many stepmothers have been crowned with success after realizing that they were facing difficult situations and they set about to solve their problems intelligently. We recall the stepmother of Abraham Lincoln, of whom Barton writes: "She transformed the home of the cheerless widower and his two motherless children into a spot of pleasant associations and happy memories."[47] Occasionally a stepmother steps into a difficult situation and does remarkably well with heavy odds against her, with the result that deep bonds of affection develop between her and the stepchildren. This also strengthens the bond between the mates.

A divorced woman remarried and the stepfather treated her son as if he were his own. The boy said his stepfather was wonderful, while he disliked his own father. In another home a boy adored his helpful stepfather. The boy's mother disliked the boy, however, and wanted to get rid of him because his behavior irritated her. She openly rejected the boy from the time of his birth and continually identified him with his father, whom she had divorced. The stepfather was a real asset in the home and served as a buffer between the boy and his mother.[48]

While many marriages involving stepchildren prove to be successful, the number may be increased by taking thought. The children and stepparent are frequently total strangers to each other. One woman made preparation for entry into the home with a twelve-year-old boy by having the boy live with her for two months before the marriage in an endeavor to become acquainted with him so that she could make good as a stepmother. This was no easy situation, since the boy for some eleven years had lived with an overindulgent grandmother. Even though the new mother did not understand children, she was anxious to learn. On the basis of this attitude she and the boy gradually became pals and he began to turn to her with his questions and problems. When a child feels that he can confide in the stepparent, the rough spots on the road to success have been quite well leveled off. The real parent can do much to prepare the children for a second marriage. One girl wrote thus:

We children were trained by our mother to respect our future stepfather, so I cannot give him all the credit for being such an affectionate father. To our mother goes much of the credit for presenting the idea of remarriage in such a sweet way, and we are much better off because of that.[49]

By reason of the stepmother stereotype many women feel a sense of uncertainty and insecurity in assuming the mother role in a reconstituted family. A woman married a widower who had two children, aged eleven and thirteen. The mother had been dead for three years and the children had lived with their grandmother, who had pampered them. About two months after the marriage the children went home. For some time they were "little angels," but soon they began to run wild as they had done at their grandmother's home. The stepmother was nonplused; she did not know what to do with them. She said that since they were not her children she could not discipline them. A social worker with a child-placing agency advised the stepmother to act as if they were her children and just as if she were a real member of the family. In a comparatively short time, with the cooperation of the father, she had the situation under control, and the children accepted the new order. In due course of time the boy joined the Navy while the girl became a Wave, and both of them wrote lovely letters to their stepmother.

Some children think that a stepmother is interested in taking advantage of them, that she is inclined to be a "gold digger." One stepmother made it impossible for any such charge to be brought against her when she refused to be made a beneficiary in her husband's insurance policy, lest the children be turned against her. She said that if he died she could take care of herself.

Partiality, actual or imputed, is the rock on which many of these marital ventures have been wrecked. To avoid any show of partiality, one stepmother would buy articles comparable, if not exactly alike, for her stepchild and for her own child. Some stepparents do more for their stepchildren than for their own children in order to avoid the accusation of unfairness. One father gave more of his spare time to his stepson than to his own children. The boy would wait for his stepfather to come home and then they would garden, read, walk, or work in their shop together. One girl wrote of her home:

We never resent correction by our stepfather because he is very just; he does not correct us as much as his own children. It always hurts us when we have to be corrected, not because of resentment, but because we admire him so much that we do not want to displease him.

Disagreement relative to the control of a child can develop friction in any home, but where a stepchild is present it is more difficult to see eye to eye on such matters. When the parent and stepparent discuss matters of discipline and then co-operate in carrying out the program on which they have agreed, the chances for a successful outcome are greatly enhanced.

Now and then any reference to a departed parent in a reconstituted home brings difficulty: it may produce jealousy on the part of the new parent or it may arouse hatred on the part of the children toward the stepparent. One stepmother assumed the care of four children and managed the situation remarkably well. One factor in the situation seemed to be that she and the eldest girl would talk freely about the girl's own mother. Even though she was not present physically, she was a real member of the family and there was no jealousy or tension connected with her.

Frequently a child feels that the new parent has supplanted him in the affections of the real parent. The new parent must exercise care in showing that he or she is not a supplanter but that the child now may be the recipient of the affections of two parents instead of one only.[50] If there is a parent fixation the situation may be sufficiently problematical to call for outside aid. A psychiatrist may be needed to bring a change in the child's attitude to avoid serious difficulty. The child needs to see that this possessiveness of his is extremely selfish and that his real parent needs the affection of the new mate.

Oftentimes a stepparent can see a child's shortcomings more clearly than a fond parent whose intimate association with the child from the very beginning has made him myopic. This does not, however, give the step-parent the privilege of setting about at once to make the child over into a new form according to his or her particular blueprint. A child tends to resent criticism and any attempt by a newcomer to make abrupt changes. Furthermore, a widower often resents this as being a criticism not only of himself but also of his departed mate. More can be done by giving the child the love and understanding of which he has been deprived through the loss of his real parent. If the child's admiration is won through a sympathetic understanding of him in his child's world, more can be done to shape his personality than through an aggressive campaign of reconstruction.

Some women, when faced with the problem of caring for stepchildren, read books on child care and training. Even though they may be "bookish" in their approach to the children, the willingness to learn and the attitude of open-mindedness lay the foundations for a successful outcome. When the books do not provide the answers, they turn to child-guidance clinics for assistance.

Many stepchildren have been won over when the new parents would share in their interests, problems, and activities. One girl had difficulties in her school work. Her mother said that she was too impatient to help her daughter, "but the stepfather," she declared, "had the patience of a saint." He gave much time to the girl, with the result that she steadily improved and began to like her studies. He was always looking for some new way in which he might help the child. When the mother, with considerable pride, stated that the daughter admired her stepfather and considered him perfect, there was no immediate danger of a rift in that family.

CONCLUSION

In popular usage the stepchild suffers from neglect, and in many ways this is all too true. Adoption, foster children, and orphans have been studied. Adoption is coming to be quite generally controlled by the state. Trained social workers investigate prospective foster parents with reference to their social and economic status as well as to their personality qualifications and moral fitness to care for children. Usually a child will be placed for a trial period, during which time the social workers keep a close check before the adoption is finally consummated.

Why should not certain safeguards be thrown about the stepchild? Should there not be some investigation made of prospective stepparents before marriage? In the state of Oregon both persons concerned in a marriage must present medical certificates in order to secure a license. Why should there not be certificates indicating suitability for stepparenthood? Since the stepchild has all the problems of any other child and usually has them in larger dosages, in addition to which he has other problems which grow directly out of the step-relationship, many of the difficulties could probably be avoided or, at any rate, minimized if certain precautionary measures were taken.

NOTES

[1]Metropolitan Life Insurance Company, "Current Pattern of Marriage and Remarriage," *Statistical Bulletin*, 34, June 1953, pp. 6–8.

[2]Bureau of the Census, *Current Population Reports, Population Characteristics*, Series P-20, No. 23, March 4, 1949, p. 1. Cf. also James H. S. Bossard, *Parent and Child*, Philadelphia, University of Pennsylvania Press, 1953, pp. 125–26.

[3]Ibid., p. 127. Used by permission.

[4]Bureau of the Census, op. cit., p. 3.

[5]Metropolitan Life Insurance Company, "The Frequency of Remarriage," *Statistical Bulletin*, 30, January 1949, pp. 8–10.

[6]Paul H. Jacobson, "Total Marital Dissolutions in the United States: Relative Importance of Mortality and Divorce," pp. 4–7, reprinted from *Studies in Population*, Princeton University Press, 1949.

[7]M. C. Elmer, *The Sociology of the Family*, Boston, Ginn & Co., 1945, p. 267.

[8]Paul C. Glick, "First Marriages and Remarriages," *American Sociological Review*, 14 (1949), p. 732.

[9]Bureau of the Census, op. cit., p. 1.

[10]Paul C. Glick and Emanuel Landau, "Age Factor in Marriage," *American Sociological Review*, 15 (1950), p. 521.

[11]Metropolitan Life Insurance Company, "The Chances of Remarriage for the Widowed and Divorced," *Statistical Bulletin*, 26, May 1945, p. 1.

[12]James H. S. Bossard, "Previous Conjugal Condition," *Social Forces*, 18 (1939), p. 244.

[13]Metropolitan Life Insurance Company, *Statistical Bulletin*, 26, May 1945, p. 1. Cf. also Paul H. Landis, "Sequential Marriage," *Journal of Home Economics*, 42 (1950), p. 625.

[14]Bossard, *Parent and Child*, pp. 129–30. Also *Social Forces*, 18 (1930), pp. 244–47.

[15]Bossard, *Parent and Child*, p. 130. Used by permission.

[16]Mortimer Spiegelman, "The Broken Family—Widowhood and Orphanhood," *The Annals*, 188 (1936), pp. 124–25.

[17]Ibid., p. 4.

[18]Cf. Glick, op. cit., p. 732.

[19]Mortimer Spiegelman, "The American Family," *The Record*, American Institute of Actuaries, 33 (1944), pp. 402–3.

[20]Kingsley Davis, "Children of Divorced Parents," *Law and Contemporary Problems*, 10 (1944), pp. 719–20.

[21]Leon C. Marshall and Geoffrey May, *The Divorce Court*, Baltimore, Johns Hopkins Press, 1932, Vol. I, p. 31. For additional data, cf. Bossard, *Parent and Child*, pp. 135–37; William Carlson Smith, *The Stepchild*, Chicago, University of Chicago Press, 1953, pp. 69–76.

[22]Paul H. Jacobson, "Differentials in Divorce by Duration of Marriage and Size of Family," *American Sociological Review*, 15 (1950), p. 239. Paul Popenoe found in his study that two thirds of the divorcees had no children when seeking divorce, although married eight to ten years. *Social Forces*, 12 (1933), p. 48.

[23]*American Sociological Review*, 15 (1950), p. 244.

[24]Paul Popenoe, "Divorce and Remarriage from a Eugenic Point of View," *Social Forces*, 12 (1933), pp. 48–50.

[25]Rex A. Skidmore and Anthon S. Cannon, *Building Your Marriage*, New York, Harper & Bros., 1951, p. 145.

[26]Harvey J. Locke, *Predicting Adjustment in Marriage: A Comparison of a Divorced and a Happily Married Group*, New York, Henry Holt, 1951, pp. 300–9.

[27]Landis, op. cit., p. 627.

[28]Thomas P. Monahan, "How Stable Are Remarriages?" *American Journal of Sociology*, 58 (1952–53), pp. 287–88.

[29]Hornell and Ella B. Hart, *Personality and the Family*, Boston, D. C. Heath, 1935, p. 109.

[30]Ibid., p. 1.

[31]*American Sociological Review*, 15 (1950), p. 239.

[32]This holds particularly true on the lower economic levels, where the rate of remarriage is higher than among professional and clerical workers. *American Sociological Review*, 14 (1949), pp. 733–34.

[33]Unpublished document.

[34]Cf. Clifford R. Shaw et al., *Delinquency Areas*, Chicago, University of Chicago Press, 1929, pp. 55–57, for an excellent case.

[35]Ibid., pp. 733–34.

[36]Spiegelman, *The Annals*, 188, pp. 121–24.

[37]Ibid., p. 122.

[38]Cf. Smith, op. cit., pp. 97–240.

[39]Paul G. Cressey, *The Taxi-Dance Hall*, Chicago, University of Chicago Press, 1932, p. 68, for an interesting case.

[40]In simple preliterate societies where it is common to live in small village groups, there are no strangers. In the event of a remarriage, the new parent and the stepchild, as members of the same primary group, are well acquainted with each other and the stepchild is not a liability.

[41]Agency case record.

[42]Unpublished document.

[43]Cf. Hermann Vollmer, "The Grandmother: A Problem in Child Rearing," *American Journal of Ortho-Psychiatry*, 7 (1937), pp. 378–82.

[44]Simple, preliterate societies are less disturbed by favoritism. Children are less the private property of the two parents and belong more to the entire primary group than in our culture.

[45]Cf. William C. Smith, "The Stepchild," *American Sociological Review*, 10, April 1945, p. 241.

[46]Agency case record.

[47]William E. Barton, *The Life of Abraham Lincoln*, Indianapolis, Bobbs-Merrill, 1925, Vol. I, p. 118.

[48]For additional case material, cf. Skidmore and Cannon, op. cit., pp. 146–48; W. C. Smith, *The Stepchild*, pp. 104–20.

[49]For role of mother in adjustments to the new family situation, cf. Allan Fromme, *The Psychologist Looks at Sex and Marriage*, New York, Prentice-Hall, 1950, pp. 240–41.

[50]Cf. O. Spurgeon English and Constance J. Foster, *Fathers Are Parents Too*, New York, G. P. Putnam's Sons, 1951, pp. 235–42.

Chapter 5

MASTURBATION

by Lester W. Dearborn

DIRECTOR, BOSTON MARRIAGE COUNSELING SERVICE, AND FORMER CHAIRMAN, AMERICAN ASSOCIATION OF MARRIAGE COUNSELORS

Since we began to study the sex life of man no other subject has been more frequently discussed, no other practice more roundly condemned and more universally practiced than masturbation. Masturbation is any stimulation of the sexual organs for the pleasure involved and for the release of tension.

What was the probable origin of the old ideas and taboos regarding masturbation? The knowledge may help to set at rest the feeling that "where there is smoke there must be fire." The fact is that many people feel there must have been a reason for the belief that masturbation resulted in harm, or otherwise the impression would not have prevailed.

When people lived in tribes that fought with other tribes, group survival was of paramount importance. The elders of the tribe considered it a social sin to waste sperm by any practice that did not procreate children. The spill of spermatozoa by Onan (which in the past has been erroneously referred to as masturbation) came under tribal interdict. The condemnation did not occur because of the loss of an easily renewable supply of spermatozoa, but rather because of Onan's anti-social attitude in refusing to father offspring.

The attitudes expressed during the twenty-two centuries marking the period from Hippocrates to Brady's[1] writings in the 1890s bear definite similarities in their obvious ignorance of body structure, causation of disease, lack of objectivity, and almost complete absence of a scientific approach to this subject. From the 1890s to the beginning of World War I there was a period of transition. During this period came a growing interest in psychiatry, the beginnings of the movement for preventive medicine, and an emphasis on the need for a scientific approach to the study of cause and result. While the notion still persisted that masturbation might cause insanity and that it was without doubt a harmful practice, we do get glimpses of a more enlightened attitude. Many insisted that the practice might be more widespread and less harmful than had been believed. For the most part, however, these pleadings for an enlightened attitude were greatly overshadowed by the persisting influence of Tissot[2] in France, who blasted the eighteenth-century world by his *Onana, A Treatise on the Diseases Produced by Onanism*. This book is steeped in ignorance and personal bias. Tissot could not be expected to have known the nature of semen or the nature of the male sex hormones. He could, however, have exercised intelligence in the deductions he made from the available facts. Tissot's book went through numerous editions and was translated into several languages. It became the main source book of those who felt impelled to write about the viciousness of "self-abuse." About this time, or in 1763, an English contemporary[3] published an unsigned booklet about tabes dorsalis, or locomotor ataxia, one cause of which he said was "the immoderate loss of so pure a fluid as the semen." Tissot agreed with him and spoke of the preciousness of the seminal fluid, the loss of one ounce of which enfeebled one more than the loss of forty ounces of blood. For these beliefs there was not, of course, the slightest scientific evidence.

Tissot attributed most of the known disorders of his day to the loss of semen; he added a few new ones born of his own observation. He accepted a statement that he had known "simple gonorrhea, dropsy, and consumption to depend on the same cause." The appalling liberties which Tissot took with scientific fact are emphasized best by his contention that sexual relations were apt to cause epileptic fits, the belief being that "coitus is a kind of epilepsy," considering the "orgasm as a convulsive symptom." Such statements, born of the man's imagination, caused immeasurable suffering for generations to follow. One effect credited to masturbation, which has been more persistently believed in than any of the others, is that masturbation supposedly caused insanity. As if Tissot had not done enough to cripple man's mind with fear, Rozier,[4] writing fifty years after the seventh edition of Tissot's work, added insanity to Tissot's list. By 1839 the belief that masturbation caused insanity was well rooted.

In 1839 a Dr. M. S. Gove[5] published her work, *Solitary Vice,* in which she quoted the sixth report of the State Lunatic Hospital at Worcester, Massachusetts, to the effect that masturbation was "third in point of power to deprive its victim of reason." Beginning with Gove appear admissions by various authors of the universality of the practice; at the same time attempts have not been made to explain why the dire consequences which they ascribed to masturbation did not manifest themselves in every case. Gove unconsciously hinted at the naturalness of masturbation in the statement that the greater part of those who communicated with her on the subject had not been taught to masturbate and did not know that anyone else did. At another point she unwittingly intimated that worry was responsible for the symptoms supposedly caused by masturbation itself.

In 1840 an anonymous writer[6] took issue with the authorities prior to him, contending that the disorders attributed to masturbation were not caused directly by it. He declared that they had *no proof* that they were so caused. Here was the first demand for a scientific approach to the whole subject. In the next sentence the writer slipped back into the old groove and described what he considered the one and only disorder due to masturbation, namely dementia praecox or schizophrenia.

Dr. E. T. Brady in 1891 was one of the first to question the part that masturbation was supposed to play in the causation of insanity. While he seemed to have no doubt about the perniciousness of the practice, he did state, "But it is very probable that its importance as an influence has been greatly exaggerated, particularly in connection with the causation of insanity." Modern marriage counselors are still having to deal with the heritage of belief and a carry-over of the old taboos.

In a paper published in 1888 in *Medical News,* Lawson Tait,[7] one of the leading gynecologists of his time, adopted what we would consider today a rather wholesome attitude toward masturbation and sex education. He said, "It is a sad misfortune that all sexual questions are so completely hidden from children at puberty." Apparently he had no doubt that there were evil effects from masturbation, but he raised a serious question as to what those evil effects might be. He was among the first to try to divorce religious morality from a condition that he considered merely physical. He seemed to feel there might be some harm in masturbation so far as the male was concerned, although he said, "The evil effects of masturbation have been greatly overrated." In women he questioned whether or not it was carried on to such an extent as to do any harm. He admitted that there were few boys who failed to masturbate at some time, but he felt the practice was comparatively rare among girls. In this he reflected the attitude of that period, when many considered that females were lacking in passion since they felt they had no need for it. This concept of female sexuality was not exploded until sexologists gathered convincing statistics to the contrary at a relatively recent date.

In 1907 Dr. Frederick Sturgis[8] attempted to make a study of the frequency of masturbation without any consideration of its supposed evils or disabling sequelae. His admittedly conservative estimate was that 60 per cent of both sexes masturbate at some time in their lives, but he held that were the whole truth known the figure would be nearer 90 per cent.

The writings of three men have probably had more direct influence upon the thinking and behavior in this country in the last half century than have those of any other writers, largely because their books when published bore the stamp of authority and were generally approved by religious leaders, educators, and social workers. The books of G. Stanley Hall,[9] Winfield Scott Hall,[10] and Sylvanus Stall[11] have probably, in the past, been on the book-shelves in more homes and schools and public libraries than is presently true of modern treatises on the subject. The influence of this last writer has been particularly bad because of the absence of any scientific approach to the subject and the wholly emotional manner in which it was handled. Stall said:

No boy can toy with the exposed portions of his reproductive system without finally suffering very serious consequences.

He favored sex education, but in this matter it was with the thought of saving boys from these terrible consequences. He says:

Nothing so much favors the continuance and spread of this awful vice as ignorance, and only by being early and purely taught on this important subject can the coming boys and men be saved from the awful consequences which are ruining morally, mentally, and physically thousands of boys every year.

After lecturing on the moral aspects of the subject he tells us that the next to suffer is the nervous system.

In the act of masturbation the nerves are wrought upon in such a manner as to produce most serious results.

Then in addition to the mental and moral changes which are supposed to have taken place he details the dreadful physical results.

I have quoted from Stall's chapter on "Self-Abuse" because he does not produce one iota of scientific evidence to substantiate any of his statements, yet his influence and that of others like him are still affecting the emotional lives of thousands of people at the present time.

The influence of Freud, the whole psychoanalytic school, and Havelock Ellis more than anyone else have made sexology a godchild of medicine. More specifically for contributions on this subject credit is given to Bernard, Bigelow, Davis, Hamilton, Kinsey, Kirkpatrick, Popenoe, and others.

Now two trends are manifest in the literature on masturbation. First is a tendency to consider masturbation in any form, under any circumstances, and with any frequency completely harmless. The writers holding this view knew that the sequelae attributed to it by preceding generations were groundless. Their newly acquired objectivity taught them to view the matter in a different light, to observe that much of animal life masturbates when deprived of any other outlet for its sexual drive. Hence they assumed it to be completely harmless.

At this same time students interested in psychiatry and psychoanalysis began to see new dangers in the practice, such as fixations, repressions, psychoneuroses, maladjustment to the sexual phase of marriage, and other mental effects. Many of these dangers have since been proven false; many are in the process of being so proved. Many of our present writings are still being influenced by the thought that we mustn't go too far in releasing restrictions for fear we may be encouraging complete abandonment which may lead to possible if not definable untoward results. However, there is a growing accumulation of modern literature which frankly reveals the truth (see bibliography).

Prevalence. What of the prevalence of masturbation? Tissot stated one reason for his writing the book was that the practice was so general. Almost without exception, particularly so far as boys were concerned, authors of treatises on this subject have expressed the belief that if it was not universal it was a habit indulged in by the majority of males. (The study of masturbation in females did not come until much later.) Sylvanus Stall said:

> *I wish I might say to you that but very few have ever known of this vice, but I do not believe that such an assertion would be true.*

In other words, he, too, accepted that it was pretty generally practiced. It is the one thing about which these early authors were right as proven by the following studies: W. L. Hughes,[12] Peck and Wells,[13] W. S. Taylor,[14] Kinsey,[15] Exner,[16] Lilburn Merrill,[17] and Dickinson and Beam.[18]

As to the prevalence of masturbation, all of the studies that have been carried on by competent investigators under well-credentialed auspices indicate that well over 90 per cent of all males have had a history of masturbation. While these studies vary somewhat in exactness, running anywhere from 90 per cent to 98 per cent, a study by Dr. A. C. Kinsey of Indiana University published in 1948 sets the figure at 94+ per cent. There will be little disagreement with this figure on the part of modern students of the subject. In 1929 Dr. Katharine Davis[19] published her study of college women wherein she reported admitted masturbation by 65 per cent of them. Since for most of them to admit masturbation was a matter of confession, we might easily add 10 per cent as a factor of error, as other studies, notably Hamilton's[20] and my own unpublished but recorded research, indicate that the figure among females runs somewhere between 75 per cent and 80 per cent if we are talking about a group of single women who have reached the age of twenty-five. In both sexes the frequency of the experience varies greatly, but the average single woman will report masturbation from two to three times a month, particularly just before or after her menstrual period, whereas the average single male reports two or three times a week. Checking this against the Hamilton report, we find that 49 per cent reported masturbation three or more times a week, and the Kinsey study, as reported by Glenn Ramsey,[21] shows 46 per cent of males who report a frequency of from one to six times weekly or more.

It may be safely assumed, therefore, from all the studies to date that were we to take the histories of men and women who had reached the age of twenty-five we would find that masturbation has played a part in the lives of more than 90 per cent of all males and about 70 per cent of all females, with the frequency running from once or twice a month up to several times a week, and that no evidence has been presented to prove that the greater frequency was any more productive of harm than the lesser.

Since all of this is pretty generally accepted by professional students of the sex life it is a dereliction of responsibility not to bring these facts to the attention of millions of people who could profit by the knowledge. In regard to this subject it might be said that today we are living in two worlds, one in which the normality of occasional masturbation for release of tension and for the physical and emotional satisfactions involved is accepted as normal, and the other, a larger world (though admittedly it is growing smaller), in which there is a persistence of the old ideas based on the dogma of the past. If you believe that I have been overemphasizing the influence of the past in present-day thinking on this subject I refer you to a statement made by Dr. Maurice Levine, who in listing misconception says that one misconception is "that masturbation causes psychoses."

> This is a misconception which has been exceedingly harmful and one which is extraordinarily persistent. In spite of the mental-hygiene teaching of the past fifteen or twenty years, many parents and doctors still believe such incorrect ideas, and still punish and threaten children who masturbate. One child-guidance clinic found recently that about 75 per cent of the parents of its child-patients remembered having threatened the children with the dangers of masturbation. It is important that physicians know that this is a mistake; many still do not.[22]

It would seem that in overcoming this problem in the larger sense we have simply to tell the truth. In doing so we must avoid the use of expressions which indicate the bias and prejudice begotten of our own early training. It is of little avail to try to release a person's fears by admitting the normality of the practice and denying that it has any unhealthy consequences, while at the same time showing your own distaste by using such words as, "It isn't nice," "Well-adjusted young people find better things to do," "You should give your attention to more constructive things," and similar condemnations. All such statements are vague, without meaning, and just as productive of emotional conflict as were the consequences attributed to masturbation in the past.

I have run across many instances where the feeling of improperness concerning the practice was having an untoward effect on personality adjustment which, if not as drastic as were the fears of the past, was definitely unwholesome in its result. Every marriage counselor has met innumerable instances in which the conflict over masturbation and its possible consequences has had a profound result in the lack of sex adjustment in marriage. In personal guidance counselors run across many cases in which worry over masturbation has been a major factor in maladjustment because of feelings of inadequacy and attitudes of self-condemnation. Whenever a person has not been particularly concerned about physical or mental consequences the very thought that the practice indicated a lack of character development still led to self-castigation and to unwholesome sex attitudes.[23]

MASTURBATION IN INFANCY

Infancy is the period in which most of the harm is done by the unwholesome attitude of adults. In their overconcern regarding this practice they engender fears and worries in the mind of the child. What is a wholesome attitude? First, we must understand that the child masturbates because he finds pleasure in it. The practice may begin very early, often when the child is still in the crib. Whether the practice begins at this time or later, it is spontaneous in the vast majority of cases. Despite the dire warnings of early writers concerning servant girls and playmates as sources of instruction in this practice, the majority of people who have talked with me cannot remember ever having received instruction from another; rather the practice began either as an urge or through some natural handling of the sexual organs. This is particularly true of the female. There are boys who report that they first became interested after hearing other boys talk about it or observing such behavior on the part of another. Even when they clearly remember sex play with other children they seem to feel that their interest in their own sexual organs preceded the group experiences. Most people claim that they do not know how or when they began but only that they have been doing it from a very early age. Many girls report that the interest came coincidentally with the onset of menstruation; an even larger number say that they had no particular interest in it until some time in their later teens.

Some recent literature* dealing with this habit in infancy has been rather forthright and free from fear-inspiring admonitions. A few writers are aesthetically critical, but the tendency is to deal with it more and more as a fact and as an accepted part of the child's development.

It is only fair to consider one factor which might give a parent some slight concern. Concerning the very young, we have no evidence that there is any tension release but rather that the organs are being manipulated because of sensory satisfactions. Because each episode does not come to a definite end, masturbation can be a prolonged activity to the exclusion of other interests, thus overemphasizing the child's pleasure interest in himself, which may later handicap his social development.

A child should be trained in good habits of hygiene, proper diet, proper elimination, and proper sleep. He should be encouraged to be active and interested in his play. If he appears to be unduly and overfrequently interested in his sex organs this problem should be discussed with the family physician, who will inquire into the possibility of adherent tissue or conditions which cause itching, thus drawing the child's attention to that area. If, however, the physician declares everything to be normal and you know that the habits of hygiene are well regulated, when you observe the child masturbating do nothing about it: do not scold or punish him or make the incident seem important. If you wish to distract his attention, do so by presenting another interest. Do it on the basis of "Let's do this" rather than "Stop doing that." If it becomes a matter of public display, then social values are involved. Correction should be a matter not of what he is doing but where he is doing it. We need have little worry, because the happy, well-adjusted child finds life so interesting and is busy at so many things that masturbation will play a very minor part in his activities.

In the unhappy child where there is obvious preoccupation with masturbation this should be regarded as a symptom of a deeper problem. Any attempt to correct the symptom without getting at the cause will undoubtedly cause greater tension and make matters worse. In a case such as this a parent is well advised to seek the counsel of a child specialist.

Masturbation is common as an adolescent practice in both sexes, with all evidence pointing to the fact that there is a higher percentage among males than among females. However, at the age of fifteen there is every indication that at least 50 per cent of the girls have masturbated and that the percentage increases as the group gets older; there are many more girls masturbating at the age of nineteen or twenty than were doing so in their middle teens.

---

*Dr. Benjamin Spock, *Baby and Child Care*, Pocket Book edition, 1946; Hannah Lees, "The Word You Can't Say," reprint from *Hygeia*, May 1944.

All that can be said about the harmlessness of masturbation in the earlier period can be repeated here. It is true, however, masturbation itself is likely to take on a somewhat different meaning to the adolescent, as each experience becomes an episode in itself, leading to orgasm, unless this climax is definitely suppressed or inhibited. It is also a psychological as well as a physiological act, as fantasy is a component part of the experience. Dr. Hamilton pointed out the desirability of fantasy construction as a part of the act and suggested that this made a more complete autoerotic experience, encouraging easier and more successful transition to heterosexual relations than does the masturbation which is purely sensory and without imagery.

There is great variety in the reported content of fantasies. Whatever it is, it consists of use of the imagination concerning sexual experience, intensifying the erotism to the point of orgasm. This can be a satisfying experience; it can help to relieve emotional tensions, and it effectively concentrates the sexual sensations in the genital area where they should be located, this being an effect especially to be desired in the female. If fear has not been engendered in the young person's mind he will quickly pass from such an episode to other life activities without particular concern, making the experience helpful and relatively unimportant. Unfortunately, because of the teachings of the past, thousands of young people still find themselves unable to pass from such an experience without deep feelings of anxiety. Consciousness of guilt, feelings of sin, and fear of consequences are the crippling sequelae of those who live in this second world. Thus the feelings of inferiority and self-condemnation, plus the anticipation of eventual harmful consequences, carry over into adult life and often adversely affect the chance for good sex adjustment. Happily, however, the type of sexual incompatibility in marriage which springs from this cause can be eliminated by proper education; this would also be true where it has been a factor in personality maladjustment.

Much credit for the successful application of modern psychology to the problem of masturbation should go to Dr. Walter F. Robie of Baldwinsville, Massachusetts, whose books, *Rational Sex Ethics, The Art of Love,* and *Sex and Life,* first emphasized the modern point of view in this field.

The physical structure of the male does not admit of a great deal of variety in masturbatory practice, and it is usually accomplished manually. However, some variations are reported, such as making coital movements against the bedclothes, or using a pillow for the purpose, or pressing against objects.

In the girl, however, because her construction permits it, there is considerable variation. While it appears that the use of the finger on the clitoris is the most usual form, running a close second is what has been referred to as thigh-rubbing, in which the girl presses her thighs together or crosses her legs and squeezes the inner muscles of her thighs, thus bringing pressure on the labia and incidentally on the clitoris. At this she may become quite skillful and can prolong the experience or bring herself to orgasm at will. Many girls who use this method, however, report that they stop short of orgasm. This may be due to the fact that thigh-rubbing is often used as a substitute after admonition by the parent who has observed some digital exploration. A frequent statement of older girls and women is that they remember having been told, "Don't you ever let me catch you touching yourself again." A household term for masturbation is "playing with oneself"; this often develops a concept in the mind of the child that the harm lies in hand contact. The girl, therefore, can indulge in thigh-rubbing with less consciousness of guilt because she is not "playing with herself."

Other methods are also reported, such as pulling panties, nightgown, pajamas, the bed sheet, or other materials tightly between the thighs, then making motions that excite the clitoris. Instrumental masturbation, that of putting something in the vagina, is not as often reported as some of these other methods.

Some forms of masturbation may act as a drawback to marriage adjustment, not because of any harm in the behavior itself, but because the transition from a particular form of masturbation to acquiring satisfactions in intercourse may later become difficult. It has been my experience that in the female those who report that they pass from clitoral stimulation to manipulation of the whole vulva, with emphasis upon stimulation of the vaginal orifice, very quickly made an adjustment to coitus; they will often report they have orgasm at the first experience or shortly thereafter. Those who for a number of years have used only the clitoris find it more difficult to make such a transition, but where they have been relieved of guilt feelings and have a co-operative and skillful husband such an adjustment will likely be made sometime within the first six months. Those girls who have denied themselves the direct form of masturbation and have used substitutive measures, such as various forms of pressure, or breast rubbing, often force themselves to stop just prior to orgasm because they have developed a fear of the orgasm, having conceived the idea that the wrong or harm lies in the release itself. In such cases, or in any case where orgasm has been suppressed, they may have developed a habit of non-response and carry this over into their marital relations, later to report that they have little or no satisfaction in coitus and an inability to come to a climax. In discouraging a form of direct masturbation in children one may be unwittingly encouraging a substitutive form which acts as a deterrent to achieving orgasm in intercourse. Also, the guilt feeling which caused a girl to withdraw from direct fondling of her own organs is apt also to cause her to resist manual stimulation on the part of the husband in his attempts at precoital excitation.

It has been my experience that the male who has masturbated with a sense of guilt which has driven him to get it over with as soon as possible and to suppress any accompanying fantasy is likely in consequence to find himself bothered in early marriage by premature ejaculation. The one who has engaged in masturbation reservatus, delaying the orgasm at will, has thus prepared himself to be a more adequate partner by having developed a technique that makes it possible for him to stay with his wife as long as it is necessary for her satisfaction.

In conclusion I wish to emphasize that every sex education program should include information concerning the normality of masturbation; this should be given to adults as well as to youth because it is through misinformed adults that the old superstitions are perpetuated. I think the kind of statement we ought to make and stand by should be something as follows:

Masturbation, according to the best medical authorities, causes no harm physically or mentally. Any harm resulting from masturbation is caused entirely by worry or by a sense of guilt due to misinformation.

I would make this kind of statement and challenge anyone to prove otherwise. Let us have respect for the normalities of life and for the good sense of our young people who have little time to be overconcerned with sex. Let's stop equivocating. Tell the truth and shame the devil!

NOTES

[1]E. T. Brady, "Masturbation," *Va.M. Month.*, 18:256–60, 1891–92.

[2]S. A. D. Tissot, *A Treatise on the Diseases Produced by Onanism*, New York, translated and published by Collins and Hannay, 1832. (First French issue prior to 1767.)

[3]Anonymous, *A Practical Essay Upon the Tabes Dorsalis*, 1763.

[4]Rozier, *Des Habitudes secrètes ou Des Maladies Produites par l'onanisme chez les femmes*, 3 ed., Paris, 1830.

[5]M. S. Gove, *Solitary Vice*, Portland, 1839.

[6]Anonymous, *An Hour's Conference with Fathers and Sons, in Relation to a Common Fatal Indulgence of Youth*, Boston, 1840.

[7]Lawson Tait, "Masturbation-Clinical Lectures," *Medical News*, 53:1–3, 1888.

[8]F. R. Sturgis, "The Comparative Prevalence of Masturbation in Males and Females," *Am. J. Dermat. and Genito-Urin. Dis.*, 11:396–400, 1907.

[9]G. Stanley Hall, *Adolescence*, 1907.

[10]Winfield S. Hall, *From Youth into Manhood*.

[11]Sylvanus Stall, *What a Young Boy Ought to Know*, 1905.

[12]W. L. Hughes, "Sex Experiences of Boyhood," *J. Social. Hyg.*, 12, 1926.

[13]M. W. Peck and F. L. Wells, "On the Psycho-sexuality of College Graduate Men," *Ment. Hyg.*, 7, 1923.

[14]W. S. Taylor, "A Critique of Sublimation in Males: A Study of Forty Superior Single Men," *Genet. Psychol. Monog.*, 13, 1933.

[15]Dr. A. C. Kinsey, Dr. Wardell B. Pomeroy, Dr. Clyde E. Martin, *Sexual Behavior in the Human Male*, 497–516, 1948.

[16]M. J. Exner, *Problems and Principles of Sex Education*, copyright by International Committee of Y.M.C.A., 1915.

[17]Lilburn Merrill, A summary of findings in a study of sexualism among a group of one hundred delinquent boys, *J. Juven. Res.*, 3, 1918.

[18]R. L. Dickinson and Lura Beam, *A Thousand Marriages; a Medical Study of Sex Adjustment*, 1931.

[19]K. B. Davis, *Factors in the Sex Life of Twenty-Two Hundred Women*, 1929.

[20]G. V. Hamilton, *A Research in Marriage.*

[21]Glenn V. Ramsey, "The Sexual Development of Boys," *Am. Journal of Psy.*, Vol. 56, April 1943.

[22]Dr. Maurice Levine, *Psychotherapy in Medicine*, 1942.

[23]Albert Ellis, Ph.D., *The American Sexual Tragedy*, 210, 1954.

BIBLIOGRAPHY

Adams, Dr. Clifford R., *Preparing for Marriage*, New York, E. P. Dutton, 1951, p. 55.

Baruch, Dorothy W., *Parents Can Be People*, New York, D. Appleton-Century Co., 1944, Chap. 9.

Ellis, Albert, *The American Sexual Tragedy*, New York, Twayne Publishers, 1954, pp. 154, 201.

Frank, Lawrence K. and Mary, *How to Be A Woman*, Maco Magazine Corp., 1954, p. 35.

Kinsey, A. C.; Pomeroy, Wardell B.; Martin, Clyde E., *Sexual Behavior in the Human Male*, Philadelphia, W. B. Saunders Co., 1948, pp. 497–516.

Levy, John, M.D., and Munroe, Ruth, *The Happy Family*, Alfred A. Knopf, 1938, p. 134.

Chapter 6

SEX EDUCATION AND THE CHILD

by Charles E. Manwiller, Ph.D.

DIRECTOR OF RESEARCH AND CURRICULUM PLANNING, PITTSBURGH BOARD OF EDUCATION

INTRODUCTION

Sex is a part of life, as is eating or sleeping. Sex is experienced in homemaking, in vocations, in social life, in clothing, in publicity, and in practically every phase of human endeavor. Sex can be regarded as normal, beautiful, natural, or as "dirty" and "unmentionable." Here sex education enters the picture with such questions as *when* and *what* should the child first learn about sex? Also *who* should teach the child?

All experts agree that sex education should begin at home and at birth, since its development proceeds simultaneously with physical, social, and emotional growth. This throws full responsibility upon the family unit; parents must be prepared for it either by having experienced good teachings in their own homes or, if not, by getting outside help from experienced people, through courses in home and family living or other counselors.

HEALTH AND HUMAN RELATIONS THROUGH HOME AND FAMILY LIVING

An awareness of sex has its beginnings in the wholesome family-life environment. Here mother and child, brother and sister, son and daughter, father and mother make sex differences obvious and normal. During the preschool years the informal and indirect general education makes for gradual and wholesome development in sex education. This should be used as a background for the later disturbing problems, emotional and psychological, brought on by adolescence.

Long before the child gets to school he has acquired at his mother's knee, or from his relatives, friends, and neighbors, basic attitudes toward others (male and female) and their standards of right and wrong, their hypocrisy, frustrations, and their attitudes toward sex and respect or lack of it for members of the opposite sex. They will have tasted of security or the lack of it in their social world called home.

The problem of child growth and development is further complicated by the differing patterns of traditions, customs, and ideals found in various sections of the country—some new, some old in the traditions of the old country. Teen-agers reflect these patterns and therefore bring to the meaning of marriage and family living the understandings, attitudes, and ideals of the cultures in which they "lived, moved, and had their being."

Frequently these culture patterns conflict with school patterns. The sex stereotypes, the mastermind father, the suppressed mother, the "free" speech, lack of respect for females, the uncensored story or joke may bring the child into difficulty with the teacher or another pupil from a different kind of home background.

A. EARLY CHILDHOOD

Early sex education is learned from love and respect of parents for each other, their kindnesses and courteous relations with each other, their freedom from fears and embarrassments. These go deeper than formal teachings or giving information, answering questions and satisfying curiosity as part of the child's effort to discover life. There is no best age to teach sex.

Sex instruction in the home must be given by precept and example. Happy parents can teach mutual courtesy, love, and kindness in their daily living.

In babyhood, lessons in general education are important. It is not always wise to let Junior have his own way about things. A good schedule carries with it regularity, abiding by the rules, and a beginning in overcoming tantrums. Learning to eat what Mother cooks is a good start toward happy married life. Similarly, learning to do chores for the family is good training for homemaking.

From three to five years of age, children begin to ask questions about self, the body, dress, and other differences as a matter of course. A straightforward answer without detailed information usually suffices at this age. The important thing is to tell the truth when a child wishes to know the origin of baby sister. Fear should be avoided.

Father must forego the role of sole disciplinarian for the family and be brought into the family circle as a partner in the creation and rearing of the offspring.

Dr. Rice[1] submits ten rules for the teaching of sex:

(1) *Parents must prepare before they can teach their child.*
(2) *They should wait until the child asks questions.*
(3) *Questions must be answered truthfully and without embarrassment.*

(4) Sex must be taught positively rather than negatively.
(5) Sex is a beautiful subject.
(6) Teaching should be as casual as possible. It is a part of living.
(7) Sex education should not be stimulating.
(8) Later teach child to look with pleasure to the time when he will have a home and family of his own.
(9) Help child acquire a decent, refined, and scientific vocabulary and acquaint him with good sources of information.
(10) Help him understand the important reasons for marriage relations and the family. Mothers must not make daughters out of sons, nor fathers make sons out of daughters.

Parents should know their children, their moods, their likes and dislikes, the things which make them unhappy, because unhappiness often leads to undesirable sex habits.

Parents should know the playmates and adults with whom the children spend time.

At this stage body cleanliness is absolutely essential. Clothes should be comfortable and well fitting, not too tight because of "hand-me-downs." If irritations appear, obtain a medical examination.

Avoid excessive fondling which may lead to sexual excitement either while bathing or toileting the child.

Use just enough cover during sleeping hours. Give him something to do immediately upon wakening. Put him to bed when sleepy. A child should not be disciplined at bedtime for misbehavior committed during the day or even the dinner hour. Going to bed should be a pleasant experience.

Every child is entitled to an adequate understanding of the nature of sex. Such training should be begun early in the child's life by the parents, who themselves recognize sex as a normal life process, and should develop and keep pace with the child's growth. The story of human origin for the five- or six-year-old and, later, the development of insight into human relations as well as a sense of social responsibility and personal adjustment should be included in the total pattern of sex education. A story which everyone should know is recorded in this sampling of good books on the subject: *The New Baby*,[2] *The Story of a Baby*[3] for the young child; *Growing Up*[4] and *Your Own Story*[5] for the preadolescent; *Your Marriage and Family Living*[6] for the high-school and college student.

B. ELEMENTARY LEVEL

All evidence from research studies on sex experiences of youth indicates (1) that an early beginning in sex education is needed; (2) that emphasis upon broad social implications of sex with regard to long-time individual adjustments is important; (3) social responsibilities associated with sex behavior need to be emphasized; and (4) the school can provide opportunities for youth to get together in wholesome, happy situations under guidance.

Every teacher should teach about sex as far as his subject or activity contributes to character building and to the shaping of ideals. He should extend understanding and facts of life and help the pupil to adjust himself socially. In the early grades when both sexes study and play together and thereby learn to observe and accept differences without bias, they are getting sex instruction. When nature-study classes or reading teachers have classroom activities involving animals, such as setting hens, rabbits, or guinea pigs, opportunity for learning about birth, care of young, and sex differences in behavior may be learned in a wholesome way before the "stork theory" or the "doctor's little black bag" gets started as a juvenile whisper campaign.

The elementary schools can give basic information in physiology and anatomy. They should be concerned with body structure and the protective functions of the body, care of the body, proper food and clothing, how to keep well and strong, community health, and personal development in mental, emotional, and social behavior. All these contribute toward background materials and educational outcomes in the form of understandings or concepts, attitudes and ideals, appreciations, and other end results which have a direct bearing on a formal course in social hygiene or on units integrated in other divisions, such as physical education, biology, home economics, social studies, and language arts.

Here on this level of instruction are developed attitudes toward personal cleanliness, clothing, medical care, exercise and recreation, infection, regular habits, self-control, acceptance by peers, security in family affection, disappointments, criticisms, parental sacrifices, sharing, new acquaintances, and responsibilities in the home. Here sex instruction must be clear, honest, and based upon fact. There is no sense in teaching a child at six the "stork theory" of birth, only to reteach the truth later. While at an early period the information given should be conservative, it should at all times be scientific and truthful.

No longer can this subject be held in abeyance for too long a time. Sex appeal has been commercialized. The child sees this in popular magazines strewn about the home, sees it in theaters, hears it on the radio, experiences it in dress and cosmetics, conversations, etc. Parents can no longer indulge in what Charles Eliot called a "conspiracy of silence."

Experiences in school systems indicate a universal need for sex education. They also indicate that lessons or approaches to this need must begin in the elementary school. Senior high school is too late to do an effective job. Educators must begin earlier and treat the problem whenever and wherever it can be introduced in a normal setting without forcing the subject. A pole among adolescent students indicates a high interest in sex problems as judged by their discussions and questions. The survey also indicates a lack of information, some misinformation, and superstitions which can and may condition their future outlooks.

Furthermore, sex instruction is more than information regarding reproduction. Information is only a phase of it. There are personal and social values to be considered.

In the early years of the child's home life he forms certain attitudes about sex from the kind of behavior he observes between his father and mother. If he sees manifestations of love, devotion, helpfulness, and sacrifice, he will register a different feeling about the pattern of social relations than if he experiences fighting, unhappiness, bickering, nagging, or selfishness between the two mates designated as homemakers and sex partners.

PARENTS AND TEACHERS

Most parents and many teachers still feel unable to talk to children about sex, reproduction, and ideals of sex behavior. Lacking vocabulary and techniques of approach, emotionally blocked by traditional teachings and old taboos, and suffering from the "silent approach" when they were children, it is most embarrassing for parents and some teachers to begin sex education at adolescence and difficult to initiate it during the child's infancy.

Frequently problems arise with foreign-born parents who do not understand the American freedom of social conduct among young people—their freedom to date without chaperons, to stay out late, to go when and where they please. Their culture patterns and social mores came from forces outside the individual, while in our culture inner protections are built up democratically through love, trust, faith, education about facts of life and consequences, and personal choice. Through co-education and the intermingling of sexes academically and socially youth learns acceptable behavior for chastity, and moral and spiritual values acceptable to home, church, and school—the institutions which exert greatest influences on them for future success in happiness, in homemaking, or in vocational adjustment.

A child exposed to secrecy, evasion, and hidden meanings at home and in school easily absorbs, without evaluative techniques or standards, the sex information, innuendoes, and sex behavior patterns of movies, night clubs, roadhouses, pulp magazines, and lurid advertising. Here are possibilities for acquiring sex misinformation about one's body, wrong attitudes toward people and/or life itself.

It is commonly conceded that children have rights. With respect to sex,

1. Children have a right to get their knowledge of sex from adults having normal and healthy attitudes.

2. They have a right to learn about sex without fears and anxieties.

3. They have a right to ask questions and get correct, straightforward answers when they ask questions from parents. Furthermore, questions need not be answered by a complete revelation of all sex facts at one sitting.

4. The children have a right to ask many questions frequently and at different maturation levels without a feeling of guilt, disturbance, or evasiveness.

In school the bottleneck in a real program of sex education is the teacher. It can be no better than the teacher. He must be free from warped attitudes, frustrations, and fears. He should have a well-rounded and well-adjusted personality. He carries no chips on his shoulders, is unbiased and at peace with the world and his fellow man. He has a love for teaching and children. They naturally gravitate toward him. He knows his subject matter and how to teach it. He is morally and spiritually sound. He has character without being a "character." He sees in this program a level of reverence for human personality and the home.

Various patterns of handling this problem have been tried by school systems. Some have been tried openly with community support and others clandestinely by teachers forced to "bootleg" discussions in biology courses between teacher and students, the latter sworn to secrecy. Such an unholy alliance only helps to deepen the mystery of sex by reinforcing the taboos and preventing free and open discussion of a subject which can stand the truth. Such secret treatment is questionable morally and spiritually. The pupil must never be made to feel ashamed of the truth.

Other school systems tried motion pictures; required courses; conferences; workshops by and for parents, teachers, welfare workers, health officials, and clergy; discussion groups with P.T.A.s, Y.M.C.A., Y.W.C.A., labor organizations, churches; parent institutes; special courses for teachers at universities; school nurses' lectures; lectures from such organizations as Family Health Association; reproduction exhibits in museums; lectures by doctors, pediatricians, and psychiatrists.

Even though many teachers feel incompetent in training and experience to tackle the job of sex instruction, educators realize now more than ever the necessity for doing the job. World War II has shown the need. They now see the task of not only giving information, but of developing attitudes and ideals, and of training the emotions. They see the individual not only as a thinking, recalling, reasoning individual capable of reading and communicating with his fellow man, but also as one having physical and social needs, drives, and impulses, all of which are educative. The emotions are important in learning. They must be considered in any phase of sex education or character education, both phases of each other.

Helping the child establish himself in his age group, helping him make and keep friends, helping him size up the status of different individuals, teaching him how to meet loneliness and need for companionship, how to accept the boy-girl status naturally, how to harmonize conflicts, to gather and weigh evidence, to establish self-confidence and self-direction, and how to know when to consult specialists in family relations, all such instruction helps that child in making good social adjustments.

Some schools offer opportunities to upper-grade students to work with and help nursery-school children. As they work with the children the older pupils discover shyness, aggressiveness, crying for attention, sex interests, temper tantrums, etc. In the process they are helped to understand themselves, their friends, their families, and neighborhoods. They recognize behavior that is immature and childish. They experience development in mental and social health.

Here is afforded background for discussions by seventh and eighth grades on such topics as:

Personality traits of a "regular guy"
Human drives for adventure, approval, interest in opposite sex, security, etc.
How to overcome personal handicaps
Relationships with young brothers or sisters
Facing personal and social problems
How we look, talk, act
Advantages and disadvantages of shyness
Use of comics
Sharing problems with others[7]

An excellent list of teaching aids and resource materials is listed in Kirkendall, *Sex Education as Human Relations,* pages 298–340. These sources, consisting of books, pamphlets, visual aids, magazines, models, exhibits, radio scripts, etc., are arranged for various maturation levels, beginning with small children to college students.

In her book, *The Normal Sex Interests of Children from Infancy to Childhood,* Strain presents on pages 31–64 an outline of the various age levels and developmental stages in sexual development of children based on observations by teachers and parents. These observations from infancy, pre-school, kindergarten, primary, elementary, junior high, and senior high school can serve as an outline for checking one's observations or as an aid to interpret and understand various expressions of sex interests as they appear in individuals or groups.

Parents and teachers can feel successful when young people express themselves openly, when conduct becomes less secretive, when hidden pictures come to light of day, when books once read behind locked doors are enjoyed openly, and when family conversation is inclusive of all.

C. HIGH-SCHOOL LEVEL

During the past quarter century sex education was introduced in the curriculum under various titles, as human reproduction, the human body, health and growth, life problems, family life education, human science, human relations, health and physical education, homemaking, education for responsible parenthood, social hygiene and health, and love and family living. Early approaches were concerned chiefly with venereal diseases, while the emphasis today is on mental hygiene, social hygiene, biological aspects of sex, family life adjustments, and normal boy-girl relationships. At first schools leaned toward separate isolated courses. The present trend is to integrate the units into such subject fields as English, home economics, physical education, science, and social studies in order to permeate all of school life and enrich the curriculum. The single-shot rifle approach with a lecture on sex, disease, or morals is unpopular and poor education.

Many educators today are still debating the problems of (1) whether instructional materials shall be presented as natural parts of other courses, in a broad program of education in human relations calling for a co-operative approach by teachers of biology, home economics, general science, physiology and hygiene, physical education, social studies, and the language arts, or (2) whether the materials should be taught in a special course or courses offered on varying maturation levels of the student. If so, what are the most desirable levels and what should be offered on each one? The first method is a long-range, co-operative enterprise. The second may be classified as a short-range, hard-hitting, emergency-need type of approach which found favor during the war in the hope of meeting problems of venereal diseases, mental hygiene, alcohol, sex delinquency, physical defects, unemployment, and accident prevention.

Both methods were tried as the old controls—fear of illegitimate pregnancy and venereal disease employed by parents as a means of warning youth against base sex behavior—were weakened by the knowledge of rapid-treatment centers for syphilis and gonorrhea and a knowledge of contraceptive devices.

It is feared by some that our standards may be changed by the success of prophylactics in preventing venereal disease through stressing prophylaxis at the expense of genetics and psychological considerations.

It is necessary, therefore, to face reality and emphasize other behavior controls based on dignity of, and respect for, human personality and happiness in home life arising out of a satisfying marriage. Thus the "facts-of-life" lecture, the lurid tales in hushed tones, and the hushed abnormal sex practices are giving way to emphasis upon personal pride, social responsibility, morality, and an understanding of human interrelations.

THE INTEGRATED METHOD

A consideration of the first method calls for a completely integrated program from kindergarten to the end of high school, or it may be delayed until the beginning of the high school and there offered by teachers of certain subjects only.

If one aim of sex education is to preserve the family, there is little doubt that it should be introduced at the nursery-school or kindergarten level and be continued throughout the high school as an integral part of a positive planned approach. Even though wholesome sex training should start in the home, the school should supplement home training, when given, and follow it through the maturation levels of the child by correlating it with subject matter and the activities in the curriculum. As he progresses, newer emphases can be given through courses in elementary science, health and physical education, home economics, social studies, biology, and the language arts, especially English. It calls for the teaching of facts which the child can understand at his maturation level, habits and attitudes which can be developed at the time. As he develops he can be introduced to the advances made in biochemistry and endocrinology and their bearing upon hygiene and physiology. The textbooks of a decade ago are no longer adequate and challenging to the modern child who is flirting with electronics and nuclear physics in some form or other or who reads about experiments with white mice or dogs. The social program and recreational activities present many wholesome opportunities for teaching social hygiene.

The success of such a plan is predicated upon certain basic factors, such as:

1. *The teacher should know his students and methods for presenting the subject.*
2. *The sex content should not be forced into units of work in any subject area. It should be integrated naturally without undue pressure.*
3. *Students should be grouped according to maturation, needs, and capacities or abilities.*
4. *The class should not be stimulated to curiosity, secrecy, or outside discussions. The subject must be impersonally and unemotionally presented.*

5. In the early stages fear and abnormal sex problems should not be presented. A positive, wholesome emphasis is to be desired.

6. The program should be gradually introduced by one teacher and then broadened to include other teachers and fields of interest.

7. Practice of having outside speakers should be discouraged.

8. Religious views and ethical differences must not be introduced into the classroom discussions.

9. Teach and inspire by facts and the truth. Don't "preach."

10. Teachers should be well grounded in biology, physiology, social psychology, and sociology, with a sound emotional attitude toward sex.

11. Some problems should be handled in personal conferences.

12. The historical approach is recommended by some in attempting to solve the personal problems later.

13. Evidence is to be desired more than opinion.

14. Materials should be selected according to age, maturity, and character of group, interests and needs of pupils.

Suggested Content for Integration with Other Courses in the Program of Studies. Perhaps a brief review of *some* of the objectives and content under subject-matter fields may indicate the contributions which each field can make to the whole pattern of health and human relations. These are not arranged in any order of importance, psychologically, or logically.

BIOLOGY—sex as a biological function; influence of glands on sex behavior; relation of mind to physical urges; development of necessary basic vocabulary; scientific attitude toward sex through study of heredity and reproduction; biological explanation of individual differences; responsibility to next generation.

ENGLISH—social phases of human relations. Teachers of literature think of their subject as coming out of life experiences of people—their behavior patterns differing geographically and chronologically. Through biography, novel, etc., study motives of other people—their successes and failures. The family in literature, marriage customs, personal and family problems, reading in the family, personalities in the family, family norms democratically arrived at. Control of sex; friendships by letter; friendship and early love; traditional inheritance; etiquette of social situations; leisure-time values; culture patterns; social hygiene in life today.

GENERAL SCIENCE—glands of body and their interrelationship; social responsibility of individual for society as a whole; effects of heredity and environment on home life; health and sanitation factors in social diseases.

PHYSIOLOGY—structure and function of sex organs; skeletal and muscular system of the anatomy; pubertal changes; how life begins; maturation of germ cells; development of fetus; communicable diseases; importance of heredity.

HEALTH AND HYGIENE (*sex, mental, personal*)

1. Sex—physical and emotional changes at puberty to understand self; sexual development; glands and reproduction; superstitions about sex; sex controls; self-control; effect of alcohol; licentious literature; building respect for opposite sex; sex and mental well-being.

2. Mental—emotional stability; self-appraisal of powers and limitations; methods of developing self-control; legitimate means of self-expression.

3. Personal—physiology and hygiene of menstruation; manifestations of sexual development; sex terminology, cleanliness, and hygiene; masturbation; dangers of venereal disease; spread of disease and social order.

PHYSICAL EDUCATION—meaning of growing up; meaning of "good sport"; physical development changes; posture, sitting, walking skills for physical fitness; games for development of muscles and organs; recreation activities, sports, hobbies, clubs; developing self-control; value of leisure time; value of clean living.

SOCIAL STUDIES—manners and customs of social life—the mores and folkways; history of marriage customs; place of family in society, marriage laws, eugenics; effect of broken homes on society; family personalities; individual personality; role of father and mother in the family; the child as a link between two generations; sex pride; sex companionship; sex delinquency; the family as a training institution for democracy; peace of home in the community; local and state agencies aiding families; venereal disease and family life; importance of birth rate to our nation.

SOCIOLOGY—family as a social unit; significance of marriage and divorce; social costs of sex misconduct, illegitimacy, prostitution.

MATHEMATICS has its contributions to make to sex education when such items as the Mendelian law, mortality tables, height-weight ratios, family budgeting, etc., are considered.

HOME ECONOMICS—problems in family living; relations between parents and children, men and women, boys and girls; value of good personality in self and others; personality development; place of interests in friendships; establishing values in love, affection, money, power, fame in life (how they operate in building standards of conduct?); social conventions; preparation for marriage; considerations for marriage; dating—single and group; crushes; normal sex interests and sex modesty; family responsibilities; parental responsibility; role of sexes in family life; child care; growth and needs of a baby; social customs around birth of baby; parenthood, heredity, and eugenics and the family; prenatal care of mothers; hygiene of child-hood; venereal disease; place of children in home; sex education of children; family adjustments by and for aged members; legal requirements for marriage; importance of cultural values in the home; fostering and building family traditions, ideals and spiritual values in the home; ways to democratic living in the home.

Home-economics teachers are laying aside some of the recipes for cookies and are tackling the problems of counseling in courtship, marriage, child rearing, and family relationships. The last war has brought us an unprecedented share of domestic and social health problems. Studies during the war revealed the alarming lack in sex instruction in home, school, or college. All too frequently youths were inadequately prepared in wholesome fundamental attitudes and patterns of sex behavior which have their beginnings early in life. This fact, coupled with emotional immaturity, marital infidelity, desertion, divorce, and excessive drinking, all of which undermine family life, are the concern not only of educators but of all who are interested in better homes. For educators it calls for marshaling of all forces in guidance, parent education, preschool programs, adult education, teen-age and adolescent clubs and activities, improved and increased recreational facilities, and clinical services. Schools must provide emphases either through courses or guidance in sex, family life, child care and development, and human relations.

There is hardly a group of teen-age or early adolescent youths who do not ask someone to enlighten them about such problems as:

1. *Getting along with other boys and girls*
2. *Attracting others*
3. *What to say to members of opposite sex*
4. *Points of social etiquette*
5. *Birth and growth of a baby*
6. *Petting, necking*
7. *Emotional controls*
8. *Changes in adolescence*
9. *Home and family living problems*
10. *Recreation problems*

Problems of Integration. One of the dangers in the integrated or fused setup is the inadequately trained, emotionally unfit, and socially embarrassed teacher who either talks too much or too little and sometimes too late. Cynicism is dangerous. Preaching is unaccepted. Idealism is essential. Overemphasis is undesirable. Teachers should be encouraged to attend health and human-relations courses. One of these was conducted at the University of Pennsylvania[8] with the following aims and topics:

1. Develop in teachers an awareness of problems in the field of sex; capacity to think constructively and without embarrassment; self-evaluation in the field by the teacher.

2. Place sex in biologic and sociopsychologic setting in growth of child to maturity.

3. Orient teacher to agency participation in guidance and remedial fields of child and family welfare.

4. Orient sex education related to delinquency, public health, and venereal-disease control.

5. Present problems of teaching and administration relating to classroom methods, development, and articulation of curriculum.

Non-Academic Activities. In the extracurricular phase of schoolwork, such activities as dancing, music, swimming, hiking, excursions, dramatics, art activities—all contribute to sex education through joint planning by both sexes and executing plans involving human relationships. These are the laboratories for the humanics for democratic living.

The school needs to recognize and work with other agencies and special groups, such as child-guidance centers, clinics, nurseries, social-welfare groups, psychiatrists, psychologists, pediatricians, and other specialists who contribute a great deal toward sex education.

THE SPECIAL-COURSE METHOD

The second method earlier referred to as the special-course method was tried in different places but perhaps not as extensively as in Pittsburgh. Briefly, the plan resolves itself into an informal, uncharted approach on the high-school level. This experiment had its inception in the war years, when the superintendent of schools called together at a luncheon meeting representative citizens from religious groups, Juvenile Court, the Parent-Teacher Association, Allegheny County Medical Association, the Child Guidance Clinic, the Department of Public Health, and the Department of Curriculum Study of the Pittsburgh schools to review problems of health and sex delinquency. At that time an outline of work and plans for administering it was presented and approved. Teachers were carefully selected in each school. Today segregated classes of twenty to thirty students are organized for six-week sessions. Students are admitted by parental permit only. There are no texts, no examinations, no assignments, no credits, no visitors. At the end of six weeks the medical doctor attempts to answer all questions unanswered by the teacher and brings the medical viewpoint into the classroom.

To date, 97 per cent of the parents have signed permits for the courses given in the ninth and twelfth grades. Students are unanimous in their praise and appreciation of this opportunity. The objectives for the courses are:

1. To understand the process of reproduction
2. To link one's own origin and development with life, based on moral and spiritual principles, together with a scientific attitude
3. To free youth from unwholesome conflicts concerning sex life
4. To help students develop a philosophy of life in harmony with sound character and social responsibility to assure successful mating and a happy family life

No doubt much of the success of the program is due to the community support gained by a proper launching, to the careful selection of teachers, small classes, to an informal approach in the classes, to assistance from the medical profession, and the short period of time required for the course.

The special-course approach may be necessary in some school centers before the integrated plan can be operated on the secondary level, since teachers feel the need for additional knowledge and methods of teaching the subject. Perhaps more colleges and universities will offer these opportunities not only to teachers already in service, but to recruits in training who require such orientation.

D. COLLEGE LEVEL

Colleges and universities are giving increased attention to the problems of home and family living and social hygiene for all students. In addition to short courses in sex, special courses in preparation for marriage, family life, parenthood, child care, prenatal care, etc., are being offered with increasing frequency.

While young people are interested in their professional careers, they are likewise asking questions about marriage and human relations. Some of these questions, reported by Carter and Foley,[9] are listed below:

1. Should a married woman seek a career? (Scaled value 8.2)
2. Should interests of man and wife be parallel? (7.5)
3. Should people marry who have great difference in age? (7.0)
4. Is a difference in formal education an important factor in determining advisability of marriage? (6.6)
5. Can difference of race and social status be overcome? (6.3)
6. Should a couple have similar standards of homemaking? (6.0)
7. Should you marry while in school? (5.8)
8. Is a long engagement advisable? (5.0)
9. What factors should a woman consider in selecting a husband? (5.0)
10. What factors should a man consider in selecting a wife? (5.0)

11. What are arguments favoring early marriage? (6.2)

12. Where is reliable information about sex and sex technique to be found? (5.2)

13. Is chastity before marriage a vital factor in future happiness and successful marriage? (4.8)

14. How can two normal parents be sure of non-defective children? (5.2)

Such questions are not uncommon when it is realized that the majority of young people received little or no sex education from their parents, because only a few feel that they can discuss sex problems with their parents. Most of what they know was derived from contemporaries or books. Attitudes toward marriage and parenthood developed early in life are not easily changed by one or two college courses or even by the accepted mores of the student-age group, though there are times when the latter are more effective than the former in influencing behavior. Frequently the need is not information so much as insight, understanding, and techniques of social control in the relationships with parents, sweethearts, or offspring.

In a study at Cornell University, of 364 juniors and seniors, the majority of whom were from homes where parents were highly educated, it was found that only about half had received a major part of their sex instruction directly from their parents. Mothers had assumed more responsibility for the sex education of their children than fathers had; in only 10 per cent of the cases had parents shared this responsibility. Brothers and sisters were sources of sex instruction in only 5 per cent and 8 per cent of the cases, respectively. In his study, Ramsey shows that boys in his case study had acquired a great deal of sex information during their preadolescent years. About 55 per cent stated that neither parent had contributed to their sex instruction.

In another study of Maryland youth, 60 per cent of the boys and 40 per cent of the girls reported that what they knew about sex was more or less limited to what friends of their own age told them.

Even though 10 per cent of the college group checked "both parents" as the source of their own sex information, 70 per cent of the group thought "both parents" should be responsible for the sex education of their children. Such facts, along with a recent public-opinion poll, may well indicate that the public may be more favorably disposed toward sex education in the schools and colleges.

Colleges and universities cannot refuse to offer courses in health and human relations or in marriage when students need to know more about the things which affect them directly in a short while either before or after graduation. They are concerned about such matters as readiness for marriage, affectional maturity, mate choosing, dating, courtship, engagement, premarital sexual adjustment, marriage laws, premarital examinations, marital adjustments (social and psychological), family administration, financial planning and management, career in marriage, sexual adjustment, parenthood and importance of children in the family, pregnancy, childbirth, husband-wife relationships before and after parenthood, family crises and how to meet them, etc.

A study of these things is important if we are to save marriage as an institution at a time when one out of three American marriages ends in divorce.

Colleges and universities can do a great deal in instructing young people about better home and family living, better health and human relations, more definite planning for homemaking as a career. Here in an adequate social-hygiene program the students may learn what constitutes good stock and how it can be maintained. Education can point up the meaning of inheritance not only as a moral and social responsibility to society, but also in mating to realize the highest ideals of love and personality. Young people can be made to feel pride in their family records and to give more serious consideration to prospective mates when they plan to marry.

NOTES

[1] Thurman B. Rice, M.D., *Those First Sex Questions,* Chicago, American Medical Association, 1940, pp. 25–28.

[2] Evelyn S. Bell, and Elizabeth Faragoh.

[3] Marie H. Ets.

[4] Karl de Schweinitz.

[5] Marion L. Faegres.

[6] Paul H. Landis.

[7] National Education Association, Department of Supervision and Curriculum Development, "Toward a New Curriculum," *1944 Yearbook,* pp. 22–36.

[8] John H. Stokes, "Sex Education and the Schools," *Journal of Social Hygiene,* Vol. 31, No. 4, April 1945, pp. 193–210.

[9] H. L. Carter and Louis Foley, "What Are Young People Asking About Marriage?", *Journal of Applied Psychology,* Vol. 27, No. 3, June 1943, pp. 275–82.

BIBLIOGRAPHY

Books

Bibby, Cyril, *Sex Education,* New York, Macmillan, 1946.

Bowman, Henry A., *Marriage for Moderns,* New York, Whittlesey House, 1942.

Bro, Marguerite, *When Children Ask,* New York, Willett Clark, 1940.

Cheeser, Eustace and Dawe, Zoë, *The Practice of Sex Education,* New York, Roy Publishers, 1946.

Corner, George W., *Attaining Manhood,* New York, Harper & Bros., 1929.

Crisp, Katharine B., *Growing into Maturity,* Philadelphia, J. B. Lippincott, 1939.

De Schweinitz, Karl, *Growing Up,* New York, MacMillan, 1928.

Duvall, Evelyn M., and Hill, Reuben, *When You Marry,* New York, D. C. Heath & Co., 1945.

Ets, Marie Hall, *The Story of a Baby,* New York, Viking Press, 1939.

Fedder, Ruth, *A Girl Grows Up,* New York, McGraw-Hill Book Co., 1939.

Foster, R. G., *Marriage and Family Relationships,* New York, Macmillan, 1944.

Goldstein, Sidney E., *Marriage and Family Counseling,* New York, McGraw-Hill Book Co., 1945.

Gruenberg, Sidonie Matsner, *The Wonderful Story of How You Were Born,* New York, Hanover House, 1952.

Hotchkiss, Robert S., *Fertility in Men,* Philadelphia, J. B. Lippincott, 1945.

Johnson, R. H., and others, *Looking toward Marriage,* New York, Allyn & Bacon, 1943.

Kirkendall, Lester A., *Sex Education as Human Relations,* New York, Inor Publishing Co., Inc., 1950.

Levine, M. I., and Seligman, Jean H., *The Wonder of Life,* New York, Simon & Schuster, 1940.

McGinnis, Esther, and others, "The Measurement of Understanding in Home Economics," in National Society for the Study of Education, *Forty-Fifth Yearbook,* Part I, University of Chicago Press, 1946.

Morris, Evangeline, *Public Health Nursing in Syphilis and Gonorrhea,* Claremont, California, Saunders, 1946.

Murchison, Carl A., and others, *A Handbook of Child Psychology,* Worcester, Massachusetts, Clark University Press, 1933.

National Society for the Study of Education, *Forty-Fifth Yearbook,* Part I, "The Measurement of Understanding," 1946.

Nelson, Janet Fowler, *Marriages Are Not Made in Heaven,* New York, Association Press, 1944.

Popenoe, Paul, *Marriage Before and After,* New York, W. Funk, 1943.

Rice, Thurman B., *Sex, Marriage, and Family,* Philadelphia, J. B. Lippin-cott, 1946.

Richmond, Winifred V., *Making the Most of Your Personality,* New York, Rinehart, 1942.

Schmiedeler, Rev. Edgar, *Marriage and the Family,* New York, McGraw-Hill Book Co., 1946.

Strain, Frances B., *Being Born,* New York, D. Appleton-Century, 1936.

——, *Sex Guidance in Family Life Education,* New York, Macmillan, 1942.

——, *The Normal Sex Interests of Children from Infancy to Childhood,* New York, Appleton-Century-Crofts, 1948.

Strang, Ruth, "Broadening the Objectives of Health Education," in National Society for the Study of Education, *Forty-Fourth Year-book,* Part I, University of Chicago Press, 1945.

Swift, Edith Hale, *Step by Step in Sex Education,* New York, Macmillan, 1938.

Todd, R. L., and Freeman, R. B., *Health Care of the Family,* Claremont, California, Saunders, 1946.

Wetherill, G. G., *Human Relations Education,* American Social Hygiene Association, New York, 1946.

When Children Ask about Sex, Child Study Association of America, New York, 1943.

Whitman, Howard, *Let's Tell the Truth about Sex,* New York, Pellegrini & Cudahy, 1948.

PERIODICALS

Advisory Committee on Social Hygiene Education of the New Jersey Department of Public Instruction, Mabel Grier Lesher, Chairman, "Education for Human Relations and Family Life on the Secondary School Level," Pub. No. A-392x, American Social Hygiene Association.

American Social Hygiene Association, "Parent-Teacher Guidance in Social Hygiene Education For Family Life," New York, 1950.

Bowman, Henry, "The Teacher as Counselor in Marriage Education," reprint from *Marriage and Family Living,* National Council on Family Relations, Chicago, 1947.

Education Committee of the New Jersey Social Hygiene Association, "An Approach to Sex Education in Schools," Pub. No. A365, American Social Hygiene Association, 1941.

Galloway, T. W., "Parent-Teacher Guidance in Social Hygiene Education for Family Life," American Social Hygiene Association, New York, 1950.

Gruenberg, Benjamin C., "How Can We Teach about Sex?" Public Affairs Committee, New York, 1946.

Health Education Council, "Suggested School Health Policies," The Council, New York, 1945.

Kirkendall, Lester A., "Health, Sex, and Human Relations in Education," bulletin of National Association of Secondary-School Principals, Vol. 28, November 1944.

———, "Sex Education Today," *National Parent-Teacher*, Vol. 39, February 1945.

———, "Understanding Sex," Science Research Associates, Chicago, 1947.

Kirkpatrick, Clifford, and Caplow, Theodore, "Courtship in a Group of Minnesota Students," *American Journal of Sociology*, Vol. 51, September 1945.

Levine, Milton I., and Seligman, Jean H., "Helping Boys and Girls Understand Their Sex Roles," Science Research Associates, Chicago, 1953.

New York Statewide Study Committee, "The School's Responsibility in Social Hygiene Education," *Journal of Social Hygiene*, October 1940.

Rowntree, L. G., and others, "Causes of Rejection and the Incidence of Defects Among 18- and 19-Year-Old Selective Service Registrants," *Journal of American Medical Association*, September 25, 1943.

Chapter 7

HOW BEHAVIOR PROBLEMS AND JUVENILE DELINQUENCY RESULT FROM INADEQUATE MARITAL ADJUSTMENT

by Richard L. Jenkins, M.D.

The poorly adjusted child tends to become the ill-adjusted partner in marriage. The parent who is maladjusted in marriage finds it difficult or impossible to be a good parent. Thus the relation between maladjusted parents and maladjusted children, who tend in turn to become maladjusted parents, is a vicious circle that tends to repeat itself.

The problems of juvenile adjustment and personal relations of parents and children may be conveniently grouped in three types.

1. *The Receiving Relationship.* The relationship of the child to the parent is chiefly one of the receiving, with little giving. The newborn infant receives everything from his parents and gives back nothing. This experience of being warmly received, of being made to feel wanted by comfort and the show of affection, as through cuddling, is essential to the normal development of the personality. As the child grows older his developing capacity for social response and the process of social training combine to aid him to develop a relationship in which he makes some small return to his parents for the great effort they expend in giving to him. Thus this relationship gradually grows in the direction of a give-and-take relationship.

2. *The Give-and-Take Relationship.* The care the parent gives the child serves the biological purpose of making the child's survival possible, and the psychological and social purpose of developing that degree of responsiveness to and confidence in other people which promotes growth into readiness for a give-and-take relationship. This relationship is first well exemplified in the peer group among children. The individual "pays his own way" in the give-and-take relationship. He meets his partner on an even footing. To make it succeed, he needs to develop a capacity for warmth of affection, for flexibility, for seeing the point of view of another person, and for some measure

of generosity. Since views of different people always differ, what appears as a fair and equal relationship to one often does not to another. For a partnership to succeed over a period of time there must be a flexibility and a tolerance that go beyond a rigid adherence to a fifty-fifty bargain. The give-and-take relation is perhaps most fully developed in the successful marriage, and next to a successful child-parent relationship early in life, it is the most significant in promoting personal growth. The attainment of a successful marriage relationship is the best preparation for successful parenthood.

3. *The Giving Relationship.* The parent-child relationship is a giving relationship. Since initially the infant is entirely helpless and has nothing to give back, the parents must find their reward in their own giving.

Successful marriage involves moving out from a situation in which the closest personal relationship has been the receiving relationship from a parent to one in which a more mature attitude in a give-and-take relationship is needful. At least three types of unsuccessful experiences in the child-parent relationship commonly cause difficulty in graduation to the give-and-take relationship. They are:

1. *Inadequate Acceptance as a Child.* The child who feels unloved and unwanted does not develop a good capacity to respond to the feelings of others. Attention is too far concentrated upon his own deprivations. He is likely to feel the world is unfair to him, to feel cheated in life, to be self-centered, selfish, overjealous and envious, and overready to interpret any small difference and neglect as due to unfair treatment or to someone's having a grudge against him. He may have an active and even pathetic desire for love and affection, but as a rule he has with it a poor capacity to return affection, or really to consider the wishes, welfare, and desires of his partner.

If this person, male or female, finds a mature, patient, and accepting mate who is able and ready to give more than is given in return, then the marriage may achieve some degree of success, and the social maturity and capacity of the less mature partner may be gradually increased.

2. *Spoiling.* If one of the partners was well accepted as a child and was given affection freely but had little training in respecting the rights of others, we are likely to find a person of charming, pleasing personality, but one who unconsciously assumes that his or her wish or word should be law. There may, consequently, be difficulty in adjusting to a real give-and-take relationship. However, the degree of unadjustability consequent to spoiling creates a minor problem as compared with the problem created by inadequate acceptance. The more difficult persons who are called "spoiled" are more likely to have had inadequate acceptance than spoiling.

3. *Conditional Acceptance.* If the child was accepted conditionally, we see another type of reaction, which I call the overconforming reaction. This occurs especially in the child who has lacked much warmth in the relationship with his parents, and where much stress has been put upon certain standards of behavior. The child comes to feel (although he does not always consciously recognize the feeling) that if he is not a good child, a conforming child, a dutiful child, his parents will not love him. Since he is dependent upon their care, he cannot afford to risk losing their love. He is therefore compelled by the pressure of his own anxiety to conform rigidly and conscientiously to their standards. He becomes inhibited, overconscientious, and inflexible. Such a person may have great difficulty in the free development of a love relationship, especially in the development of sexual responsiveness. Like the spoiled child, but to a greater degree, he is likely to be parent-tied. He is conspicuously likely to be sexually inhibited and to have difficulty in establishing sexual adjustment.

4. *Prolonged Dependence on the Parent.* Spoiling and conditional acceptance both contribute to prolonged dependence on the parent. There is another important cause—the unwillingness of a parent to relinquish the child. Overdependence on a parent places obstacles in the way of the wholehearted development of a love and marriage relationship and gives rise to the mother-in-law problems emphasized in our popular humor. Successful parenthood depends on an emotional readiness for parenthood more than on any other factor. This readiness is usually best manifested in a good marriage adjustment that has passed at least the acute phase of the honeymoon period. While happy parents often acclaim parenthood as not involving hardship, yet, objectively considered, the inconveniences and sacrifices of parenthood are substantial. When they are not experienced as hardships it is probably because the satisfactions of parenthood outweigh them. In general they are best carried by those individuals of reasonable emotional maturity who are happily married, although certain exceptions may be noted. The unhappy mother is not likely to be able to give her children the love and acceptance they need for their socialization and social development. She is likely to have too large a feeling of resentment over the sacrifices inevitable to maternity, and this resentment too frequently breaks through in irritability, impatience, or frank hostility.

Occasionally the good marriage adjustment may contribute to an unreadiness for parenthood. This is true in the permanent honeymoon marriage, in which the children may appear somewhat as interlopers in the perfect love relation.

Sometimes a parent, especially a wife with a considerable capacity for parental feeling, may find in maternity a compensation for unhappiness in the marital relation. Such a situation bears risks that the parent may seek from the child satisfactions which would more normally be found in a mate, and may have particular difficulty in permitting the child to grow into independence.

The first prerequisite for the socialization and social adjustment of the young child is a warm accepting attitude on the part of the parents, and particularly of the mother, since her relation is normally the closest with the young child. It is almost impossible to exaggerate the importance of this early acceptance. In the person who has not experienced some measure of it was typically seen a deeply distorted personality, characteristically hostile and aggressive toward others and discouraged with himself. He usually lacks social feeling and is without remorse for the hurts he may cause others. He is selfish and self-centered, yet easily depressed.

Many children who are not rejected by their parents *feel* rejected to varying degrees. An important cause of this feeling is the jealousy between children and their rivalry for parental love and favor. The fuss made over the new baby often leads older children to feel unloved and rejected. An older child may respond by bad and provocative behavior which excites parental anger and brings parental punishment. This, in turn, confirms the child in the belief that he is unloved and leads to more rebellious and hostile behavior. Unless the parent has sufficient understanding to recognize what is happening to the child, and sufficient maturity to give evidence of acceptance in the face of provocative behavior, a vicious circle of parental punishment and child resentment and even desperation may develop.

Richard, an eleven-year-old boy, has been truanting intermittently for four years. Up to the age of seven he was an only child and was indulged by parents and relatives. Then a baby brother was born and became the center of attention. Richard regressed to babylike behavior, refused to dress or feed himself, and had severe temper tantrums.

A year later a baby sister was born. Richard's attitude toward her has been more accepting than that toward his brother, whom his parents fear he may injure.

Richard lived with his maternal grandparents two or three weeks at the birth of each new baby. He also lived with them four months when he was ten. During this time he was obedient toward his grandparents and did not truant.

On the other hand, Richard disregards his mother's directions. Several times she has ordered him out of the house. On these occasions he walked several miles to his maternal grandparents' home and told them, "My mother doesn't want me."

Both the parents and the schoolteacher threatened Richard with reform school if he continued his truancy.

Richard's actions are the result of his feeling that he was crowded out and rejected at the birth of a younger brother; his behavior and even personality revert to a more infantile level. The boy was better able to accept the birth of his younger sister, but he has not recovered from his feeling of rejection at the birth of his younger brother. He likes his grandparents' home better than that of his parents.

Here is an extreme case, but most illustrative:

Robert, a fourteen-year-old boy, was described by his mother as "the meanest devil God ever gave any mother for a son."

Robert was born two months after the marriage of his nineteen-year-old mother to his twenty-eight-year-old presumed father.

Robert's mother had numerous sexual relationships. She threatened suicide to bring about her marriage but later stated the man she married was not Robert's father. Robert was frequently in boarding homes in his first seven years and, when he was not, his mother frequently kept him tied up and allowed him little freedom. There was conflict between Robert's mother and her husband. The mother said that she hunted for things to hurt her husband's feelings and finally felt most successful using Robert.

At fourteen Robert had shown violence toward his mother and threatened her life. He had temper tantrums and fits of jealousy of his sister, seven years younger, and it was believed that he attempted her life on two occasions when she was about a year old.

In company with three other boys, Robert burglarized two gasoline stations and stole a series of cars. At the age of fourteen he had spent two periods in a county juvenile home and one in a state training school for delinquent boys.

A rather special result which may occur in cases in which a child becomes a pawn between two parents in conflict with each other is that such a child may develop considerable skill in playing off one adult against another. Such a background can contribute to the development of an adult who even takes pride in a rather unscrupulous persuasiveness and who may use this skill to take advantage of others by embezzlement or otherwise.

After love and acceptance, the greatest need of the child is for room to grow—he needs respect for his individuality and an area in which he can make his own decisions. If his life is all arranged on the basis that "Mother knows best," his opportunity to develop any reasonable sense of individuality is interfered with. In this event, depending upon the toughness and resilience of his own striving, he may become rebellious or sink into becoming a mere appendage of his parent.

John, two years and eleven months, a boy of very superior intelligence, caused his parents much concern by his thoroughgoing pattern of resistance and rebellion. He particularly resisted being dressed or undressed but commonly resisted being fed or helped in the daily routine.

John's parents were both college graduates. They had very definite ideas of child training and were in agreement on them. They often noted the misbehavior of their friends' children and agree that such behavior would not be tolerated in their own.

Their program of training was a good one except that it was overdone. John was not helped to feel that there was any area of action that was his, or that his own desires or wishes received any respect. His contact with training was entirely one of being required to conform to the wishes of someone else. Being a spirited youngster, he thoroughly rebelled. When the parents assumed a more relaxed and considerate management there was a rapid improvement in John's behavior.

A particularly unfortunate situation is that in which a child receives neither adequate acceptance as a person nor adequate room to grow as an individual. This situation may be the product of a sense of parental duty or pride without real parental feeling. The mother in particular may lack real maternal response yet may feel the need to prove to the world that she is a good mother. She goes through the gestures although the feeling is not there. The result may be an emphasis upon parental responsibility, authority, and control without significant warmth, affection, or emotional resonance with the child. He is treated as a responsibility, but not as a personality in his own right. As a consequence, his contacts with his parents may be chiefly sources of frustration to him. In severe instances the child may leave the externals of his life to be dominated by his parents and withdraw into a world of fantasy. As a result of such withdrawal, he may fail effectively to relate himself to the real world around him. Such tendencies have some effect of predisposing individuals toward the functional psychosis, schizophrenia, which fills about a quarter of all our hospital beds. A study by Joseph Mark of attitudes of 100 mothers of male schizophrenics compared with attitudes of a control group of mothers of male non-schizophrenics, revealed that out of 139 statements there were fifteen with each of which the mothers of schizophrenics agreed more frequently than the control mothers, to an extent that would not occur by chance once in a thousand times. These statements are as follows:

1. Children should be taken to and from school until the age of eight just to make sure there are no accidents.

2. A mother should make it her business to know everything her children are thinking.

3. If children are quiet for a little while, Mother should immediately find out what they are thinking about.

4. Children should not annoy parents with their unimportant problems.

5. A devoted mother has no time for social life.

6. A watchful mother can keep her child out of all accidents.

7. *Playing too much with a child will spoil him.*
8. *A parent must never make mistakes in front of the child.*
9. *Parents should sacrifice everything for their children.*
10. *When the father punishes a child for no good reason, the mother should take the child's side.*
11. *A mother has to suffer much and say little.*
12. *Most children are toilet-trained by fifteen months of age.*
13. *Children who take part in sex play become sex criminals when they grow up.*
14. *A child should not plan to enter any occupation that his parents don't approve of.*
15. *Too much affection will make a child a "softie."*

Although it may be that none of the mothers agreed with all of these statements, the series gives us something of a composite picture of differences between the two groups.

The sense of maternal responsibility is reflected here (for example, in statements 1, 2, 3, 6, 9) and with it maternal authority and control (2, 3, 14). There is a martyred self-pity on the part of the mother (5, 9, 11). Standards are unrealistically high (12) and backed by an overanxious concern about behavior (13) coupled with an absence of concern about or response to the child's feelings and desires (4, 7, 15).

These, of course, are statistical tendencies certainly not reflected in every case. It is not maintained that parental attitudes cause schizophrenia. On the other hand, it seems clear that some parental attitudes may constitute a predisposing factor rendering the individual otherwise predisposed more likely to break down in this psychotic pattern. The combination of a lack of emotional acceptance and a lack of encouragement or opportunity to grow is a bad one, for it so frequently results in a personality lacking confidence either in acceptability to others or in his capacity to deal with life himself.

The third need of childhood is for training, guidance, and supervision. In order for the training to work successfully, the first two needs must be met. But the social training must be in an acceptable group and along acceptable lines if the child is to fit into the larger society. The loyal gang member is a socialized individual who accepts his gang as his social group. Such a development is common in boys but uncommon in girls. In such boys, usually the early relation with the mother was emotionally healthy. The failure of the home is a failure of omission rather than a failure of commission. It lies in the failure of the guidance, training, and control of the preadolescent and the adolescent, and this is more a paternal than a maternal function. As a result of this failure, the child may fall under the influence of delinquent companions. The problem exists particularly in those neighborhoods which are somewhat disorganized and in which there is some tradition of delinquent activity among the youth. The failure of the home is the failure to provide any effective supervision or any positive patterns of behavior sufficiently strong to offset the fascination of the appeal and excitement of the delinquent depredations of the street gang. Under these circumstances the development of membership in a delinquent gang may occur essentially as a normal process of social growth.

> *Michael, at the age of fifteen, was returned to a state training school for delinquent boys from which he had run away. Michael was returned after he was arrested for participation in an armed robbery in which a man was shot and seriously wounded.*
>
> *Michael was the third of seven children of a hard-working man and a healthy maternal woman. The marital adjustment was never very good, and as time went on Michael's father began to drink more and more heavily. When intoxicated, he was physically abusive to his wife and children. When Michael was ten his father was physically thrown out of the house by his two older sons when he came home drunk and started to beat his wife. He did not return.*
>
> *It was then necessary for the mother to move with the children to a low-rental area. The oldest boy went to work and the next one soon followed. Michael began to associate with boys on the street who taught him to steal fruit from the fruit stands. He joined them in "junking" expeditions in which they stripped anything salable from vacant houses. Soon he became part of the closely knit delinquent gang which stole and stripped cars. His older brothers sought to separate him from his companions, but he was sullen and defiant. At the age of twelve he was apprehended with an older companion in the theft of a car and was put on probation. At the age of thirteen he was found to be involved in several car thefts and committed to a training school for delinquent boys. After several months he ran away and joined two of his older companions in a holdup. They were committed to prison. He was returned to the training school.*

Although participation in an organized gang is unusual for girls, their delinquency proceeds from much the same psychological causes as does that of boys. Unhappiness in the home and the failure of effective parental guidance make the girl turn away from the home and look in other directions for her real satisfactions in living. She is likely to find solace in the interest that boys of her age or older show in her. If her parents seek to interfere with this she becomes rebellious and is unwilling to give up her good times. Usually she begins sexual intercourse more as a means of retaining male interest, or of paying her way, than out of direct sex desire. While sexual behavior is certainly not to be considered other than normal in itself, and while at the present time it is not unusual for girls of good family background to enter into premarital sexual relationships when they feel they are in love, yet the occurrence of casual or promiscuous sexual behavior is generally related to some substantial failure of home acceptance or home guidance and supervision.

One of the risks of child training is the risk of overtraining. Training may invade too large an area of the child's life. Or it may assume too great an intensity on unimportant things. Particularly if it is coupled with a lack of warm acceptance, the child may come to feel that his acceptance, his position in the family, is dependent upon a high degree of conformity to parental expectations. This situation results in the overconforming child—tense, anxious, overinhibited or overconscientious, or both, and predisposed toward psychoneurotic breakdown later in life. The development of an unhealthy anxiety over parental approval and, with it, timidity and lack of self-confidence are early signs of this reaction.

Inconsistency in training results in confusion in the child and contributes to insecurity. Ill-health of parent or of child, or any elements which break down the child's confidence in himself, in the presence of a strong training program, contributes toward insecurity and an overconforming reaction.

At the age of eighteen, after four months' service, Henry was discharged from the Army because of a psychoneurosis. He had chronic anxiety and frequent attacks of palpitation of the heart.

Henry's mother was a quiet woman, lacking warmth and rather dominated by her husband. Henry's father was a severe and perfectionistic man, always pushing Henry to more effort and never satisfied with his attainments. As a child Henry feared his father's criticism and disapproval. Henry became hardworking in school and studious, but was tongue-tied and trembled when called upon in class in grade school. In high school he was shy and did not date. In the Army he was very much afraid of doing the wrong thing. He was quite afraid of officers. He soon developed pounding of the heart during drill and believed he had heart disease. After hospital study he was discharged as psychoneurotic.

The typical mistake in the upper social and educational classes is overtraining rather than inadequate training. The training in modesty given girls in such families too often protects them not only from premature sex experience but from any capacity for experiencing sexual love at all. The overtrained, timid, dutiful, "nice" girl often becomes the tense, neurotic, frigid wife, if indeed she is able to marry at all. The overtrained, conscientious, mannerly, diligent boy may, years later, be the overdriven, overstrained, overanxious man whose health breaks down under the effort of his work.

Those relationships generally work out best which are accepting and affectionate without being indulgent, which give respect for the child's personality, which give some gentle guidance and, when necessary, a dependable firmness.

Yet while an unhappy childhood is a poor start for successful marriage, nothing is more characteristic of the human race than the capacity it has shown to rise above its own beginnings by virtue of consistent and directed effort. When we seek the best start for our children we should not feel too far weighted down by imperfections in our own home backgrounds.

Chapter 8

ADOLESCENT PREPARATION FOR SUCCESSFUL MARRIAGE

by Katharine Whiteside Taylor, Ed.D.

SUPERVISOR OF PARENT EDUCATION, BALTIMORE DEPARTMENT OF EDUCATION

In the deepest sense preparation for marriage begins in the first year of life. But puberty and adolescence are of unique importance in laying groundwork for really satisfying marital adjustments. There was real wisdom in the pubic ceremonies among primitive peoples that emphasized the great significance of puberty as the dramatic period during which the individual changes from child to young adult. Although the process continues until twenty or thereabouts, puberty as the entry into this important period should really be welcomed rather than ignored or even hidden, as is still too often the case.

Parents often bemoan the fact that young adulthood is approaching, saying, "Isn't it too bad! We are losing our little girl. If only we could keep her sweet and innocent," or "We are keeping our son so busy he won't have time to think about girls. We don't want him to grow up too fast."

All parents feel this way to a certain extent; it is hard to give up the satisfactions of having little children to love and be dependent upon us. But if we want to help them to the joys of genuine maturity we should look forward ourselves to the deeper satisfactions of companionship with mature sons and daughters. We should be able to say with honest enthusiasm, "Isn't it wonderful to have a young woman [or man] in the house! It is so much nicer than when she [or he] was a child. We are proud she [or he] is growing up."

The importance of this cannot be overemphasized. During pubescence and the beginning of adolescence, often continuing for several years, the young person is in the throes of a real conflict within himself as to whether it is really better to go on to the greater freedom and joy but greater demands of adulthood or sink back into the easier requirements and safer, well-tried ways of childhood. This struggle may in times of stress be severe. The joys of childhood were very real and what was required of one so much less! Yet in wholesome youngsters the urge toward maturity is strong and will win out if not impeded by undue desires in parents to prolong the joys of having a child look to them alone for guidance and for love.

Even the most understanding and freedom-giving parents may be temporarily rejected during this period of struggle for autonomy and self-direction. Just being near parents during these conflicts is apt to make the young person feel *little,* like a child again, since for many fulfilling years he or she has been their little child. If the parents still derive major satisfactions from keeping their adolescents dependent and in the little-child role psychologically, the young person's revolt must be stronger to save his emerging maturity from destruction or impairment. The wise role for parents then is to accept signs of temporary rejection by adolescents as a normal, even wholesome sign of maturation and give all the leeway to independence consistent with the young person's safety and that of others. With reasonably reliable youngsters this leeway is apt to be wider than most parents tend to realize, and the only way a person's judgment can grow is through independent exercise.

Further, parents must be ready to allow their young adults to do more and more as well as to decide more and more on their own. Teen-agers should also be encouraged to contribute in ways appropriate to their new status. For instance, instead of *helping* get dinner, a teen-ager should be permitted to get it entirely on her own. If Mother is sufficiently mature not to see this as competition for prestige through good cooking, she will welcome such a contribution. So will a father who is really secure in himself welcome his son's wish to take over the full responsibility of caring for the family car instead of just washing it on Saturday afternoon. And such opportunities for accepting more and more responsibility are highly valuable for the young adult, not only for developing his independent abilities, but also in promoting growth toward the true adulthood essential for sustaining marriage.

The opportunity and capacity to contribute in thought and effort in ways recognized as valuable by important persons, including parents, are basic in the young person's establishing the feelings of autonomy and self-worth, underlying healthy growth of personality brought out in the findings of the Mid-Century White House Conference on Children and Youth.

While the seeds of these attributes must be sown from earliest childhood on, the onset of puberty brings these growing capacities a new chance to flower.

Until physiological maturity has been reached, the child must be chiefly on the receiving side. The growing body needs to absorb large amounts of food just for building tissue. When maturity has been reached much energy is released for constructive work and creative activity. In like manner, the growing personality must receive an abundance of love, appreciation, and response to grow into even the beginnings of maturity. If growth has progressed wholesomely, puberty marks the point when real love and interest in others outside the family can begin.

If we are to be ready to welcome puberty and help our boys and girls welcome it as a happy step in progress toward maturity and capacity for marriage, we must understand the signs that indicate the process has begun. Since girls reach puberty on an average between eleven and thirteen and boys between twelve and fourteen, some of the internal and external changes may be starting as early as nine in some girls and ten in some boys. The onset of the cycle may, however, start as much as three or four years later for either sex and still be within the normal range.

SIGNS OF MATURATION

At the beginning of the cycle there is usually a slowing down of growth, followed by a rapid spurt just before puberty, followed again by a slowing down until physical growth becomes complete. But growth does not proceed evenly in all parts of the body. For example, bones grow more rapidly than muscle tissue, producing the typically awkward length of arms and legs of early adolescence, causing the individual to look ungainly, knock things over, and perhaps even stumble about just when he or she is beginning to be really interested in making a good impression! Differentials in rate of growth also make for temporary disharmony in features. A typical adolescent worry is over a nose which grows out of all proportion to the rest of the face. Added to this, the reorganization of the glandular system often causes pimples, blackheads, and scraggly hair, adding extra complications to the problems of pleasing appearance. Then when the lad's voice starts squeaking unexpectedly and doing other strange things, he is apt to feel he has all the trials there are. Parents who understand what is going on and who welcome the fact their son or daughter is maturing can help the youngster also to an acceptance of, possibly even a cheery attitude toward, the discomforts that mean he or she is becoming a young adult. One lad, for instance, was encouraged to "keep tabs" with a friend across the street as to how many times their voices cracked in an hour. They then laughingly compared notes.

The reorganization of the glandular system often makes for swings in mood and energy level which the whole family needs to understand. Bursts of energy and enthusiasm may be offset by periods of slowing down to the point of being what is called lazy. These slowed-down spells need to be respected, as they are Nature's way of protecting the growing organism from overfatigue. There may be extra strain also because of the fact that all the organs do not grow at the same rate. Indeed, at certain periods heart and lungs may not yet be large enough to carry with ease the new size and length of the body. There may be frequent swings in mood and erratic behavior which are often more difficult to accept than the fluctuations in energy. The young adult may find it decidedly difficult to live with himself. Part of him is eager to grow up, to accept adult responsibility and the normal satisfactions of adult life, including marriage and all it means. Yet the part that is still a child may be frightened at the demands of adulthood and particularly frightened at the thought of sex. The fact that his or her own body is no longer that of a child, but capable of full sex response, may be frightening if the surrounding atmosphere either at home or in the neighborhood has held attitudes that sex is wicked and shameful.

Particularly important for the future marital happiness is understanding and acceptance by these young folk of the development of their own sex organs, the appearance of secondary sex characteristics, and the evidence that their capacity to become parents has begun. Serious emotional problems often include shock at the first nocturnal emission or menstruation. One girl who had not been prepared and whose grandmother was dying of cancer, seeing blood on her own underclothing, lay for hours sick with fear that she also was dying of cancer, while all the adults in the family were too busy with the grandmother's needs to notice hers.

Education as to reproduction should be given in answer to questions, from the earliest years of childhood on, and if no questions are asked parents should make opportunity to explain, using some of the excellent books now available for parents and also for children. Then as puberty approaches, parents should prepare themselves to explain to both sons and daughters that when the baby is developing inside its mother it must have an extra supply of blood from the mother, and that when there isn't any baby developing the blood passes away at monthly intervals; and that this is called menstruation from the Latin word *mensis,* meaning month.

MENSTRUATION

It should be explained also that while menstruation typically occurs monthly there is individual variation even at maturity, and usually considerable irregularity during the first few years, until the function is thoroughly established; also, that the capacity to reproduce is usually not present until several years after the first menstruation. Moreover, girls today should not be burdened with the idea that one is "unwell" at that time, or that it is a "curse" which makes one miserable. Indeed, there is some indication that girls and women who have happy, accepting attitudes toward their role as women may actually feel a heightening of energy and well-being during the menstrual period.

Boys also need to understand that girls may have to refrain from swimming and violent exercise at that time and may need a little extra consideration.

Boys of course need particularly to understand the real meaning of nocturnal emissions. They may be told that they carry the sperm cells which must be carried over into the mother's body to join with the ovum in hers to form a baby. These are carried in a fluid called semen. But this is not needed until they are ready to become fathers; therefore, from time to time it passes out of the body, not regularly as with girls, but whenever there is a sufficient accumulation.

Beyond this, all young adults need access to good books and pamphlets, including adequate diagrams. I have supplied a list at the end of this chapter. Wise parents will look it over, make sure their children's knowledge is adequate, and provide for any lacks by supplementary reading.

The young adult should feel he can talk freely to his parents about these problems. The emotions and attitudes parents bring to such discussions are really more important than the words they say. Many of us who are parents do have hang-overs of unwholesome attitudes from our own childhood, such as that sex is "dirty, sinful, low, and vile." Some of us, perhaps, need consciously to weed out such attitudes and supplant them with the realization of the deep beauty and sacredness of love between a man and a woman, the creative power which brings new life into the world. One of the best ways to do this, perhaps, is to read aloud together some of the good materials listed and, if possible, to attend good lectures on the subject in order to be ready to talk it over casually as occasion makes possible in an atmosphere of naturalness and relaxation.

Parents need to accept the fact that the capacity for sex response and some handling of their own genitals on the part of boys and girls are normal and to be expected as the sex organs develop. The chapter on masturbation discusses this problem fully.

In spite of the fact that relationships change, relationship between parents and adolescents is fundamental to successful living and in laying the groundwork for happy marriage. In the penetrating study, *Predicting Failure or Success in Marriage,* by Drs. Burgess and Cottrell, there were two factors in the histories of happily married people twice as important as any other:

these were a warm sustaining relationship of children with their own parents. The other important factor in predetermining marital happiness was the relationship of parents to each other.

ATTACHMENT TO PARENTS

If they are to be of genuine help, all parents need to understand the normal changes in their own relationship to their adolescent son or daughter, and of the young person's to groups and persons outside the home. In spite of the young person's growing need for independence and his or her tendency to reject both parents for a time, soon after puberty the young adult normally draws close to the parent of the opposite sex, sensing new meaning in the relationship. For a short time, indeed, some of the closeness of infancy may be reactivated. Parents whose own needs are not adequately met may tend to seize on this response and cling to it. This would tend to impede the young adult's maturation.

The girl, for example, becomes increasingly aware of her father and sensitive to his smile and warmth or to his aloofness and disapproval. It is particularly important for a father to understand and accept his daughter's increasing femininity appreciatively. By so doing he builds up her sense of security and feeling of worth. Girls who are secure in their fathers' love and appreciation, yet feel free to develop friendships outside the home, seldom get into sex difficulties. Indeed, serious sex misdemeanors in girls are often found to be a result of insecurity, especially in their relationship with their father.

As she draws toward her father, the girl is likely for a time to draw away from her mother, resent her suggestions, and even see her as a rival for the attentions of the father. And if the mother is not quite secure as a woman she may resent this new contestant for feminine supremacy in the home.

The daughter is likely to seek feminine ideals in teachers and others outside the home. As she becomes more mature, however, she will turn back to her mother in a new relationship based on real equality which may be deeply satisfying to them both. This happens best where the mother is secure and happy in her own life so that she does not feel rejected and can give her daughter the freedom she needs. A mother who is truly fulfilled as a woman both in her home and in her community contacts, is most helpful in providing her daughter with a picture of adulthood worth striving for.

In early adolescence the boy tends to draw toward his mother and feels devoted to her in a new way. To a certain extent he relives some of the closeness he felt during infancy. At this time it is particularly necessary for mothers to lead truly fulfilling lives lest they prolong this precious period unduly. It is particularly difficult for unhappy mothers wholeheartedly to approve of their sons getting interested in other feminine persons, as they must do if they are to become real men.

At this time also the boy is likely to develop strong antagonism toward his father and to seek masculine patterns outside the home, which is the counterpart of the girl's behavior. And fathers who are not quite secure in their capacity for evoking love may also resent this potent rival for masculine supremacy in the family. A new and deeper understanding and real friendship may be established, however, when the young man has gained full emotional independence.

The boy in one way has an even bigger job of emancipation than the girl in our culture, since it is he who must make the living for his future family. The girl in most instances will not need to attain economic independence before she is considered marriageable. It is equally essential, however, for both sexes to become completely freed from childlike dependence upon parents, not only in capabilities and independent judgment, but also from the need to lean upon them emotionally.

It cannot be emphasized too often that this emotional emancipation must go two ways to be complete. Parents must be ready to give up dependence upon children for their major satisfactions. Having real fulfillment in marriage and as persons with going lives of their own is the best insurance that the new freedom can be a two-way street!

Nothing is more important from the point of view of successful marriage than growing up emotionally. This means that you have learned to carry your full share of responsibility in any situation except when ill, to make decisions upon the basis of your own scheme of values and the reality factors in any situation, and to work out a life pattern that carries sufficient fulfillment so that you do not need to exploit others to gain satisfactions. Further, it means that you have a rich and full capacity for giving sympathy, tenderness, and love to others, at the same time maintaining your integrity. Therefore, the grownup does not need to be always on the receiving end of a relationship, as is a small child, but is equally ready to give. It means further, however, that you do not need to be always on the giving side to show your superiority, as in the case with some immature folk, but that you can enter into a reciprocal, interdependent relationship where you both give and receive when that is necessary. All of us have times when we are tired or ill, when things have gone wrong, when we do not feel very mature. But those who really love us get joy from helping us. One of the best things about real marriage is that each can find real satisfaction both in giving help and love and in receiving them from the loved person.

Genuine maturity means further that we do not stop at our own front door, but that our love flows out in ever-widening circles to neighbors, community, and world. In the final analysis we pour out effort in work, help, and love not primarily for the prestige, recognition, and response that we get out of it, but for the real joy of giving what we have to give.

Obviously with this definition of maturity, few attain perfection, nor does it come about quickly. It is rather a process of growth through gaining satisfactions in the use of one's powers, building a satisfying scheme of values, and perhaps most of all through finding satisfying experiences in relationships through giving as well as receiving love.

ATTACHMENTS TO ONE'S OWN SEX

As the young adult passes through the stage of attachment to the parent of the opposite sex his main focus shifts for a time to primary interest in his own sex. The first phase is typically a strong sense of group belonging. Out of this group attachment there usually emerges a deep friendship with a member of the same sex. This is sometimes derisively called a "crush" among girls. It should, however, be accepted by parents and all who deal with young adults as not only a normal but an essential part of their growth toward maturity. It is typically far deeper than the easy friendships of childhood and is usually the young adult's first experience of really loving someone outside his own family. It is, therefore, the first chance to sense deeply the feelings and longings of another and is important in deepening the capacity for emotional response. It may or may not include some degree of physical interest in each other. Its value lies in the depth of real feeling involved and the part that it serves simply as one phase of development.

Appreciation of one's own sex has the additional value of helping establish the young adult's sense of identity also essential to the development of a wholesome personality. The feeling it is fine to be a member of one's own sex, that one can be as valid and important as a person of the opposite sex, is as necessary for self-acceptance as to accept one's race, creed and family background as worthy and good.

It is a real tragedy for either a boy or a girl to become fixated at what may be termed this homosexual level, however, even though it is a normal phase to pass through. People are said to be fixated at this level, even if they have never had any interest in physical intimacies, if they still find their greatest satisfaction in being with members of their own sex. Unfortunately this is true of some people who have been married for years and may have had several children. But they may have never established a really mature relationship on a give-and-take basis with their marriage partner. There is in such cases a tragic loss of genuine fulfillment in their lives and lack of genuine security for their children.

SIGNS OF NORMAL SEX DEVELOPMENT

Two things are necessary if we are to make sure our own young adults pass safely through the homosexual phase into a normal focus upon the opposite sex as the chief center of interest. The first is an abundant exposure to attractive members of the opposite sex. The second is a wholesome education not only as to the reproductive process, as mentioned earlier, but in attitudes toward the whole of the relationship of the sexes to each other. One very important phase of this is the attitudes expressed by parents toward their own youngsters' first signs of interest in the opposite sex.

One particularly happily married young man related that when he was about sixteen his father said to him, "Well, Henry! I notice you are beginning to slick down your hair and are asking your mother to press your trousers every few days. And I know what that means. You are getting interested in some of those nice girls you meet at school. And I'm glad you are! There is nothing nicer than having a fine time with really lovely girls, and I want you to have your share of it."

Other crude manifestations of interest such as risqué pin-up girls and dirty stories may be a good deal harder for parents to take. But they, too, are quite normal manifestations and are a part of the youngster's self-education in getting used to the contours of the opposite sex. If there is excessive interest in dirty stories, however, it usually means that the youngster has not had enough of the right kind of education, or possibly that he is insecure and tries to build himself up by showing off his sophistication.

The first approach to interest in the opposite sex may be distant and tentative, such as groaning at love scenes at movies, writing for pictures of one's favorite movie stars, and possibly writing letters to members of the opposite sex at long range whom one hasn't met. One boy, for instance, pinned love notes onto the back of girls' dresses without their knowing who did it.

Just as with members of the same sex, the first major contacts between members of the opposite sex are typically those in groups. Kissing games like post office are a tentative tryout at intimacy, with the whole group there for protection! There is likely to follow, as the youngsters grow up a bit, considerable experimental hand holding, "necking," and kissing. It is a normal manifestation, and usually if parents discuss standards of decency with their youngsters there is little danger that they will go too far. Particularly if they feel secure in their parents' love, will they tend to accept their standards.

Parents who are not prudish or overly severe will keep the channels open for discussion of such matters, which in itself is a good safeguard. As one wise father said when his son started off on a date, "You are lucky to have such a nice girl to take out. Do everything you can to give her a wonderful time. And it doesn't hurt if you 'neck' just a little. Of course you know where to stop, and I can trust you to do it. The wonderful experience of complete intimacy can be had in the right way only in marriage."

As couples begin to pair off, "going steady" relationships start. There is a tendency for these to begin too early in many high schools just because it is the vogue. Such relationships should not be established before they can have the meaning of two people really wanting to know and share each other's lives. Also, they tend to limit contacts and development of personality through varied companionship.

When young folk are old enough to enter into such relationships seriously (and that is a matter of maturity rather than chronological age) they may grow thereby in their capacity for mature relatedness on a give-and-take basis. Better than frowning upon such relationships, parents would do well to emphasize emotional sincerity, mutual responsibility and growth together as the sound basis for maintaining them.

That warm interest and love between the sexes be accepted and appreciated as valid and good by every adolescent's parents is an important aid and support in his developing capacity for real intimacy, also now recognized (see White House Conference report) as essential for healthy personal growth. It lies at the very heart of a capacity for real friendship, true marriage, and even for the most fructifying parenthood. Yet in our culture it is too often damaged by the projection of parental anxiety regarding the dangers of sex onto children at this very point of the young adult's first awakening to the beauty and power of sex love.

WHEN ADOLESCENTS FALL IN LOVE

The great moment that parents should be ready to understand and accept is when their young folk really fall in love. When a boy or girl comes in all aglow, saying, "I have met a person I would just die for!" parents should not derisively say, "Oh! That's just puppy love." Even though the object of such affection may not be worthy of it, the important thing is the feeling inside the heart of the boy or girl. It is a tremendous thing to feel one would be willing to give one's life for another person. It is not an emotion of childhood but an initiation into one of the deepest feelings of adulthood. Even though these first loves usually do not last, they are usually very important steps in growth toward real maturity.

One of the times when understanding parents can be of the greatest help is when the young adult is suffering from what is called "a broken heart" at the cessation of one of these love affairs. Whether it is because the boy or girl has been turned down or has become disillusioned as to the quality of his or her love object, the suffering can be some of the most severe in human experience. Particularly if one has been rejected, there is great need for parents and other wise counselors who can help the young person understand the traits in himself and his partner which caused the break, and re-establish his own sense of worth. Such crises, lived through with understanding, can be great factors, making for the growth of a person of any age toward greater depth, sensitivity, and appreciation of the utter preciousness of love when it is deep and mutual.

When young adults become seriously interested in marriage, parents should make sure that they have access to some of the excellent books on preparation for marriage. The other chapters in the present volume will be of great value to parents wanting to guide their young folk into lasting marital happiness.

Earnest talks between young adults and their parents can add much in clarifying and underlining what is read. It is a great help, for instance, when parents emphasize and exemplify that marriage is a process which continues over the years and grows deeper and more meaningful as understanding and mutual helpfulness increase; that it is not merely a 50-50 proposition but rather a 100-100 enterprise, with each giving everything he has to making it go; that it is even more important to ask, "what am I giving?" than to wonder, "what am I getting?" It may help to bring out further that there is no discipline like the discipline of love for making us grow toward greater maturity. Life offers no greater motivation for the effort involved than the longing to understand and provide for the comfort and joy of the loved person and to deepen the love that is flowing between.

ENGAGEMENT AND THE FAMILY

The time when the son or daughter becomes engaged is almost inevitably something of a crisis in the lives of parents. Even though they want their child to be happy, it is often difficult, particularly for the mother, to accept the fact that the young person is almost ready to leave the home nest. Sometimes it is the parents' own unfulfilled needs which blind them to the really fine qualities in the mate-to-be and put undue obstacles in the path of their child's happiness.

For this reason, and also because it is the best possible preparation for their child's lasting happiness, parents should do all possible to work out and maintain a really sound adjustment as marriage partners. Persons with a relationship that is not as fulfilling as it ought to be should have no more hesitancy in going to a good family-counseling center than in going to a physician for a physical ailment. If the difficulty is with the individual person rather than chiefly in the relationship, a good psychiatrist may be able to help immeasurably. The comfort and new zest for living which can come from the utilization of such services are almost unbelievable to those who have not actually seen the results.

Among the greatest unused resources in the world today are the capacities of middle-aged women who have been tempered and disciplined and developed emotionally through their own family experiences, and whose hands are empty when their children leave home. Wise women will plan ahead for the ways they may contribute when their nest is empty, for their own sakes, their children's, and for what they can give their communities.

As life remains interesting and zestful to them they will have more to contribute to their own marriage relationship, which may well remain sweet and sustaining to the very end of life. Indeed, many couples report that after the menopause, when there is no fear of conception and no daily care for their children who are married and living away, they grow closer together and find a new depth and beauty in their own marriage.

BIBLIOGRAPHY

Books for Parents

Baruch, Dorothy, *Living with Our Teen Agers*, New York, McGraw-Hill Book Co., 1953.

Havighurst, R. J., and Taba, H., *Adolescent Character and Personality*, New York, John Wiley, 1947.

Landis, Paul H., *Adolescence and Youth*, New York, McGraw-Hill Book Co., 1945.

Mid-Century White House Conference on Children and Youth, *A Healthy Personality for Every Child*, Raleigh, N.C., Health Publications Institute, 1951.

Strain, F. B., *New Patterns in Sex Teaching*, New York, Appleton-Century, 1936 (recently revised).

———, *But You Don't Understand*, New York, Appleton-Century-Crofts, 1949.

Taylor, Katharine Whiteside, *Do Adolescents Need Parents?* New York, Appleton-Century, 1938.

Wilmer, H., and Kotinsky, R., *Personality in the Making,* New York, Harper & Bros., 1952.

Books for Teen-Agers

Crawford and Woodward, *Better Ways of Growing Up,* Philadelphia, Muhlenberg Press, 1949.

Faegre, Marion, *Understanding Ourselves,* Minneapolis, University of Minnesota Press, 1944.

Strain, F. B., *Teen-Days,* New York, Appleton-Century, 1946.

Taylor, Katharine Whiteside, "Do You Understand Your Parents?" *Junior Red Cross Magazine,* February 1954.

———, *Getting Along with Parents,* Chicago, Science Research Associates, 1952.

Chapter 9

PARENT-CHILD RELATIONSHIPS AND THE FAMILY COUNCIL

by James H. S. Bossard, Ph.D., L.H.D.*
PROFESSOR OF SOCIOLOGY AND DIRECTOR OF THE WILLIAM T. CARTER FOUNDA-
TION, UNIVERSITY OF PENNSYLVANIA

The problems of parent-child relationships are perennial, but certain recent changes in family situations tend to focus increased attention not only on these problems but also on the social technics that may be utilized to deal effectively with them. One such device is the family council.

FAMILY COUNCIL: ITS MEANING AND CHANGING NATURE

The family council, as a more or less formalized meeting of members of a family group, is as old as the primitive family and extends down to the present day. It changes in form and functions as the family and society in which it operates change.

The Family Council in Primitive Society. In primitive society the family council is composed of selected representatives of the kinship group, usually the males of adult status. Women sometimes are admitted, but children usually are excluded. In the deliberations of the council, the elders have precedence in decision over the younger. Its ideology is communal, not individualistic, with the survival and welfare of the group as its basic purpose. Customarily there is a definite time, place, personnel, and procedure for its meeting; the range of its deliberations is all-inclusive, from domestic relations to war and crime; the power of its decisions are absolute and complete where the group is isolated from external law, and where not, it acts as an intermediary between the group and the law.

The description which Schapera gives of its operation among the Bantu of South Africa may be cited as an illustration of the family council in primitive society:

---

*NOTE: For aid in the preparation of this chapter, the author is indebted to Dr. Eleanor S. Boll, research associate of the Carter Foundation.

Nearly all cases affecting family relations, such as disputes between husband and wife, or the non-fulfillment of kinship obligations, are first discussed by a family council, embracing all the near male relatives of the parties concerned. It is convened and presided over by the senior man of the kinship group. Where women are directly involved the mothers and wives will be included in the council. The matter is, if possible, settled here, and if it is one involving the payment of damages the council will suggest that the usual amount be paid. But it cannot enforce such payment, nor can it inflict any penalty on the offender without his consent. Where the parties cannot come to an agreement, or the offender refuses to accept the decision, the case will be referred to the local court.[1]

The Family Council in Civil Society. As civil society comes into being, the power of the state and the rights of the individual begin to emerge. The law takes away from the family council its power of decision on matters such as property interest, personal liberty, and criminal behavior. However, the process of using the council as an intermediary and advisory body, standing between the state and the family, survives and seems to do so with greatest vitality in those societies where there is least centralization of government, less concentration of population in large cities, and where the kinship or extended type of the family remains strong and stable. Under the civil code, it was relatively strong in central, southern, and western Europe and in Japan. In these areas it retained many elements of the older pattern, such as selected representatives from the family group, precedence in decisions to elders, and definite arrangements for meeting and procedure. Modifications that came to be accepted were the inclusion of a representative of the law, the selection of a non-family member as president of the council, and the relegation of the family members to a consulting and deliberating role.[2]

The Family Council among American Immigrant Groups. With the coming of large immigrant groups from these countries, the idea of the family council was brought to the United States. This was most conspicuously true of the French who came to Louisiana. Under the name of the Family Meeting, it was given a legal status in the Civil Code of the state, which it retained, aided by strong popular support, until 1934. Quotations from this code indicate some of its formal features.

Family meetings, in all cases in which they are required by law, for the interest of minors or of other persons, must be composed of at least five relations, or in default of relations, friends of him on whose interests they are called upon to deliberate. . . . These relations or friends must be selected from among those domiciled in the parish in which the meeting is held. . . . The relations shall be selected according to their proximity, beginning with the nearest. . . . The appointment of the members of the family meeting shall be made by the judge. . . . The family meeting shall be held before the recorder of the parish, a justice of the peace, or notary public appointed by the judge for the purpose.[3]

The purposes for which the family meeting was held concerned such crises situations as the separation, death, or imprisonment of the parents; the remarriage of a mother; or matters of property in which the child had a stake. Its functions were consultative and deliberative. It had no power of decision.

Among the other immigrant groups, a less formal type of family council was brought to the New World. As ordinarily developed, it took the form of a conclave of several generations and of several degrees of kinship and involved chiefly the right of kinsfolk to have a "say" about problems of primary family interest, such as business, religion, education, occupations, marriage of the children, control over the children's money, family feuds, and the like.[4] It is seen in its closest likeness to the European model in areas of first settlement, but it keeps its form with difficulty, and for a number of reasons. First, many immigrant families did not migrate as units. If the entire family did come, it often did so piecemeal; in other instances, the complete family unit never was established here. This can be illustrated clearly in the case of Japanese immigrants. Smith refers to this in these words:

> In Japan the family council is an important regulatory device. When any matter of consequence is to be considered, such as the marriage of a daughter, the council, made up of relatives, convenes and deliberates. Since grandmothers, uncles, and mothers-in-law did not migrate to America in a body it is impossible to call these conclaves.[5]

Obviously, this happens in the case of the Chinese and various European immigrant groups. Second, residential mobility in the United States often broke up families, particularly the larger kinship groups. Third, the state and other social agencies make more encroachments upon family rights or take over former family functions. Fourth, immigrant parents are less equipped to cope effectively and intelligently with family problems in the United States and tend to hesitate in the application of older methods.

The Contemporary Form of Family Council. This is a more simplified and informal type than has prevailed in the past. It tends to be a family gathering in which all members participate on a relatively equal footing, at least so far as discussion is concerned, in which differing points of view are aired, with expression of the conflicting claims of individual interest, all against the broader background of family solidarity. Osborne writes:

> The idea is relatively simple. When decisions affecting the family must be made, all its members come together and discuss the steps that should be taken. Vacation plans may need to be formulated; the amount the family can afford

to put into war bonds decided upon; the questions of whether Mother should take a job discussed pro and con. Where there are very young children, the simpler problems should be discussed and the discussions kept very informal.[6]

In terms of formalized definition, then, the modern family council may be regarded as a gathering of the family personnel to discuss, advise, deliberate, and, if possible, to agree on matters of common family interest. Its basic implications are that the family is a unified group of interacting personalities, in which each member has his rights, roles, and responsibilities. Applied specifically to the children, it means a rejection of the traditional point of view that they are "silent members" whose prime duty is that of obedience, and the acceptance of the idea that they are to be regarded as co-operating members in a democratically operating household. True, there still are families where recourse to the council is utilized by an older member to dominate rather than to lead, but these are increasingly out of focus with the mental atmosphere of the times.

Occasionally one hears of modern family councils which are organized in more pretentious manner, with a definite time, place, procedure, rules, and regulations. Father may be the presiding officer; there is a secretary to keep a record of the proceedings; decisions are made formally by majority vote. More and more, however, the contemporary family council dispenses with formalities of this kind and becomes an informal get-together of the family group for joint discussion of its common problems.[7]

RECENT CHANGES IN FAMILY SITUATIONS

The preponderant portion of American families are small in size. Contemporary birth rates translated into terms of family units mean the small-family system. This affects family counseling in several ways. It permits greater ease, with less formality, in family conferences. Just as small classes permit more effective teaching, so do small families make possible a more satisfactory family council. It encourages the full inclusion of its children, with sufficient opportunity even for the very young ones to participate. Furthermore, the small family emphasizes the personal relations of all its members with each other and the need of adjustment of these relations.

The role of the family council in larger families, however, must not be ignored. A recent study of the large-family system made by the author stresses its importance in the promotion of family happiness and harmony. In those large families where the father or mother or older brother is a good organizer, leading the family as a project in group living, the children living in these families invariably rate them as happy and satisfactory.[8]

The decline of the patriarchal authority and dominance of the father or oldest male has been a feature of the changing American family, closely associated with changes in the bases and purposes of family living. The authoritarian male family head was a product historically of the time when the family had to be a closely knit and integrated group for purposes of economic production and physical safety. Contemporary economic conditions and prevailing forms of social organization and responsibility no longer require this, and the way is paved for more democratic forms of family life, one of which obviously is the family council.

Contemporary family life tends to be characterized by a diversification in occupations and interests of its members. Father may be a lawyer, Mother is a teacher, Mary is at college, John is in high school, and Jane is attending a specialized private school. This makes, on the one hand, for a richness and variety of backgrounds of the family personnel. Each is a distinct person, and each has his own contribution to make to the family life and its planning. On the other hand, each member of the family, under these conditions, has his own problems, and these may conflict with those of other members or of the interests of the family as a whole. Still another problem is the difficulty of getting all of its members, with their divergent interests, together sufficiently so that the home becomes at least a satisfactory base of operations. The role of the family council, in utilizing effectively this diversified background, its possibility of adjusting conflicting demands and interests, and its potential value as a counterattraction, should be evident.

Another change of the most fundamental importance is the increasing democratization of family life. In part this is the inevitable product of recent changes within the family; in large measure it is but a taking over into the family of concepts which are increasingly emphasized in all segments of American life. To talk constantly about democracy in political life, in industry, in international relations, and then to omit its incorporation into family life is both incongruous and indefensible, if not impossible. Children particularly are alive and susceptible to these "voices in the air." Moreover, they are being given increasingly a training in democratic procedures, in the symbols of expression, and in habits of conferring. Democracy within the family, which is the essence of the family council, comes easily and naturally in keeping with its application in other areas of life.

Contemporary parent-child relationships must be considered against a background of mobile populations and rapid cultural change. The former involves change, often repeated change, from one culture to another, so that members of the family at different age levels come to be conditioned by differing cultural influences and pressures; the latter, by its very nature, increases the cultural differences between successive generations. When these two factors are combined, as has been the case in immigrant families and, to a lesser extent, in country-to-city migrations, the effects upon parent-child conflicts are doubly marked. In such situations of culture differentials between generations, attempts at parental domination tend to defeat themselves. Obviously, co-operative counseling is a far better way out.

All these changes must be considered in relation to the changing functions of the family, so much emphasized in the recent literature on the family. Burgess and Locke note the shift in the family from institution to companionship, with its consequent implications for family functions.[9] Others point out the family's increasing concern with the personality development of its members, particularly its child members. Much of the lament over the decline of the family results from a failure to recognize that while older functions of the family are passing newer ones are emerging. These newer functions tend more and more to be of an advising, counseling, administrative nature, through which the family aids the child in the wise selection and effective utilization of the various specialized services that are available. This change is of revolutionary importance in parent-child relationships because it means that leadership in the modern family now calls for the tactful direction of its members to the diverse opportunities and specialized services now open to them. This calls for qualities, not of physical dominance, but of keen judgment; instead of authoritarian control there must be wise counsel; instead of regulation the demand is for instruction and self-discipline.

SELECTED ASPECTS OF MODERN FAMILY COUNSELING

The Family Meal. One such aspect is the family meal.[10] The generic importance of the family meal has long been recognized. Christianity has immortalized it in the ceremonial of the Last Supper and renews this recognition endlessly in the communion rite. Dramatists stage it with frequent effectiveness. To the novelist, it is a constant device for character delineation or plot facilitation. Even the essayists, like Dr. Holmes, clothe their sage observations around the framework of the breakfast table. Obviously it is important, too, for the student of family life, and particularly of the family council, and for several reasons.

First, the family meal is a distinct aspect of the family's life. In lower-class families especially, the dining rather than the living room is apt to be the social center of the household. Second, it holds the members of the family together over an extended period of time. The length of time and the details of the occasion naturally vary from one family to another, but in general a family meal is an extended session of the family personnel, with a relatively high rate of attendance. Today, under stress of the differing interests of family members, it may be the only time that its members come together. Third, it is at dinner that the family members are likely to be at their greatest ease, both physically and psychologically. The times that the family is at its best are perhaps most often on the occasions of its more leisured dining, just as the family entertaining at the dining table is the family on exhibition. This more felicitous generalization does not overlook the fact that the family meal also represents at times the family in haste, operating with direct bluntness, or the family at war, disturbing the emotions of its members and upsetting the gastric processes. Fourth, one must recall the continuing repetition of the family meal. Some families meet around the table three times a day; most families do so at least once a day. Over a period of years the simple arithmetic of this is enough to emphasize its quantitative effectiveness. Finally, the family meal is likely to represent the family in its most democratic mood. Now, more than at other times, the younger members have their opportunity to blossom verbally. Well-fed elders accept with impunity remarks from juveniles which might otherwise not be tolerated, just as Mother has long recognized that Father is most susceptible and generous after a satisfactory dinner. This democratic mood is particularly important in the present connection.

Many features of family life which develop in connection with the family meal are germane to the development of family counseling. Six will be summarized briefly.

(a) The individual's role in the family group comes to be clearly defined around the family table. Since the entire family is together, relationships between individual members are brought out into the open. Feuding members are seated at opposite sides of the table, for example. Covenants secretly arrived at become manifest. Group choices are made—in seating arrangements, in the serving of food, in the assignment of leftovers, in priorities in conversation.

(b) This table audience, both in responses which it gives to and which it withholds from its individual members, carries the greatest weight in the molding of personal traits. Its intimate nature and repetitive force make it often the family's best corrective disciplinarian. Children especially are frank, often quite brutally so, in their reactions to one another, and perhaps nowhere are they so with as much self-assurance as under the protective custody of the family meal.

(c) The family meal is a kind of personality clinic, with both students and clients in attendance. Particularly is this true if the family is of any considerable size. Each member comes to be analyzed, dissected, catalogued, and processed by the other members. This procedure is all the more devastating because it goes on before the entire group. Undesirable traits and personal weakness may be particularly identified and castigated.

(d) The family meal, particularly the dinner one, is the clearinghouse for most of the family's information, news, and experiences. Jack tells about the substitute teacher; Jane about the neighboring girl's new coat; Daddy refers to the fact that Mr. Davis is complaining about the number of government questionnaires and threatens to go out of business; Mother thinks that Bill is coming down with the grippe. The family dining table is like a crossroads through which flows the news of the world as the respective members of the family see it and experience it. Much of this traffic of information and ideas flows swiftly and unobtrusively past, noticed more in its absence than in its presence, but it is there for all to see, hear, and assimilate.

(e) The family meal is constantly serving as a forum for the discussion of matters of interest and concern to the family members. Questions are asked, answered, or evaded in turn. The range of topics covered may be wide and varied, or monotonous in the recurrence of a few items of interest. Significant for all are the topics meticulously avoided as well as those assiduously discussed. The selection of topics for the family forum is in itself a cultural choice.

(f) The family meal serves constantly as an evaluating conference, especially on the experiences, needs, and interests of the family members. There is group discussion. Individual views are expressed, modified, and reconciled often as a family judgment, choice, decision, or attitude emerges. Arrived at experimentally in democratic conference, or imposed by an autocratic parent, these evaluations are absorbed on the basis of their emotional relations to the family, so that the line between the two may often be quite indistinct.

The Family Guest. A second aspect of family life important in this connection grows out of the presence of guests. The role of the guest has long been neglected, in large part, in the study of the family. A research project completed by the William T. Carter Foundation for Child Development of the University of Pennsylvania, and based on four hundred case documents, indicates that this is a serious omission. This study suggests a number of conclusions pertinent to this chapter. The outstanding impression from the project as a whole focuses upon the importance of family experience with the guest as source material in the learning (and counseling) process that goes on within the family, with particular reference to its child members. Guests come into the home, generally with some, and often with relatively complete, acceptance by the parents. They are outsiders, but less so than other persons. They constitute a sort of intermediate stage between the child's confined family contacts and the more formal contacts with persons from the world outside. Furthermore, they come to the child's attention on a distinctive plane. They come with the attractiveness of novelty and often with an interpretive coloring by the adults in the family group. Particularly would this be true of the approved guest in upper-class homes, where family entertainment has a relatively selective character. That is to say, guests are invited into the home because the family wants them.

From this it follows that guests often are the agents through which is brought into the home, and to the child's vivid attention, a consciousness of the variety of life, of different people, diverse ideas, contrasting mannerisms and interests. An analysis of 117 autobiographies, in which the authors comment on the role of guests in their families, made as a part of the above-mentioned research project, shows a very general emphasis upon the importance of guests in extending the horizon of beliefs and customs of family members, the introduction of public issues as well as problems of etiquette and other forms of personal behavior, and a knowledge of conflict situations hitherto unknown. At the same time there are frequent references to the fact that guests in the home facilitated comparisons which gave family members a conception of their own family status.[11] Often elders in the family consciously manipulate this use of the guest.

After the guests have left the home, "post-mortems" may follow. There are analyses, comments, and evaluations concerning many things relating to the guests: their behavior, their occupations, their planes of living, their patterns of expenditures, the attitudes which were expressed. Sometimes the family appraisal of these may be made "in front of the children" and with their participation. Such situations offer an excellent opportunity for the family council to function.

Family Projects. Modern life is rich with opportunities for family projects which afford an excellent opportunity for the development of family councils. It may be the erection and furnishing of a summer shack, the building of an outdoor grill, the cultivation of a vacant lot or flower bed, the development of a family hobby, or the acquisition of a domestic animal. Many families, for example, have found the training and breeding of a dog a family project exceedingly useful in the training of younger family members in toilet habits, and the education of all in the differences and processes of sex.[12] Or the projects may be more ambitious—a lengthy program for the education of the children, the purchase of a piano, plans for a summer vacation for the family, or the establishment of a business. Concrete projects of the kind indicated above can be made to serve as excellent frameworks for effective family councils.

Family Rituals. Many families develop what might be called family rituals. These are certain prescribed patterns of family procedure which come to be accepted by the family members and, in course of time, come to have the support of family tradition. The following brief excerpts from a large collection of family rituals will illustrate their nature as well as their possibilities for family council.[13]

Every night, when it is possible, I will go into my parents' room prior to retiring and review the day's events. They criticize and give opinions on subjects which to me are problems. I ask questions and also venture ideas. We discuss family affairs, each of us giving a bit to the conversation. This to me is the dearest of all our rituals because it brings me closer to my parents than at any other time, and gives me invaluable aid.

Every Saturday night they would have what they called a "lamb slaughter," which really meant they had a few arguments about anything (all participating), and those who couldn't give much contribution to the discussion they called the slaughter lambs. The children mostly opened the argument asking their father's or mother's opinions about religion, education, love, or anything, but they would wind up arguing with each other. In summer these arguments took place on the porch. When the arguments would become too heated one of the boys would say, "Let's have some music." [This is a description of a Negro family.]

The Clark family consisted of father, mother, and two children. The children were of high-school age and were employed each Saturday during the school year. The father's and the children's employment extended into the late hours of Saturday evening. The custom developed early for the family to come together in the kitchen between eleven and twelve o'clock on Saturday evening. Invariably the mother would provide a midnight supper. Earnings of the week were totaled, expenditures were planned, experiences at work were exchanged. Usually these sessions lasted until 2 A.M. on Sunday mornings. After a time they became a family event which each member looked forward to, and made a definite part of the weekly schedule. This ritual continued for a number of years, and now, although the children are married, they still come "home" for the Saturday-night family supper.

The over-all conclusion that emerges from the study of family rituals is their relation to family integration. An integrated family is a well-knit family, one that functions smoothly as a unit. Rituals contribute to this end by accustoming members of a family to do things together. Families are held together best by doing things together.[14]

POSSIBLE VALUES OF THE FAMILY COUNCIL

The extent to which the family council obtains as a form of internal family organization in the United States is not known, but a study by Mather is suggestive in this connection. Analyzing the family histories written by two hundred college students, he identified four types of family control in the following proportions: (a) dominance by the father, 37.8 per cent; (b) mother dominance, 20.2 per cent; (c) joint dominance by father and mother, 28.4 per cent; (d) family-council control, 13.6 per cent.[15] Whatever the proportion in the population as a whole, its utilization has been extensive enough to justify some tentative conclusion of its possible values. These are stated here in summary form.

(a) The family council may serve as an educational device in acquainting all of the members of the group with the family needs and problems. Personal problems are merged into a group problem, and each may see his or her problem and needs, both in relation to those of each other member, and of the group as a whole.

(b) A family group consciousness may be built up through the family council. What is good for the family as a group? How can the family name be upheld? How can the family put its best foot forward? These are considerations which may be involved in the purchase of common possessions, necessitating in turn the curtailment of some individual expenditures. Family achievements which result from co-operative family effort make for family pride. Persons familiar with college and university students will have no difficulty in recalling instances of family planning over a period of years to accomplish the college education of successive members of the family group.[16] Mather's study revealed that family affection, social life, loyalty, solidarity, co-operation, joint use of family property, and celebration of family birthdays and holidays were found in greatest number where the family council prevailed.[17]

(c) Increased wisdom of family decisions is possible under the family council. This is so because such decisions are likely to be based on more adequate and complete information. Where each can express his needs and viewpoints, the ultimate decision is more likely to recognize the interests of all.

(d) Group decisions tend to be supported by group authority. It is not just the authoritarian father but the entire family that expects you to accept its decision. Here is but another illustration of the sociological principle that the group is the best disciplinarian of its individual members.

(e) The family council facilitates specialization of role and responsibility within the family. Group organization focuses attention upon individual aptitudes, interests, and knowledge. This in turn often leads to the assignment of responsibilities in such a way as the group considers most advantageous to itself. This again has the added value of establishing duties on the basis of group approval rather than parental domination. Such group specialization is highly meaningful, as students of gang life so clearly reveal. Perhaps the most significant aspect of this is the subtly effective transfer of responsibility for specific functions from older to younger members of the family.

(f) Perhaps as significant as any value inherent in the family council is the sense of security which it may give to the individual family member. Here is not just a family into which he happened to be born and in which he is made to do things by order of an authoritarian head. This is his family, in which he has his say, in which he co-operates in doing his part. It is a family which does things as a family, and (albeit this may operate below the level of conscious reflection) just as it does things for all, so it may be depended upon to do things for him. The family council satisfies the sense of being wanted, the longing to belong.

NOTES

[1]L. Schapera, *Bantu-Speaking Tribes of South Africa*, London, George Routledge and Sons, Ltd., 1937, p. 213. For survival of this form of family council in modern peasant society in India, read Hilda Wernher, *The Land and the Well*, New York, John Day, 1946.

[2]For a summary of Family Council Law in Europe, the reader is referred to *Family Council Law in Europe*, prepared and issued under the auspices of the Eugenics Society of England, 1927–29.

[3]*The Civil Code of the State of Louisiana, Revision of 1870*, Vol. I, Articles 281–85, pp. 166–68.

[4]For an interesting description of the attempts of a Russian Jewish family in the United States to engage their daughter to a man of their selection, the reader is referred to Rose Cohan, *Out of the Shadow*, New York, George H. Doran Co., 1918, Chaps. XLIV and XLV.

[5]William C. Smith, *Americans in the Making*, New York, D. Appleton-Century, 1939, p. 88.

[6]Ernest G. Osborne, "The Family Council," *The National Parent-Teacher*, September 1943, pp. 25–27.

[7]For a readable account of the operation of a family council, see Lillian M. Gilbreth, *Living with Our Children*, New York, W. W. Norton, 1928. See also Hazel A. Price, *Living with the Family*, Boston, Little, Brown, 1942.

[8]James H. S. Bossard, *Parent and Child*, Philadelphia, University of Pennsylvania Press, 1953, Chaps. V, VI. A completed study of 100 large families is now awaiting publication.

[9]Ernest W. Burgess and Harvey J. Locke, *The Family*, New York, American Book Co., rev. ed., 1953.

[10]James H. S. Bossard, *The Sociology of Child Development*, New York, Harper & Bros., rev. ed., 1954, Chap. VIII.

[11]For a complete report of tne autobiographical part of this study, the reader is referred to James H. S. Bossard and Eleanor S. Boll, "The Role of the Guest," *American Sociological Review*, April 1947.

[12]James H. S. Bossard, "The Mental Hygiene of Owning a Dog," *Mental Hygiene*, July 1944, pp. 408–13. See also Bossard, *Parent and Child*, Chap. XII.

[13]James H. S. Bossard and Eleanor S. Boll, *Ritual in Family Living*, Philadelphia, University of Pennsylvania Press, 1950, Chap. IV.

[14]Ibid., Chap. X.

[15]W. G. Mather, Jr., "Defining Family Types on the Basis of Control," *The Family*, 1935–36, Vol. 16, pp. 9–12, also 181–82. Consult also Mildred B. Thurow, *A Study of Selected Factors in Family Life as Described in Autobiographies*, Cornell University Agricultural Experiment Station, Ithaca, New York, 1934.

[16]The author had as an undergraduate student recently a widow aged 61, who was working for a degree as a part of a twenty-year family-council plan, in the course of which three children had previously obtained professional degrees.

[17]Mather, op. cit.

PART V

Social Problems of Sex and Marriage

Chapter 1

SEX AND THE SOCIAL ORDER

by *Georgene H. Seward, Ph.D.*
UNIVERSITY OF SOUTHERN CALIFORNIA

CULTURAL DEFINITION OF NORMS FOR SEXUAL BEHAVIOR AND SOCIAL SEX ROLES

Not long ago sex was viewed as one of the constants of human nature, an instinctual force struggling against social forces attempting to control it. More recently, cultural anthropology has taught us that "human nature" cannot be abstracted from cultural context and that the only "constant" is the constant interaction between the individual and his society. Individual behavior must be interpreted in the light of the social frame in which it inheres. Consequently, if one wishes to determine the role of sex in a given culture, one must first determine the basic values of that culture.[1] A cross-cultural survey bears out this point.[2] Sex may carry the meaning of sin or pleasure, nurture or dominance, according to the prevailing value system.

Even within the confines of Western culture there is wide diversity in the interpretation of sexual behavior from one subculture to another. In working-class groups, for example, more direct heterosexual activity is acceptable, in accordance with the greater permissiveness of impulse expression in general. In fact, status is acquired through early sexual experience.[3] Masturbation, however, is more apt to be disapproved as a perversion among the underprivileged, and sexual outlets to be narrowly channeled in coitus with little variation in technique and foreplay.[4]

Across the color barrier, the social-class differences still hold. Although Victorian sex mores are even more coercive for middle-class Negroes than they are for comparable white groups, they are less binding for the most disadvantaged.[5] For example, in a study of Negro children in Cincinnati, the poorer ones showed greater freedom from restraint both in indulging in sexual relations and in discussing them than those from a higher socioeconomic level.[6] Supporting evidence comes from an investigation of lower-class urban Negro girls whose standard of sex morality corresponded more closely to the more lenient conduct expected of middle-class white boys![7] A very different sex code prevails in the Italian slums of Eastern City, where a premium is placed on virginity at marriage. This ideal is upheld by strong legal and institutional sanctions and is supported by equally strong sentiments. For a "corner boy" to have "laid" a virgin is to incur the severe censure of his group.[8]

In the social roles ascribed to the two sexes, cultural relativity is no less apparent than in the evaluation of sexual behavior. In most societies there is a definite "sex line" as to what constitutes appropriate personality and behavior. "Masculine" usually means a higher dominance level than "feminine." Men are more often expected to perform tasks involving direct contact with the environment while women must tend the home fires and care for the young. In societies where the sex-personality line is tightly drawn, the situation is fraught with risk of failure to fit into the prescribed mold and of consequent social punishment for deviation. Some cultures wisely meet this difficulty by providing safety valves for those likely to deviate. Examples are the institutionalized sex-role reversals of the berdache among the Plains Indians,[9] the "manly hearts" of the North Piegans,[10] the two-way exchanges of the Mohaves,[11] and others.

In Western culture, fluidity has marked the history of social sex roles since the days of antiquity. Today, behavior expectancies change from one generation to the next, and even during the course of individual development there are shifts and discontinuities from one stage to another. What is appropriate conduct at one age level may be highly inappropriate a little later. For example, "being good at games" was found to increase in importance for boys at the first, third, and fifth grades, while "being quiet" had almost dropped out as a desirable masculine attribute by the third grade.[12] Thus a boy with characteristics that carried status in the first grade may find his prestige lowered by the time he reaches the fifth by merely maintaining the previously rewarded traits. Analogous shifts occur in desirable feminine personality patterns—the prepubertal "little lady" ideal giving way to the "good sport" and "glamour girl" design at a junior-high-school level.[13] These ever-shifting standards make it difficult for the developing youngster to know what is expected of him.

No less confusing are the adult sex roles that he is to emulate. The transition from a dominant father to a democratic form of family structure is causing many dislocations and inconsistencies in the roles of both men and women. The situation is further complicated by the fact that changes in feminine social role and personality pattern are proceeding more rapidly for single than for married women.[14] A common dilemma among college girls is that of deciding when to "play dumb" on dates and when to play up to the "modern" role that an equalitarian education calls for.[15] In one group of students, the only girls who escaped sex-role conflicts were those from sheltered, conservative homes.[16] For married women the choice seems to be among three wifely roles: the traditional, the companion, and the partner, with the last outstripping the other two in popularity among the younger generation.[17]

The cultural transition which is responsible for shifts and readjustments in the feminine role necessarily brings with it concomitant changes in the masculine. The loss of patriarchal status with its clear-cut directives concerning economic support and authority in the home has sometimes shown a boomerang effect, resulting in role reversals rather than the adoption of a partnership. There seems to have been some tendency for women to usurp the abdicated masculine domestic authority, leading to extreme cases of dependency, or "momism."[18] Recent studies of the father role, however, indicate an increasing recognition of the importance of companionship with their children and of sharing the disciplinary function with the mother.[19]

CULTURAL DEFINITION OF SEXUAL DEVIATION

"Normal" sex and sex role behavior is relative not only to a given society but to local areas and to age, and ethnic groupings. The conflict and confusion inherent in the complex patterns that constitute our culture make it easy enough to understand the prevalence of sexual deviation. It is not so easy, however, to understand the particular forms the deviation may take. Two cases with the same label may have altogether different meanings in the history of the patient. For example, a theft may have been committed in order to obtain articles for a sexual partner, for fetishistic enjoyment, or merely for the perverse erotic excitement aroused by the danger. Widely different surface manifestations may reflect the same inner dynamics. In the case of a fetishist, burglary, theft, and assault may all represent the means of obtaining the erotic object on which his sexual gratification depends. People who deviate sexually are neither vicious monsters nor supernatural vampires. Even the insane contribute sparingly to their numbers.[20] Sex offenders are for the most part people whose orientation toward their reproductive functions and social sex roles has not been properly channeled. In other words, they are anomalies of development. Biological maturation accounts only for sexual drive; learning, for its direction. This has been amply demonstrated in animals of various species.[21] Behavior that may be appropriate at one developmental period or at one time or place becomes a "perversion" under other circumstances.

Perversion of Sex Object. Since the biological end of sexual behavior is procreation of the species, the direction of sex interest toward objects other than the biologically adequate adult of opposite sex is a perversion. The commonest one is masturbation, in which the individual gratifies his sexual needs by stimulating his own genitals. Long before the sex organs are capable of reproductive function they have become the focus of interest to the child. This interest might be utilized constructively or destructively by society.* Autoerotic practices usually decrease as other sources of gratification become available. In cases where they are continued into adult life no generalization is possible since masturbation is differently motivated in different personalities. For the neurotic who has failed to free himself from family ties it may represent an escape from the more exacting demands of heterosexual relations; for the well-adjusted individual it may be merely one of the many forms of sex play he enjoys, while for the celibate youth or aging widow it becomes a means of eliminating distracting tensions. Whether the practice is "good" or "bad" depends on its significance for the person concerned. No absolutely good or bad effects have been scientifically established. Where it is a symptom of underlying maladjustment and represents a failure to grow up sufficiently to undertake adult sexual relationships, the treatment should be aimed at the underlying problem.

Another potential misdirection of sexual interest is toward members of the immediate family. To guard against this possibility and to ensure co-operation between groups through exogamy, most societies have erected strong taboos against incest. Although conspicuous exceptions exist, such as the Egyptian Ptolemies, the incest taboo is almost universal. In the intimate family structure of contemporary Western culture strong incestuous tendencies have to be counteracted by equally strong social sanctions; as a result incestuous attachments are usually deeply repressed and do not ordinarily reach the point of overt expression. Even so, incest occurs more often than is commonly supposed, the chief offenders being widowers and their daughters.[22] When incestuous relationships are begun in childhood they might be expected to constitute a serious threat to later adjustment. Whether or not traumatic aftereffects will follow, however, seems to depend on the existing security level of the child at the time of the experience.[23]

Similar considerations hold for cases in which sex relations occur between children and unrelated adults. The child's later development is not as seri-

---

*We may contrast the Marquesans, who encourage it among their children with the generally negative attitude that prevails in our own.

ously threatened as might be supposed. Aggressions occurring before puberty do not seem to predispose the individual toward the development of mental disorders in adult life.[24] Contrary to popular belief, the child, far from being the pitiable victim of sexual attack, frequently acts as the aggressor, apparently deriving positive satisfaction from the experience.[25] The chief danger to the child from such precocious sexual relationships lies in the possibility of acquiring negative attitudes toward sex that may be unfavorable for normal heterosexual adjustments and ultimately lead to homosexuality.[26]

As for the adult participating in sexual associations with children, one frequently finds a timid soul whose inadequacy to cope with the complexities of adult relationships leads him to escape into the simpler intimacies with children.[27] Mr. L, for example, was arrested at the age of thirty-eight for the fourth time for improper approaches to little girls. His background revealed a combination of browbeating on the part of his domineering father and oversolicitude by his mother that prevented him from developing normal feelings of self-esteem. With the building up of his confidence in himself his erotic interest in children disappeared. Lowering of inhibitions in senility or following the use of alcohol may also result in regression from adult adjustment patterns to the more infantile love of children.[28]

One of the most common sexual aberrations in many cultures is orientation toward the same sex. The significance of this disorder varies with local circumstance. Intimate friendships between comrades in arms were glorified in ancient Greece and Persia, in Japan during the period of chivalry, and most recently in the *Bruderschaft* of modern Germany.[29] Among certain preliterate peoples a homosexual stage is considered essential to the attainment of sexual maturity. The Keraki Indians of southern New Guinea provide an example in their "making-of-man" cult.[30] They believe it necessary for boys to pass through a passive and an active homosexual stage before they are prepared for full adult sexuality. In our own society, temporary homosexual interests are regarded as part of growing up and are supported if not induced by the many sex-segregating influences to which the developing individual is subjected. This represents a passing phase that is reversible, giving way easily when heterosexual opportunities arise. Later in life, if unusual situations occur in which homosexual behavior is rewarded, the individual may revert to this form of adjustment.[31] Prison life, for example, not only involves long periods of segregation of members of the same sex but it is so far beyond the pale of what is normal outside the walls that new customs are likely to develop. Social stratification is often along homosexual lines, with status differentials following proficiency in obtaining "gals."[32] Similar social organization was reported for an institution segregating subnormal Negro and white girls. In this extraordinary context the scarcer Negresses enjoyed superior social status which they expressed as aggressive behavior toward the white girls. The latter, in turn, responded with sexual interest. "The social origin of the homosexual dominance behavior on the part of the Negro girls came out clearly when they dropped the masculine role they had assumed toward white girls in order to play the feminine role toward another Negress."[33] From armies to monasteries, sex-segregated groups that remain an integral part of the larger social structure accept the official taboo against homosexual practices, punishing overt offenders, although there may be clandestine indulgence.[34]

Although the weight of scientific evidence indicates that social factors are the most important in inducing homosexuality,[35] genetic[36] and hormonal[37] also contribute to the condition. Where the biological distortion is extreme, homoerotic attachments are conceivably acquired more readily, but even in such cases the environment would have to provide the opportunity for the deviant learning. In other words, training may enrich natural predispositions or it may run counter to them. In either event, the training is the differential in the individual's ultimate behavior.

Cases of deeply embedded homoeroticism often have their roots in the early family situation and may reflect a variety of unwholesome influences. Failure of the parent to provide an appropriate sex model often leads to cross-sex identification, as does his failure to provide the child with an opportunity to try out appropriate sex-role behavior. Irreparable harm has been done by disappointed parents in their futile attempts to thrust upon the child the role of the desired sex. Little boys whose baby curls are kept too long or who are dressed up in Sister's clothes for the amusement and admiration of female relatives may become the transvestites of the next generation. A case in the making was Nancy, whose father wanted a son and whose mother rejected her own femininity. In a family where everything desirable was on the side of being male, it was natural for Nancy to want to be a boy. She wore shorts, insisted that other children call her "Bill," and refused to play the role of mother or little girl in "house." Her futile efforts to change her sex led her into conflict everywhere.[38]

Perhaps the most convincing evidence of the importance of social factors in psychosexuality comes from the pseudohermaphrodites who show discrepancies between biology and behavior. In a recent review of eighty-four cases from the medical literature. Ellis concluded that although physical sexuality may be biologically determined, it is experience that determines the more inclusive psychosexuality that ultimately develops.[39] As an illustrative case we may take S. M., with the anatomy of a male, who was reared as a girl and completely accepted the feminine role. At the age of seventeen, failure to menstruate led to the discovery that "she" had undescended testes and predominantly male secondary sex characters, while the only suggestion of female anatomy was a large clitoris. In this case the feminine social orientation began with an early identification with the mother entrenched by fear of the father.[40]

The rarer perversions that have as their objects animals, corpses, non-genital parts of the body, inanimate objects, and others are the products of unfortunate conditioning no less than the more common forms. Among the goatherds of southern Italy and Sicily who spend so much of their time with animals it is not uncommon for them to have sexual relations with animals.[41] Under the conditions of modern urban life, however, such a sexual orientation is symptomatic of severe pathology. Sometimes a perversion is the result of a single vivid association between a particular object and sexual excitement, although retraining may be a long, uphill process.

Perversion of the Sex Act. Perversion of the sex object is not the only way in which sexual deviation may occur. The means by which gratification is attained may include activities as irrelevant to biological mating as stealing, arson, and murder. More common perversions involve deriving erotic satisfaction from infliction of injury upon others (sadism) or the self (masochism). These distortions may occur in a homosexual as well as in a heterosexual context. Olkon and Sherman describe a transvestite male who behaved sadistically and also sought chastisement from his wife and family.[42] In another case the clearing up of transvestite and paranoid symptoms following electroshock also suggests a masochistic overtone.[43] It is not unusual for a number of perverse attitudes to be combined in the same individual, as in the case of J. S., a meek and mild middle-aged New Englander who was arrested for homosexual practices with little boys. The children were coached to act out the punitive role of the irate father. The background suggested a female identification, expressed in a childhood preference for girls' games for which the patient was severely punished. In this case, prefrontal lobotomy apparently relieved the obsessive, masochistic fantasies and anxieties.[44]

Sexual satisfaction in some cases seems to depend on what is normally a preliminary step in the sex act, namely, exhibiting and viewing the genitals. Again we must evaluate the behavior in the light of the cultural setting. It becomes pathological only where there are social sanctions against genital display. Among the South African Bantu, for example, prepubertal boys may freely reveal the penis, even decorating it with bells, although after circumcision the glans must be concealed. With so little restriction, exhibitionism is a rare occurrence and is mainly found among city Negroes in relation to

European women.[45] In our own culture, where display of the sex organs is regarded as obscene, the genitals acquire correspondingly high valence and their demonstration becomes a distorted attempt to win social approval! The exhibitionist is often the shy, overconscientious, well-bred son of a domineering mother, who feels compelled to display his genitals in order to prove his masculinity.[46] A case answering this description came to my attention; it concerned a brilliant young scientist whose success in research was unparalleled. His mother's sexual frigidity and resentment at having borne a son rather than a daughter led to the development of this patient's exhibitionistic compulsions. The continual threat to his career and to his marriage was ended by suicide.

Analogous considerations hold for cases of voyeurism, where there is the reverse tendency to spy on others in order to see their genitals or to watch them perform the sex act. Like pornography, voyeurism is a cultural product of the secrecy with which sex relations are surrounded. The concealment generates excessive interest in the subject, and as "peeping Toms" timid, ineffectual, and sexually impotent men may find sublimation for the sexual needs they dare not express directly.

Behavior that is normal in one culture may be abnormal in another. The interpretation of a specific form of aberration cannot be understood categorically but only within the personality context of the individual patient. Sex offense is a symptom of total personality maladjustment. It may represent the gamut of emotional disturbance, including psychoneurosis, psychopathic personality, and, more rarely, psychosis. The basic cause, not the superficial symptom, should be treated. A physician does not treat a fever or a hallucination; he treats a case of pneumonia or schizophrenia. It is just as futile to try to cope with exhibitionism or homosexuality without discovering the underlying personality disturbance they represent. When the "treatment" is some kind of punishment, incarceration, castration, or other serious frustration, it is not only futile but harmful.[47] Each offense should be handled individually and the distinctive psychodynamics worked out.[48] The psychiatric approach is no less important in dangerous cases where segregation is necessary for the protection of the community. The more the hospital replaces the prison, the more we may expect in the way of personal and social reclamation of the sex offender. The ultimate ideal of prevention rather than reclamation may be hoped for only when by intelligent social planning we may be able to relieve individuals of the major sources of anxiety and hostility.

Deviation from Heterosexual Mores. Even in cases where the individual's sex development has reached adult heterosexuality his behavior may be socially deviant though not biologically perverted. In our culture acceptable sex behavior is restricted to monogamous marriage. Frequent breaches of this requirement are bound to occur. In fact, the mores themselves are undergoing progressive change in the direction of increasing permissiveness of premarital intercourse especially between engaged couples.[49] Some observers have gone so far as to suggest more drastic modification of the mores in the interests of better adaptation to current realities. For example, one recent writer remarked, "When an important part of the people does not live in marriage and a great number of women cannot find a mate, marriage can scarcely continue to be the only institution in which sex life is legitimate."[50] Under present circumstances, however, the unmarried mother and the "illegitimate child" continue to be symptoms of our social pathology.

The American Negro has contributed a large share of illegitimacy, though through no fault of his own, since marriage was seldom legalized during slavery.[51] Under those circumstances no stigma was attached to the "unmarried mother." On the contrary, she enjoyed relatively high status for maintaining the family group. With urbanization and the migration to the North, her respectability was lowered as a result of the unequal competition with the dominant whites by whose standards of conduct the Negro was now judged.[52]

Another related social factor often associated with illegitimacy is culture conflict. Confusion between two sets of mores may go a long way toward explaining the high incidence among girls of foreign parentage.[53] During the recent war parental neglect, manifested by poor social identification and inadequate sex instruction, was held responsible for the increase in sex delinquency among underprivileged teen-agers.[54] Similar background conditions were also more recently found among lower-class unmarried mothers in an attempt to analyze the dynamics of anxiety at different social levels.[55]

The results of maternal neglect do not stop with the unmarried mothers but unfortunately are transmitted by them to their illegitimate offspring. Evidence on this point is presented in a recent study showing a significantly greater proportion of illegitimate children suffering from feelings of being unwanted than among a matched control group. These feelings were correlated with maternal rejection and lack of interest in the children's problems.[56] Other factors that contribute to the difficulties of children of unmarried mothers are the absence of a father figure and the general social rejection that occurs when their status becomes known. If the stigma of illegitimacy were removed and the children born out of wedlock afforded the same legal status and the associated inheritance rights and social security that other children enjoy, a big step would have been taken toward the amelioration of one major social sex problem. Prevention through better education for sex living would of course represent a more fundamental attack.

Another form of deviation from the official institution of matrimony is the subinstitution of prostitution. Since the problem will be treated in detail in the following chapter we shall merely present a case to emphasize the importance of the individual approach in this social disease. The patient was a girl of strict religious training and good education who had to undertake the support of her two children after an unsuccessful marriage. Financial difficulties made it necessary for her to live in a neighborhood where prostitution was the norm. In this atmosphere she first indulged in some casual promiscuous relationships; later in prostitution. That the prostitution actually filled a deep emotional need was revealed by psychoanalysis. She harbored an unconscious hostility toward her father that found vent in her behavior. When a stronger motive was mobilized by pointing out the undesirable effects on her children, the practice was suddenly stopped despite a worse financial status. Thus the economic need was only a secondary factor serving as a rationalization for the primary unconscious motive.[57] This case indicates the need for scientific handling of the problem.

Escape from the monogamous standard is sometimes sought in an extramarital affair. Although such irregularity may occasionally happen among the happily married it is more often an index of maladjustment.[58] Sexual relationships outside of wedlock are paradoxically motivated less by sexual need than by the need for reassurance.[59] They may also serve the purpose of working off unconscious hostilities toward the spouse. In any case, extramarital tendencies should be recognized as symptoms rather than causes of conjugal disharmony. Probing beneath the fling to the underlying factors may or may not reveal incompatibility so serious as to make the continuation of the relationship undesirable. However that may be, separation on the basis of symptom alone, no matter how legally and socially defensible, may break a marriage that could be saved and contribute needlessly to personal unhappiness and the divorce rate.

CULTURE AND SUCCESSFUL MARRIAGE

Intramarital Disturbance. Even when there is outward conformity to the mores there may be internal sources of tension that threaten to disrupt the relationship. The friction may be reflected in impotence, frigidity, painful intercourse, or as any of a large number of related psychosomatic symptoms.[60] The important point is that such disturbances are merely *symptoms* and not in themselves *causes* of the maladjustment. The underlying difficulty frequently has its roots in the ambiguity and confusion of current sex-role expectations. Formerly, personal happiness of the mates was subordinated to their obligations and duties to the larger grandparental family groups they represented.[61] Under these auspices the erotic was paradoxically likely to be divorced from the marriage and driven underground in the more casual relationships with mistress or prostitute. In contrast, the contemporary family focusing on the personal relationship between married partners theoretically provides them with the opportunity of developing an intimate companionship in which the erotic supplies the vital spark. Actually, however, the new sex equality has too often merely opened up a new avenue through which the competitive pattern of the culture may find expression. We may have outgrown some of the authoritarian forms, but we have not yet grown up enough to accept the implications of the democratic family design.

Suggested Solutions. A variety of solutions for handling the problems created by the re-evaluation of sex roles has been suggested in the recent literature. For example, Erich Fromm[62] points out the fallacy of equating difference with deficiency. For him, equality of opportunity affords the basis for the development of differences, resulting in the fullest realization of individuality. In his opinion, sex differences in biological role have certain personality overtones which blend with those directly produced by culture, and so do not warrant casting men and women in different social roles.

Margaret Mead[63] also stresses certain core differences between the sexes which she discovered in societies widely diverse in the surface patterning of social sex behaviors. In all, achievement appeared as the chief male preoccupation, while for women, nurturing activities were paramount. Unlike Fromm, Mead believes that social sex roles should follow these biological cleavages, with women finding their self-expression in the service areas while men remain free to engage in competitive achievement.

Agreeing with Mead's basic assumptions, Lundberg and Farnham[64] would go farther in an effort to restore the balance between the sexes which was lost when the Industrial Revolution removed the feminine functions from the home. According to these authors, to re-establish woman's sense of personal worth, it is not enough that she be permitted to follow her nurturing interests into the world beyond the home. Within the home itself, her unique and essential contribution of mothering should be elevated to a social status commensurate with that accorded competitive achievement. To implement this notion, the authors suggest recognition of successful childbearing and rearing by government subsidies and academic honors.

In view of the importance of culture in playing up or playing down whatever sex differences may be traced to biological process, any dichotomizing of social roles is risky for the individual. Greater differences may be found among members within one sex than between the sexes. This overlapping has led Komarovsky[65] to comment with respect to education that woman's "nature" would be just as much violated by being forced into a "feminized" curriculum as by the so-called "imitation" of men. She suggests a rich and flexible offering in which the talents of individuals irrespective of sex are fostered. In previous work[66] the present writer, expressing a similar view, pointed out that the educational groundwork should be begun long before college age. If men and women are to develop co-operative attitudes and more harmonious marriages, they must begin their basic training in childhood. As little boys and girls they must learn the distinction between biological and social roles, accepting their complementary biological functions, and at the same time respecting one another's freedom in the choice of social role. While such education would not eliminate the problem of adjusting to changing and often confusing sex-role demands, it would provide the individual with better preparation for it. In so doing it would provide him with an important technique for successful marriage.

NOTES

[1]G. Bateson, "Sex and Culture," *Ann. N. Y. Acad. Sci.*, 1947, 47; 647–60.

[2]G. H. Seward, *Sex and the Social Order*, New York, McGraw-Hill Book Co., 1946.

[3]A. Davis, "Socialization and Adolescent Personality," *Yearb. Nat. Soc. Stud. Educ.*, 1944, 43; 198–216.

[4]A. C. Kinsey, W. B. Pomeroy, and C. E. Martin, *Sexual Behavior in the Human Male*, Philadelphia, Saunders, 1948.

[5]A. Kardiner and L. Ovesey, *The Mark of Oppression*, New York, Norton, 1951.

[6]A. T. Childers, "Some Notes on Sex Mores among Negro Children," *Amer. J. Orthopsychiat.*, 1936, 6; 442–48.

[7]M. Brenman, "Urban Lower-Class Negro Girls," *Psychiatry*, 1943, 6; 307–24.

[8]W. F. Whyte, "A Slum Sex Code," *Amer. J. Sociol.*, 1943, 49; 24–31.

[9]R. Benedict, "Sex in Primitive Society," *Amer. J. Orthopsychiat.*, 1939, 9; 570–74 and R. Linton, *The Study of Man*, New York, Appleton, 1936.

[10]O. Lewis, "Manly Hearted Women among the North Piegan," *Amer. Anthrop.*, 1941, 43; 173–87.

[11]G. Devereaux, "Institutionalized Homosexuality of the Mohave Indians," *Hum. Biol.*, 1937, 9; 498–527.

[12]J. W. Macfarlane, "Study of Personality Development" (in R. G. Barker, J. S. Kounin, and H. F. Wright, *Child Behavior and Development*), New York, McGraw-Hill Book Co., 1943, 307–28.

[13]C. Tryon, "Evaluations of Adolescent Personality by Adolescents," *Monogr. Soc. Res. Child Developm.*, 1939, 4, No. 4, and "The Adolescent Peer Culture," *Yearb. Nat. Soc. Stud. Educ.*, 1944, 43; 217–39.

[14]G. H. Seward, "Sex Roles in Postwar Planning," *J. Soc. Psychol.*, 1944, 19; 163–85.

[15]M. Komarovsky, "Cultural Contradictions and Sex Roles," *Amer. J. Sociol.*, 1946, 52; 184–89.

[16]G. H. Seward, "Cultural Conflict and the Feminine Role," *J. Soc. Psychol.*, 1945, 22; 177–94.

[17]C. Kirkpatrick, "Techniques of Marital Adjustment," *Ann. Amer. Acad. Polit. Soc. Sci.*, 1932, 160; 178–83. J. Walters and R. H. Ojemann, "A Study of the Components of Adolescent Attitudes Concerning the Role of Women," *J. Soc. Psychol.*, 1952, 35; 101–10.

[18]E. A. Strecker, *Their Mothers' Sons: The Psychiatrist Examines an American Problem,* Philadelphia, J. B. Lippincott, 1946.

[19]L. P. Gardner, "A Survey of the Attitudes and Activities of Fathers," *J. Genet. Psychol.,* 1943, 63; 15–53. R. J. Tasch, "The Role of the Father in the Family," *J. Exp. Educ.,* 1952, 20; 319–61.

[20]K. M. Bowman, "The Challenge of Sex Offenders: Psychiatric Aspects of the Problem," *Ment. Hy.,* 1938, 22; 10–20. S. H. Ruskin, "Analysis of Sex Offenses among Male Psychiatric Patients," *Amer. J. Psychiat.,* 1941, 97; 955–68.

[21]F. A. Beach, "Execution of the Complete Masculine Copulatory Pattern by Sexually Receptive Female Rats," *J. Genet. Psychol.,* 1942, 60; 137–42, and "Female Mating Behavior Shown by Male Rats after Administration of Testosterone Propionate," *Endocrinology,* 1941, 29; 409–12. W. Craig, "Male Doves Reared in Isolation," *J. Animal Behav.,* 1914, 4; 121–33. M. Jenkins, "The Effect of Segregation on the Sex Behavior of the White Rat as Measured by the Obstruction Method," *Genet. Psychol. Monogr.,* 1938, 3; 457–571.

[22]W. M. East, "Sexual Offenders," *J. Nerv. Ment. Dis.,* 1946, 103; 626–66.

[23]C. Landis, A. T. Landis, and M. M. Bolles, *Sex in Development,* New York, Hoeber, 1940. P. Sloane and E. Karpinski, "Effects of Incest on the Participants," *Amer. J. Orthopsychiat.,* 1942, 12; 666–74.

[24]C. Landis, et al., op. cit. L. Bender and A. G. Grugett, Jr., "A Follow-up Report on Children Who Had Atypical Sexual Experience," *Amer. J. Orthopsychiat.,* 1952, 22; 825–37.

[25]L. Bender and A. Blau, "The Reaction of Children to Sexual Relations with Adults," *Amer. J. Orthopsychiat.,* 1937, 7; 500–18.

[26]W. M. East, op. cit. L. W. Ferguson, "Correlates of Marital Happiness," *J. Psychol.,* 1938, 6; 285–94. G. V. Hamilton, *A Research in Marriage,* New York, Boni, 1929. S. Harrison, "Psychogenic and Constitutional Factors in Homosexuality," *Psychiat. Quart.,* 1934, 8; 243–64.

[27]B. Apfelberg, C. Sugar, and A. Z. Pfeffer, "A Psychiatric Study of 250 Sex Offenders," *Amer. J. Psychiat.,* 1944, 100; 762–70. J. H. Conn, "The Chronic Offender," *J. Crim. Law and Criminol.,* 1942, 32; 631–35. J. Frosch and W. Bromberg, "The Sex Offender," *Amer. J. Orthopsychiat.,* 1939, 9; 761–76.

[28]B. Apfelberg, et al., op. cit.

[29]H. Licht (Paul Brandt), *Sexual Life in Ancient Greece,* London, Routledge, 1932. H. Blüher, *Die rolle der Erotik in der männlichen Gesellschaft,* 2 vols., Jena, E. Diederichs, 1921.

[30]R. Benedict, op. cit.

[31]M. C. Greco, "Social Psychological Differentials in the Initiation and Retention of Chronic Homosexuality," *Amer. Psychologist,* 1946, 1; 240(A).

[32]G. Devereaux and M. C. Moos, "The Social Structure of Prisons and the Organic Tensions," *J. Crim. Psychopathol.,* 1942, 4; 306–24.

[33]T. M. Abel, "Negro-White Interpersonal Relationships among Institutionalized Subnormal Girls," *Amer. J. Ment. Def.,* 1942, 46; 325–39, and "Negro-White Interpersonal Relationships in a Limited Environment," Trans. *N. Y. Acad. Sci.,* 1943, 5; 97–105.

[34]G. Devereaux and M. C. Moos, op. cit. H. Elkin, "Aggressive and Erotic Tendencies in Army Life," *Amer. J. Sociol.,* 1946, 51; 408–13.

[35]G. W. Henry, *Sex Variants,* 2 vols., New York, Hoeber, 1941. A. C. Kinsey, W. B. Pomeroy, and C. E. Martin, op. cit.

[36]J. Bauer, "Homosexuality as an Endocrinological, Psychological, and Genetic Problem," *J. Crim. Psychopath.,* 1940, 2; 188–97. T. Lang, "Studies in the Genetic Determination of Homosexuality," *J. Nerv. Ment. Dis.,* 1940, 92; 55–64.

[37]S. J. Glass and B. J. McKennon, "The Hormonal Aspects of Sex Reversed States," *West. J. Surg.,* 1937, 45; 467. A. Myerson and R. Neustadt, "The Bisexuality of Man," *J. Mt. Sinai Hosp.,* New York, 1942, 9; 668–78.

[38]H. E. Jones and K. Read, "Sex Education for the Preschool Child," *Hygeia,* 1941, 19; 360–62.

[39]A. Ellis, "The Sexual Psychology of Human Hermaphrodites," *Psychosom. Med.,* 1945, 7; 108–25.

[40]J. E. Finesinger, J. V. Meigs, and H. W. Sulkowitch, "Clinical, Psychiatric and

Psychoanalytic Study of Male Pesudohermaphroditism," *Amer. J. Obstet., Dis. Wom.,* 1942, 44; 310–17.

[41]J. Wortis, "Sex Taboos, Sex Offenders and the Law," *Amer. J. Orthopsychiat.,* 1939, 9; 554–64.

[42]D. M. Olkon and I. C. Sherman, "Eonism with Added Outstanding Psychopathic Features: A Unique Psychopathological Study," *J. Nerv. Ment. Dis.,* 1944, 99; 159–67.

[43]S. Liebman, "Homosexuality, Transvestism, and Psychosis: Study of a Case Treated with Electroshock," *J. Nerv. Ment. Dis.,* 1944, 99; 945–58.

[44]R. S. Banay and L. Davideff, "Apparent Recovery of a Sex Psychopath after Lobotomy," *J. Crim. Psychopathol.,* 1942, 4; 59–66.

[45]J. J. Honigman, "A Cultural Theory of Obscenity," *J. Crim. Psychopathol.,* 1944, 5; 715–33.

[46]B. Apfelberg, et al., op. cit. A. J. Arieff and D. B. Rotman, "Psychiatric Inventory of 100 Cases of Indecent Exposure," *J. Nerv. Ment. Dis.,* 1942, 96; 523–28. N. K. Rickles, *Exhibitionism,* Philadelphia, J. B. Lippincott, 1950.

[47]B. Apfelberg, et al., op. cit. J. H. Conn, op. cit. F. A. McKendry, "A Note on Homosexuality, Crime and the Newspapers," *J. Crim. Psychopathol.,* 1941, 2; 533–48.

[48]J. Frosch and W. Bromberg, op. cit.

[49]L. M. Terman, *Psychological Factors in Marital Happiness,* New York, McGraw-Hill Book Co., 1938. A. C. Kinsey et al., op. cit. A. C. Kinsey, W. B. Pomeroy, C. E. Martin, and P. H. Gebhard, *Sexual Behavior in the Human Female,* Philadelphia, Saunders, 1953.

[50]K. Frankenthal, "The Role of Sex in Modern Society," *Psychiatry,* 1945, 8; 19–25.

[51]F. E. Frazier, "The Negro Family" (in R. N. Anshen [ed.], *The Family: Its Function and Destiny*), New York, Harper, 1949, 142–58. A. Kardiner and L. Ovesey, op. cit.

[52]F. E. Frazier, "Sociologic Factors in the Formation of Sex Attitudes" (in P. H. Hoch and J. Zubin [eds.]), *Psychosexual Development in Health and Disease,* New York, Grune and Stratton, 1949, 244–55.

[53]A. T. Bingham, "Determinants of Sex Delinquency in Adolescent Girls Based on Intensive Studies of 500 Cases," *J. Crim. Law and Criminol.,* 1923, 13; 494–586.

[54]B. Johnson (chm.), "Sex Delinquency among Girls," a report of the Committee on Sex Delinquency among Young Girls, which met in New York, November 23–24, 1942, *J. Soc. Hy.,* 1943, 29; 492–501. M. L. Webb, "Delinquency in the Making; Patterns in the Development of Girl Sex Delinquency in the City of Seattle, with Recommendations for a Community Preventive Program," *J. Soc. Hy.,* 1943, 29; 502–10.

[55]R. May, *The Meaning of Anxiety,* New York, Ronald, 1950.

[56]S. Harrison, "A Comparative Study of Behavior Problems in Illegitimate and Legitimate Children," *Smith Coll. Sud. Soc. Work,* 1944, 15; 120–21 (A).

[57]J. F. Brown and D. W. Orr, "The Field-Theoretical Approach to Criminology," *J. Crim. Psychopathol.,* 1941–42, 3; 236–52.

[58]C. Landis, et al., op. cit.

[59]E. W. Burgess and L. S. Cottrell, Jr., *Predicting Success or Failure in Marriage,* New York, Prentice-Hall, 1939, A. H. Maslow, "Self-esteem (Dominance Feeling) and Sexuality in Women," *J. Soc. Psychol.,* 1942, 16; 259–94.

[60]R. L. Dickinson and L. Beam, "A Thousand Marriages: A Medical Study of Sex Adjustment," Baltimore, Williams and Wilkins, 1931. K. A. Menninger, "Impotence and Frigidity," *Bull. Menninger Clin.,* 1937, 1; 251–60.

[61]F. Znaniecki, "The Changing Cultural Ideals of the Family," *Marr. and Family Living,* 1941, 3; 58–62, 68.

[62]E. Fromm, "Man-Woman" (in M. Hughes [ed.], *The People in Your Life*), New York, Knopf, 1951, 3–27. E. Fromm, *"Sex and Character"* (in R. Anshen [ed.], *The Family*), New York, Harper, 1949, 375–92.

[63]M. Mead, *Male and Female: A Study of the Sexes in a Changing World,* New York, Morrow, 1949.

[64]F. Lundberg and M. F. Farnham, *Modern Woman; the Lost Sex,* New York, Harper & Bros., 1947.

[65]M. Komarovsky, *Women in the Modern World; Their Education and Their Dilemmas,* Boston, Little, Brown, 1953.

[66]G. H. Seward, op. cit., 2 and 14.

Chapter 2

PROSTITUTION IN THE UNITED STATES

by Walter C. Reckless, Ph.D.

PROFESSOR OF SOCIOLOGY, OHIO STATE UNIVERSITY

THE CONCERN ABOUT PROSTITUTION

In many countries, in times past, prostitution was considered a "necessary evil"—a sort of safety valve for the sexual drives of men. At the same time, the resort to prostitution by men was a part of the general pattern of the double standard of morality—men's ways as contrasted to the ways of respectable women. Modern society, especially in Western civilization, has increasingly challenged the double standard of morality as well as the concept of prostitution as a necessary evil.

The semi-official view as to why prostitution is a social problem and why it should be suppressed in the United States today is expressed by the American Social Hygiene Association, which cites the following counts against prostitution:

1. It strikes at the home and family, breeding deceit and disloyalty, degrading the marriage relation, undermining character and self-control.

2. It injures public health, affording the greatest opportunity for the spread of venereal disease.

3. It exploits young people for the profit of "third-party" interests. Both boys and girls are victimized.

4. It increases graft, allying itself with other lawless, anti-social forces which corrupt susceptible public officials.

5. It encourages sex delinquency, since it offers dangerous outlets to the play impulse of youth and promotes immature sex curiosity and leads to promiscuity.

6. It undermines national defense strength by striking at the health of manpower and weakening moral integrity.[1]

It seems safe to assume that these points represent the prevailing view of the public as well as the view which is officially expressed by most local, state, and federal governments. Tacit, and sometimes open, disagreement with these points is often expressed by officials, medical doctors, and certain segments of the public, but such disagreement is a minority view.

I would put the case against prostitution in the United States in this way: it is a threat to sex morality, a threat to family life, a threat to health, a threat to the welfare of vulnerable girls and women, and a threat to local government. It should be expected that in other modern countries the concern about prostitution would take a different form. It is likely, however, that practically all nations would be concerned about the venereal disease aspect of prostitution and the welfare of women and children. The moral issue and the issue of corruption of local government are likely to be of greater concern in the United States than in other countries.

NOT AN INSTITUTION IN U. S.

The nearest approach which prostitution made to being an institution in the United States was during the period of the toleration policy which many police departments followed a generation ago. Police in those days took little action against the practice of prostitution in so-called segregrated districts. One could not tell whether this was due to the fact that police earnestly believed that prostitution could be controlled only by some sort of corralling in a district where they could keep an eye on it or to the fact that police made arrangements with keepers of houses to give "protection" in return for monetary and other considerations. The sporting public and political machines believed in a "live-and-let-live" policy for prostitution and houses of prostitution. Many doctors also claimed that open prostitution was a necessary evil, as a safety valve to the aggressions of the polygamous male. The majority opinion of the United States was not in favor of tolerated houses of ill fame. An anti-vice crusade gathered momentum before World War I, forcing the law-enforcement officials and the minority public to recognize that prostitution was not an accepted institution. This was the main achievement of the anti-vice crusades rather than the permanent closing of houses of prostitution.

FICTITIOUS WHITE-SLAVE TRAFFIC

The United States has not been the scene for a heavy and elaborate traffic in prostitutes, incidental to recruiting women for houses of prostitution. Concurrent with the anti-vice crusade was the anti-white-slavery movement. The American public, particularly the religious and middle-class part of it, became greatly alarmed and agitated. But when looked for, the white-slave traffic could not be found in proportions even remotely approximating the dimensions of rumor propaganda, and the great anti-white-slave prosecutor of Chicago, Clifford Roe, had little real evidence of an organized traffic in women.[2] The Chicago Vice Commission report found little evidence for a traffic;[3] the New York Commission,[4] likewise. Some recruitment did take place a generation ago and still does take place, but not on a large or important scale. Recruitment of women and girls for prostitution in the United States never approached the vicious proportions it used to have in the Far East, North Africa, Central Europe, and Latin America.[5] There appears to be good evidence to believe that the traffic in women and girls is abating in most regions of the world.[6]

One direct legislative result of the anti-white-slavery crusade was the passing of the federal Mann Act, which was approved about the beginning of World War I. This law gave the United States Government the right to prosecute cases in which a woman was transported over state lines for immoral purposes. It aimed at the curtailment of recruitment of girls and women for houses of prostitution. Actually there have been few instances of actual white-slave cases in more than a generation.[7] Most of the cases prosecuted under the Mann Act have been those of men who unwittingly took a woman over state boundaries, paid her expenses, and was found to have had sex relations with her. The arrangements were personal and not for recruitment into prostitution.

There were six, four, two, and eleven cases filed for importing aliens for prostitution in 1948, 1949, 1950, and 1951 consecutively (fiscal years) in the United States, and there were 261, 191, 238, and 229 cases filed under interstate transportation for prostitution (Mann Act) in 1948, 1949, 1950, and 1951 consecutively (fiscal years) in the United States. The United States reported to the United Nations that during the fiscal years 1948–50 there were only three cases of international traffic in women: one case involving a woman from Cuba and an alien man; a second involving a woman and a man, both residents of Cuba; a third involving a U. S. citizen and two prostitutes from Canada.[8]

PROSTITUTION AS A CRIME

Prostitution or any connection with it is a crime in the United States. The offenses of soliciting for prostitution or being in houses of prostitution are misdemeanors and call for fines and/or sentences for less than a year. Pandering is usually a felony, although, like rape, it is hard to get a clear case. In the United States the prostitutes and the "keepers" are the ones who have been most drastically acted on by law enforcement. The male customers have never been dealt with drastically. If taken down to the police stations, they usually are let go on a small bond, which is forfeited for non-appearance at court hearing, which in turn is expected. The male runners and hangers-on of houses of prostitution are usually dealt with in about the same category as keepers—not too severely. The real keepers or owners are seldom prosecuted in the United States because they have the immunity through protection or the "fix."[9] Their hirelings, who happen to be on the premises at the time of a raid, usually "take the rap" for them. This is especially true where syndicates of houses of prostitution are operated by underworld characters who have affiliations with gangsters and corrupt political machines in American cities.

According to FBI reports, 28,094 persons were charged and held for prosecution by the police for prostitution and commercialized vice in the year 1952. As would be expected, the rate of arrest for these offenses is the greatest in the largest cities. Included under this offense listing are such offenses as soliciting for or practicing prostitution, keeping a bawdyhouse, procuring, detaining against will, and transporting. Out of twenty-five types of offenses reported to the FBI, prostitution and commercialized vice ranked fourteenth in volume rate in the 1952 figures. Drunkenness ranked second; disorderly conduct, third; gambling, ninth; liquor laws, eleventh; sex offenses (not rape and not prostitution), sixteenth; narcotic drug laws, twentieth— to give some idea of incidence comparison.[10]

SUPPRESSION DURING WAR II AND POSTWAR REACTION

The operations of solicitors in public places and the operations of houses of prostitution are the most vulnerable to law-enforcement effort, if and when made, in the United States. That prostitution, in its openly available form, can be suppressed to almost a vanishing point was borne out by experience during World War II.[11] Under powers to proceed against prostitution in military and defense-factory centers, the federal government, through the May Act, held the whip hand over local law-enforcement authorities and caused them really to clamp down. Previous to this experience local law enforcement in American cities had blown hot and cold in its policy toward the business of prostitution. The result was that the business of open prostitution was never seriously curtailed for any sustained period of time. The provisions of the May Act were extended permanently by the Congress, approved by the President, May 15, 1946.[12]

Soon after the termination of World War II some relaxation in control was noted by the field reports of the American Social Hygiene Association.[13] An independent observer also reported that the business of prostitution staged a post-war comeback.[14] Since 1948, however, the field agents of the American Social Hygiene Association reported that conditions have improved, and it appears that open prostitution in the United States is less in evidence than ever before.[15]

Whether soliciting in public places and the open operation of brothels will return to their prewar effrontery is conjectural. That prostitution in its less open forms will be curtailed in the United States is doubtful. Law enforcement would need much greater goading than it had under the May Act in order to eradicate and suppress the sub rosa practice of prostitution; it would need almost prohibitively expensive investigational service to show results. One of the cheapest and most effective ways to combat the less open forms of prostitution is to have hotel management do a thorough job of self-discipline in their own hostelries and not hoodwink sub rosa and extra-territorial practice of prostitution in their establishments.

PROSTITUTION AS A TRADE OR A SCHEME OF LIFE

Prostitution has been and is a trade or vocation, which is practiced at quite different levels of operation, according to the point at which the woman drifts into prostitution and gravitates after she is in. The author has described elsewhere modern operational types of prostitutes: the brothel prostitute; the call-girl prostitute, who is available by telephone via hotel intermediaries; the street or public prostitute, who makes direct solicitations and uses her own arrangements for assignation; the unorganized professional prostitute, who operates in her own apartment and reaches the upper class of patrons.[16] The prostitute, for the most part, is aware that she plies an illegal trade, but for various reasons, not clearly understood, she is willing to take the risk just as others are willing to take occupational risks. She may be a lucky or well-organized person who manages to keep away from involvement with law-enforcement officials, venereal infection, gynecological involvements, pimps, drugs, alcoholism, and shoplifting. Usually she is somewhat less fortunate than this and falls victim to one or more of these more frequent occupational risks. Most prostitutes know that there are occupational risks prior to their entrance into the trade. The prostitute does not usually conceive of herself as a criminal because she plies an illegal trade. She does not think herself as reprehensible as the non-commercially promiscuous girl, who is likely to be looked down upon because of undermining competition.

THE PROSTITUTE IN TERMS OF PROMISCUITY

After ten years' experience in attempting to do a case-work treatment job with prostitutes in the city of Baltimore, Miss Mazie F. Rappaport comes to the conclusion that it is practically impossible to define or find "the prostitute personality." She looks upon prostitution or the prostitute as a legal term and contends that it is more appropriate to view the prostitute as a promiscuous girl or woman. Prostitutes, in the sense of promiscuous women, have one basic common denominator, according to Miss Rappaport, namely "their inability to develop with another human being a relationship with meaning and continuity."[17] The sexually promiscuous girl who becomes a prostitute is one who is ordinarily mobile, uses aliases, evades police and family, lacks self-respect, is unable to put down any social roots, is unable to allow her personal possessions to have any real meaning for her. "Beneath the hard shell, the casualness or the sharp and ready humor of the promiscuous girl, there is likely to be an unhappy, bitter person no longer in control of her own life."[18] Miss Rappaport observes some changes in the promiscuous girl during the last ten years. She is less likely to be a non-resident of Baltimore. She is much less likely to have left a small town to come to the big city or to follow servicemen to neighboring camps.[19]

WOMEN ASSIST WOMEN

The American girls drift into prostitution without much help from men directly. They find their way themselves. If they have any aids to help them get placed, their own women associates who know the ropes are likely to be the main instrumentalities. Women help women to start in prostitution more than men.[20] There are pimps who dominate the lives and finances of prostitutes, but this parasitism is not the rule. The few American girls who have pimps acquire them after they get into their vocation rather than before. It is rare, indeed, to find a case in the United States in which a girl who has never been in prostitution was placed into it by a pimp.

VULNERABILITY FOR DRIFT INTO PROSTITUTION

The most vulnerable girl for drifting into prostitution is the girl of poor personal and social resources.[21] It may be the girl from a poor family or a disorganized family, a girl without much education and without vocational skills, a girl without good instrumental contacts for finding a job, a place to live, and a respectable world in which to live.[22] It may be the disorganized girl, the girl lacking good acumen, the emotionally disturbed girl, the girl showing psychopathic trends and other mental vagaries. Two studies[23] of women delinquents in the United States, composed largely of prostitutes, confirm this position. Kemp's study of Copenhagen prostitutes gives added support to this view.[24]

Most observers agree that the girl who becomes a prostitute has had previous sex experience, mostly unfortunate, in or out of wedlock. The sexually deviate girl or woman of good social and personal resources is not a likely risk for prostitution. She is able to command a career usually on a much higher level than prostitution, either in or out of marriage. The girl of poor social and personal resources, plus previous unfortunate sex experience, is the one, we may assume, who is most vulnerable to the drift into prostitution. However, if the drift into prostitution was merely determined by these vulnerabilities, we should then expect to find a very much larger proportion of the sex-delinquent girls who get referred to our juvenile courts and get sent to our training schools (for delinquent girls) being reported as ultimately becoming prostitutes. Evidently there is a factor in addition to vulnerability. The best guess is that this factor consists of contact with persons in or on the fringe of prostitution. The vulnerable girl, it can be assumed, must be shown the way by associates. The hypothesis presented earlier may be repeated again at this point, namely, that we should expect the practitioners of prostitution to show girls and women the way into prostitution in the United States more so than panderers, pimps, and other males associated with it.

In many instances the practice of prostitution is a parallel drift. The girl is already an entertainer, a barmaid, a waitress, a domestic. She has already had unfortunate sex experience. She may have received attentions for presents or even money. The movement over to prostitution from this parallel stream is not too difficult. The drift into prostitution can be much more downward and sudden, from so-called better circumstances. However, it is best to assume that there has been a parallel drift prior to entrance.

PSYCHIC TRAUMA AND GUILT

How traumatic the actual entrance into prostitution is is not known. For those of the quick descent it can be assumed that the psychic trauma is great. For those of prepared entrance from parallel or closely allied schemes of life it can be assumed that the trauma is slight, other things being equal. These girls quite likely accommodate themselves to their new trade as readily as they would to any other shift in job.

There is no reason to believe that the modern American prostitute looks upon herself as a "lost woman" when she enters into the actual practice of prostitution. However, one might expect a possible class differential in the matter of handling the "guilt reaction" when becoming a prostitute. Girls from middle-class upbringing might be expected to show more psychic trauma, guilt reactions, and sense of degradation and might be more neurotic about their situation than girls from the lower classes of society, who have been less protected and have a less disturbing set of moral values. Just how the individual girl handles the crisis of entrance into prostitution is something which the psychiatrists and psychologists should determine. It is possible that the subnormal girl, the emotionally disturbed girl, and the psychopathic girl present problems at initial orientation to prostitution.

SOCIAL PROCESSING

After the girl is in prostitution the "life" or experience does something to her, just as the stage, newspaper reporting, professional baseball, the merchant marine, hoboing do things to people. Something happens to the attitudes, habits, schemes of values of the prostitute herself. She is socially processed by the "life" itself and by its traditions which are carried by other prostitutes. She must accept the role of a sexual servant of men. She tends to develop an argot, special arts and services, bartering patterns, impersonality, and rationalizations for the life of a prostitute. Presumably she can acquire many of the patterns of a prostitute by herself, but it is more likely that she is assisted by her co-workers, who soon put her wise.

There is a long tradition back of prostitution. It is one of the world's oldest professions; almost as old as trade itself. Prostitution has a lore, and the current practitioners get some of this lore from previous practitioners and will hand something over in turn to the neophytes. This heritage of prostitution is not transmitted to our girls in the United States as completely as it was to the entrants into prostitution in Japan, China, India, the Near East, North Africa, Southern Europe, and Latin America in previous years.

PROSTITUTION NOT A CASTE IN THE UNITED STATES

Prostitutes in the United States form less of a social caste than elsewhere. They move in and out of prostitution with greater ease in accordance with greater freedom of movement and action, which again are characteristic of American society. When prostitution is a caste vocation and prostitutes form a social caste, the lore of prostitution is more readily transmitted to the neophytes.

If we had the caste system of prostitution in the United States the social processing of the personalities of the prostitutes would be much more complete and the possibility of their rehabilitation would be much more difficult. The nearest approach to the caste system of prostitution in the United States was the practice of prostitution in the brothels of the so-called "red-light" districts. The girl who drifted into prostitution in the "segregated districts" had some difficulty in getting out of the life, although this was not too difficult. However, the concentrated, open life of prostitution in these tolerated areas was conducive to the transmission of heritages of prostitution and the social processing of women by underworld society.[25]

DOWNWARD DRIFT AND DEMORALIZATION

Something happens to a prostitute because she practices the life of a prostitute and comes into contact with carriers of the heritages of prostitution. After the woman has become a prostitute there are various tendencies. Undoubtedly a small number of prostitutes make certain advancements in their scale of living and in their political and clientele contacts. They are probably the more resourceful individuals, who are able to rise above the occupational risks of prostitution, such as arrests and jail sentences, venereal infection, sickness, and marginal living. However, the drift is more likely to go the other way, namely, downward. When it does, the process can be called demoralization. The nth degree of demoralization is a derelict status. The occupational hazards are real in prostitution. The chances of arrest, infection, sickness are great. The chances of resorting to alcoholism and drugs as palliatives and escapes are great. The chances to have demoralizing connections with crime and the underworld are good. The chances of resorting to "jackrolling" and shoplifting are fair. It is not easy to resist the demoralizing force of the occupational risks in prostitution, although it probably takes years of downward drift before a prostitute becomes a complete derelict. While the long-time drift in prostitution is usually to lower levels of adjustment to life, it is possible for the prostitutes in the United States to escape by their own election or to be helped to escape.

THE SOCIAL PROTECTION PROGRAM

During World War II a social protection program for the control of the problem of prostitution emerged as a national policy under the immediate direction of the Social Protection Division of the Federal Security Agency.[26] The approach to the problem of prostitution as it finally developed was multilateral; that is, an attack from every and all sides. The approach involved the co-ordination of local, state, and national agencies and resources which touched the problem in any effective way: adequate legislation and good law enforcement, venereal-disease control, rehabilitation services for promiscuous girls and women at court, in detention, and in the community, and a breadth of preventive measures. Field agents of the Social Protection Division were available to local communities and states who were actively interested in coming to grips with any or several aspects of America's so-called "fifth column," as prostitution and venereal disease were patriotically labeled. In some instances federal aid was granted to help initiate programs of control of prostitution and venereal disease. The lessons learned from this experience were manifold, but they can be reduced in the main to these points: a national policy is possible; co-ordination of local, state, and national resources is essential; federal aid is necessary; a many-sided community approach to the problem is most effective, involving law enforcement and venereal-disease control, rehabilitation of the individual girl or woman, and preventive measures. The second session of the Seventy-ninth Congress gave this program a definite setback when it refused to continue social protection assistance to the states.

REHABILITATION OF THE PROSTITUTE

The resources to rehabilitate prostitutes in the United States are weak and spotty, although they compare favorably with those in other countries.[27] The jail and workhouse have been the primary resources heretofore. The programs here are custodial in the main, with attention in recent years to the infectious state of the committed prostitutes. Usually the girls are held in these institutions for short sentences until they are considered to be in a non-infectious state. The few jails and workhouses which have a social-service staff and a "training" program are in a position to do something more constructive for the rehabilitation of the individual girl or woman than those institutions which have merely a custodial and medical program. The state reformatories for women sometimes receive habitual prostitutes and prostitutes committed on other charges. One should expect the women's reformatories to have a better training program and better follow-up planning and supervision than the average local jail and workhouse.[28]

Where police departments have well-developed women's bureaus,[29] whose policewomen are able to do short-contact work with the girls needing help and wanting help, a big step forward in the rehabilitation of prostitutes is taken. A policewomen's bureau, such as exists in the Metropolitan Police Department of the District of Columbia, in which the staff consists of trained social workers, is a real asset to a community both for prevention as well as rehabilitation. The reality is, however, that there are few well-developed policewomen's bureaus in the United States. A manual of good practice for policewomen to follow in their work with women and girls in need of protection against moral hazards has been prepared and is available.[30]

Since prostitution as a practice is mainly a misdemeanor, the handling of cases usually comes before the lower courts in the United States. Few of these have full-time paid probation service, let alone a probation service approximating case work. Adequate probation service on a case-work basis can be one of the most effective agencies of rehabilitation.

Likewise, at the public tax-paying level, local health departments have frequently operated special clinics for the treatment of venereally infected persons and have supplied clinical service in jails and workhouses.

At the voluntary and private support level, there have been shelters and homes for unfortunate women, mostly under religious auspices. They, too, have been limited in their retraining programs and program for follow-up help after the woman or girl is released. Residence homes or hostels, available to ex-prostitutes, have been few and far between.

THE CASE-WORK APPROACH

The problem of rehabilitation, over and above the medical and training aspects of institutional care, is one of helping the woman or girl understand her needs, arriving at a state of wanting to accept help, and of developing a plan with the client which can effectively keep her from drifting back into prostitution because of the lack of support, proper lodging, and persons interested in her welfare.

This sort of rehabilitation service was scarce before World War II and is still scarce.[31] Private and public case-work agencies are seldom able to be of much help. Their limitations of intake and service, made necessary by local policy and budget, prevent their usefulness in this special area. Besides, there has been no precedent set by the prostitutes themselves for accepting voluntarily the services of case workers. As a matter of fact, one might even say there is a sort of barrier against accepting help from case workers. Law-enforcement personnel, court personnel, jail and workhouse personnel, as well as personnel in private shelters and rescue missions, unless they are trained in social work or have good understanding as to how to use case-work-agency services, likewise are not disposed to refer girls and women to case-work agencies.

However, some advance was made during World War II, assisted in part by the field consulting services of the federal social protection program, toward setting up channels for referral of women to case-work agencies.[32] As an example, mention can be made of the plan developed in Baltimore, Maryland.[33]

PROTECTIVE SERVICE OF THE DEPARTMENT OF PUBLIC WELFARE, BALTIMORE, MARYLAND.

This service, one of four divisions of the Department of Public Welfare, was established as an outgrowth of the attempt in Baltimore to marshal community forces to control the carriers of venereal disease. It specifically was created to provide case-work services for the "known" promiscuous girls and the known prostitutes.

Cases are referred by the law-enforcement and health agencies and the penal institutions. Effort is made to acquaint the girls and women with the service and to help them decide whether they voluntarily want to accept help. Clients who voluntarily request help are not held under any court order.

However, girls and women are referred to the service by the courts and police magistrates, usually for a one-year period of probation supervision. The service assumes probation authority in these cases. It capitalizes on this authority given it by the court and uses it constructively.

The girls and women are given immediate help as needs dictate: help in finding a job, in providing shelter, advance in money until first payday, medical service, transportation home, and so forth.

The clients are "eligible" so long as they try to quit prostitution and promiscuity. This eligibility is continually re-evaluated with the girls through the case movement. The girl "must come to grips with the fact that [prostitution] is not the way she wants to live before she can move away from it."

According to reports, the experience of this service shows that girls can quit prostitution and that it is easier for the agency to help and the girl to be helped if she comes to the agency on probation, since the authority of the court is a "powerful dynamic" for the girls.

TREATMENT-RESPONSE TYPES

While it has been difficult for the usual public or private case-work agency to meet the needs, rehabilitation-wise, of prostitutes and promiscuous girls and women, there is growing evidence to support the notion that some prostitutes do not respond favorably to case-work plans or any sort of social treatment, and not because they have any trade prejudices toward social workers. On the other hand, there seem to be certain types of cases which respond much more readily. Marsh attempted to formulate the treatment-response types which might be expected to confront the case-work agencies in New York City.

The first is composed of those who are "young" in the business, a factor not necessarily related to chronological age, and who have not established habit patterns or personal connections that are hard to break. Rehabilitation may well follow referral to a private social agency if it is equipped to ascertain the character of the pressures which resulted in prostitution and ready and able to meet the needs both financial and emotional which are revealed.

The second group, usually with a long history of sexual delinquency, is composed of those who are disillusioned as to the satisfactions they once thought

*were to be found in the business, or who never really wanted to engage in it.
Included here are the women who prostitute themselves to obtain money to buy
drugs, where prostitution is a secondary effect of the drug habit. This group
obviously needs more help of all types—medical and social—and over a longer
period than those in the first category. In both, the desire on the part of the
individual to change her way of living is the* sine qua non *for effective case work.
The complex of emotional problems of most of these women means, however,
that the client is not likely to show initiative in the case-work relationship, a factor which needs to be faced and dealt with both by the agency and case worker.*

*A third group is composed of women who engage in prostitution for no other
reason than to obtain a none too secure livelihood. Provision for comparable
financial security, with the added satisfaction which comes from living in a
socially acceptable fashion, can serve the need of this group. While it cannot
be stated with certainty, it is probable that many Negro recidivists, especially
those in the early years, are in this class.*

*The fourth group is composed of those not likely to respond voluntarily to any
social plan. It includes the women for whom prostitution has no moral or social
significance, but is simply a more successful way of making money by which to
obtain luxuries as well as necessities. There are also women whose connections
with rackets and racketeers have greater strength and are more satisfying to
them than any plan that a social agency can offer. For some the satisfaction
may come from the element of danger and excitement that such connections
possess. The mentally defective and the psychotic obviously require hospitalization or institutionalization if the community is to be protected, and they, also,
fall in this fourth group. In addition, certain women, because of psychically
traumatic experiences, are suspicious of the good will of others and reject any
and all offers of help.*[34]

DIRECT PREVENTIVE MEASURES

Since it is usually the sexually promiscuous girl who is vulnerable to
prostitution, an excellent place to do prevention work is by readjusting
the sexually delinquent girls that come to the attention of juvenile courts
and girls' training schools. At the juvenile-court level the problem is one
of having adequate probationary case-work service for the girls and good
local resources to use in the social-treatment process. At the training-school
level the problem is to have personnel and program which can do an effective
job of retaining sexually delinquent girls and which can effectively prepare
them for release and effectively supervise them on release.

Since girls seem to enter prostitution because of the lack of resources, it
would appear secondly that another excellent place to do preventive work
would be at the community level, where the girl or woman is left on her own.
The Travelers Aid work for stranded and out-of-town persons is covering an
important area of hazard. Surveillance of stations and public places by
policewomen in the interest of spotting girls on the loose is another measure

of preventive service. Provision for lodging for homeless girls, especially those who are recent and unsophisticated migrants to the large cities, has likewise been conceived as important. Protection for the woman in the job-finding process has also contributed its share to preventive work. The operations of unscrupulous private employment agencies have been seriously curtailed in the United States.

Since places of moral hazard are the places where sex delinquency can be engendered and where women can meet women and men who have contacts with the underworld and with the practice of prostitution, it would appear thirdly that here is another important area for preventive work. Legislation has attempted to protect minors from such hazards, but it is not able in the United States to protect women over twenty-one from these hazards. The hazards are mainly in recreational centers and centers of leisure time, especially where liquor is sold. There are hazards in certain fields of work for women workers, especially waitresses and entertainers, again where liquor is sold and the hours of night life are long. No matter how completely the laws may give protection to women and girls, it is up to the law-enforcement authorities to do a good surveillance job and to elicit good co-operation from the owners of places of moral hazard. A well-organized policewomen's bureau is one of the most effective ways of covering this particular area of prevention.

INDIRECT PREVENTION

While these three approaches to the prevention of prostitution in America are the most direct, there are other approaches which are less immediate and less direct. The potentially most important one of these indirect approaches is sex education. Practically it is hard to apply at the right time and the right place. The recipe for effective sex education in the home and the school has not been found, although considerable effort is being made. Marriage counseling, available locally for young persons, likewise has excellent theoretical possibilities. The problem here is to establish local counseling service and then get the most vulnerable young people to seek help from the counseling agency. The same comment can be made for vocational-guidance and vocational-education programs. Prevention of prostitution can proceed still more indirectly. Claims are made that better housing can help, that prohibition can help, that social security can help, and so forth. Attention, however, needs to be called to the point that the further we travel away from the factors which are specifically close to the drift into prostitution, the less likelihood that the preventive effort will be effective.

If the experts in this field could develop an "aimed" approach, specially aimed at the processes by which women get into prostitution, our society could make intelligent progress with its preventive efforts.

The first three suggestions given consideration for good preventive potentials have the virtue of being related to the processes by which girls and women become prostitutes. They cover elements mainly in the confronting environment or situation. How to give girls and women who as personalities are vulnerable to sex delinquency and prostitution the moral fiber, the maturity, the stability, the emotional satisfaction necessary to prevent their own drift into prostitution is a much different matter. Theoretically one can say that counseling, psychotherapy, group therapy, and mental hygiene contain the potentialities for diverting personalities from lower levels of adjustment in life. There are some efforts along these lines. But the coverage is very, very poor and the cost is tremendous.

NOTES

[1]*Journal of Social Hygiene,* Vol. 35, No. 4, April 1949, p. 166. Adapted and paraphrased.

[2]Walter C. Reckless, *Vice in Chicago,* 1933, pp. 36–39.

[3]The Vice Commission of Chicago, *The Social Evil in Chicago,* Chicago, 1911, pp. 176–77.

[4]Edwin R. A. Seligman, *The Social Evil in New York,* second edition of the Committee of Fifteen report, New York, 1912, p. 27.

[5]League of Nations, Report to the Council, *Commission of Enquiry into Traffic in Women and Children in the East,* Official No. C 849. M393, 1932 IV, Geneva, 1933, pp. 22–96.

[6]United Nations, Economic and Social Council, *Traffic in Women and Children,* summary of annual reports for the period 1948–50, prepared by the Secretariat, August 25, 1952, New York.

[7]John Edgar Hoover, "Organized Protection against Organized Predatory Crimes: V. White Slave Traffic," *Journal of Criminal Law and Criminology,* Vol. 24, 1933–34, pp. 480–81.

[8]United Nations, *Economic and Social Council,* op. cit., pp. 21–22, 23.

[9]One of the most notorious and dramatic exceptions is the case of Charles (Lucky) Luciano, who was committed to prison from New York City in 1936 for "compulsory prostitution" operations. Luciano was the chief operator of organized prostitution in New York City at the time and was prosecuted by Thomas Dewey, who was then prosecutor. On January 3, 1946, Dewey, now governor of New York, commuted Luciano's sentence so as to allow his deportation to Italy, which took place February 10, 1946.

[10]Federal Bureau of Investigation, *Uniform Crime Reports,* Vol. IV, No. 1, 1953, pp. 50–51.

[11]Philip S. Broughton, *Prostitution and the War,* Public Affairs Pamphlet No. 65, New York, 1944; Joanna C. Colcord, "Fighting Prostitution," *Survey Midmonthly,* Vol. 78, No. 8, August 1942, pp. 214–15.

[12]See House of Representatives, bill no. 6305, Seventy-ninth Congress, 2nd session.

[13]*Journal of Social Hygiene,* Vol. 32, No. 5, May 1946, p. 226.

[14]Albert Deutsch, "Prostitution Racket is Back," *American Mercury,* Vol. 63, September 1946, pp. 270–77.

[15]Paul M. Kinsie, "Prostitution—Then and Now," *Journal of Social Hygiene,* Vol. 39,

June 1953, pp. 246–47; see also "Prostitution Conditions in the U.S.A.: A 12-Year Survey," *Journal of Social Hygiene,* Vol. 38, April 1952, pp. 186–87.

[16]Walter C. Reckless, *The Crime Problem,* New York, 1950, p. 226.

[17]Mazie F. Rappaport, "After 10 Years: Helping Prostitutes Help Themselves," *Journal of Social Hygiene,* Vol. 39, May 1953, p. 209.

[18]Ibid., pp. 211–12.

[19]Ibid., p. 212.

[20]This point is borne out partly by a Copenhagen study of 530 prostitutes. The immediate cause for 13 and 8 per cent of the women entering prostitution was found to be influence of sisters and women friends and influence of a pimp, respectively. See Tage Kemp, *Prostitution,* Copenhagen, 1936, p. 190.

[21]Walter C. Reckless, "A Sociologist Looks at Prostitution," *Federal Probation,* Vol. 7, No. 2, 1943, p. 13.

[22]One must be prepared for exceptions, as in the instance of a wealthy call girl reported by *Time,* Feb. 2, 1953, p. 20.

[23]The earlier of the two studies is by Mabel Ruth Fernald, et al., *A Study of Women Delinquents in New York State,* New York, 1920. "We note two lines of influence which seem to have a bearing on the problem of delinquency among women, namely, (1) poor economic background with few advantages or opportunities, including such conditions as poor homes, very limited school opportunity, early age at starting work, and meager industrial training; and (2) a somewhat inferior mentality." (p. 525) The later of the two studies is by Sheldon and Eleanor T. Glueck, *Five Hundred Delinquent Women,* New York, 1934. It was found that the women "were born and bred in households in which poverty or near poverty and its attendant evils and miseries were the common lot. Their parents were on the whole of low mentality and in large measure illiterate. There was misunderstanding and friction. The moral standards of a great many of these families were low. The disciplinary practices of the parents were often unintelligent or worse. An abnormally high proportion of the homes were early broken by the death, desertion, or divorce of the parents. The women are themselves on the whole a sorry lot. Burdened with feeble-mindedness, psychopathic personality, and marked emotional instability, a large proportion of them found it difficult to survive by legitimate means. In educational achievement they fell considerably below the average. Few had the advantage of vocational guidance or training. Too early in life most of them were thrown into the industrial maelstrom. Employed largely as factory hands, or domestics, their competency as workers ranged as a rule from only fair to poor; their status was essentially that of irregular workers; their earnings were miserably low." (Pp. 299–300.)

[24]Kemp found that varying degrees of defective intelligence and psychopathy were the most frequent mental abnormalities among the 530 Copenhagen prostitutes. Hypersexuality or sex abnormality was discovered only infrequently, while mental disease among them was rare. Whether abnormal or normal, the prostitutes displayed varying amounts of criminality, wanderlust, alcoholism, work shyness, marital instability, characterological debility, and rudimentary sentiment development. The immediate causes for entrance into prostitution were found to be situational factors such as poverty and dire need, fondness of dancing and restaurant life, influence of associates, and so forth. The overwhelming majority of the prostitutes came from the servant class (81 per cent) and they had emerged out of unfavorable childhood environments. Op cit., pp. 39, 121, 174, 190.

[25]Kemp's observations oppose somewhat the view that prostitutes are socially processed by their life and experience. He contends that the Copenhagen prostitutes did not bear evidence of their way of living, except in instances of the older, coarse prostitutes. He claims there is no longer a "harlot type." Op. cit., pp. 122–23. My interpretation of Kemp's observations is that he denies finding the earmarks of a caste of prostitution, which is in line with what we should expect in a modern Western city. However, I doubt that he would deny the existence of the subtler effects of non-caste prostitution on the social attitudes, values, and habits of the prostitutes.

[26]Eliot Ness, "Federal Government's Program in Attacking the Problem of Prostitution," *Federal Probation,* Vol. 7, No. 2, pp. 17–19; Raymond F. Clapp, "Social Treatment of Prostitutes and Promiscuous Women," ibid., pp. 23–27; Social Protection Division, Federal Security Agency, Challenge to Community Action, Washington, D.C., 1945.

[27]League of Nations, *Enquiry into Measures of Rehabilitation of Prostitutes,* Part III and Part IV, Official No. C83. M.43. 1939. IV. Geneva, July 1, 1939.

[28]Miriam van Waters, "Study and Treatment of Persons Charged with Prostitution,"

Federal Probation, Vol. 7, No. 2, pp. 27–30; also Helen Hironimus, "Survey of 100 May Act Violators Committed to the Federal Reformatory for Women," ibid., pp. 31–34.

[29]Captain Rhoda J. Milliken, "The Role of the Police Woman's Bureau in Combatting Prostitution," ibid., pp. 20–22.

[30]The National Advisory Police Committee on Social Protection of the Federal Security Agency, *Techniques of Law Enforcement in the Use of Police Women with Special Reference to Social Protection,* no date, Washington, D.C.

[31]Marguerite Marsh, *Prostitutes in New York City: Their Apprehension, Trial and Treatment, July 1939–June 1940,* Welfare Council of New York City, pp. 121–25, June 1941.

[32]See Walter C. Reckless, "A Sociologist Looks at Prostitution," op. cit., pp. 14–15, for a preliminary statement on the Louisville, Kentucky, plan of assigning case workers to the workhouse from the Municipal Bureau of Social Service, to develop release plans with the prostitutes prior to actual release from custody.

[33]Summarized from Mazie F. Rappaport, "A Social Agency Helps the Prostitute on Probation," *National Probation Association Yearbook,* New York, 1945, pp. 124–35; also Rappaport, op. cit., pp. 209–15.

[34]Marsh, op. cit., pp. 122–23.

Chapter 3

VENEREAL DISEASES

by R. A. Vonderlehr, M.D.

MEDICAL DIRECTOR, COMMUNICABLE DISEASE CENTER, U. S. PUBLIC HEALTH SERVICE, ATLANTA, GEORGIA

Venereal disease has been a cause of maladjustment in marriage in all civilized countries. There are three common venereal diseases and two others which seldom occur in the Temperate Zone but are more frequent in the tropics. The three common venereal diseases are, in order of most frequent occurrence, gonorrhea, syphilis, and chancroid. The uncommon ones are known by the technical names granuloma inguinale and lymphogranuloma venereum.

Gonorrhea and chancroid have existed in civilized communities for centuries; they were known in the Orient more than five thousand years ago and occurred in European countries before the time of Columbus. There is some doubt regarding the origin of syphilis. Two schools of thought exist—one, that the disease originated in the Western Hemisphere and was carried to European and Asiatic countries after the explorations of Columbus and those who followed him; the other theory is that it existed in Europe and Asia before Columbus' time but was confused with other diseases.

GONORRHEA

Gonorrhea is caused by a germ called gonococcus. Ordinarily it can be identified only through laboratory methods which involve the use of a high-powered microscope and other procedures such as staining and culturing.

The gonococcus needs moisture and approximately the same degree of warmth as the human body to live and multiply. It cannot survive long when dry or at much higher or lower temperatures. Consequently this germ has a definite affinity for the mucous surfaces of the human body, especially those of the genital tract and of the eye. Ordinarily it lives on no other surface of the body, with the exception of the mucous membrane of the rectum. Because of these requirements of the gonococcus, the disease is usually spread by direct contact between the genital organs of infected and uninfected persons. An exception is the occasional transmission of the germ in young boys and girls by inanimate objects such as infected rectal thermometers and soiled linens. Most authorities now believe, however, that infection by inanimate objects in young girls and boys is uncommon; infection in children is most often due to precocious sexual practices among the children themselves.

In both men and women gonorrhea first manifests itself by the formation of pus in certain parts of the genital and urinary tracts. In men the first symptom is usually a burning sensation on urination; when the man examines himself he finds that a drop or two of pus can be squeezed out of the urethra, the canal that leads from the bladder through the penis to the outside. This pus contains thousands of germs and is highly contagious, not only to other people, but when carelessly transferred to the patient's eyes or rectal area these parts may also become infected. This is one reason why it is important for all persons infected with gonorrhea to wash the hands thoroughly after handling the generative organs. The urethral discharge usually lasts for a period of several weeks in untreated cases. It is most abundant during the first week and, as time elapses, gradually diminishes in amount and becomes more mucus-like in appearance.

Certain complications can occur with gonorrhea in the male. These are produced when the germ spreads into the prostate gland at the base of the bladder, into the seminal vesicles on either side of the prostate gland, or into the tubules (epididymis) leading from the testicles. In each of these cases there is pus formation followed by other symptoms, which vary depending on the location and function of the part involved. Gonorrheal inflammation of the epididymis, for instance, usually leads to sterility if it occurs on both sides. Fortunately, with new methods of treatment these complications are rare. They are likely to occur if treatment is neglected or if an infected male has sexual intercourse, engages in prolonged sexual excitement, or if he does heavy work with his bladder filled with urine.

In women gonorrhea may begin in several different ways. The urethra or tube that leads from the bladder to the vulva (external genitals) usually becomes inflamed and pus forms. There is likely to be a burning sensation on urination. Furthermore, the glands, which are so numerous in the mucous lining of the canal of the womb, usually become infected. These glands exude pus which reaches the vagina, and the woman has a severe vaginal discharge. Mucous glands of the vulva may also become infected and abscesses may form; pain may be particularly severe on walking in such women with acute gonorrhea. In other cases the infection produces few symptoms and the women notice only a more or less severe leukorrheal discharge.

Sexual intercourse, prolonged sexual excitement, and high-pressure douches may also result in complications of gonorrhea in women. Fortunately, however, these complications are also comparatively uncommon under modern methods of treatment. One of the more frequent complications, when treatment is neglected by the unco-operative patient, is involvement of the Fallopian tubes. These structures lead from the ovaries to the womb and carry the ovum from the ovary to the body of the womb. When the Fallopian tubes become inflamed, pus forms and abscesses often result. If, as frequently happens, the abscess breaks, the pus scatters through the lower part of the pelvis and the woman is then said to have pelvic inflammatory disease. Involvement of the Fallopian tubes in the gonorrheal process frequently renders the woman sterile because the tubes are permanently closed and the ovum cannot pass through.

Especially serious about gonorrhea in women from a public health point of view is the fact that they often become carriers of gonorrhea germs. In the female the disease tends to become chronic and may persist for months. During this time it does not cause symptoms, or perhaps only mild leukorrheal discharge. Yet such women harbor the gonococcus in the mucous glands of the genital tract, and these germs may infect any male with whom they have intercourse. The woman who has chronic gonorrhea without symptoms, therefore, is the serious problem in the transmission of this disease. This is particularly significant when we recall that it is the female who can have the larger number of sex contacts in a given period of time. The infected woman is responsible, on an average, for the infection of a larger number of people than is the infected man. These facts show the urgent need for vigorous repression of prostitution and control of promiscuity if the venereal diseases are to be controlled.

In men or women other severe complications of gonorrhea rarely occur, such as heart-valve involvement (gonococcal endocarditis); gonorrheal arthritis, especially of the knee joint; and gonorrheal inflammation of the eye, which even under modern treatment may lead to varying degrees of blindness. Ophthalmia neonatorum (blindness in the newborn) may also result when the baby's eyes are infected in passing through the birth canal.

SYPHILIS

The germ that causes syphilis is an active corkscrew-shaped organism called Spirochaeta pallida (the pale spirochete). The pale spirochete of syphilis, like the gonococcus, requires an environment that is closely within the temperature and moisture range of human mucous surfaces. The spirochete lives best on mucous surfaces of the genital organs and the mouth, but it has the ability to enter through the skin and mucous membrane if infected material touches them. The germs of syphilis are most frequently transmitted by sexual contact, but they may also be spread by kissing or inanimate objects that are contaminated with infectious material from a person with syphilis. Remember, however, that the germ on inanimate objects must remain moist until it reaches the mucous surface or skin of uninfected persons because it promptly dies as soon as the infectious material dries. Traditionally the soiled toilet seat is the most frequent inanimate object blamed for a syphilitic or gonorrheal infection. The fact that the germs of both diseases die at once on drying indicates the fallacy of this belief, because few people use a toilet seat that is wet or soiled.

When a person of either sex is infected with syphilis, the following manifestations occur in the absence of treatment: After the spirochete first gets into the body, three to four weeks pass without symptoms. This time, known as the incubation period, permits the germs to multiply. When the germs increase to a sufficient number, a sore develops at the place where the spirochete entered. Because syphilis is usually transmitted by sexual contact, this sore is most often found on the generative organs. In the male the sore is practically always on the external organs. In the female, because of the anatomy of the genital organs, the sore is located on the internal organs about half of the time, particularly the mouth of the womb. This circumstance, together with the fact that subsequent manifestations of syphilis may be missed or incorrectly interpreted, causes a large number of infected women to be unaware of their syphilitic infection.

The first sore of syphilis, known as chancre, remains for a period of from three to six weeks. The sore gradually heals and in the absence of treatment a skin rash develops. In addition the infected person with a rash may develop sores on the mucous surface of the mouth or on the genital organs. There may also be headache, backache, and pains in the joints; all, as a rule, worse at night. In adults, syphilitic disease of the eye may seriously impair vision. There is a great deal of variation in the intensity of the rash and other symptoms, so that some persons may not recognize the disease in the early stage.

The symptoms in the preceding paragraph, when present, last for from two to six months. Then the syphilitic person passes into the symptomless stage and for many years may feel entirely normal. It is during this stage that syphilis can be detected only by a blood test. It must be remembered, however, that occasionally the blood test for syphilis may be positive in the presence of other diseases than syphilis and a diagnosis of syphilis should not be based on one positive test. In other words, if positive, the blood test should be repeated and a second positive test and a physical examination obtained before treatment is started. It is also in this symptomless stage that the first evidence of involvement of the central nervous system in the syphilitic person can be detected by the examination of the spinal fluid. The alert physician often requests permission of the patient to do a spinal tap.

The end of the symptomless period is gradual and the untreated person becomes aware of vague manifestations of one sort or another. These symptoms vary greatly, depending on which of the organs is involved by syphilis. Late complications, coming on in the absence of adequate treatment several to thirty years or more after infection, may be syphilis of the central nervous system and syphilis of the heart and the great blood vessels leading away from the heart. Syphilitic disease of the heart and great vessels may cause a leaking heart valve with ultimate symptoms of heart failure. Degeneration of the large artery leading away from the heart (aortitis or aneurysm) is common. Syphilis of the central nervous system may be of several kinds, but the most frequent are known as general paralysis of the insane (paresis or syphilitic insanity) and tabes dorsalis (locomotor ataxia). Cirrhosis (hardening) of the liver is sometimes a late manifestation of syphilis. Any of these late complications may come on when the patient is not properly treated.

Less serious types of late syphilis may be inflammation and thickening of the bones, particularly the long bones of the leg and the bones of the skull. Chronic ulcers and indolent skin eruptions may occur. Naturally, no one patient has all of the complications of late syphilis, although combinations of two forms are frequent.

Unfortunate particularly about inadequately treated syphilis is the fact that usually it is transmitted from the infected mother to her unborn child. The disease never spreads directly from an infected father to an unborn child, but always from the mother, who may have been infected by the father. The unborn child infected with syphilis may die before the end of the gestation period, and the mother's pregnancy then terminates in a miscarriage. If the child is born with syphilis, serious skin eruptions may occur within the first few weeks of life. The liver is often involved early in life, and frequently there are inflammatory changes in the bones of the infant. If the syphilitic baby survives the first year of life he is subject to later attacks by Spirochaeta pallida. Disease of the eye and deafness due to syphilis are frequent. Otherwise the attacks in older children resemble late syphilis in the adult.

OTHER VENEREAL DISEASES

The importance of other venereal diseases in marriage may be said to be limited almost entirely to chancroid. Chancroid causes an ulceration of the external generative organs, and it may be confused with the first sore of syphilis. Indeed, sometimes syphilis and chancroid develop together. Chancroid heals promptly with proper treatment, but all people who have genital sores should remain under the care of a physician for several months, during which blood tests for syphilis should be repeated periodically to be sure that a combined chancroidal and syphilitc infection did not occur.

Granuloma inguinale and lymphogranuloma venereum are different diseases in spite of some similarity of the names. They produce serious destruction and deformity of the external genitals and adjacent parts. These diseases are uncommon in the Temperate and Frigid Zones.

TREATMENT

Antibiotics are now employed almost to the exclusion of other drugs in the treatment of the venereal diseases. These new preparations have greatly simplified the method of treatment, have shortened the time necessary to obtain a cure, and have prevented most of the severe complications that formerly occurred. They also have shortened greatly the period when the person with a venereal disease is contagious and, therefore, have contributed greatly to the control of these diseases.

In order of popularity, penicillin takes first place. Terramycin is probably the second antibiotic of choice, and streptomycin and the other antibiotics follow. It is fortunate that we have a number of antibiotics, because sometimes patients become sensitized to one of these drugs, and it is necessary to switch to others in the group. This is particularly true of penicillin, which is so widely used in the treatment of many diseases today. Also, there is some difference in the efficacy of one antibiotic as compared to another in the treatment of some of the five venereal diseases, and the competent physician often prescribes the antibiotic he believes has a more specific action against a given disease.

In the treatment of chancroid and lymphogranuloma venereum, one of the sulfa drugs (sulfadiazine) is still utilized extensively. Even with these two diseases, however, the antibiotics give evidence of increasing efficacy. It is possible that treatment with some of the new antibiotics may ultimately replace the use of this sulfa drug, and in that event the antibiotics would become the unanimous choice of physicians in the treatment and control of all of the venereal diseases.

PUBLIC HEALTH CONTROL

Venereal disease can be successfully controlled by intensive and rapid case finding, early treatment of all infected persons, and prophylactic treatment for all persons sexually exposed to a known infectious case. These diseases cannot be prevented by vaccination or immunization in the way that smallpox, yellow fever, and diphtheria may be prevented. Because of complex social and moral connotations there is great need for some method of vaccination or immunization against venereal disease. Such a preventive method would place their control on a purely scientific basis, and the social and moral problems would be given their respective places in sociology and theology.

There is another method for the prevention of the venereal diseases, but because of the human equation this method, known as a prophylaxis, is effective only when applied to groups of people under rigid discipline. The method, which involves the use of chemical and mechanical agents, is therefore largely limited to the armed forces. In the civilian population under no discipline, prophylaxis fails because of an aesthetic dislike for the agents, because of overconfidence in the paramour's health, because of the use of alcohol, and because of ignorance.

The more important social measures which should complement the venereal-disease-control program are repression of prostitution, attempts to decrease promiscuity, and a service to locate infected persons who do not seek treatment voluntarily. Strange to say, experience has shown that many people who have gonorrhea and syphilis in contagious stages do not report promptly to a physician. This is ordinarily due to ignorance. It is therefore necessary for each venereal-disease clinic to employ persons who are especially trained in finding the cases. Even though it may sound difficult to the uninitiated, these people become adept at learning of the sex contacts made by patients who voluntarily seek treatment for syphilis and gonorrhea. The confidential information thus obtained is used most tactfully in approaching the contacts of the person known to be infected. This approach, which may take the form of a telephone call, a letter, or a visit, helps to inform the alleged contact that he has been exposed to a serious contagious disease and that he should go to a designated clinic or to his personal physician for examination. Studies made by trained people in the field of case finding have shown that syphilis and gonorrhea are spread in small epidemics in a community, and that sometimes the infection of one promiscuous person may lead directly or indirectly to the exposure and possible infection of dozens of other people. The goal of health workers is to bring in promptly for medical care all persons infected with venereal diseases.

Naturally, if exposure to a venereal disease can be avoided, there will be no infection and no need for case-finding work, examination, or treatment. It has been repeatedly shown, for instance, that prostitutes may have sex contact with as many as several dozen men in twenty-four hours. Other promiscuous people may expose an average of two or three people each day to a venereal disease. No sure method exists to protect people who are promiscuous or who have intercourse with prostitutes. For these reasons it is necessary to repress prostitution and to prevent promiscuity in order to stop venereal-disease transmission.

Laws have been passed in all of the states against prostitution and promiscuity, but these measures are ineffective unless given active support by the public. We must choose between promiscuity and prostitution, with high venereal-disease prevalence on the one hand, and effective social and moral measures, with low venereal-disease prevalence on the other. When we make the choice we should also remember that neither promiscuity nor prostitution contributes to the number of happy marriages.

The question frequently is asked as to how many people are infected with gonorrhea and syphilis. There are no figures for gonorrhea. An estimate of the number of people infected with syphilis is also difficult to obtain because so many people do not seek treatment and some are not even reported anonymously when they go to a physician or clinic. The best figures available on the extent of syphilis were obtained during World War II, when a routine examination of selectees for military service showed that approximately $4\frac{1}{2}$ per cent of all men coming into military service had repeated positive blood tests for syphilis. Comparing this information with that from other sources, it is believed that from 2 to 5 per cent of the total population is infected. This estimate makes allowance for sex, racial differences, and other factors.

The frequency with which one encounters syphilis has given active support to the enactment of state laws aimed at the prevention of the transmission of syphilis to an uninfected spouse at the time of marriage, and to the unborn child. One would think that a person contemplating marriage or a pregnant woman knowing she had syphilis would be examined and seek treatment if necessary. The syphilitic infection, however, is frequently missed. To detect these infected people, experience shows that it is not only necessary to do a complete physical examination on all prospective spouses and expectant mothers, but to use routinely a blood test for syphilis as part of the examination. The blood specimen should be taken by the physician who does the examination and sent to a laboratory known to do reliable work. By 1954, thirty-nine states had satisfactory premarital laws, according to the American Social Hygiene Association. The same authority reports that forty-two states have satisfactory prenatal laws for the prevention of the transmission of syphilis from an expectant mother to an unborn child.

Infection of a marital partner with a venereal disease is almost conclusive evidence of infidelity. Venereal diseases in marriage, therefore, have been one of the common causes of separation, divorce, and broken homes. The moral and ethical aspects of adultery vary under different circumstances, whether or not the problem of venereal disease enters the picture. In many instances conditions exist which make it highly undesirable to dissolve marriage because of a single instance of broken fidelity. The injured spouse should remember that intelligent action will promptly eliminate venereal disease from consideration because modern treatment for gonorrhea and early syphilis leads to cure.

Chapter 4

DIVORCE

by Kingsley Davis, Ph.D.
PROFESSOR OF SOCIOLOGY, COLUMBIA UNIVERSITY

Like everything else in marriage, divorce concerns not one person but at least two or more. Ordinarily, in connection with marital relations, one can assume that the marriage itself is considered valuable by both parties and that the aim of both is to preserve or improve it. But when a desire for divorce has been expressed, this assumption can no longer be made. For either the husband or the wife, or possibly both, the marriage itself is no longer valued. It is conceived rather as an obstacle to be eliminated, even at some mental or material cost.

The conflict of interest in divorce is at a minimum when both parties want a dissolution. Even in this case, however, plenty of room is left for possible bitterness and for disagreement over such matters as property settlements, alimony, and custody of children. In such cases the state, according to law, must play the unpleasant role of opposing a divorce which both parties want, at the same time arbitrating the conflict of interests over subsidiary matters.

The more typical cases are those in which one party wants the divorce and the other really does not. Such a case strongly tempts neighbors and friends to take sides in the emotional struggle. Presumably a marriage counselor would attempt to remain neutral, simply trying to give the couple insight into their own motives and some knowledge concerning the possible psychological and social effects of their actions. But since people who do marriage counseling are usually sponsored by religious, social work, or government agencies, their moral evaluation with reference to divorce is likely to be somewhat conservative and hence not strictly neutral.[1] Consequently the party who wants a divorce is likely to stay away from such advice. He is likely to feel that by traditional standards he is in the wrong unless he can show a morally acceptable reason for his goal. If he is merely bored with his mate or he happens to like someone else better, he may well fear a concealed opposition. He is more likely to rely upon his lawyer, who by profession is pledged to look after the interest of his client. Indeed, the lawyers do more marriage counseling and more intelligent balancing of interests than anyone else in divorce cases, ill prepared as they may be for this difficult role.[2]

The truth is that divorce poses the problem of conflicting interest in an acute form. For this reason, once the decision to obtain a divorce has been made by one or both parties, the chief role of the marriage counselor refers no longer to marital adjustment but rather to a divorce adjustment.[3] Those who believe that the incidence of divorce can be greatly reduced through the counseling of couples after they have already sought divorce are probably mistaken. By that time marital discord or ennui has usually grown too deep to be banished by verbal dissuasion.

Since divorce is an old institution and is embedded in the social structure in many ways, there already exist agencies for handling its different aspects. First, divorce is a legal matter, with an elaborate legal machinery and a traditional legal philosophy for handling it. Second, it is a cultural and statistical fact, with fluctuations in time which respond to concurrent economic and social changes. Third, it is an emotional and personal process, with psychologic and psychiatric ramifications. Finally, it is a moral fact, with official and unofficial attitudes toward it that are mutually opposed. All of these aspects must be kept in mind if divorce is to be understood.

DIVORCE AND THE LAW

When the legal aspect of divorce is mentioned, one naturally thinks of divorce laws. But the stipulations and intent of legislative acts, constitutional clauses, and established precedents are not the whole legal story. Another part of the story lies in the way the law is actually used, and for what purposes. Perhaps in no other field of legal practice is the divergence between the intent of the law and its actual use so great as it is in divorce litigation. American divorce law today ideally sets out to accomplish one goal but in fact accomplishes the opposite, and it rests its logic on one set of assumptions but in practice operates on a contrary set. This hiatus between law in theory and law in action is partly a result of the rapid changes in our society which have affected divorce attitudes and behavior much more than they have affected formal divorce law. But the hiatus is also due to the fact that much of our family law, including that of divorce, had its origin in ecclesiastical jurisprudence but is now applied by secular courts in a secular state. The ecclesiastical system from which stems our present family law, however, happens to have been one which did not admit of absolute divorce, whereas under modern secular law this has become the main form of divorce.[4]

Sometimes it seems that the formal law of divorce has not changed at all, but only the social role and practice of the law. But actually during the last three or four decades there have been some changes, among which the following may be singled out for brief attention.

1. *An increase in the number of legal grounds and a liberalization of their interpretation and character.* Under the traditional theory, a divorce can be obtained only by the "innocent" party coming into court and proving that the "guilty" party has committed one of the unbearable "faults" which the state legislature has laid down as legitimate "ground" for divorce. This view of divorce—known as the adversary theory—has never been 100 per cent pure; there have always been in various states grounds of divorce—impotency, insanity, epilepsy—which can hardly be construed as a matter of willful fault. However, during recent decades the adversary theory has been shaken in new ways. Not only has the number of grounds of divorce tended to mulitply under state legislation, but the nature of some of these grounds, either by definition or by interpretation, is contrary to the old view.

The most striking of the non-adversary grounds is "incompatibility." During the nineteenth century several states allowed divorce for incompatibility of temperament, but the statutes were subsequently repealed.[5] But in recent times three jurisdictions (Alaska in 1933, New Mexico in 1935, and the Virgin Islands in 1944) have included incompatibility among the grounds. Obviously, incompatibility is not a fault; it cannot be blamed on one party and not the other. A man can commit adultery, but he can hardly commit incompatibility.

In addition, at least five jurisdictions have amended their laws in order to permit divorce because of voluntary separation.[6] Eleven others do so on the ground of protracted separation, which at least in some cases may be voluntary. Such separation is certainly different from the old-style "desertion." Like incompatibility, it is a mutual matter. "No charge of desertion nor assumption of guilt is necessary; if the parties voluntarily live apart for the given period, either may get the divorce on this ground alone."[7]

Still another modification of the adversary theory is reached through the "cruelty" channel. No less than forty-two states allow divorce for cruelty. Eight of these specifically mention "mental" cruelty in their statutes, and virtually all the others (except Alabama and South Carolina) seemingly admit mental cruelty as a cause in actual divorce cases.[8] While such "cruelty" appears to fit with the adversary theory, it actually does not to the extent that mutual contempt (i.e., expressed incompatibility) is construed as fitting the definition and to the extent that the cruelty need not be intentional. Similarly, ten jurisdictions allow divorce for "indignities" suffered by the plaintiff. Generally, the indignities need to have been intentionally inflicted, and so this cause does not overlap with incompatibility to the same extent that mental cruelty does, but its liberalizing effect is nevertheless plain.

These changes in the grounds of divorce therefore represent an adjustment of American legal theory in the direction of actual practice. The law is beginning to sanction divorce by mutual consent. Everyone knows that it has always done so in practice (and increasingly as time has gone by), but only recently has it begun to do so in theory.

2. *Vacillation with respect to migratory divorce.* American divorce litigation is confused and complicated by the fact that it is handled by forty-eight different state jurisdictions and several territorial jurisdictions. Although all of these grant absolute divorce, the circumstances and conditions under which they grant it differ greatly. The result has been, as everyone knows, to allow people to escape the more severe legal restrictions of conservative states by going to more liberal states for divorces. A state has jurisdiction over divorce if the plaintiff is domiciled there. Competition for the divorce business has led some states to lower the residence requirements to a few weeks or months.[9] This, plus the increasing ease of travel and mobility of the American people, has made migratory divorce easier, though it remains true that such divorces account for only a small portion (something around 6 per cent) of the total.[10] The determination of the validity of these migratory divorces and the adjustment of the consequent rights and obligations of the divorced parties and their dependents have led to an enormous amount of confused litigation and a great outpouring of legal literature.

The legal theory is that, by the full faith and credit clause of the Constitution, a divorce granted in one state must be recognized by the other states, provided the state in question has jurisdiction—that is, provided the plaintiff is a resident of the state when the action is initiated. By a legal fiction, however, this theory is not applied in practice, so that out-of-state or migratory divorces, which in theory are impossible, nevertheless occur. In other words, divorces are regularly granted by states really lacking jurisdiction, and these divorces are treated as valid.[11]

The basis for the legal fiction lies in the ambiguity of the notion of "domicil," on which jurisdiction depends.

Domicil in this country has lost much of the stability it possessed in earlier times. . . . People are in the habit of changing their homes frequently from state to state. In many cases they have homes in several states. Again, married women are permitted to have domicils different from their husbands'. Under present conditions, therefore, it is frequently difficult, if not possible, to ascertain where the domicil of a person is.[12]

The legal definition is subjective: a bona fide domicil is a place which the person *regards* as his home and where he *intends* to stay more or less indefinitely. But a subjective definition cannot be applied in practice consistently unless it is transformed into an objective one—that is, unless certain ascertainable criteria are admitted as proof of the subjective state of mind. The states in fact lay down the requirement that a person must *reside* in the state for *a certain length of time* before he can initiate divorce action there. This is not what the ordinary person, the Supreme Court, or our legal philosophers mean by domicile, because they are thinking of intentions. A man who takes a vacation from his New York job and leaves his apartment in New York for six weeks to go to Reno, secures a divorce, and comes back to his job and his apartment in New York has had no intention of establishing a "residence," a "legal domicil," in Nevada. He simply went there to get a divorce by a legal fiction—a fiction kindly connived at by the state of Nevada itself. In statements of theory by the courts, a state to which the party "has moved immediately prior to the divorce and from which he removes immediately afterwards is uniformly held not to be the domicil of the party in question."[13] Yet this is exactly what most persons getting out-of-state divorces do. Presumably, then, if the law practiced its theory, it would treat nearly all such divorces as void. But it does no such thing. The courts continue to grind out divorces for out-of-state applicants, the persons who obtain these decrees practically never get prosecuted, and when the validity of the divorce is challenged, the courts in other states often refuse to reopen the case out of respect for the doctrines of estoppel and *res judicata*.

Most divorces in the United States (about 95 per cent) are the result of mutual agreement.[14] This does not mean that both parties "want" the divorce, but simply that neither will try seriously to compel the other party to stay married. As a result, after the divorce is granted neither one is likely to challenge the decree, and usually no one else is interested in doing so. This means that in the great majority of cases an out-of-state decree can serve without penalty as a basis for subsequent conduct, such as remarriage. But suppose somebody does challenge the decree later, will the courts then treat it as void? In case of remarriage, will they recognize the first spouse as the legitimate heir in preference to the second one? Will they refuse to admit the "void" divorce as a valid defense in suits for alienation of affection? The answer seems to be no. "Oddly enough, it is only in the case of a prosecution for bigamy that one can be certain that such results will follow, and prosecutions for bigamy after anything which resembles an effort to obtain a divorce are so rare that, for practical purposes, they may be and are ignored."[15]

The law rationalizes its unwillingness to treat a "void" divorce as void by two devices. First, it invokes the doctrine of estoppel when both parties have appeared in action and have not contested the court's jurisdiction. Each is, by his participation in the "void" divorce, estopped from subsequently questioning the jurisdiction of the court that granted it. Second, the law invokes the doctrine of *res judicata*. Even if the person has fought the action and has not remarried, he may nevertheless be forbidden to question the validity of the divorce. "It is simply not true that a divorce rendered in a state to which both parties resorted solely for the purpose of obtaining the decree is without legal effect. On the contrary, it has the precise effect which the parties desire."[16]

Of course if the defendant spouse does not enter the action or accept service in any way, he or she may bring suit in the state of real domicil either for another divorce or for a settlement of property and custody, but it seems virtually impossible, by direct attack on the out-of-state decree, to re-establish the marriage.

The use of legal fiction to accomplish out-of-state divorces has obviously led to suggestions of reform. Proposals have been made to have "domicil" federally defined for purposes of divorce, all states thus being similar in this respect. On May 6, 1953, the United States Senate passed a bill attempting to confine divorce jurisdiction to the last state in which the parties were domiciled together as husband and wife.[17] The idea has been put forward that intrastate divorces should be handled by federal rather than state courts, and that these courts should have the power to determine the facts of domicile and thus decide which state's laws should govern the action.[18] In the meantime, the volume of interstate divorces is tending to increase. They represent a convenient means of escape from the rigid laws of divorce in some states.

3. *The drive to supplement adversary procedures with administrative arrangements in divorce cases.* Recognizing that the old adversary theory of divorce is not only breaking down in practice but fails to fit the facts of modern life, many individuals and states are working to reorganize the handling of divorce cases. One measure being taken in this direction is the establishment of special family courts to deal with family litigation. In these courts preside judges and referees specially selected for their ability to deal with family problems, and the court is furnished with trained family counselors, social investigators, and psychiatric consultants.[19] An effort is thus being made to acquaint the court with the real facts of the cases that come before it, so that matters will not be decided on the basis of purely legal technicalities and fictions.[20] In addition, the legal-aid societies that have been growing in number and scope are also of help in straightening out divorce tangles. These and other social agencies help not so much with reference to

the main issue of divorce as in the ancillary judgments with respect to alimony and custody. Doubtless as the law loses its adherence to an outworn theory of divorce as a matter of conflict, guilt, and punishment, this humanizing tendency will continue.[21]

4. *The increasing role of the separation agreement.* Although on its way, the modification of the litigious process in divorce has not gone very far yet. In the meantime it is interesting that couples appear to be placing more and more reliance upon the separation agreement to settle their property and custody problems in connection with divorce.

The emphasis on an adversary determination of questions of guilt and innocence (usually completely unrelated to the real marital difficulty) and the absence in most parts of the country of any judicial machinery capable of surveying a total marital picture have resulted in a situation where the court rules on the technicalities of the divorce while the essential questions are settled by the parties extra-judicially, usually by negotiating and entering into a contract known as a separation agreement.[22]

Ordinarily the court tends to accept the terms of the agreement, without really examining their merits in the particular case. Since the agreement is almost invariably worked out by the two lawyers in the case, it is in a sense the lawyers who are serving as the fact-finders, mediators, counselors, and lawmakers in cases of divorce. Thus the ponderous formality of the law has resulted in a certain abdication, the people who want divorces taking things into their own and their lawyers' hands and working out agreements which somehow get the job done.

STATISTICAL ASPECTS

It should be remembered that divorce is not the only way of dissolving a marriage. Other legal ways are by annulment and by formal separation. Non-legal ways include desertion and informal separation. From an adjustment point of view these other ways of dissolving a marriage raise as many problems as divorce, for their effects on the mates and their children are in many ways more complex and more serious than those that divorce creates.

Certainly, too, these other forms of marital dissolution are as important as divorce from a statistical standpoint. It has been estimated that the number of desertions occurring each year is perhaps half the number of divorces.[23] Since the average number of children affected by desertion is greater than the number affected by divorce, this means that the total impact of desertion on the American family is sizable. In the 1950 census there were 1,169,000 wives who were separated from their husbands.[24] This almost equaled the number of divorced women in the population (1,373,000). Those reported as "separated" in the census probably included deserted wives as well as women who were legally or informally separated, but in any case it appears that desertion and separation taken together probably account for as many marital dissolutions as divorce does. In thinking of family breakdown, people give a disproportionate amount of attention to divorce because it is a legal process, is better measured, and catches the popular imagination; but it must always be remembered that divorce represents only half the problem of marital dissolution.

In the United States as a whole, annulments constitute only a small proportion of legal dissolutions. In 1946 they represented only 3.5 per cent of the total. But according to Jacobson, they were much more important in California and New York.

Thus in California, annulments constituted somewhat more than one ninth of all legal marriage dissolutions in 1948. In New York they were an even larger proportion of the total; almost one quarter of the marital dissolutions in 1940, and since 1946 almost one third. In at least five counties in New York, the number of annulments now exceeds the number of absolute divorces.

Year	Rate	Year	Rate	Year	Rate
1881	5.1	1905	9.6	1929	17.3
1882	5.3	1906	9.9	1930	16.3
1883	5.4	1907	10.1	1931	15.9
1884	5.3	1908	9.8	1932	14.0
1885	5.2	1909	9.9	1933	14.2
1886	5.6	1910	10.0	1934	17.8
1887	5.9	1911	10.5	1935	18.8
1888	6.0	1912	10.8	1936	20.1
1889	6.5	1913	10.2	1937	21.0
1890	6.6	1914	11.0	1938	20.1
1891	6.9	1915	11.1	1939	20.4
1892	6.9	1916	11.9	1940	21.2
1893	6.9	1917	12.5	1941	22.7
1894	6.8	1918	11.7	1942	23.7
1895	7.2	1919	14.0	1943	25.0
1896	7.5	1920	16.5	1944	27.0
1897	7.7	1921	15.0	1945	33.5
1898	8.0	1922	13.7	1946	40.1
1899	8.5	1923	15.0	1947	30.0
1900	9.0	1924	15.3	1948	24.4
1901	9.7	1925	15.4	1949	22.4
1902	9.5	1926	16.0	1950	22.1
1903	9.8	1927	16.8	1951	21.5
1904	9.7	1928	17.1		

TABLE 6. DIVORCES PER 100 MARRIAGES

In this table the divorces are not related to the marriages in the same year, but to marriages occurring in the previous ten years. That is to say, the table shows the number of divorces per 100 marriages occurring each year on the average in the ten years previous to the year in question. This ratio is taken because most divorces represent the breakup of marriages that were formed during the preceding ten years. The figures are derived from data contained in the releases of the Bureau of the Census and the National Office of Vital Statistics.

New York State has this high annulment rate because it grants divorce only for adultery but gives annulments for any one of eight different grounds, many of which are ill defined.[25] The Catholic influence in the state is clear.

Coming back now to absolute divorces, we know that the divorce rate in the United States has experienced a long secular rise. It jumped up sharply after World War I, fell back slightly in the early twenties, dropped noticeably during the depression, then rose sharply again in connection with World War II. A peak was reached in 1946, after which the rate declined noticeably. In 1951 the rate stood slightly lower than in 1942. The accompanying chart shows the trend. There is evidence of a saturation point being reached. The divorce rate in the United States has risen more slowly than it has in most other countries, so that today our rate does not exceed that of, say, European countries as much as it used to.[26] Nevertheless, the rate here has risen to the point where, over a long period, roughly a third of the marriages formed will end in divorce.[27]

DIVORCE AND THE CHILD

The most serious aspect of divorce concerns the child, particularly in our culture. However, it is still true that most divorces and annulments occurring in the United States in 1948 were to couples with children. The average number of children per divorced couple with children was 1.8. In other words, about 313,000 children under age 21 were involved in the 421,000 absolute decrees granted in 1948.[28] (This figure of course does not include children in homes broken by separation and desertion.)

There are several features of our family system that make the problem of the divorce child peculiarly difficult. First, because of our pattern of low fertility and high geographical and social mobility, the effective family unit is small in size and extremely isolated from other kinsmen. Second, because of our urban economy, the nuclear family has remarkably few functions and activities in common and consequently must depend heavily on sheer sentiment to hold it together. Third, our family organization is extremely democratic and permissive, with a minimum of fixed patterns to serve as guides in domestic conduct. As a result of these features, the parent-child relation tends to be at once emotionally close but conflictful, so that any tension between the parents tends also to involve the child. Furthermore, when the marriage is broken, the household is usually broken up too. There is no stable milieu wider than the small family to which the child can remain attached, as there is in many cultures. There is no relative who can immediately substitute for a missing parent.[29]

Both parents are entitled to feel they have an equal claim upon the child, which sets the stage for conflict over custody in divorce cases. Although the child's welfare is supposed to be the guide in determining custody, "welfare" is still too subjective to be determined accurately.[30] One parent, most often the father, is required to support the child, and yet he may live far from him and see him relatively infrequently. The parent who keeps the child most of the time may be forced to work or may enter a second marriage. The child may be shunted back and forth from one parent to the other. In any case, he remains the sole remaining link between the parents and thus is sometimes used as the instrument for the continued expression of antagonism. In sum, the child of divorced parents is placed in a peculiarly anomalous situation laden with potential conflict and insecurity. How well he actually fares, however, depends largely on how intelligently and calmly the parents handle the situation.

The child of divorced parents is in a potentially better situation than the one who has lost one parent through death. He stands the chance of receiving the economic support and affection of both his parents, even though they are divorced. If one or both parents remarry, the child may find a new home better than the old, depending again on how matters are handled. In this connection it is worth noting that the rate of remarriage after divorce is quite high. It seems probable that close to four fifths of those getting divorced today will eventually remarry, most of them soon after their divorce.

PSYCHIATRIC ASPECTS

Occasionally there is a tendency to regard divorce itself as a mental disorder or at least as an evidence of such disorder. This, however, is merely a sly way of condemning divorce. Since divorce is merely the legal dissolution of a marriage, it may or may not be a result of neurosis in one or both of the parties concerned. Unless the term "neurotic" is defined loosely, it cannot be used to explain the majority of divorces. Certainly the divorce itself does not constitute evidence of neurosis without independent confirmation. Divorces are in fact so much a part of American folkways and mores that they cannot be regarded as abnormal. Only when divorce occurs two or more times to the same person can it be taken as suggestive of neurosis. Many of us will have observed second marriages that work out extremely well, their success being due perhaps in part to experience with the realities of life gained in a first but unsuccessful marriage.

In those cases in which mental disorder appears to be involved, the help of a psychiatrist is of course desirable—not necessarily to save the marriage, for that may be the wrong tack, but possibly to save the individual from another unhappy venture. Sometimes a divorce itself will prove of benefit to such a person, but in other cases it will have little effect upon his mental illness or will exacerbate it.

Divorce does not necessarily end the relationship between the erstwhile married pair. Shreds and vestiges of the former bond remain. Through alimony payments, through the children, through mutual friends, through continued interest, the relationship tends to live on.[31] The neurotic has much the same difficulty adjusting to the modified relationship that he had in adjusting to the former one. If he needed help in the first instance, he also needs it in the second.

Even if neurosis is not involved, even if divorce is wanted by both parties, the actual dissolution often comes as a crisis. To be sure, the main emotional crisis may have come earlier, when the decision to obtain a divorce was first made. The actual decree, when it comes later, may seem an aftermath. But somewhere along the line the erstwhile partners are likely to experience the breakup of their marriage as a shock. "In our society divorced persons are presented with no socially approved means of adjustment to this crisis such as those available to the bereaved." Instead, they are often faced with hostile or at least uncertain reactions on the part of the community, for divorce is still a negative value among us.[32]

A BRIEF SUMMARY

Divorce offers a peculiar challenge because it raises the problems of conflicting interests in an acute form. Yet the increase of divorce in our society makes it a somewhat normal and regular outcome of matrimony. Even American law, conservative as it may be, is beginning to admit divorce as a matter of mutual agreement and has facilitated the evasion of strict state statutes by refusing to practice its own theory with reference to "domicil." Those who advise regarding marriage must meet the issue of divorce with great frequency. One cannot regard it simply as an abnormality suggestive of neurosis. Rather it must be accepted as a normal feature of our popular mores. We are, in effect, returning to the old custom of trial marriage. Our young people get married at a remarkably early age (earlier than in any other industrial nation). They do so knowing full well that if it does not work out a divorce can be obtained, if not in their own state, then in some other state. Many of them do get divorced, and they do so for the most part within a short time after they get married (usually within two or three years). Most of these speedily marry a second time, and most of these unions work out. The custom of divorce is linked with other aspects of our social order and is not likely to change unless the rest of that order also changes.

NOTES

[1]The literature on marriage counseling suggests a conservative attitude toward divorce, but a more professional, or disinterested, attitude is emerging. It is recognized that the goal of making marriages work does not preclude the possibility that divorce itself may be desirable. See Emily H. Mudd, *The Practice of Marriage Counseling*, New York, Association Press, 1951, Chaps. 1, 9–10.

[2]Harriet F. Pilpel and Theodora S. Zavin, "Separation Agreements: Their Function and Future," *Law and Contemporary Problems*, Vol. 18, Winter 1953, pp. 33–38.

[3]Further analysis of the problem of conflicting ends in marriage counseling is found in the writer's paper, "The Application of Science to Personal Relations," *American Sociological Review*, Vol. I, April 1936, pp. 236–51.

[4]For a fuller discussion of the backgrounds of our divorce law, see readings by Llewellyn and Pound in *Selected Essays on Family Law*, Brooklyn, Foundation Press, 1950, pp. 27–95, 872–80.

[5]Lester B. Orfield, "Divorce for Temperamental Incompatibility," *Michigan Law Review*, Vol. 52, March 1954, pp. 659–63.

[6]Arizona (1931), Arkansas (1937), District of Columbia (1929), Louisiana (1932), Maryland (1937), and Nevada (1934). See Chester G. Vernier, *American Family Laws, 1938 Supplement*, Stanford University Press, 1938, p. 46.

[7]Joseph K. Folsom, *The Family and Democratic Society*, New York, Wiley, 1943, p. 515.

[8]Orfield, op. cit., pp. 674–75.

[9]Arkansas (1947), 60 days; Florida (1943), 90 days; Nevada (1934), 6 weeks; Wyoming (1945), 60 days; Virgin Islands (1944 and 1953), 6 weeks; Idaho (1947), 6 weeks.

[10]No one knows how many out-of-state divorces are granted in the United States, because in theory no such divorces occur. A rough estimate made by the writer for the year 1950 places the proportion at 6.4 per cent. Of course in those states having severe divorce laws, a much larger proportion of the residents go elsewhere for their divorces. In the case of New York, for example, more of its citizens get divorces out of the state than inside it. See Paul H. Jacobson, "Marital Dissolutions in New York State in Relation to Their Trend in the United States," *Milbank Memorial Fund Quarterly*, Vol. 28, January 1950, pp. 25–42.

[11]Fowler V. Harper, "The Myth of the Void Divorce," *Law and Contemporary Problems*, Vol. 2, June 1935, pp. 335–47.

[12]Ernest G. Lorenzen, "Extraterritorial Divorce—Williams v. North Carolina II," *Yale Law Journal*, Vol. 54, December 1944, p. 805.

[13]Harper, op. cit., p. 338.

[14]Alfred Cahen, *Statistical Analysis of American Divorce*, New York, Columbia University Press, 1932, p. 43.

[15]Harper, op. cit., p. 339.

[16]Ibid., p. 341.

[17]For a description and critique of this bill, see William D. Ferguson in *Cornell Law Quarterly*, Vol. 39, Fall 1953, pp. 148–53.

[18]Lewis Mayers, "Ex Parte Divorce: A Proposed Federal Remedy," *Columbia Law Review*, Vol. 54, January 1954, pp. 54–69.

[19]For a discussion of the family court idea and a review of such courts in different states, see Charles L. Chute, "Divorce and the Family Court," *Law and Contemporary Problems,* Vol. 18, Winter 1953, pp. 49–65.

[20]In Michigan, the Wayne County Circuit Court, which has jurisdiction in divorce matters, has since 1929 had attached to it the office of "Friend of the Court," the function of which is to ascertain the facts and bring in evidence of aid to the court. See Edward Pokorny, "Observations by a 'Friend of the Court,'" *Law and Contemporary Problems,* Vol. 10, Summer 1944, pp. 778–89; "The Enforcement of Foreign Decrees for Alimony," ibid., Vol. 6, Spring 1939, pp. 274–82.

[21]See Paul W. Alexander, "Let's Get the Embattled Spouses out of the Trenches," *Law and Contemporary Problems,* Vol. 18, Winter 1953, pp. 98–106; and John S. Bradway, "Family Dissolution—Limits of the Present Litigious Method" in *Selected Essays on Family Law,* pp. 881–96.

[22]Pilpel and Zavin, op. cit., p. 33.

[23]Folsom, op. cit., p. 509.

[24]There were, in addition, 839,000 wives whose husbands were absent from the home but not separated.

[25]Jacobson, op. cit., pp. 35–37.

[26]See Kingsley Davis, "Statistical Perspective on Marriage and Divorce," *Annals* of the American Academy of Political and Social Science, Vol. 272, November 1950, pp. 18–19.

[27]See Paul H. Jacobson, "Total Marital Dissolutions in the United States" in George F. Mair (ed.), *Studies in Population,* Princeton University Press, 1949, pp. 9–11.

[28]Metropolitan Life Insurance Company, *Statistical Bulletin,* Vol. 31, February 1950, p. 1.

[29]Kingsley Davis, "Children of Divorced Parents: A Sociological and Statistical Analysis," *Law and Contemporary Problems,* Summer 1944, pp. 711–12.

[30]Carl A. Weinman, "The Trial Judge Awards Custody," *Law and Contemporary Problems,* Vol. 10, Summer 1944, pp. 737–46. The whole issue of this journal is devoted to "Children of Divorced Parents." The articles as a whole comprise the best discussion of the subject in print.

[31]Catherine Groves Peele, "Social and Psychological Effects of the Availability and the Granting of Alimony on the Spouses," *Law and Contemporary Problems,* Vol. 6, Spring 1939, pp. 283–92; Willard Waller, *The Old Love and the New,* New York, Liveright, 1930.

[32]Ernest W. Burgess and Harvey J. Locke, *The Family,* New York, American Book Co., 1945, pp. 646–47.

Chapter 5

SEX BEHAVIOR AND PROBLEMS OF THE CLIMACTERIC*

by August A. Werner, M.D.

FORMERLY ASSISTANT PROFESSOR OF INTERNAL MEDICINE, ST. LOUIS UNIVERSITY SCHOOL OF MEDICINE

DOES LIFE BEGIN AT FORTY?

People say that "life begins at forty." If this phrase refers to intellectual and social activities, the expression may to a degree be accepted literally. At forty years of age normal persons should have had sufficient experiences through education and human interrelationship to have developed sound judgment or values about social relationships. At this age they should have a high degree of understanding and be mellow and tolerant toward the weaknesses, frailties, and personal peculiarities of their fellow men. Their financial and social positions should be established, and they should at least begin to have a clear vision of the future and the goal which they wish to attain. If these accomplishments are complemented by good health, then life can begin at forty.

Forty has also been described as "the dangerous age"; it can be dangerous for several reasons. At this age many persons develop a desire or have an urge to stray from the beaten path in more ways than one. They seem to sense or fear that the tide of life may ebb and they want to take a last fling at new experiences; youth in the opposite sex and flattery seem attractive. This is the age at which persons of stable character remain "hitched."

Forty can also be dangerous for reasons pertaining to health. Many persons at this age and during the succeeding decade develop disorders of the ductless glands, especially those related to sexual function. These glands are the pituitary (anterior lobe), the ovaries in the female and the testicles in the male, the adrenals, and the thyroid.

---

*Dr. August A. Werner died December 20, 1953. Dr. Morris Fishbein has edited this chapter for this edition.

DUCTLESS GLANDS WHICH INFLUENCE SEX DEVELOPMENT AND FUNCTION

The thyroid gland is the accelerator of the body functions. Thyroxin, which is the active principle of the thyroid, stimulates the chemical activity of all body cells. If there is insufficient secretion of this gland, then all body processes will be slowed; if the thyroid is too active or hypersecretes, then all activities will be accelerated. Thyroxin affects sex function indirectly by its influence on the cellular activity of the sex-related glands.

The adrenal glands produce several internal secretions, one of which is known as adrenosterone, a male sex hormone. This hormone, or secretion, at times causes disturbances in the menstrual cycle and may cause varying degrees of masculinization in women.

The pituitary gland is about the most important piece of tissue in the organism. It is about the size of a large green pea. This important structure is in the most invulnerable part of the body, a bony cavity situated at the base of the brain, about the center of the head, where the possibility of injury is remote. The pituitary has more diverse functions than any of the other ductless glands. The secretions of the pituitary gland here most concerned are the gonadotrophic or sex-gland-stimulating substances or hormones. There are two of these, one of which stimulates the development of an ovum or egg in the ovary, and the other one which produces changes in the follicle or cavity of the ovary from which the egg has been extruded.

The cells lining the small cavity in which the egg develops secrete the female sex hormones, estrogen and progesterone. Estrogen is the ovarian secretion, which at puberty stimulates secondary development of the external and internal genitals (sex organs) and breasts and changes the girl through adolescence to womanhood. Estrogen also stimulates growth of the mucous membrane which lines the cavity of the uterus or womb during the menstrual cycle. During approximately the last ten days of the menstrual cycle progesterone further stimulates this membrane in conjunction with estrogen. This is a periodic preparation each month of the womb to receive a fertilized egg and is necessary for pregnancy. If there is no fertilized egg, then pregnancy cannot occur and the cyclic preparation of the mucous membrane of the womb is of no avail. Complicated secretory glandular readjustments then take place, the mucous membrane exfoliates or sheds off, exposing small capillaries which bleed, and the woman menstruates. She then proceeds through another menstrual cycle. If all of the glands which are instrumental in maintaining the menstrual cycle function normally, and if no other adverse influences such as sickness or disease intervene, then the menstrual cycle will continue until the age for the climacteric or menopause to occur.

THE CLIMACTERIC OR MENOPAUSE

The term menopause, literally meaning cessation of menstrual flow, is commonly used to designate that critical period in a woman's life more correctly spoken of as the climacteric. Menstrual pause may occur at any time during active sexual life from various causes. Disturbances of menstrual flow, such as irregularity, profuseness, scantiness, or cessation, are only visible evidences that there is some disturbance of the function of the glands which control the menstrual mechanism. Some women believe that they are through the change of life when menstruation ceases at the climacteric. They are mistaken, for menstruation ceases only because the ovaries do not function sufficiently to produce the growth in the womb that results in bleeding. It is the decrease or absence of ovarian function that initiates all of the difficulty and not the absence of menstruation. The disturbance of, or the cessation of, menstruation is only one of the phenomena which occur at the climacteric. It is the one sign which is objective and therefore it attracts most attention, but it is far from being the most disturbing factor of the climacteric.

The so-called "change of life" is not an actual change; it only marks the end of the childbearing period in a woman's life. The ovaries, which have been primarily responsible for the sex life of the woman, begin to lose their function and their responsiveness to stimulation by the pituitary gland, which is their activator. The pituitary gland becomes secondarily disturbed, and since the pituitary exercises stimulatory influence on other glands, such as the thyroid and the adrenals, a complex crisis or climax occurs.

The climacteric is further complicated by the fact that these ductless glands exercise varying degrees of regulatory influence on the two nervous systems, namely, the central or voluntary nervous system (brain and spinal cord) and the autonomic or involuntary nervous system. Both the voluntary and the involuntary nervous systems are interrelated, but the autonomic or involuntary nervous system is seemingly more disturbed, for it is the nervous network which controls the vital life processes of the organism, over which we have no control.

Among physiological activities which are under autonomic control may be mentioned the emotions to a great extent, and the sense of physical and mental well-being, the heart and the respiratory rates, the digestion of various foods, and the marvelous chemical reactions which occur in the body and the various tissues, especially in the liver.

With disturbance of function of the ovaries and other interrelated glands and the imbalance of the nervous systems, a train of subjective symptoms occur which render the person uncomfortable. Perhaps all women experience some discomfort at the climacteric, but in many it is so mild as to be negligible; others have a more severe disturbance. In these women the symptoms can be alleviated by proper endocrine (glandular) treatment.

DURATION OF THE CLIMACTERIC OR MENOPAUSE

The climacteric varies in duration with each person. A few women enter the climacteric at about thirty-eight years of age, while others do not experience difficulty until they are approximately fifty years old. A woman need not be of climacteric age to have all of the symptoms characteristic for the menopause. Since these symptoms are initiated by a decrease or absence of ovarian function, they will occur in women whose ovaries have been removed and younger women who have decreased function, regardless of age. A woman will not be free of symptoms until she develops the glandular equilibrium characteristic for the postmenopausal period. In some women glandular balance may occur within three to six months, while in others the imbalance may last five, six, or even more years. There are also some women who claim not to have had any appreciable disturbance at the time of cessation of menstruation and who perhaps five to ten years later, at ages fifty to sixty years, develop the typical symptoms of the climacteric; they still have glandular instability. Practically all these women respond nicely to treatment with estrogenic (female sex) hormones.

SOME CAUSES FOR DECREASED OR ABSENT FUNCTION OF THE OVARIES

Decreased ovarian function may be due to degeneration or inflammatory processes in the tissues of the ovary or those adjacent to the ovaries. Examples are inflamed tubes or appendicitis, which may cause degeneration in the glands. Decrease in ovarian function may be secondary to constitutional disease processes as some anemias, tuberculosis, or malignancies. Vitamin deficiency in the diet may cause it. It may be primary, as in some cases in which the ovaries fail to develop, or the ovaries may never attain full development and function. It may be secondary to secretory deficiency of the pituitary gland (which secretions are necessary to stimulate function of the ovaries), as in some types of infantilism, or in some obese girls and women. It may occur after partial castration, when one ovary has been removed or only a small part of one ovary remains. It will be complete when both ovaries are removed, unless there is accessory ovarian tissue. It always occurs at the climacteric.

SYMPTOMS CHARACTERISTIC OF DEFICIENCY OR ABSENCE OF OVARIAN
FUNCTION, AND THE CLIMACTERIC

The disturbances which accompany deficiency or absence of ovarian function and which occur, especially at the climacteric, may be divided into objective signs and subjective symptoms.

Objective Signs. The objective signs are, first, various types of menstrual disorder occurring separately or with varying degrees of combination, such as irregularity, scantiness of flow with decreased duration, and, finally, cessation of menstruation. Excessive bleeding at menstruation and irregular bleeding between the menstrual periods also occur at times, but these two conditions are more likely to occur in women who are approaching the natural menopause than in those of younger age. Cessation of bleeding usually follows removal of the ovaries, as for infections or tumors.

Obesity, characterized by a generalized deposition of fat or a localized deposition over the hips and fatty enlargement of the breasts, also occurs at the climacteric. The localization of fat over the hips and in the breasts usually occurs in younger women who have decreased ovarian function and in castrates following operation, after they reach the age of approximately thirty years. Many obese girls, when they attain the age of puberty, have delayed, irregular, or scanty menstruation, or they may have complete absence of menstruation; this is usually due to a complex glandular disorder. Following the termination of pregnancy, a complicated glandular readjustment must occur in the woman. Frequently the glands do not strike a normal balance, with the result that a certain number have various types of menstrual disorder and some of them date their onset of obesity from one of their pregnancies. Other signs of deficient ovarian function are shrinkage or decrease in the size of the sex organs and breasts and loss of hair about the genitals and under the arms. The lining of the vagina becomes thin and pale and it may be tender and painful during sexual relationships.

Subjective Symptoms. The subjective symptoms accompanying decreased ovarian function render the patient more uncomfortable than do the objective signs. These subjective symptoms may be classified as nervous, circulatory, and general in origin.

NERVOUS SYMPTOMS. Subjective nervousness is an intense feeling of nervous tension. Many patients state that they feel jumpy or trembly inside their body; a common expression is that they have "butterflies in the stomach." Some state that they feel like screaming, or as though they might lose their mind. In most instances they do not have a tremor, but occasionally this nervousness may become so extreme as to cause some tremulousness.

Excitability is a nervous state in which the persons respond to ordinary stimuli in an exaggerated manner, especially in regard to their psychic response. Unfavorable news, slight mishaps, arguments, all manner of little occurrences that would not disturb a normal individual cause quite a nervous and mental flurry.

These people are irritable and easily aggravated or excited to anger by deed or word. They are hard to please. Noises of playing children, the radio —almost anything stirs them to action. In fact, they need no special stimulus. They are simply hard to get along with. In many instances they acknowledge this condition but state that they cannot help themselves.

Headaches of various types and locations occur, but they are rarely migrainous. Migraine is a sick headache, usually located on one side of the head, and it may be accompanied by nausea and vomiting. When migraine occurs with glandular disorders, it is probably only initiated or aggravated by the glandular irregularity. The usual headaches may be described by the patient as dull to severe and not neuralgic in type. They may occur irregularly or may be continuous. Patients have been observed with headaches lasting continuously for thirty to forty days which were relieved by proper glandular treatment. Their location may be over the temples, in front of the head, or above the eyes, and there may be a sensation of pressure back of the eyes. Patients also complain of a severe ache in the top (vertex) of the head; they describe this as if a great weight were resting on the head, and some state that they feel as if the top of the head wanted to push out.

Among nervous symptoms may be classed psychic depression, commonly called "the blues." When in this state these patients do not have interest in ordinary activities. They cannot "cheer up." It is an effort to smile or laugh; they do not want company or care to enter into pleasurable entertainment. Frequently this depression is accompanied by crying without reason. They state that they cannot prevent this. This condition, if untreated or unimproved, may progress to anxiety psychosis in which the patients feel ill at ease. They have a fear of impending danger which they cannot explain. They worry unnecessarily and feel that something dreadful will happen to them, their loved ones, or others. At times they imagine that someone is watching them or that they hear strange noises. Some patients, especially in the menopause, become self-accusatory and others, whose past life had been rather bohemian, develop an extreme religious outlook.

Decreased memory and ability to concentrate are observed. They forget where they put things. They cannot remember, especially recent events. The mental processes are slow and they cerebrate slowly. The mind seems hazy or fogged. If they read an article they cannot tell what they have read and frequently must reread it three or four times before it registers.

Formication, a sensation as if ants or insects are crawling over the skin, especially on the arms, back, and body, is complained of frequently. There also may be prickling or tingling of the skin.

A large majority of these patients complain of sleeping poorly. They may be restless, sleeping only for short intervals during the night. Some fall asleep quickly upon retiring, only to awaken within a half-hour and remain awake for varying lengths of time. Others do not sleep upon retiring until after midnight. Some complain that they sleep well until 2 or 3 A.M. and then remain awake until morning. This is known as insomnia.

Patients who do not sleep at night find themselves exhausted the next day and must sleep during the daytime. This desire to sleep during the daylight hours must not be confused with somnolence. True somnolence is a condition characterized by inability to remain awake either night or day. These people are sleepy most of the time. They sleep soundly all night and fall asleep when they sit down during the day. Patients have been known to fall asleep while driving automobiles and go into the ditch or strike objects or other cars and have been accused of being drunk, especially if injured and rendered unconscious.

CIRCULATORY SYMPTOMS. Hot flushes have always been considered positive proof that a woman is in the menopause. This is not literally true, for some patients who have many climacteric symptoms do not have hot flushes. Hot flushes are characterized by sudden redness of the face and neck, upper chest, and at times most of the body. This is akin to blushing and is due to a dilation of the superficial capillaries of the skin. It is a very uncomfortable sensation and generally is of short duration, but it may last for half an hour or even longer, if the statements of some patients are correct. Frequently they are described as a smothering sensation. They may be accompanied by dizziness, spots before the eyes, or tingling or prickling sensations over the head, neck, and body. They are frequently accompanied by profuse perspiration. Occasionally hot flushes alternate with or follow chilly sensations over the same areas. Hot flushes may accompany disturbances of the heart and blood vessels, especially hardening or thickening of the vessels with high blood pressure, but these conditions can be eliminated by proper diagnosis.

These patients notice rapid heart rate, palpitation, and shortness of breath more than usual upon moderate effort, without any disease condition to account for it.

They also complain of easy fatigability; sweeping, ascending a flight of stairs, walking a block to the store—almost any moderate effort causes them to fatigue more than normally. With this they may have mild to moderate palpitation, increased heart rate, and shortness of breath. Patients frequently state that they are more tired upon arising in the morning than when they retired the night before.

Dizziness with change of position and even while changing position in bed is another frequent symptom, generally more annoying than serious.

Frequently there are dark spots or silvery specks floating before the eyes. Dizziness, ringing in the ears, and spots before the eyes often occur concurrently and of these dizziness is the most frequent.

Cold hands, feet, and extremities are commonly found in this condition. The pulse rate is usually not changed much, unless there is thyroid disturbance. In some instances the blood pressure may be increased, but this usually returns to normal with proper treatment.

GENERAL SYMPTOMS. Constipation is frequently found in people of climacteric age, but is probably not directly attributable to the glandular disturbance. In the vast majority of patients constipation is probably due to improper habits, diet, or gastrointestinal disorders.

Patients complain of vague pains, and their location may be as legion as is the distribution of the sensory nerves. One of the most common pains is a boring ache which may be located below the lower angles of the shoulder blades or in the center of the upper part of the back. Again, it may be anywhere along the spine, especially in the lower back, and the legs may ache. Pain in the chest, over the region of the heart, is frequently complained of; usually this pain over the heart is in the chest wall and is not due to any heart condition.

A condition known as menopausal arthritis is characterized by soreness in various joints throughout the body, without redness or much swelling. The joints most commonly involved are those of the fingers, hands, wrists, shoulders, and the spine, especially in the lower part of the back. In some instances there is some thickening of the joints in the fingers, which is painful.

The average age of onset of symptoms in women with the climacteric or menopause whom I have seen was 40.8 years. One must always remember that it is not necessary for women to have absence of menstruation to have this group of symptoms. Cessation of menstruation is not the climacteric; it is only the visible evidence that the woman is having insufficient function of the sex glands, and whenever this occurs she is liable to develop this group of symptoms for which she will need treatment, whether she does or does not menstruate.

CLIMACTERIC PSYCHOSIS (INVOLUTIONAL MELANCHOLIA)

Probably the first biologic urges of primitive man were for food, security, sex, and association with his fellows. Closely associated with the satisfaction and frustrations of these drives are the emotions. The emotions represent psychic responses to internal and especially to external stimuli. These responses are mediated through the central and autonomic nervous systems and the secretions (hormones) of the ductless glands.

Disordered function of the ductless glands, by over- or undersupply of these secretions, can so disturb persons emotionally that they manifest psychoses. The hormonal conflicts of pregnancy and the necessary readjustments following labor may cause profound disturbances of the personality and psychosis.

After an extended observation of a large number of patients over a period of years, with mild to extreme menopausal symptoms, I have concluded that so-called involutional melancholia is only the severest manifestation of the disturbances at this period in life.

THE MALE CLIMACTERIC

Men are subject to decreased function of the sex glands, just as women are, especially in later life. Both men and women have a pituitary-sex gland relationship.

In the girl at puberty the sex-stimulating secretions of the pituitary gland stimulate the ovaries to function, with the development of a follicle in the ovary and the production of an egg. The cells lining the follicle secrete the female sex hormone, which in turn stimulates development of the breasts, the internal and external genitals, and the configuration of the body, which changes from that of the girl through adolescence to womanhood.

In the boy at puberty the pituitary sex-stimulating secretions stimulate the testicles to function. Certain cells in the testicles, known as interstitial cells, are stimulated, and these secrete the male sex hormone, which initiates development of the secondary sex characteristics and the other changes as he develops from boyhood through adolescence to normal manhood.

The most obvious and fundamental difference which occurs as a result of this pituitary-sex gland relationship in the human male and female is the fact that the normal woman menstruates.

The menstrual cycle may be looked upon as an extra phenomenon in the woman and not as an occurrence necessary for her sense of well-being. If the uterus or womb is removed and the ovaries are healthy and their function is not disturbed, her pituitary-sex gland relationship will continue as it does in the man and she can and will feel perfectly normal until the climacteric is reached.

Cessation of menstruation is not the climacteric and is not of such great importance as it was formerly supposed to be. Cessation of menstruation is only visible evidence in the woman that there is beginning decrease or cessation of the function of her ovaries. The climacteric is the result of the glandular imbalance and not the result of the menstrual disturbance.

As a result of the overemphasis which has been placed upon the cessation of menstruation in the woman and because the man does not have this phenomenon, many believe that the man does not have a climacteric. There is absolutely no basis for the belief that the man does not have a decrease in sex function in later life and that he cannot have a climacteric. To be in the climacteric does not necessarily preclude the possibility of sexual relationship, but there is a decline in sex desire and the ability in the man to have sexual relationship as frequently as in earlier life; this also applies to the woman. Women of climacteric age have no more sex potency than have men of the same age; the seeming difference is only a matter of anatomical structure.

In the woman the disturbed menstruation is objective evidence that she is having a disturbance of the function of her ovaries and is in the climacteric. Because of the absence of this phenomenon in the man it is seemingly more difficult to make the diagnosis of the climacteric, unless one has this group of symptoms in mind. I believe, from experience with male patients, that practically as many men as women experience some degree of glandular disturbance, with characteristic symptoms, if the conditions are recognized and if correct information is available.

The climacteric usually occurs later in men than in women. If at any time after the onset of sexual function there is a definite decrease in this function, regardless of age, the person is liable to develop the climacteric symptoms. (While they may not have reached the physiologic climacteric, they reach it psychically.—Ed.)

Decreased sex function in men may be primary or secondary. In primary insufficiency of the sex glands, normally placed testes have never functioned to a normal degree. Secondary decreased function of the testes occurs when these glands apparently have functioned normally and later there is a decrease in their secretory activity. Secondary failure to function normally may occur at any time during the period of actual sexual life of the individual, and it may result from insufficient stimulation of the testicles by the pituitary gland, or failure of adequate response of the testicles to normal stimulation by the pituitary. The testicles may be subject to decreased function following toxic conditions, infections, and various other ailments. Insufficient function of the thyroid gland is sometimes responsible for the insufficient secretion of the testicles, by failure to stimulate normal chemical cellular activity of all body structures, including the sex glands.

Complete or partial loss of function of the testicles can also occur from any of the following conditions, namely, castration or bilateral inflammation of the testicles from any cause, especially mumps or following operations for hernia (rupture), if the circulation to the testicles is markedly impaired. X-ray radiation of the male genital organs in the region of the testicles may injure these glands so that they will lose their function, if they are not properly protected. In some instances it is necessary to use the X ray for treatment, as in malignant conditions. If any of these harmful conditions occur after the patient has had normal sex function, severe glandular imbalance will result in the appearance of the symptoms characteristic for the climacteric, and these symptoms may persist with varying intensity until the time for the individual to develop a normal glandular balance, which may be an indefinite number of years.

SUBJECTIVE SYMPTOMS

After a man has developed normally and has functioned normally sexually and then has decreased or absent function at some later date, the diagnostic evidence for the condition is chiefly subjective rather than objective. The group of symptoms which will be described result from functional imbalance between the pituitary and the sex glands (the thyroid and adrenal glands may be secondarily involved), with disturbance of the autonomic and central nervous systems. The symptoms are, necessarily, chiefly functional. They have been classified as nervous, circulatory, and general.

Nervous Symptoms. Most of the patients complain of an intense subjective nervousness. There is a feeling of tension and a sensation of inward tremulousness; they are "jittery." Many state that this is especially noticeable upon arising in the morning or during the night. It is accentuated by excitement, effort, or fatigue, and then a tremor may be noticeable.

There is decreased ability for mental concentration, the mental processes are slow, and these persons are forgetful, especially for recent events. If they read an article they cannot tell what they have read and must reread it several times before it registers; names, figures, and dates are especially difficult to remember.

Depression, commonly called "the blues," is an important symptom; when this is present the patients have a loss of interest in their work, in their home, or in their past pleasurable diversions; they want to avoid people, and do not care for social activities. They realize that there is something wrong within themselves; they become introverts, are ill at ease, have fear of some impending danger, and worry unnecessarily. There is a loss of self-confidence and a feeling of futility. At this stage of the condition these patients verge on psychosis, may be self-accusatory, have thoughts of self-destruction, and may actually commit the act. This extreme stage has previously been referred to as involutional melancholia; it is a psychosis, but of definite glandular origin, and should be entitled "climacteric psychosis."

Circulatory Symptoms. Some few men have hot flushes similar to those of women. Hot flushes are characterized by a sudden redness of the face and neck, upper chest, and at times most of the body. It is a very uncomfortable sensation, generally of short duration, but it may last an hour or even longer.

General Symptoms. Lassitude and fatigability are often present. Some of these people state that there is pronounced decrease of endurance and that they fatigue easily. Others complain that they are constantly tired, or that on arising in the morning they are unrested or feel more exhausted than when they retired the night before.

These people also complain of vague pains, and their location may be in any part of the body or extremities. Frequent sites of pain are in the shoulders, wrists, fingers, and along the spinal column. This pain is usually not accompanied by redness, swelling, or temperature, and is frequently spoken of as rheumatoid arthritis and climacteric arthritis.

Most of these men state that they have noticed a decrease in sex function. Decrease in sex function does not necessarily mean that the desire and ability are entirely lost, for these may persist in varying degrees throughout the life of the individual. In many instances the decline of sex function and the persistence of desire cause many men to consult the physician.

Many of these patients complain of gastric (stomach) distention and eructation after meals; in most instances this is probably a nervous indigestion and disappears with proper treatment. Constipation is frequently present during the climacteric, but in the vast majority of patients it is probably due to improper habits, diets, or other conditions.

The great majority of my patients volunteered the information that their sex desire and potency were decreased or absent, but this condition, with few exceptions, was not their chief concern. They were more interested in having relief from their symptoms, especially those which were nervous and psychic; they wanted to feel well so that they could work. One can almost surely promise a climacteric patient relief from his symptoms and a feeling of well-being by treatment with the proper sex hormones.

INTERSEXUALITY

Each individual results from the union of two sexual cells, an ovum (egg) and a spermatozoon (male germinal element). Therefore, each individual is primarily bisexual and has the rudiments of both sexes. The development of the sex structures, up to a certain point, during the first few weeks of pregnancy is from the same tissues and is the same for both sexes. Because of this condition, excessive stimulation by the opposite glandular sex secretions can modify sex structures and male or female characteristics.

Intersexuality is a condition in a person or an animal characterized by the coexistence of both male and female sex structures. These structures may vary markedly in their degree of development. Just what influences determine whether the fertilized ovum or egg shall produce a normal male or female have not as yet been satisfactorily explained. The conditions which cause intersexuality must be operative very early during pregnancy.

Intersexuality has been produced experimentally by injecting large amounts of male or .female sex hormones into pregnant rats. Injection of excessive amounts of male sex hormone affects the female progeny, so that they have sex structures characteristic for both sexes, but it does not disturb the normal sex development of the male offspring. However, just the opposite effect will be produced if the experiment is reversed and excessive amounts of female sex hormones are injected; then the males will be intersexual and the females will be normal.

HERMAPHRODITISM

Intersexuality in man is designated as hermaphroditism, and the condition may be true or false.

True hermaphroditism is of extremely rare occurrence. It is characterized by the presence in an individual of ovarian and testicular tissues, both of which tissues should be capable of functioning. As a result of the presence of functioning tissues of both sexes, the internal and external sex organs may show all degrees of differentiation between male and female development, as may also the bodily configuration.

False hermaphroditism is characterized by the presence of the functioning organs of one sex (ovaries or testicles), with some marked secondary sex characteristics of the other, or a combination of both, with various conceivable anomalies of development of the genital organs.

ABNORMAL MODIFICATION OF THE SEX STRUCTURES AND CHARACTERISTICS

The degree of modification of the sex structures and characteristics depends upon the time during which the excessive amount of either sex hormone is operative. If it occurs during pregnancy, before the birth of the child, the modification will be more definite than if it occurs after birth. If the child is sexually normal at birth and then develops some condition which causes excessive secretion of the opposite sex hormone, there will be masculinization of the female or feminization of the male.

If this adverse sex stimulation occurs after the person has reached adult age, when modification of body structures normally ceases, the changes will not be so noticeable as when they occur during childhood and adolescence. These changes are probably more noticeable in the female than in the male.

PRECOCIOUS PUBERTY

Precocious puberty is a condition in which secondary sex development occurs before the normal time for its appearance. It may occur at any time, from birth to the normal age for onset of puberty.

It is characterized in the male by early increase in the size of the external sex organs, appearance of hair about the genitals, under the arms, and on the face, accompanied by evidence of sex function. In the female usually the first objective evidence of precocious puberty is very early development of the genital organs and the breasts, early onset of menstruation, and the appearance of hair growth characteristic for the woman. The voice also changes from that of child to the adult type.

DELAYED PUBERTY

There may also be delayed puberal changes. If the child is markedly undersize for age and there is delay in the development of the secondary sex characteristics, it is designated as "infantilism." A boy or girl having normal growth may also have delayed sexual development, and this condition may be due to retardation or failure of the sex glands to develop and function. In this condition the girl will have absent or late onset of menstruation, and the menstrual cycles may be irregular and the flow of short duration and scant. The condition may be inherent in the sex glands, which fail to develop and function; or the pituitary gland, which stimulates the sex glands to function, may be deficient.

MASCULINIZATION AND VIRILISM IN THE FEMALE

There are two sets of paired glands, the secretions of which can, under abnormal conditions, cause masculinization in the woman. These are the ovaries and the adrenal glands.

The center of each ovary of the woman contains rudimentary testicular (male) tissue, which normally remains dormant. Under certain conditions this undifferentiated, dormant male tissue may become active and secrete male hormone, which may override the primary female tendency with the possibility of inhibition of the female sex function and the production of various degrees of modification of the female sex characteristics. In extreme cases a woman who has previously had normal feminine characteristics and function may cease menstruating, the breasts become smaller, masculine-type hair growth appears on the face, chest, abdomen, and the extremities, the feminine bodily contour becomes more like that of the male, and the voice becomes deeper because of changes in the larynx. The external sex organs also show marked changes.

Some women at the climacteric develop varying degrees of masculine-type hair growth, especially about the upper lip, chin, and the face. This is called "virilism." At the climacteric the ovaries lose their responsiveness to stimulation by the sex-stimulating hormones of the pituitary gland, with the result that there is decrease and finally absence of secretion of female sex hormones by the ovaries. With the absence of the female sex hormones, the dormant male tissue in the center of the ovary may become sufficiently active to stimulate the development of the abnormal hair growth.

The adrenal glands, which rest upon the upper pole of each kidney, are at times potent disturbers of femininity. The tissues from which the ovaries and the cortical portions of the adrenal glands develop lie in close proximity at the very beginning of pregnancy. Because of this, small pieces of adrenal cortical tissue may occasionally be found in the ovaries. The adrenal cortex produces a male sex hormone known as adrenosterone. If the adrenal cortex secretes too actively, or if there is a tumor of the adrenal cortex, which secretes excessive amounts of this male hormone in the woman, or if there is an active tumor composed of this adrenal cortex tissue, situated in the ovary, then the woman will become masculinized. This male sex secretion of the adrenal cortex may also cause mild virilism (masculine-type hair growth) in the woman at the climacteric, after the ovaries have ceased to function and the inhibitory influence of the female sex secretion is absent.

If married couples have knowledge of the above sexual phenomena, many marital difficulties can be avoided. Love rests upon the solid foundation of respect for the individual and his or her rights, and if this is realized and an honest and true effort is made toward mutual understanding and co-operation, marriage can continue to be the happy institution that the young couple intended.

Chapter 6

WOMEN'S CONFLICTING VALUES IN RELATION TO MARRIAGE ADJUSTMENT

by Emily Hartshorne Mudd, Ph.D.

EXECUTIVE DIRECTOR, MARRIAGE COUNCIL OF PHILADELPHIA, AND ASSISTANT
PROFESSOR OF FAMILY STUDY IN PSYCHIATRY, UNIVERSITY OF PENNSYLVANIA,
SCHOOL OF MEDICINE

Marriage is entered into and carried out successfully or fails in the United States primarily on the basis of the interpersonal relations of the two people who agree to undertake it. Women are concerned with various values which may be conflicting. Conflict is discord manifested in actions, feelings, or effects. Conflict is significant because it is the base of conscious life. Conflicting values can be world-wide, as in contemporary global tension, or they can be local and relate to such simple things as individual opinions about the use of electric washers or the clothes one wears. All human beings live in conflict and have conflicting values. Variation is evident in the intensity and degree to which a conflict disturbs the activity of an individual person and those with whom he is associated.

Do women as human beings have conflicting values, or is it that men have conflicting values about women? Or is the society in which men and women live responsible for forming and nurturing conflicts? Woman is a complex but oriented organism. She has well-focused needs and goals; she has the desire and ability to attain these goals—goals of physical and mental maturity, the chance to love and be loved, to reproduce her kind, to participate actively in the worth-while work of the world; in other words, to be a person in her own right, to realize in the fullest sense creativity.

Undoubtedly one of the clues to the emotional conflicts or satisfactions of women lies in the religious concepts of any given society. Sophie Drinker points out that the Romans, for instance, expressed their relation to the higher powers in a prayer: *"Sive deus, sive dea* [whether god, whether goddess] . . ."* To them, Life Force manifested itself through both male and female. By today the industrial revolution has removed much of the economic value of woman as the producer of products essential for homemaking. The increasing mechanization of life has limited even further woman's own feeling of worth. Actually, the easy availability of the necessary commodities may relieve toil, but it has also removed the importance and much of the skill and uniqueness from the position of mistress of the small apartment. The routine tasks become more or less monotonous drudgery, requiring little ingenuity and utilizing only a fraction of the ability of the average woman. In addition, many college women—handmaidens of higher education, with its emphasis on the intellectual—have believed that actual housework and the physical care of children do not utilize their training to the best advantage of society.

Constant improvements in living conditions are in the direction of further mechanization. The home is depicted with even more labor-saving and comfort-giving devices. Rooms may have electrically charged wire to which dust particles will be drawn, thereby eliminating cleaning and much laundering. Homes come in ready-to-order sections, functionally adapted to the changing needs of the family, one section for the bride and groom, which can be varied appropriately for the type adapted to baby. Other sections, suitable for young children, can be traded in later when "daughter dates Dick." Nearing perfection are house-heating devices using atomic energy, while the same power is used to produce rays capable of killing bacteria in food so that refrigeration will not be necessary.

All of this may eliminate labor, but it will not eliminate human feelings, needs, and desires. Does it not merely present us with an even more drastic challenge to understand and develop competence to meet these needs and desires as real and vital essentials to life? Serenity of the heart and soul will not be achieved by having things done to you and for you. Being a turner of switches, a watcher rather than a participant, does not make for inner satisfaction and feelings of worth.

It is small wonder that in certain instances the attitude of depreciation of the role of wife and mother only, plus the practical difficulties of adequate child care if she has a job away from home, plus the sex discrimination and competition in the job world, induce a variety of conflicts in the modern woman which definitely deter her growth and spiritual development and her feelings of belief in her value as a woman. Ensuing complications, both physical and emotional, are often evident. An illuminating description of some of these problems is found in *Women after College*. Strecker shows how the results of these often unresolved conflicts are reaped by the helpless, sometimes hopeless, children of the "American Mom." Lundberg and Farnham, in their controversial book, *Modern Woman: The Lost Sex*, reiterate that the woman of today, rejecting, overprotecting, or dominating her children, is bringing up a race of neurotics. Margaret Mead scrutinizes astutely the relationship between women and men in many of her books, Simone de Beauvoir decries the Second Sex, and a somewhat different emphasis is introduced through Ashley-Montagu's controversial volume, *The Natural Superiority of Women.*

The combination of spiritual starvation, mechanization, and dual roles has been overwhelming to some contemporary women who have found it difficult to surmount the barriers to normal activity. Many a woman thus finds herself tossed hither and yon by the pressures of her world, her parents, her job, her husband, her children, or her social milieu, or she charts a stormy course and steers with determination, in spite of combined pressure, toward a beacon, an ideal. Some women try every type of compromise; others exhibit every type of protest. Some ask for too little, denying their value; others demand too much, overasserting their frustrations and feeling of inequality. The results of these conscious and unconscious conflicts propel some women to the physician's office, to the counseling service, to the divorce court, or unhappily to one of the thousands of untrained and unethical advisers who live profitably from the misery of others.

A marriage counseling office finds discouraging evidence of the practical effect on individual personality growth, on marriage and on family life, and so on the community, of situations in which conflicts remain unresolved. The following are illustrations of situations for which clients, men as well as women, sought help. So often the conflicts are the result of different expectations of one or both partners in a marriage of the role of the other; expectations which were built up in the childhood of each and in turn were dependent on the cultural conditions of the particular family group, a concept amplified by Pearl Buck in *Of Men and Women.*

The situation of Mrs. A shows how the activities of a machine age have changed and in part removed the concept of value from the homemaker.

Mrs. A was the "girl back home" when Mr. A, an ambitious, intelligent man in his thirties, had married. She was all his mother had been and more—a good cook, a neat housekeeper, a devoted mother who asked for no more than to perfect her home and dedicate her life to her man. In a large city Mr. A, as a successful businessman, found himself thrown with men whose wives were of a different vintage. Modern equipment, small apartments, and few children left them with the feeling that domestic activities were beneath them and of little value. They were aggressive in their appearance and manner, sophisticated in their glamour, their entertaining, and their lack of household duties, active in clubs and community. Their days, as their husbands', were full of "keeping up with the Joneses" in clothes, cars, schools, entertainments—competition, as Margaret Mead contends, in goals of triviality. Mr. A now had money in plenty. He wanted his wife to take her place with "the other girls" and do him proud. He told her so, at first gently and later accusingly. Helpless, frightened, and confused (as Lundberg and Farnham claim so many American women are), Mrs. A clung to her familiar world with tenacity. Mr. A became disgusted, bored, abusive, and resentful in turn. It took him only a short time with the counselor to realize that Mrs. A needed help, reassurance, encouragement, and kindness to learn gradually to try herself and her abilities in a new and strange world, a world which measured success so much in the doing and attached so little importance to the being. Gradually she began to realize that this new effort did not threaten her basic value as homemaker, mate, and mother. And her competence in adjusting herself to her husband's changing needs strengthened when she developed faith in herself as a dynamic unit of society, able to create human relationships.

Mrs. B's behavior was very different from Mrs. A's. Mrs. B exhibited marked protest against her environment and resented her womanhood. She reconciled herself to her sex by becoming a designer and by attempting to associate with men as professional equals. Having adopted this attitude, she married another designer. Now, however, her impulses as a woman asserted themselves, and she found herself disturbed by the criticism of her friends that a woman could not be successful as a career designer and as a wife. She was not able to resolve this conflict successfully and alternated between being an artist and a wife. Her dilemma was not that she was uncreative in the matter of design, but that her energy was spent in denying the value of womanhood as a creative force. Her identification with men *in her career injured her spirit as a creative woman.*

The case of Mrs. C shows in still another way how a woman can become discouraged by her particular social milieu. Mrs. C asked for so little that she reminded the counselor of the proverbial worm. It was the beginning of the turning of this inner worm that led her to seek professional help. Mrs. C had been trained as a teacher. Because she was a woman, marriage was the answer to her desire for children. Because her contacts were limited she married an almost illiterate man who was trying to earn his living as a laborer. Forced to do manual work, she found herself in circumstances for which she was unprepared by temperament, training, and background. One by one she gave up her old interests in a constant struggle to adjust herself. At the age of forty her life was drab and humdrum. Her sole connection with the outside world was a friendship with the wife of a teacher in another state. So after twenty years of marriage she felt herself a failure, and she felt her marriage was a failure too. In this situation also the criteria held by society in regard to the duties of a married woman were so inimical to the development of her inner life that she did not have the stamina to assert herself. Society so often puts little value on the possible contributions of womanhood, with the result, in Helene Deutsch's words, that "there is hardly a woman in whom the normal psychic conflicts do not result in a pathological distortion, at some point, of the biologic process of motherhood."

The next situation shows a woman who demanded so much that her marriage relationship became almost unbearable. A librarian by profession, Mrs. D was a woman of great energy and ambition. She married a man who was equally ambitious and gave up her paid position because of the concept held by her and her young husband that "man was the provider and woman's place was in the home." She found housework and the care of three children tedious and not broad enough to give scope to her talents. She attained middle age discontented and bitter. She was dissatisfied with her children who, incidentally, had turned out remarkably well; she did not feel that her husband's outstanding success in business was worth the sacrifice of her own career—a feeling apparently shared, if not verbalized, by many women, according to Della D. Cyrus.[1] She demanded complete devotion and constant attention from her husband. Her unreasonable demands finally drove him to seek distraction elsewhere. Mrs. D's frustration begat a domineering attitude which brought strain and unhappiness to her whole family. Here again we see a woman who did not find sufficient opportunity in her limited conception of her role and whose husband did not know how to help her by attributing equal value to her contribution. What she lacked was more a feeling of the worth-whileness of herself as a person rather than an actual lack of opportunity for the use of potentially constructive energy.

Mrs. E was like Mrs. D in her ability and aggressiveness, but her marriage differed in that her husband was neither brilliant nor successful. Mrs. E, therefore, had ample opportunity to contribute within the supposed limits of marriage. She made such good use of her abilities that she became not only the housekeeper but the sole support of the family. Her husband, thus outdistanced, made little effort to find congenial work and finally gave his affection to a sweet little clinging vine for whom he divorced his wife. During the process of realizing what was happening Mrs. E was precipitated into severe conflict and sought counseling help. She knew that she was contributing more than he as an effective person in their social group, but at the same time she wanted to preserve her family. Her type of conflict was the result of her failure to exert her powers toward the goal of creating a human relationship in which her husband could feel himself as of equal value to her and to their children.

SEXUAL ADJUSTMENTS, BASIS OF CONFLICTS

Wherever there are conflicts in marriage which continue over a period of time to cause increasing frustration for one or both partners, almost inevitably there is difficulty in the sexual adjustment of the couple. Either a mutually adequate sexual adjustment is never achieved, or if this experience of loving exchange has been achieved, the completeness and harmony of the relationship lessen and finally may be totally impaired. As D. H. Lawrence puts it, "It was from herself she wanted to be saved, from her own inward anger and resistance—and suddenly—it was gone, the resistance was gone, and she began to melt in a marvelous peace—and further and further rolled the waves of herself away from herself, leaving her, till suddenly—she was gone. She was gone, she was not, and she was born; a woman." Esther

Harding contends that "nothing but devotion to a faith in the rightness of one's own nature can release energy, be it sexual or spiritual." When a woman's emotional conflicts are resolved in favor of the naturalness, rightness, and spiritual power of sexual intercourse, then, and then only, is she freed to give herself, to unite with her man, to achieve the essence of womanhood.

That women have been a "Force in History" has been proved beyond doubt by Mary Beard. Although we have so far emphasized women's conflicting values and cases in which their conflicts have not been resolved, fortunately many women in our times do find satisfactory solutions even within the complexities of the present social order. Such women achieve a degree of comfort, a serenity in being themselves, which in turn brings comfort and serenity to those around them. Usually this finding of themselves as women comes through emotionally satisfying orientation to one or a combination of the three general roles which existing cultural patterns leave open to women. In any one or a combination of these roles such women feel themselves to be of value and are so recognized by others.

THE ROLES OF WOMEN IN LIFE

Marriage, Motherhood, Aid to Husband. The first of these roles satisfies women who feel that their finest contribution can be made through marriage, motherhood, and identification with the creative activities of their man. Who better illustrates this than Emma Wedgwood Darwin, wife of the great scientist Charles Darwin, whose writings on evolution have so revolutionized modern life? Darwin was always physically frail and would, in all probability, have been unable to cope with the complex responsibilities of life and a family—plus creative research—had it not been for the unswerving devotion of this wonderful woman. Lady Darwin put at the disposal of her husband an absolute belief and confidence in the things which were vital to him—his researches. She took over the management of his comfortable income, his house and children; she protected her scientist from interruptions and worries that would distract his singleness of purpose; she helped in the preservation of specimens and notes; in addition to all this, she bore him five sons and two daughters. In part, as a result of this devotion, three of these sons have been knighted for outstanding achievement in their own right.

Again, in this first group, we think of Madame Pasteur, whose devotion and loyalty to a brilliant and, at that time, an often misunderstood chemist carried her to rural communities, exposed her to ridicule and persecution, put her loyalty to the test through the illness and death from typhoid fever of two of her three children. At all times she accepted the vagaries of a household whose routine revolved around the exotic and untimely events of an experimental laboratory, believing that the hoped-for results of her husband's creative mind merited the means. This great woman found courage even to fortify her own beloved daughter, at the moment of her approaching motherhood, for the continued absence of her young husband who was closeted behind locked doors in her father's laboratory, to tell her that this was part of the life of a great man's wife and daughter—to help her find strength to bear it. Cosima Liszt Wagner summed up this philosophy with the words, "Women are put into the world to help great men."

The majority of American women quite consciously identify themselves with this role, and many, like Mrs. Mamie Eisenhower; Lady Franks, charming American wife of the British Ambassador and mother of five; Mrs. Grace Richards Conant, wife of Harvard's former president, later High Commissioner of Germany; Mrs. Walter B. Cannon, wife of the famous physiologist; and Mrs. Alfred Kinsey, make a striking success of it. As one modern and prominent wife puts it, "To be a successful wife is a career in itself, requiring, among other things, the qualities of a diplomat, a businesswoman, a good cook, a trained nurse, a schoolteacher, a politician, and a glamour girl. It can be the most utterly rewarding of all careers."[2] It is natural and to be expected that the names of women in this group are seldom known beyond the confines of their families and friends unless their husbands become famous. As a generic type, however, they constitute the large majority of women in this country and are the backbone of our civilization, a fact well recognized in popular song and literature, where they have long been enthroned.

Contributor to the World's Work Without Marriage. The second of these roles satisfies women who almost completely sublimate their instinctive biological drives in creative work outside of childbearing. In this group we find the great reformers of the past century. Such leaders as the fearless Susan B. Anthony, advocate of equal rights for women; Florence Nightingale, the courageous and indomitable nurse; Dr. Anna Howard Shaw, a great leader in woman suffrage; Jane Addams, the interpreter of the lives of the underprivileged; and Cecilia Beaux, the artist. In our own day we find Federal Judge Florence Allen, mentioned as a candidate for the Supreme Court of the United States; Dr. Alice Hamilton, famed for research in industrial hazards and former woman member of the Harvard Medical School faculty; Catherine McBride, president of Bryn Mawr College; Dr. Florence Seibert, prize-winning researcher in tuberculosis; Malvina Hoffman, illustrious sculptress whose sensitive creations people the Hall of Man at Chicago's Field

Museum; Emily Green Balch, winner of the Nobel prize in 1946 for her work toward world peace; and Helen Keller, who, although blind and deaf herself, has contributed so greatly to the betterment of other persons similarly afflicted. These women have each and all left an imprint on social, professional, educational, and humanitarian standards.

As Contributor in Addition to Marriage and Motherhood. There is the third group, women who have the drive to contribue through creative work and yet as earnestly desire wifehood and motherhood and who in one way or another—with the help of their husbands—succeed in all three. That amazing and unbelievable Englishwoman, Elizabeth Fry, is among the first women in the nineteenth century who leads this group. At a very early age she consecrated her life to the service of humanity and religion. During all her years she never wavered in her mission on behalf of the miserable and the distressed, in spite of the fact that she reared a large family, eleven children in all. By the time of her death she had spread her propaganda on prison reform through every quarter of Europe.

Madame Marie Curie was the mother of two daughters, co-worker and discoverer with her husband of radium, first woman to be given the Nobel prize, and the only person ever to have received the Nobel prize twice. Incidentally, Marie Curie carried on her work after the sudden death of her husband and lived to see her two daughters excel in their own fields, one as a musician and writer, the other as physicist. This last daughter, Irene Curie Joliet, also married a physicist and continued with her husband to work with her mother, in turn receiving, with her husband, the Nobel prize.

We have all been familiar with the great cinema actress, Marie Dressler, with her devotion through grueling years to an invalid husband, whom she comforted and supported through her professional achievements. Obviously there are many examples among our contemporaries of women who have made outstanding contributions to husbands and children and to the needed work of the world. Queen Elizabeth II has endeared herself not only to England but to the world in her capacity as stateswoman, wife, and mother. In our own country we take pride in Mrs. Franklin Delano Roosevelt; Oveta Culp Hobby, Secretary of Health, Education, and Welfare; Clare Booth Luce, diplomat; Margaret Sanger, world worker for planned parenthood; Cornelia Otis Skinner, the popular and witty monologist; Pearl Buck, the famous novelist; and Millicent Carey MacIntosh, president of Barnard College and mother of five. In addition, literally hundreds of women writers, actresses, artists, educators, government and welfare workers, as well as those who have become successful in the business world, have proved beyond question that women who realize the full potentialities of their womanhood are creating in other ways also than in the making of children and homes.

The women of whom we have just spoken were able to live creatively and, therefore, satisfactorily within the limits imposed by their environment. They found opportunity to convert their energy and ability into constructive activity. Other women similar to those whose situations were discussed earlier are less fortunate, or less strong or able, or less mature, and so fail in using their energy and ability satisfactorily. The emotional and physical giving and sharing involved in the day-by-day demands of marriage, jobs, or a combination of both are too much for them, and they retreat from the responsibilities of the fulfillment of their womanhood and project their unresolved conflicts on others. This is not the fault but the misfortune, rather, of the individual woman whose personality pattern is not ingenious or hardy enough and whose competence is not sufficient to surmount the obstacles of the present environment.

Whatever the difficulties, whatever the solution, in each and every woman I believe that there can be found some spark of divine unrest, some residue of the collective consciousness of that past in which women were accepted by their world as contributors of equal value to men in creative power. "No risks," says Lawrence Frank, "are great enough to block the human need for aspiration and striving." The clue to this has been suggested by Kirt Lowin, who has shown that there must be in the individual an uninterrupted and free flow between the plane of reality and the plane of unreality, and to that extent to which the individual's plane of unreality—call it fantasy, imagination, hopes—is restricted, his capacities for dealing with the actual world around him are by so much limited." Is not a realization on the part of men and of other women that all *women* need this free flow between the real and imaginative, that they are striving to recapture it, one of the most important resolutions of women's conflicting values?

There are now, happily, indications that this affirmation of womanhood, so long held in check, is about to become a creative force again. That new ideals for women are being incorporated into formal education is illustrated by the following quotation from the president of Bryn Mawr College. "The student must have a knowledge of fundamentals . . . the perspective that will enable her to live in the midst of change. . . . Courses taught as most of ours are taught not only contribute to maturity, it should be noted, they require it."[3] In discussing ways in which the college could be of help to women, Dr. Mirra Komarovsky states convincingly, "The touchstone of a liberal education is not its uselessness for a vocation—but its perspective and scope, the range of principles which underlie it, the generality of the relationships which it reveals, the significance of the values it treats." Leading educators believe that such processes will serve women after college as a vitalizing springboard for the complex demands of job, husband, home, and children. In support of this, we find Kenneth Appel, past president of the American Psychiatric Association, asserting that women are more mature than men in personality attributes that make for civilization.[4]

After school and college the large majority of girls become wives and mothers. During this phase of life miracles of modern medicine and surgery have already removed many of the physical ills which formerly sapped so much of women's strength. The spacing of children, too, has liberated them from the bondage of excessive childbearing. Mothers are now able to regard nature not as an end in itself, but, as all intimate relations with life should be, as a means of spiritual growth through full experience. Among the younger women many can now be found who run their simple homes with grace and capability, who believe in the beneficence of motherhood, the generous qualities of love mutually shared by men and women, and the importance of children as independent human beings.

As society accepts the concept of woman as a potentially mature human being—creative in body, in mind, and in spirit—the conflicting values which women have experienced will tend to disappear. If woman can again be conditioned to have the proper confidence in her capabilities, if she can imaginatively place herself in a creative relation to life, she can then bring to marriage a contribution that only women can bring to it. Of course women will have to compromise and develop competence now as formerly in meeting the exigencies of the times. So will men. So have all human beings through the ages. Conflict which necessitates compromise is a condition of life but is balanced in nature by the principle co-operation and mutual aid.

May we suggest the thesis that our world—the world of now—with all its difficulties, needs not men *or* women, most certainly not men *against* women, or women *against* men, but rather men *and* women, together shouldering the load and working to lighten it?

Men can encourage women, and women can encourage other women in their search to be of value. Men and women shoulder to shoulder can achieve real partnership, the sharing of two persons of equal value in the enterprise of marriage and of living. Marriage must contain the fundamentals of satisfaction, for marriage forms the nurturing ground for the attitudes and behavior of future citizens.

NOTES

[1]Della D. Cyrus, "Why Mothers Fail," *Atlantic Monthly*, Vol. 179, No. 3, March 1947, p. 57.

[2]Mrs. Theodore Roosevelt, Jr., "What's Wrong with American Marriages?" Town Meeting of the Air, February 13, 1947, New York.

[3]Katherine McBride, "Education at the Crossroads," *Bryn Mawr Bulletin*, December 1946, pp. 9–11.

[4]Kenneth E. Appel, "The Role of Women in Personality Growth," lecture for the National Committee for Mental Hygiene of Canada and McGill University, Montreal, February 1946.

BIBLIOGRAPHY

Ashley-Montagu, M. F., *Natural Superiority of Women*, ed., New York, Macmillan, 1953; *The Meaning of Love*, New York, Julian Press, 1953.

Beard, Mary, *Woman as Force in History*, New York, Macmillan, 1946.

Bergler, Edmund, *Unhappy Marriage and Divorce*, New York, International Universities Press, 1946.

Buck, Pearl S., *Of Men and Women*, New York, John Day, 1941.

Daniels, Anna Kleegman, *The Mature Woman: Her Richest Years*, New York, Prentice-Hall, 1953.

de Beauvoir, Simone, *The Second Sex*, New York, Knopf, 1953.

Deutsch, Helene, *Psychology of Women*, Vol. I, II, New York, Grune and Stratton, 1945.

Drinker, Sophie H., *Music and Women*, New York, Coward-McCann, 1948.

English, O. Spurgeon, and Pierson, Gerald, *Emotional Problems of Living*, New York, Norton, 1945.

Foster, Robert G., and Wilson, Pauline P., *Women after College*, New York, Columbia University Press, 1942.

Frank, Lawrence K., *Nature and Human Nature*, New Brunswick, N.J., Rutgers University Press, 1951.

Gruenberg, Sidonie M., and Krech, Hilda Sidney, *The Many Lives of Modern Woman*, New York, Doubleday, 1952.

Harding, Mary Esther, *Women's Mysteries*, New York, Longmans, Green, 1944.

Hollis, Florence, *Women in Marital Conflict,* New York, Family Service Association of America, 1949.

Jung, C. G., *Modern Man in Search of a Soul,* New York, Harcourt, Brace, 1934.

Kinsey, Alfred, *Sexual Behavior in the Human Male; Sexual Behavior in the Human Female,* Philadelphia, W. B. Saunders Co., 1948, 1953.

Komarovsky, Mirra, *Women in the Modern World,* New York, Little, Brown, 1953.

Lawrence, D. H., *Sons and Lovers; Lady Chatterley's Lover; Women in Love,* The Modern Library, New York.

Lundberg, F., and Farnham, M. F., *Modern Women: The Lost Sex,* New York, Harper & Bros., 1947.

Mead, Margaret, *Male and Female,* New York, W. Morrow, 1949.

Menninger, Karl, *Love against Hate,* New York, Harcourt, Brace, 1942.

Mudd, Emily Hartshorne, *The Practice of Marriage Counseling,* New York, Association Press, 1951.

Saul, Leon J., *Emotional Maturity, Development and Dynamics of Personality,* Philadelphia, J. B. Lippincott, 1947.

Sirjamaki, John, *The American Family in the Twentieth Century,* Cambridge, Harvard University Press, 1953.

Steiner, L. R., *Where Do People Take Their Troubles?* Boston, Houghton Mifflin, 1945.

Strecker, Edward A., *Their Mothers' Sons,* New York, J. B. Lippincott, 1946.

Suttie, Ian D., *The Origins of Love and Hate,* New York, Julian Press, 1953.

Chapter 7

EDUCATION AND FAMILY LIFE

by Muriel W. Brown, Ph.D.
COMMUNITY EDUCATION SPECIALIST, U. S. OFFICE OF EDUCATION

A French philosopher once wrote a clever essay on love in America. "America," he began, "appears to be the only country in the world where love is a national problem. . . . Nowhere else can one find a people devoting so much time and so much study to the relationship between men and women." In a spirit of gay condescension he discourses on love, democracy, and cookbooks and finally concludes that someday love in this country will cease to be "a hunting ground for reformers" and become, "as everywhere else, a personal affair, very much worth the effort it takes to examine it."[1]

As a matter of fact, there is no country in the world, including our own, where love is not both a personal affair and a national concern. We are not, as M. de Sales implies, willful children determined to make love "work" because we want more of the pleasure we know it can give us. We are seriously trying to learn what love is and how we can work *with* it. We are intent upon doing this because we believe that the hope of this troubled world lies, ultimately, in man's ability to experience and express love in appropriate ways in all of his relationships with other human beings and with God. We believe that the most central purpose of family life is to foster the growth of love and teach people how to use constructively the power it releases. Because of these beliefs, we feel obliged to try to find out how homes in which this kind of learning can go on are established and maintained. If this be "reform," let us make the most of it! Actually it seems to us more sensible to think of this "movement" as basic human education. Usually we call it family-life education or education for family living.

Education for family life is as old as the family itself. In the past, and in many parts of the world today, cultures have perpetuated their patterns of family living through systems of indoctrination which have left most of the people concerned in little doubt about their duties and responsibilities as sons, daughters, fathers, mothers, husbands, wives. With the total support of tightly organized societies, children have been taught by their parents the values and folkways of their forebears. Codes of conduct handed down from one generation to the next have been useful over long periods of time because the life situations in which they have been successfully applied have changed slowly during many centuries. Tradition, until very recently, has been the force which has stabilized and given continuity to human experience.

As social changes take place with increasing rapidity, however, tradition inevitably becomes a less and less reliable guide for use in meeting new situations. This began to be true in the early days of our own history. England, France, and Spain were too far away from us to be able to impose their value systems on us for long. Survival in colonial America depended on ingenuity, adaptability, and co-operative action. Only by men and women who had learned to think fearlessly and creatively could this continent have been conquered and this nation built. The Yankee shrewdness which amuses and sometimes shocks the rest of the world is the inevitable result of our long apprenticeship in problem-solving. It has become our habit to challenge assumptions that seem unreasonable; to ask questions when we are in doubt; to try to find out what the matter is when something goes wrong; to invent new solutions and create new possibilities when old approaches to problems no longer serve.

This dynamic approach to life has bred in us a great deal of self-confidence and a tremendous respect for the ability to co-operate effectively with change. As far as most of us are concerned, there is no forever Forbidden City in man's search for knowledge and for truth. If an aspect of life is puzzling, we explore it. If problems multiply in an area of special importance, we analyze them with special care. The heart may have reasons that reason does not know, but we expect that eventually reason will bring these to light.

In view of all this, it is not surprising that ours should be one of the first countries—if not *the* first—to develop a dynamic concept of education for family living and to implement this with planned programs of study. These programs seek the continuous improvement of family life through the intelligent application of insights, knowledge, and skills acquired to the everyday problems of the home and the family. They are sometimes described collectively as a "folk" movement because they have tended to develop in response to popular demand and because the lay people who take part have so much to do with the organization and direction of so many of them.

Family-life education has been defined as "that part of a total education which equips individuals for effective membership in the family so that each contributes to home and community life according to his capacity."[2] Activities within this broad field are conducted under many different auspices, in many different ways. They include the programs for parents called, originally, mothercraft, then child study or parent education. They include home-making education for children, youth, and adults—that part of home economics which "is centered on home activities and relationships and enables the individual to assume the responsibilities of homemaking."[3] They include the local, state, and national programs of marriage counseling, social hygiene, and mental hygiene which are developing soundly against sometimes heavy odds. They include the courses in marriage and family living now being given in many colleges, and a wide variety of offerings in the curricula of elementary and secondary schools (in addition to home economics)—the units on the family in most social-studies courses, the home-living units in the lower grades, the sex instruction sometimes given in science and health education, the classes in personality development and human relations. They also include a great many different kinds of community projects under the sponsorship of a wide variety of community groups.

Education for family living is carried on in the United States by an unknown number of governmental and non-governmental agencies and organizations. It is also carried on by persons trained in many different professions, including particularly psychiatrists, lawyers, psychologists, social workers, teachers, pediatricians, sociologists, ministers, nurses, and family doctors. In 1948, 104 of our national organizations were emphasizing some phase of family life education in their programs to an extent which justified their participation in the National Conference on the Family held during that year. This number did not include the twenty-seven federal agencies and the seventeen foundations also working in this area. Today there are undoubtedly many more groups active in both categories.

Among the agencies and organizations most active in this field of education are the schools, colleges, and universities; the churches; the social agencies; the libraries; the Cooperative Extension Services of federal and state departments of agriculture, and many large voluntary groups with nation-wide memberships, both lay and professional. To give a reliable over-view of the principal channels and sources of leadership is probably impossible, so varied are the auspices under which activities in this field are promoted. At the federal level, there is a family-life specialist in the Extension Division of the U. S. Department of Agriculture. In the Department of Health, Education, and Welfare there are family experts in the Office of Education, the Public Health Service, and the Social Security Administration, which includes the Children's Bureau and the Bureau of Public Assistance. The total programs of both of these departments are geared to the study of problems affecting families in a number of ways. The Inter-departmental Committee for Children and Youth, staffed by the Children's Bureau, is broadly concerned with family welfare and co-ordinates informally many of the activities of the constituent agencies in this general area.

Many national women's organizations, such as the General Federation of Women's Clubs and the American Association of University Women, stress home and family life in their programs of work and prepare materials for their members to use in studying family problems. The labor organizations are also emphasizing work in this field. The national church organizations are, of course, all actively interested, and the national social welfare associations are giving increasing attention to educational, as distinguished from therapeutic, aspects of both group work and case work with families.

Of the specialized agencies giving national, professional leadership in family-life education, the National Council on Family Relations is perhaps the largest and the most consistently interdisciplinary. Other important professional groups are the American Association of Marriage Counselors, the Planned Parenthood Federation of America, the Child Study Association of America, the American Institute of Family Relations, the Association for Family Living (Chicago). The National Congress of Parents and Teachers and the American Home Economics Association both have special departments which stimulate and guide their activities in parent education, child development, and homemaking. Several foundations, including the Woman's Foundation of New York, and the Grant, Field, and Rosenberg foundations, have indicated their interest in education for home and family living.

The Groves Conference on Marriage and Family Living is an annual meeting which provides opportunities for the presentation and informal co-ordination of research in the family field. The chief professional magazine for family-life specialists is *Marriage and Family Living,* the journal of the National Council on Family Relations. *Parents' Magazine,* the outstanding popular publication in parent education, now reaches more than a million families each month. Commercial magazines for families are widely available through department and food stores and other business channels.

State governments participate in family-life education through state departments of health, education, and welfare, and through the Cooperative Extension Service in Agriculture in each state. A few state departments of public instruction have specialists in parent- or family-life education on their staffs; all (including the Territories and the District of Columbia) have supervisors of home economics who give full time to the homemaking programs, including those for adults, sponsored by the public schools in their states. The Cooperative Extension Service in twenty-five states employs one or more full-time specialists in family-life education, and in nine other states responsibility for this area is assigned to other specialists who have had training in child development and family relations.

It is on the local level, in city neighborhoods, in towns, and in country villages, that one senses most vividly the great vitality of this movement. In these places, teachers, parents, home demonstration agents, health educators, social workers, youth leaders, and ministers of all denominations are engaged in a great, if informal, joint effort to help families improve their living. Here are courses in family living for children in school, classes and study groups for out-of-school youth and adults. Here are community projects, co-operatively organized, in which local family problems that can be generalized are studied in the light of new knowledge which bears upon them. There is probably no state today in which at least one community has not had at least one well-attended family-life conference, institute, or workshop for lay and professional people, sponsored by one or more local groups.

The following letter, addressed to a member of the staff of the Home Economics Education Branch of the U. S. Office of Education, shows the spirit and scope of many of these grass-roots activities. It comes from a minister in a small Midwestern city and says, in part:

We noted the increase in divorces in our county, rising to a high of 51 per cent. The Ministerial Association called in the lawyers of the county for a supper. We ate and talked and found a lot of common ground which perhaps most of us did not know existed to this extent. A committee on recommendations for a later meeting was appointed. I am chairman of that committee. The committee includes three pastors and three representing the lawyers: judge of the Common Pleas Court, judge of Probate Court, and president of the Bar Association. Our recommendations, after many committee meetings, are tentatively the following:

1. That a course be offered in all county high schools (city high schools too) which would study the related factors in harmonious marriage and happy family life. A course is now being offered in one of our high schools, with the approach from the health side; the course is given by the physical-education department.

2. That a course on "The Essentials for Success and Harmony in Marriage" (or some similar subject) be offered in —— periodically (probably 9 or 10 months out of the year); this course to be especially for premarried and newly married couples and others who may wish to attend.

3. That a counseling service be set up in —— to which all interested individuals and agencies may be referred; namely, all personnel directors in our factories, social-welfare agencies, school principals, county Bar Association, county health department, etc., would be solicited to refer people in need to this service.

In spite of our national tendency to explore and experiment, developments in this crucial area of education have taken place slowly. Each of the specialized programs mentioned above has had to overcome opposition originating in ignorance, indifference, or fear. Several years ago two well-known women, one from abroad, the other an American, found themselves dinner partners at a banquet in New York.

"Your name is very familiar," the foreign visitor said to her neighbor. "May I ask what your work is?"

"Parent education," replied the American.

There was an awkward pause.

"Parent education!" the woman from overseas finally exclaimed. *"Really? How amusing!"*

The word "amusing" used in this connection is packed, of course, with hidden meanings. If she had fully spoken her mind that night, the guest from Europe would probably have said, as people in our own country still sometimes do:

"Education for marriage and parenthood? Nonsense. A mother instinctively knows what to do for her baby because she loves it. The things people need to know to make a success of love, marriage, childbearing, and child rearing they must learn from experience. If one should feel the need of more information than he happens to have about any of these things, he can always turn to a book—or a friend. These are intimate, personal experiences with which each person has a right to deal as he sees fit. And, really, after all, how ridiculous to suppose that logic and reasoning have anything to do with love!"

Even those phases of family-life education conservative enough to find their way into public-school curriculums have developed gradually. In 1841, for example, Catherine Beecher, the sister of Harriet Beecher Stowe, wrote an excellent textbook for use in women's colleges called *A Treatise on Domestic Economy*. It would be hard to paint a more inspiring, more comprehensive, or more practical picture of the duties, responsibilities, and privileges of the American homemaker. A succession of able home economists have enriched and enlarged upon the concepts introduced by Miss Beecher. Yet it has taken approximately one hundred years for leaders in home economics to establish homemaking as a functional area in American education and to demonstrate that the teaching of homemaking can be as vital, rich, and varied as life in the homes served by our schools.

Nevertheless, the United States has, at last, become "family-conscious." As the letter quoted earlier indicates, increases in juvenile delinquency and divorce following the war have forced us to recognize weaknesses in our social structure which we have not been too willing to face in the past. Parents, at present, are the scapegoats, charged with every crime against children known to psychiatry. Riding high on the band wagon, radios, newspapers, magazines, even the chain grocery stores, are bombarding the public with information and advice on every conceivable phase of family living— child care and guidance, family relations, marriage, sex, and the technical problems of homemaking. Sometimes these and other special-interest groups make contributions to family education that are extremely valuable. Sometimes, unfortunately, they use the most subtle psychological tricks to sell bills of goods, playing mercilessly upon the emotions of worried people, chiefly upon their fears.

Because systematic education in the essentials of good family living has not been an integral part of his basic education, the average American does not know what to do about all this furor over his alleged failure as a homemaker. When his family is in trouble he seeks advice, not as a rule from those trained professionally to deal with problems like his, but from those in whom he has confidence for other reasons—relatives, the corner druggist, the bartender. Less frequently, according to studies,[4] he goes for help to a clergyman, a labor leader, a ward boss, or a policeman.

A recent analysis of 6,422 letters received from women during a one-year period by an advice columnist writing for a popular monthly magazine shows how urgent and widespread is the need for help with family problems. Of these correspondents, 87 per cent indicated a need for sex information, 73 per cent for birth-control information, 52 per cent for information about agencies which might help with specific problems, 30 per cent for legal advice, 23 per cent for information about venereal diseases, 22 per cent for help in deciding whether or not to get a divorce, 14 per cent for advice about how to get a second party to agree to marriage, 13 per cent for advice about how to prevent a divorce. Altogether, the lives of roughly 38,897 immediate relatives were affected by the decisions made by these "people in quandaries."

"Why," asks the author of this study,[5] "did these women write to an advice columnist? There appears to be one basic reason. It is because somewhere along the way someone has failed. That failure may lie in the home, the school, the church, the community, or in society itself. . . .

"It appears, therefore, that the challenge for family-life education is there. Ways must be found to extend and enlarge upon the work now being done in classrooms, marital clinics, through counseling services, and in parent-education groups."

It would, of course, be naïve to imply that professional education has any easy short cuts to success in family development. The whole problem of learning in relation to life adjustment is extremely complicated, and to oversimplify it is dangerous. There are four principal sources of knowledge in the world—the findings of scientific research, the revelations of religion, the insights of artists, and the observations made currently and in the past by people in all walks of life. From these sources come the "raw materials" of understanding—facts, hunches, doctrines, opinions, descriptions of experience, problems. These "raw materials" are gradually brought together, evaluated, and organized into bodies or fields of knowledge, which have to be related to each other. It is then the business of education to deal with these syntheses, making generalizations, pulling out principles, showing how these may be used as guides and tools in solving life problems.

It has not been easy to organize knowledge pertaining to family life, partly because we have had little experience in dealing with the kinds of "raw materials" involved; partly because this whole area is so heavily mined, emotionally, that we have been afraid of it; partly because nature continues to operate, however blindly, without our intervention. As small increases in understanding have pointed the way to greater happiness and satisfaction in family living, interest in the study of this field has grown. We have begun to assemble our data from religion, from the arts, from the sciences, from life. This comprehensive manual, *Successful Marriage,* is, in itself, good evidence of the progress we have made. Already we know a great deal about human growth and development, and about the history of the family as a social institution. We have had some fruitful research on specific aspects of sex behavior. We know some things which seem significant about present-day family living in our own and other cultures. There have been spectacular developments in the technologies of homemaking. Unfortunately, the biggest lag is at the place where insight is most needed—the study of human relationships.

The important fact, in this connection, however, is not that knowledge is still limited, but that we are not making full use of the knowledge we do possess. As in the case of the possibly fictitious farmer, "our doin's need to catch up with our knowin's!" Three fairly recent publications have suggested partial answers to at least three of the most basic questions it is possible to ask about family life: (1) What makes families strong? (2) What are families for? (3) What is *good* family living?

One of these publications is a report of a study[6] made between 1940 and 1943 which seems to throw a good deal of light on *the first of these questions.* It is an analysis of the experiences during this period of 62 low-income families living in New York City. In the 24 months of the study, these families had a total of 109 serious troubles. But here is the interesting thing! Fourteen of them had no troubles at all during this time. When the investigator rated all of these 62 families on the quality of their family living, he found that, judging by his criteria, family troubles tended to increase as family organization weakened. The 14 families without troubles from 1940 to 1943 were average or better in the following respects:

1. Each person in the family knew his place or role and knew what to expect of each other member of the family. As one father put it, "If everybody has a job in the family and does it, we get along all right."
2. Each member of the family was willing to put the good of the family ahead of his own good.
3. Each family provided some means for family members to meet their needs and satisfy their interests within the family.
4. Each family had a goal or plan and was moving in the direction of it. Everybody in the family wanted this goal and was helping to reach it.

This study puts new substance into family-life education. It does not highlight any given system of family practices, but it does show what some of the specifics probably are in successful family organization. Each one of these seemingly "fortunate" families had found out how to work together for something that seemed important to both parents and children. This joint striving toward common goals gave form, direction, and meaning to family life. So long as these goals or values were clear in the minds of those seeking them, the material circumstances of life could change again and again without disturbing family morale. Each such change was just a new challenge to "take what they had and make what they wanted."

It is in knowing *what to want* in family life that most young people contemplating marriage, and many married couples, are at a loss today. In helping them to find out, family-life education has, perhaps, its greatest opportunity for social usefulness. The most important goals for American families are goals which must be stated in terms of action. What should we expect families to do for their own members, for their communities, for their country, and for the great family of nations which is the world? In short, *the second of our three key questions: What is the family for?*

Too often in the past the answers to this question have been unsatisfactory because they have not been based on knowledge and experience that were sufficiently broad. To be universally meaningful, they must be acceptable to the religious leader, the artist, the scientist, and the man in the street. The second of the publications mentioned earlier in connection with this question is a report[7] of an attempt to get such a consensus of opinion. This document was prepared in 1945 for the Woman's Foundation of New York by a committee of specialists in anthropology, education, psychiatry, psychology, religion, and sociology. It proposes a statement of the distinctive functions of family living in our society which is so far-reaching, yet so comprehensive and fundamental, that it may well serve as a platform or charter for programs of family-life education under any auspices, anywhere. According to this statement, these functions or tasks are:

1. To provide a way of living for members of the family group in which basic physical needs can be met and emotional security and personal fulfillment can be attained.

2. To provide in marriage for the achievement of a sustained relationship between a man and a woman in and through which they may seek fulfillment of their intimate, affectionate needs and desires.

3. To bear and rear healthy children in the setting of a home and of family life.

4. To provide the kind of family living which fosters the development and maturation of personalities able to maintain a democratic way of life in the family and in society generally.

5. To transmit, transform, and develop cultural traditions from one generation to the next, especially in the area of interpersonal relations.

6. To integrate, mediate, and interpret the demands (which the environment makes upon the individual) and the possibilities (which it has for him).

7. To provide a socially sanctioned situation in which co-operative living and division of labor can be developed according to the interests, needs, and abilities of the family group.

This brings us to *the third question: What is good family living?* If in our society we depend upon the family for certain essential contributions to personal and social development, then as far as we are concerned "good" families are families which make these contributions in a reasonably adequate manner. It is important to notice that the purposes or tasks for family life just quoted are stated in terms of action. It should also be noted that this action must be co-operative, since no single member of a family group can perform any one of these functions by himself. The *sine qua non* of good family living in our culture is, therefore, the ability to maintain co-operative relations among family members. We call relationships of this type "democratic," meaning by that word not some vague form of friendly association, but a kind of behavior which frees the energies of the human spirit for creative, co-operative living.

A definition of democracy which seems capable of releasing untold amounts of energy for more effective living in families is the one to be found in the report of a study of democratic practice in American schools published in 1941 by the Educational Policies Commission of the National Education Association.[8] On the basis of this definition, the democratic society is one in which

1. There is co-operative action for the common good.

2. The welfare of each member is sought by all the rest.

3. All members take part, according to their ability, in planning, carrying out and evaluating the results of group activities.

4. The experimental method of free inquiry based on faith in informed intelligence is freely used in solving problems.

5. Controversial issues are freely studied and discussed in order that truth may be discovered through the dispassionate examination of all available facts and many different points of view.

6. Each member has freedom with responsibility *in action.*

These three sets of conclusions dovetail neatly because they spring from the same basic philosophy. They are positive guides for family action. Their chief value is that they can never be used as formulas. They offer no ready-made solutions for family problems. Their purpose is to show us what the job is and how it can be done. Their full meaning becomes apparent only as we begin to work with them, delving for the facts behind the generalizations. How, for instance, are family roles determined? What are basic human needs? What can families do to meet these? What is emotional security? How is it attained? What does it mean to "achieve" in relationships? What can a family do to give children a true appreciation of the riches coming into our culture through the art, music, literature, crafts, and customs of all the people joining us from other lands? Can success and failure in marriage be predicted? Can young people be taught *how* to love before they fall in love? How are habits of co-operative living formed? How does a family learn to discuss controversial problems? To what extent and how is it possible to educate children for responsible freedom?

These and countless other questions are the subject matter of education for home and family living today. It is obvious that much of this education must be "on-the-job" training. The best time to teach the fine art of diapering, for example, is when a young girl or boy has a baby to care for. This does not mean, however, that everything waits for the wedding. Into adequate preparation for marriage and family living go a multitude of attitudes, skills, and abilities which are "content" for learning from infancy on up.

This seems to indicate that major responsibility for giving basic, systematic instruction in homemaking and family development must rest with the school. Among our many educational agencies, this is the only one in a position to offer fundamental education for family living to all of our people. This does not mean that full recognition is not given to the value of educational opportunities in this field provided by other agencies and many professions. The school alone cannot possibly meet all of the needs of family members of all ages for help with all kinds of family problems. As a matter of fact, the school can do little or nothing, even in its own technical sphere, without the wholehearted support of all other agencies and organizations able in any way to extend, interpret, enrich, reinforce, encourage, help direct and apply its teachings.

It is clear that there is not yet agreement among the professions concerned as to what the specific objectives of family-life education should be. The following statement,[9] however, is one which seems to be meeting with increasing favor as teachers and school officials experiment with it as a basis for curriculum planning:

1. An appreciation of the importance of the family in American life and some specific understanding of its functions as a social institution.

2. A specific understanding of what good family living means in terms of the student's own family experience.

3. A desire to establish and maintain families which are good by the highest standards the student can realistically set for himself.

4. A specific yet broad understanding of what the resources for family living are in the communities where students live.

5. The skills and abilities needed for finding these resources and using them effectively. These abilities include among others:

(a) The ability to buy wisely within the limits of family income.

(b) The ability to resist the propaganda, high-pressure salesmanship, and the trickery which now keeps so large a proportion of American families in perpetual debt.

(c) The ability to work effectively with other families to develop new resources, make better use of resources already available, and/or solve family problems of common concern.

(d) The skills of good housekeeping and home management.

6. The ability to maintain democratic relationships in family life—to be a good family citizen.

7. The ability to participate effectively in the establishing and maintaining of wholesome family-community relations.

8. The ability to recognize and conserve values in family living as family patterns change.

These are exciting goals but, at this point, it becomes necessary to face a very fundamental question. The abilities listed are, for the most part, facets of a single, basic one: the ability to express in one's relations with other people the attitudes and values which characterize American democracy. *What kinds of learning experiences help people develop and organize what kinds of value systems, and how is progress in this sort of learning evaluated?*

It is generally understood that *knowing about* and *really knowing* are two quite different things. If family happiness and stability depend, in the last analysis, on the ability of family members to express certain qualities of personality in their relations with each other, then the study of personality development must have a central place in family-life education. And in studying personality development we can no longer content ourselves with the ego-centric approach so commonly made in the past. Education for living in the democratic family in the United States in this mid-decade of the twentieth century requires that we concern ourselves simultaneously with the effects of family membership on the individual at all stages of growth and the effect upon the family of the behavior of the individual family member.

It is indeed difficult, as Montaigne once remarked, to lay hold of "the many little nimble motions" made by two such active systems of variables. Recently, however, there have been a number of promising new leads. The 1950 White House Conference on Children and Youth has put Erikson's "ground plan" for normal personality development directly into the "stream of consciousness" in the social sciences. This concept makes wonderful sense both as a springboard for research and as a practical guide for people working with parents and children. For example: In this scheme the first developmental task for the newborn baby is the achievement of a sense of basic trust in the people around him and in the world in which he finds himself. Lacking this feeling of security, the infant becomes fearful and must draw heavily on energy needed for growth to protect himself in what probably seems to him a terribly dangerous environment.

Assuming that this hypothesis is correct, the most important thing that parents can do for a young baby is to learn how to feed, clothe, bathe, and love him in ways that help him to trust life. If his family can help him to "make the grade" in this special sense as he meets each of the major growth crises of life, the trusting baby will, in all probability, become the kind of person who can do the same thing, in due time, for his own children and for his marriage partner.

This White House Conference material has helped to make much more specific the parallel concept of family stages, the outstanding contribution of the 1948 National Conference on the Family, formulated by Evelyn Duvall and Reuben Hill. Much further work needs to be done in knitting the two together. A recent trend in family-life research is toward the study of the total family as a small group, over periods of time sufficiently long to permit the tracing of developmental processes from their various beginnings as they weave themselves into the patterns of family and family-society interrelationships which they create. As this kind of research matures, ways will be found of exploring more effectively than is now possible the intricate problems of role determination in family life. We certainly need more insight into the causes of family tensions and better techniques for resolving those which arise from feelings of hostility, guilt, doubt, or shame owing to deep-seated dissatisfaction with one's own family role and the roles of other family members.

What this new content will mean as it comes to enrich family-life education, we cannot yet really know. To be able to handle it, teachers will certainly need more intensive training than most teachers colleges now offer in functional approaches to the study of child, group, and family development. More attention will have to be given to ways of helping people in positions of administrative leadership gain deeper insight into the meaning of human communication, and more skill in establishing human relations in which people can actually communicate with each other.

It will surely be necessary to develop better methods of helping teachers to understand themselves, particularly their own motivations, before we can expect them to be able to help students, on any educational level, understand better their own family behavior. Perhaps the task most immediately before us is to learn how to use more effectively some of the procedures and techniques already known. The sociodrama, for instance, is a method which has much more to contribute to emotional education than most of us know how to get from it.

Far as we still have to go, we have just cause for optimism as we review accomplishments in the broad field of education for family living in recent years. All of the familiar educational problems beset us in this as in other kinds of teaching—problems of motivation, ego-involvement, attitude change, carry-over into behavior. On the other hand, we see encouraging evidences of progress. We see an increasing number of co-ordinated family-life programs in schools reaching an increasing number of pupils. We see increasing richness of psychological and social content in these programs, with increasing emphasis on school-community co-operation in discovering the needs of students and their families. We see increasingly more dynamic and realistic methods of teaching coming into use. We see an increasing emphasis on educational aspects of the work of many other agencies and organizations serving families, and an increasing readiness for interdisciplinary co-ordination and co-operation in planning, executing, and evaluating joint family-life education projects.

One of the most interesting and significant of recent developments has been the growth in the number and effectiveness of community programs of education for home and family living under the direction of local family-life councils. As community concern is focused on local conditions of family living, communities are showing increasing initiative and ingenuity in meeting problems. One thinks, in this connection, of the successful family health program carried on for the past four years under the auspices of the Family Life Program in Obion County, Tennessee;[10] of the fathers and mothers in countless places organizing study groups, nursery schools or play groups, child-care centers, co-operative laundries, and other services needed to supplement the efforts of individual families to meet family needs. This, indeed, is democracy in action since, by definition, a democracy is a society in which each citizen helps to create the conditions under which he wishes to live. It is also functional family-life education.

In the 1930s a little band of refugees from the dust bowls of Arkansas and Oklahoma trekked north. They stopped on the outskirts of Wichita, Kansas, because they had no means of going further. They lived as well as they could in the shelter they could find—houses no one else wanted, tin shacks and old chicken coops. There was no work to be had even for the most capable and the most willing. At last the time came when children stayed home from school because they had no shoes to wear; when families huddled at night in their ragged coats because they had not enough quilts or blankets to keep them warm when the cold winds of winter blew across the prairies.

A community family-life program was organized in Wichita in 1938, and among its other activities arrangements were made for a teacher provided through the public schools to work with these families. The Lend-a-Hand Club previously organized by the families themselves became a sewing class in which donated garments were renovated and made to fit. Quilts were made for beds and rag rugs for floors. Soon a full-fledged Self-help Center began to operate, with hours of credit on clothing and other household necessities given for hours of work on the project.

Finally the day arrived when it seemed not too farfetched to think of better housing. All possible improvements were made in the homes then occupied, with the help of the Vocational Education Department of the Wichita Public Schools and many other co-operating groups. Much conversation about buying, renting, etc., revealed the fact that no one in the Center knew much about housing. With an initial loan of $300 from friends the group undertook to learn about houses by building a little house in the manner of old-fashioned barn-raisings. An attractive three-room dwelling was finished completely and sold to a young family for $500, the details of financing being also a part of the study.

In the short space of nine years this family-life-education project developed to the point where Center families owned their own clubhouse, belonged to the National Association of Credit Unions and the Blue Cross. The Lend-a-Hand Club long ago became the Source Class which studied and made recommendations to the membership concerning any new activities or policies the Center might be considering.

This experiment has been both a fulfillment and a promise. It justified the belief that people with meager resources can generate plenty of power to raise their own standards of living through thoughtfully planned co-operative action. It gave us a preview of what education may be like when we have learned to think, feel, and act more creatively about it and the concept of learning by doing has gained real respectability.

In many parts of the world, the same principles of community organization for better family living which operated in the Wichita program are now being applied in programs of village development. Families in places as far apart as the Lebanese province of Saneen, the South Pacific island of Palau, the village of Mit Halfa in the ancient valley of the Nile, the crossroads settlement of Tin Top, Texas, made famous by the Ford Foundation radio project, *The People Act*—families in all of these places are finding ways and means of dealing with problems of housing, health, sanitation, agriculture, industry, and education which have defied governmental efforts for generations.

Not long ago an African chief was discussing the United Nations. "The U.N.," he said, "that is the council which is sewing the world together in one piece." One of the most effective ways in which we can help with this "sewing"—which certainly needs to be done, and done quickly—is to give high priority here at home to the programs of education for democracy which we call education for home and family living. From homes which foster the growth of love and understanding between people flow, as David Mace once said, "tides of peace and sanity which renew from age to age the deepest purposes of life." To strengthen the movement which is bringing such homes into ever closer and more dynamic relationships with each other, in our own country and in other lands, must surely be the most effective answer to the destructive forces which, from time to time, marshal against us out of the dark night of time.

NOTES

[1]Raoul de Roussy de Sales, "Love in America," *The Atlantic Pocket Book*, Pocket Book 397, New York, Pocket Books, Inc., 1946, pp. 7–21.

[2]U. S. Office of Education, *Vocational Education in the Years Ahead*, Washington, D.C., Federal Security Agency, 1945, p. 191.

[3]Ibid.

[4]Earl Lomon Koos, *Families in Trouble*, New York, King's Crown Press, 1946, p. 86.

[5]Christine H. Hillman, "An Advice Column's Challenge for Family Life Education," *Marriage and Family Living,* Vol. 16, No. 1, pp. 51–54.

[6]Earl Lomon Koos, *Families in Trouble,* New York, King's Crown Press, 1946, pp. 33ff.

[7]Consultants' Report, *The Place of the Family in American Life,* New York, Woman's Foundation, 1945, p. 15.

[8]Educational Policies Commission, *Learning the Ways of Democracy,* Washington, D.C., National Education Association, 1941, pp. 127–28.

[9]From an unpublished memorandum on the needs and purposes of family-life education at the secondary level, U. S. Office of Education, Washington, D.C., 1947.

[10]Muriel W. Brown, *With Focus on Family Living,* Vocational Division Bulletin No. 249, Home Economics Education Series No. 28, U. S. Office of Education, Washington, D.C., 1953, Chap. 6, pp. 66–93.

Index

INDEX

A

Abnormal characteristics, psychology of: American Indians, 418; Bantu customs, 423; berdache, 418; *Bruderschaft,* 421; cultural influences on sex norms, 417–19; deviation from heterosexual mores, 424–26; Egyptian Ptolemies, 420; exhibitionism, 423; Germany, 421; Greece, 421; homoeroticism, 422; homosexuality, 77, 396, 421; incest, 420; Japan, 421; Keraki Indians, 421; Marquesan culture, 420; masochism, 423; masturbation, 417; men and animals, 423; Mohave Indians, 418; narcissism, 5, 111; norms of sex-role behavior, 417–19; norms in various cultures, 418–21; oriental norms, 421; "peeping Toms," 424; penal institutions, 421; Plains Indians, 418; psychoneurosis, 424; psychosexuality, 422; New Guinea, 421; rare cases of, 423; reversal of masculine and feminine roles, 418–19; sadism, 423; sex act, 423–24; sex object, 423; sex reversal, 418; sexual deviation in Western culture, 418; voyeurism, 424

Abortion, 195–206; ancient method of contraception, 267; Bourne Abortion trial, famous English test case, 202–3; Caesarean, 203; care of, 200–1; caused by abnormal reproductive organs, 199; death rate in Russia, 205; death rate in United States, 204; English Abortion Act of 1860, 202; habitual, 196; illegal, 195, 203–4; intercourse, should not be undertaken immediately before or after, 193; normal abortion, 198; self-induced,

Abortion—(*cont.*)
204; spontaneous, 85, 196–97, 201; statistics, 196; superstitions about, 199; syphilis, not a cause of, 199; therapeutic, 85, 195, 201–3; Vitamin E, used in treatment of, 200

Abortion Act of 1860, in England, 202

Achondroplasis, mutation rate of, 226

Achondroplastic dwarfism, hereditary cause, 225–26

Activities. *See* Recreation

Adaptability. *See* Adjustments

Addams, Jane, 491

Adjustments: childhood and family influence on, 119–20; during engagement, 25–26; factors in maladjustments in marriage, 168–80; importance of background, 119–20; marriage, 25–26, 113–26; personality and temperament, factors for happiness, 117–18, 124; sex-adjustment aptitude, 115; sexual adjustments in marriage, 98–112; test for marital happiness, 113–14; wedding and honeymoon, 127–36; women's adjustments to marriage, 25, 485–94

Adolescence: age period, 288; attachment to one's own sex, 396; courtship, 28–38, 42; dating, 17–18, 28–34, 46–47; delinquency, 379–88, 425; engagement, 18, 28–38; engagement and the family, 399–400; going steady, 18, 32–34, 398; in love, 398–99; masturbation, 77, 355; maturation and learning, 301–2; medical examinations advised, 56; menstruation, 392–93; normal sex development, 397; parent attachment, 5, 9–10, 169–73, 394–96; parents' influence, 6, 14, 15,

Economics—(*cont.*)
problems of parenthood, 212–13. *See also* Financial planning

Education: effect of overtraining, 387; effect on marital adjustments, 19, 41, 114, 122; in the family council, 412; family life, 497–512; organizations for family, 499–500. *See also* Sex education

Educational Policies Commission of the National Education Association, 506

Egg (ovum), 69; abnormal chromosomes in egg cause abortion, 197; in girls and during development, 243–44; fertilization, 80, 84, 217; heredity, 217; during menstruation, 72, 245; in ovary, 232, 233, 234; diagrams, 68, 81

Egg trap, 69; diagram, 81

Egypt, Ptolemaic approval of incest, 420

Eisenhower, Mrs. Mamie, 491

Ejaculation, elements and quantity of, 76

Ejaculatory duct, 74

Ellis, Dr. Albert, 162

Elopement, escape from marriage, 132; unsuccessful, 22, 128–29

Embryo: circulation of, 252; extent of development in abortion, 198; normal development in early pregnancy, 250–52; placenta furnishes food to, 252, 253; diagram, 250, 251

Emission, rhythmic release in the male, 85, 393

Emmenagogue. *See* Drugs, abortifacient

Emotions: aroused by petting, 43, 46; depression during climacteric, 475, 477–78, 480; fear, an inhibition to sexual and marital adjustments, 103, 128, 132; infatuation, 6–8, 22; interdependence, necessary for marital adjustment, 21; jealousy, 7; love, 3–13, 104; maturity of, 21, 30; parent attachment, 169–73, 394–95; "puppy love," 5; sexual, expression of, 104

Endocrinology. *See* Glands, ductless

Engagement, 18, 35–37, 40; adjustments during, 24–27; adolescents, 399; conduct during, 46–47; decision of ethical, financial, and domestic principles, 25; factors in selection of mate, 14–27; limitation of petting, 36; period of planning, 36; premarital relations, 36, 40–50; test of

Engagement—(*cont.*)
compatibility, 117–18; weddings and expenses involved, 127–36

England, Abortion Act of 1860, 202

English, as a course, contribution to sex education, 369

Environment: child's interest in his, 309; church, 19; economic status, 20; family relationships, 19; friends, 19; influence of maladjusted parents, 379–88; membership in organizations, 19; problems of stepchildren, 327–45; social factors, 18–19

Epididymis, 74, 80; gonorrhea in, 449; diagrams, 75, 82, 83

Epiloia, mutation rate of, 226

Erectile bulbs, diagram, 81

Erection: in female, 70; in male, 77; lack of in male, rare, 84

Ergot, abortive drug, 205

Erotic response, seat of, 70, 71–72

Erythroblastosis fetalis, inherited blood condition, 223, 247

Estrogen, hormone: in ovaries, 234, 235; stimulates ovulation, 72; stimulates sex development, 244, 471; treatment during menopause, 473

Estrogenic preparations, artificial, 235

Estrone, hormone, used in treatment of abortion, 200

Estrus, fertile period, 232

Ethics: decided during engagement, 24; premarital, 40–50; value of mutual standards in marital adjustment, 22–24; virginity, 46, 48. *See also* Divorce; Prostitution

Exercise: after childbirth, 265; avoid strenuous activity during pregnancy, 248; effect on abortion, 198–99

Exhaustion, factor in sexual inhibition, 95

Exhibitionism, 424

Expenses, financial. *See* Financial planning

Extramarital relations, 157–67; adultery, 161–62; men as offenders, 163–64; motivation for, 165, 166; premarital affairs, 87; prostitution, 432–45; statistics, 157, 160–62; women as offenders, 164

Eye, danger of contracting syphilis, 449; disease due to syphilis, 450; treatment with silver nitrate at birth, 262

F

Fallopian tubes: during conception, 245; during ovulation, 233, 234, 244; during pregnancy, 252; infection due to gonorrhea, 450; sterilization by blockage, 80; sterilization by removal, 275; diagrams, 68, 81

Family: customs, 411; education, 497–512; guests, 409–10; influence on homosexuality, 422; marital adjustment depends on, 4, 9, 119–20; mealtimes, 407–8; parent-child relationships, 402–13; projects, 410; religion in, 16; source of recreation, 44; wants, 139–40. *See also* Children; Divorce; Father fixation; Financial planning; Heredity; Home; Mother fixation; Parents; Sex education

Family council, its meaning and nature, 402; family counseling, 407; parent-child relationships, 402–13

Family life, problems of: adoption, 313–25; child psychology, 299–312; children, growth and development of, 281–97; contraception, 267–76; divorce, 457–68; education and family life, 497–512; home management, 137–56; juvenile delinquency, 379–88; need for help with, 503; parent-child relationships, 402–13; remarriage, 327–45; sex education and the child, 360–75; stepchildren, 335–45

Family Life Program, Obion County, Tenn., 511

Family relationships, 19, 402–13

Family Service Association, role in marriage counseling, 61

Fantasy, factor in masturbation, 356

Father. *See* Parents

Father fixation, psychological attachment of child, 169–70, 192, 394–96. *See also* Mother fixation; Parents

Favoritism, problems arising from stepchildren, 340, 341

Fear: causes contraction of vaginal canal, 79; fears of the bride, 132; inhibition to sexual and marital adjustments, 103, 128; not a cause of abortion, 199; resulting from masturbation, 353–54, 355–56

Federal Food and Drug Administration, control of condoms, 269

Federal Security Agency (Social Protection Division), control of prostitution, 439

Female anatomy: breasts, 90, 105, 245, 263; cervix, 69, 71, 78, 79, 84, 96, 234, 253, 273; clitoris, 69–70, 72, 77, 88, 90, 93, 94; coccyx bone, 70; egg, 69, 72, 84, 85, 217, 233, 234, 243–45; egg trap, 69, 72; embryology and pregnancy, 72, 85–87, 92, 196–97, 200, 214–16; Fallopian tubes, 80, 233, 234, 244, 245, 252, 275; genitalia, 69–71; gonorrhea, 449–50; hymen, 69, 70, 71, 77–79, 84; intersexuality, 481–82; labia, 69; meatus, 70; mons, 69; ovaries, 69, 72–73, 84, 233–34, 253, 473, 474–75, *et seq.*; perineum, 261; premarital examination of, 54; prepuce, 76; pubic bone, 69; sacrum, 70; syphilis, 450–52; urethra, 70, 449; uterus, 69, 71, 72, 79, 84, 244, 245, 253; vagina, 69, 70, 71, 79, 90, 189, 449; venereal diseases of, 448–53; vulva, 73; vulvovaginal glands, 71; diagrams, 68, 82

Fertile period, 73, 236–37

Fertility, 84, 232–42; contraceptives, harmless, 55; cyclical events in the ovary, 233–34; determined by temperature, 73, 237–42; fertile period, 73, 236–37, 274; menopause, 242, 472–78; method of conserving male fertility, 238; ovaries, function of, 233–34, 237–38; premarital examinations for, 51–57; rhythm of reproduction, 232–33; after sterilization, rarely restored, 276; statistics, 51; diagrams, 81, 82, 277. *See also* Infertility; Sterilization

Fertilization, 80, 84; artificial insemination, 85; defective ovulation 197; determined by body temperature, 73, 237–42, 274; ovulation, 73, 233, 235–36

Fetus. *See* Embryo development

Financial planning: automobile, 148–49; budget reduction, 155; clothing, 144–46; cost per child, 212; family, 152–54; food, 143–44; health, 149–51; housing, 146–48; insurance, 151, 155; maternity, 212; recreation, 151–52; savings, 156; trousseau, 129; wedding, 130; who does what, 140–42

Growth—(*cont.*)

307; pubertal growth, 292; race or nationality, 289. *See also* Maturation

Guests, in family life, 409–10

Guilt complex: masturbation, 354, 358; prostitution, 437

H

Hair, appearance during puberty, 311; clipped in preparation for labor, 259; female genitalia, 69; feminine facial growths of, 484; male genitalia, 93

Haldane, John Burdon Sanderson, on mutation rates of certain genes, 225–26; on Rh factor in infant mortality, 223

Hall, G. Stanley, 351

Hall, Winfield Scott, 351

Hamilton, Alice, 491

Hamilton, Dr. G. V., 161

Happiness, marital: child and family background, 119–20; church, 120; divorce predictions, 123–25; education, 114, 121, 122; friends, 121; husband's occupation, 122; income and saving, 20, 122; measurement of, 113–15; number of children, 122; parents' attitude, 119, 121; personality and temperament, 5, 20–26, 30, 117–19, 124–25; sexual adjustment, 115–16; talented people, 115, 116; tests for, 113–14, 116–18; unemployment, 121–22; wife's occupation, 120

Headaches, 475; migraine accompanied by nausea, 475; ovary deficiency causes, 475

Health: budgeting for family needs, 149–50; during climacteric, 470–84; influence on marital happiness, 122; influence on parenthood, 211–12; insurance, 150–51, 155–56; marriage hygiene, 181–94; venereal diseases, 448–56. *See also* Health and hygiene of marriage; Sex education

Health, Education and Welfare, Department of, 499

Health and hygiene of marriage; anatomy and physiology of sex organs, 67–87; childbirth, 255–66; cleanliness essential,

Health and hygiene of marriage—(*cont.*) 183–84; climacteric period, 470–84; disparity of sex organs, 189; douches, dangerous, 191; douches suggested, 96; erotic response, 71–72; excessive childbearing, 187; female genitalia, 69–73; feminine hygiene, 96, 184; fertility, 232–42; frequency of sexual intercourse, 186–87; genital odors, 96, 184; how to select a physician, 246; hygiene of the bedroom, 185–86; influence on marital happiness, 122; intercourse, 88–97; intercourse among elderly, 193; male genitalia, 74–77; masculine hygiene, 96; masturbation, 348–58; miscarriages and abortions, 195–206; nudity, 186; ovulation, 72–73; pregnancy, 85, 243–54; prevention of conception, 190–91, 267–76; purposes of sex relations, 181–82; safe period, 73, 238, 240; sex relations, 88–97; sterility, 80–85; timing in sexual intercourse, 189–90; venereal disease, 448–56

Health insurance, 150–51, 155–56

Health test. *See* Medical examinations

Heart diseases, caused by venereal diseases, 452

Heart-valve involvement, caused by gonorrhea, 450

Heat flashes. *See* Hot flashes

Height, grid method of recording, 289–92; physical growth of boys and girls compared, 284; tables and graphs, 285, 286, 287. *See also* Growth; Weight

Hemophilia (hereditary bleeding), 222; abortion desirable during pregnancy in cases of, 202; mutation rate, 226

Hemorrhage, cause of death during maternity, 248

"Hemorrhage," dilation, 79

Heredity, 217–30; achondroplasia, 226; albinism, 220; alkaptonuria, 220; allele, 219; anemia, 224; birthmarks, 226; blood factors, 223; color blindness, 222; deaf mutism, 220; dystrophy, 222; and environment, 227; erythroblastosis, 223; fallacies regarding, 226; genes, 218–21; hemophilia, 222, 226; heterozygous genes, 219, 228–29; homozygous genes, 219; ichthyosis fetalis, 220; mechanism of sex inheritance, 218; Mediterranean

528 INDEX

Heredity—(*cont.*)
fever, 224; modern methods of studying,
225; mutant genes, 219, 224; mutation,
219; mutation rates, 226; nervous diseases, 221; phenylketonuria, 220; predetermination of sex, 227–28; race crossing, 229–30; radiation induced mutations, 227; Rh factor, 223, 247; sex-
linked dominants, 222; sex-linked recessives, 221–22; sickle-cell anemia, 224;
sterilization of unfit, 228; twins, 225
Hermaphroditism (intersexuality), 482
Hernia, sterility sometimes caused by
operation for, 53, 480
Heterosexual customs, 424–26
Heterozygous genes, 219, 228–29
High school, suggested courses in sex education, 367
Hill, Reuben, 509
Hobby, Oveta Culp, 492
Hoffman, Malvina, 491
Home economics and management, 137–
56; adequate family diets, 143; budgets,
143; clothing, 144–46; costs of family,
152–54; family expenditures, 144; food,
143; health, 149–51; subject in school
curriculum valuable to sex education,
369–70; who does what, 140–42
Home life and education. *See* Family life
Home management and finance, 137–56;
adjustment to changing wants and
changing income, 154–56; automobile,
148–49; budget reduction, 155; clothing, 144–46; cost per child, 212–13;
family resources, 137–38; family's wants,
139–40; health, 149–51; house, 146–48;
maternity, 212–13; planning for the long
life of the family, 152–54; recreation,
151–52; techniques of financing planning, 142–43; who does what, 140–42
Homoeroticism, 422
Homosexuality: adolescence, habits of, 77,
396, 421; considered normal in various
countries, 421; narcissistic personalities,
110, 111; in penal institutions, 421;
sexual relations unattractive to, 159. *See
also* Masturbation
Homozygous genes, 219
Honeymoon, adjustments during, 133–35;
expenses, 133; selection of place, 133

Hormones: abortion, treatment for, 200;
activity begins at puberty, 102; activity
decreases at climacteric, 242, 471;
adrenal, 471; adrenal cortex, 484; adrenosterone, 484; climacteric, 471; effect on pregnancy, 244–45; estrogen,
72, 234, 235, 244, 471, 473; estrogenic
preparations, 235; estrone, 200; female,
72, 73, 242, 244, 245, 471, 484; fertility,
stimulated by, 234; male, 74, 235, 483;
influence on sex development, 471; masculinization, caused by deficiency of,
471; during menopause, 242, 471, 484;
during menstruation, 245; ovulation,
72–73; pituitary, 72, 244, 471; placenta,
200; progesterone, 73, 200, 245, 471;
sexual modifications, caused by, 482;
sterility, resulting from lack of, 84;
testosterone, 235; thyroid, 201, 471;
treatment for abortion, 200; treatment
for infertility, 235; Vitamin E, 200
Hospitalization (insurance), need of
family budgeting for, 150, 151, 155, 156
Hot flushes: in men during climacteric,
481; in women during menopause, 476
Housing: apartments, 24, 140; expenses
and budgeting, 146–48; location, 140; in
metropolitan areas, 140; ownership, advantages, 139, 147; ownership, percentage in United States, 138; renting, 148
Husband: concept of wife's role in marriage, 11; conduct on honeymoon, 133–
36; extramarital relations, 157–67; role
in financial planning, 141–56. *See also*
Men
Husbands, choice of. *See* Mate, choice of
Hygiene. *See* Health and hygiene
Hymen, 69, 77–79; dilators, use of, 78–79;
douche used to stretch, 78; effect of
menstrual tampon on, 78; stretched by
physician, 78–79; treatment of, 57, 78–
79; virgin, 56–57, 70, 77; diagrams,
68–81

I

Ichthyosis fetalis (hereditary disease), 220
Idealism and idealization: daydreaming,
12; infatuation, a cause of, 7; social factors, influence in adolescence, 311–12

Idiots, hereditary cause of, 220

Imbeciles, hereditary cause of, 220

Immigrants, family council introduced in United States by, 403–4

Incest: taboo in Western culture, 420; use of abortion in cases of incestuous pregnancy, 202

Incisor teeth: baby, 293; permanent, 293

Income: budgeting, 142–43; managing, 140–42; marital happiness, influence of, 20, 122; resources, 137–38; statistics, 138

Incompatibility, legal grounds for divorce, 459

Indians, American, sex behavior of, 418

Individualism, 15

Infancy, age period, 288

Infant. *See* Baby

Infant mortality, caused by hereditary Rh blood factor, 223

Infanticide, primitive custom, 267

Infantilism, delayed puberty, 483

Infatuation, 6–8, 22. *See also* Affection; Love

Inferiority complex, problems of, 6

Infertility: causes, 69, 80–87; fertility rarely restored after sterilization, 276; gonorrhea, 449; in man, 53, 80; menopause, 242, 472–78; premarital examinations, 51–57; rates of male and female, 80; treatment for, 235; in women, 80; diagrams, 81, 83. *See also* Fertility; Sterilization

Infidelity, 162–67; causes, 163–64, 426; statistics, 160–67. *See also* Adultery; Prostitution

Inflammation: of cervix, 78; of fringes, 84; gonorrhea, as a cause of, 84; of penis of young boys, 96; of ovary, 84

Inheritance (physiological). *See* Heredity

Inheritance laws affecting adoption, 320–21

Inhibitions to marital adjustment, 95, 128, 132

Insanity, masturbation not a cause of, 349; syphilitic, 452

Insecurity. *See* Security

Insomnia, symptom of menopause, 476

Insurance: automobile, 155; fire, 155; group plan, 151; hospitalization, 151, 155–56; life, 156

Intelligence, effect on marital adjustments, 114, 121. *See also* Education

Intercourse: among elderly, 193–94; anatomy, 67–87; cleanliness, 183–84; coitus interruptus, 268; dangerous douches, 191–92; duration, 76, 189–90; excess, dangers of, 95, 186–87; female orgasm, 90, 94; feminine hygiene, 96–97; fertile period, 73, 236–37; first experience, 89; frequency, 76–77, 94–96, 186–88; hymen, method of stretching for, 57; lateral or side position, 92; male orgasm, 76; man-above position, 91; masculine hygiene, 96; masturbation, effect of, 348–58; nudity, 186; orgasm, 71, 76, 88, 90, 94; positions, 77, 91–93; during pregnancy, 193, 199, 249; premarital abstinence, 40–47, 85–87, 158; problem growing out of adolescent petting, 44; rear-entry position, 92; safe period, 73–74, 274–75; seat of feminine sensation, 90; statistics, 54–55, 157; temperature, effect on, 237, 238; woman-above position, 91. *See also* Contraception; Fertility; Infertility; Sterilization

Intersexuality, 481–82; hermaphroditism, 482

Interstitial cells, 478

Intra-uterine contraceptives, dangers of, 55, 191, 272

Introverts, 21

Investments: financial, 138; insurance, 150–51, 155–56; savings, 154

Irritableness during menopause, 475

J

Japan, family council, 404; homosexual customs, 421

Jaundice, caused by Rh factor, 247

Jealousy: caused by insecurity, 9; problem among stepchildren, 335–42

Jellies and creams as contraceptives, 55, 189, 192, 271

Jews, rate of illegal abortion, 204

Juvenile delinquency, 41; gangs, 386; overtraining, effect of, 387; parent-child relationships, 379–81; prostitution, effect

Juvenile delinquency—(*cont.*)
on, 436–37, 443; spoiling of children,
380. *See also* Child psychology

K

Kansas, 511
"Keeping company," 18. *See also* Dating
Keller, Helen, 492
Keraki Indians, 421
Kidney, infection of during pregnancy,
264
Kinsey, Dr. Alfred, 91, 161, 352
Kinsey, Mrs. Alfred, 491
Kissing: adolescent games, 397; arouses
emotions, 90, 105
Komarovsky, Dr. Mirra, 493

L

Labia, 69; diagrams, 68, 81
Labor, 256–57; baby, immediate care of
after birth, 262; choice of physician,
246; confinement, 256; delivery, 261;
delivery technique, 261; drugs used to
relieve pain during labor, 260–61; duration of labor, 257; examinations before
labor begins, 259; mother, care of, 262;
position of baby in uterus, 252, 258–
59; postpartum care, 264–65; predicting
date of birth, 255; pregnancy, 214–16,
243–54; puerperium, 262–64; signs of
labor, 256–57; stages of labor, 257;
when to call physician, 256–57
Landsteiner, Karl, discoverer of Rh blood
factor, 223
Laws and legislation: adoption, 318–23;
divorce, 458–63; Food and Drug Administration, control of condoms, 269;
health certificates, 53; inheritance after
adoption, 322; premarital examinations,
state control, 455; prenatal laws for prevention of transmission of syphilis, 455;
syphilis test, 247
Learning, child psychology of, 301–4. *See
also* Education

Lend-a-Hand Club (family-life organiza-
tion), Wichita, Kan., 511
Leukorrhea, as a disease, 55–56
Leukorrhea, natural, 55, 74. *See also* Mucus
Leukorrheal discharge, caused by gonorrhea, 450
Levine, Maurice, 353
Life insurance, family budgeting for, 156
Lincoln, Abraham, 342
Liver, cirrhosis of by venereal disease, 452
Locomotor ataxia, caused by venereal
disease, 452; masturbation, no effect on,
349
Louisiana, Civil Code regarding the family meeting, 403
Love, 3–13; in adolescence, 5, 13, 398–99;
affection, 22; concept of roles, 11; counselor, 12–13; environment, 11–12; infatuation, 4, 6–8, 22; interests and activities, 11; love and infatuation, 6;
military service, effect on, 9; motion
pictures, as an influence on, 8; narcissism, 5, 111; negative, critical, or doubtful elements in the couple's relationship,
10; parent fixation, hindrance to, 5;
pattern of development, 11; persons not
prepared to fall in love, 5–6; "puppy
love," 5, 13, 398; relation to things of
the loved one, 10; relationship to other
people, 9; social factors, influence on,
8–9
Lubrication, sexual, 71, 74, 88; artificial
lubricants, 88
Luce, Clare Booth, 492
Lymphogranuloma venereum, venereal
disease, 453

M

McBride, Catherine, 491
MacIntosh, Millicent Carey, 492
Male genitalia: anatomy, 74–80; epididymis, 74, 80; gonorrhea, 448–50; hygiene
of, 96; intersexuality, 481–82; meatus,
74, 84; penis, 69, 72, 74, 76, 84, 88,
91–93, 96, 189; premarital examination
of, 53–54; prepuce, 76; prostate gland,
74; scrotum, 74, 84; spermatic cord, 74;

Marriage counselor—(*cont.*)
selor, 61–62; marriage-counseling organizations, 61; premarital counseling, 26; professional man as marriage counselor, 62, 109–10; use of counselor, 109–10; women, adjustment to marriage, 487. *See also* Counseling

Marriage law in relation to divorce, 458–63

Marriage relations, technique of: feminine hygiene, 96–97; first sexual act, 89; lateral or side position, 92; man-above position, 91; masculine hygiene, 96; masturbation, 356, 357, 358; as means of self-expression, 182; procreation, purpose of, 181–82; purposes, 181–83; rear-entry position, 92; seat of feminine sensation, 90; sedentary positions, 92; standing position, 93; woman-above position, 91. *See also* Intercourse

Masculinization, caused by deficiency of hormones in women, 483–84

Masochism, abnormal sexual pleasure, 423

Masturbation: adolescence, 77, 355–57; facts, 352, 357–58; false beliefs, 348–50; fantasy, as a factor in, 356; harmless, 54, 351, 358; infancy, 354; insanity, not caused by, 349; marriage, effects on, 54, 352, 357–58; men, 54, 77, 85, 350, 356; methods, 356–57; normality of, 352; norms in various cultures, 420; prevalence of, 352–54; puberty, sexual adjustment, 102; repression, results of, 102; women, 77, 350, 352–53, 356–57

Mate, choice of: adjustment in engagement, 24–27; affection and sex, 22; church, 19; common interests and values, 22–24; dating, 17–18; desire for children, 23; determination to succeed in marriage, 25; domestic interest, 23–24; economic status, 20; education level, 19; emancipation of women, 15–16; emotional interdependence, 21; emotional and social maturity, 21; engagement, 18; engagement adjustment, 25; family relationships, 19; favorable and unfavorable personality traits, 20–21; flexibility, 25; friends, 23; going steady, 18; individualism, 15; "keeping company," 18; leisure-time preference, 22–23; life values and career, 24; marriage

Mate, choice of—(*cont.*)
as companionship, 16–17; membership in organizations, 19; number of friends, 19; past customs of selection, 14; preparation for marriage, 26; private understanding, 18; in remarriage, 329; secularization of life, 16; social background, 18–20; temperament and personality, 20–22; urbanization, 15

Maternity: baby, immediate care of after birth, 262; birth, 255–66; children, number of, 214–16; choice of physician, 246; confinement, 256; delivery, 261; delivery technique, 261; drugs used to relieve pain during labor, 260–61; duration of labor, 257; economic problems, 212; employment during pregnancy, 213–14; examinations before labor begins, 259; health values, 211; menstruation, return of, 265–66; mother, care of, 262; nursing, 263, 265, 266; position of baby in uterus, 252, 258; postpartum care, 264–65; predicting date of birth, 255; pregnancy, 214–16, 243–54; psychological factors of, 210; puerperium, 262–64; signs of labor, 256–57; stages of labor, 257; time between pregnancies, 214–16; when to call physician, 256

Mathematics, in school curriculum, contribution to sex education, 370

Maturation, physical development in adolescence: anatomy, 67–87; child psychology of, 301–4; emotional and social, prerequisites for marriage, 21; growth, 292–93

May Act, federal control of prostitution, 434

Mead, Margaret, 427, 487

Mealtime, used as a family council, 407–9

Meatus, urethra opening: in the female, 70; in the male, 74, 84; diagrams, 68, 75

Medical care, family budgeting for, 149–51

Medical examination, 51–57; premarital requirements, 53

Mediterranean fever (thalassemia), hereditary, 224

Melancholia during climacteric, 477–78; in men, 481; in women, 475

Memory, effect of menopause on, 475

534

Perversions—(cont.)
418; oriental norms, 421; "peeping Toms," 424; penal institutions, 421; Plains Indians, 420; psychoneurosis, 424; reversal of masculine and feminine roles, 418; sadism, 423; sex act, 423–24; sex object, 420–23; sex reversal of, 418; sexual deviations in Western culture, 417; suggested solutions, 427–28; voyeurism, 424

Pessary: as a contraceptive, 272; dangers of infection from stem pessaries, 191; used to correct displaced uterus, 79

Pessimism, undesirable trait for marital adjustment, 20

Petting: definition, 43; dangers of excess, 45, 46; during engagement, 36, 37; marital relations, 89, 105; habit forming started, 43; "heavy petting," 43; how far to do, 45; leading to coitus, 44; to orgasm, 43, 78, 87; premarital relations not desirable to marital adjustment, 36; as substitute for coitus, 87

Phenol, a dangerous douche, 191

Phenotype, 220, 221

Phenylketonuria, 220

Physical attraction: emphasized by infatuation, 22; overemphasized by books, movies, radio, television, 8

Physical attractiveness, 29

Physical education, in school curriculum, contribution to sex education, 370

Physical examinations, premarital requirements: blood tests for gonorrhea and syphilis, 53; certificates required, 53; contraceptives, 54, 55; degree of fertility or sterility determined by, 51; diaphragm, 55, 57; hymen, treatment for, 57; laws governing, 53; leukorrhea, 55; men, examinations of, 53–54; statistics, 55; virginity, 56–57; women, examinations of, 54–55

Physical exercise. See Exercise

Physician: how to choose a physician during pregnancy, 246; as counselor on sex hygiene, 52; as marriage counselor, 62, 109–10

Physiology. See Anatomy

Physiology, as a school subject, contribution to sex education, 369

Pimps, prostitutes, 436

Pittsburgh, 372

Pituitary gland: function, 471; ovulation stimulated by, 72, 233, 235; relation to sex glands, 478; sex development influenced by, 471; stimulation of ova, 244; testicles affected by, 479

Placenta: estrogen abundant in pregnancy, 234; means of embryo nourishment before birth, 252, 253

Plains Indians, 418

Pneumonia, as a cause of abortion, 199

Postnatal period: mother, immediate care of, 262; menstruation, return of, 265–66; nursing, 263, 265; postpartum care, 264–65; puerperium, 262–64

Postpartum, care after delivery, 264–65

Preadolescence, 310. See also Children; Adolescence

Precocious puberty, 483

Predetermination of sex, methods of, 227–28

Pregnancy: abnormalities revealed by X ray, 259; abortions, 195–206; after abortion, 201; anatomy of early pregnancy, 85; Aschheim-Zondek test for, 245; baby, immediate care of after birth, 262; birth of the baby, 255–66; birthmarks not caused by mother's emotions, 226, 249; bleeding, should be reported, 200; blood deficiency and abortion, 197; blood test for syphilis, 247; choice of physician, 246; conception occurs during ovulation, 236; conception possible on every day of cycle, 245; confinement, 256–57; contraception, 73–74, 86, 96, 190–91, 267–76; delivery, 261; delivery technique, 261; diet during pregnancy, 248; drugs used to relieve pain during labor, 260–61; duration of labor, 257; emotions during, 249; employment during, 213–14; examinations before labor begins, 259; exercise during, 248; false pregnancy, 246; fraternal twins, 73; hereditary factors, 229–41; hospital or home delivery, 259; how baby is formed, 260; identical twins, 73, 226; intercourse during pregnancy, 193, 209; intercourse technique during, 92; labor, 256–57; life history of abortion caused by defective germ plasm, 196–97; menstruation, return of, 265–66; miscarriages and abor-

Puerperium: interval after birth, 262–64; need of sleep during, 264–65

Punishment, influence on child's future marital adjustment, 119

"Puppy love": emotions of puppy love contradict real love, 5; painful experience, 13

Pure Food and Drug Act, control of fake abortifacient drugs, 206

Puritans, arranged marriages of their children, 14

Pus: contagious germs, 449; sign of gonorrhea, 449

Q

Quarrels, inhibit marital adjustment, 136

R

Race crossing, hereditary effects of, 229–30

Radiation: causes damage to sex glands, 227; germ-plasm mutations may be induced by, 227

Rappaport, Mazie F., 435

Rational Sex Ethics (W. F. Robie), 356

Records, adoption, 321–22

Recreation: can control premarital sex relations, 44, 45; common leisure-time preferences during engagement, 22; criteria for companionship, 11; factor in selection of mate, 11; financial planning, 151–52; importance to sex education, 372; important factor in dating, 30–31; influence on marital adjustment, 19; organizations, 19, 31, 32, 45; source for in church, YWCA, YMCA, 31, 32

Religion: Catholic views on abortion, 201; Catholic views on contraceptives, 238; church sanction increased divorce, 16; diminished in family life, 16; influence on marital adjustments, 19–20; place of church in providing recreation for adolescents, 31, 32; role of church in mar-

Religion—(*cont.*)
riage counseling, 61; secularization influence of on marriage problem, 16

Remarriage and the stepchild: extent of remarriage, 327–28; factors in problematical situation, 337–42; favoritism, 340, 341; grandparents' influence on stepchildren, 340; increase in, 328; mate selection, 329; problems due to stepchildren, 335–37; stepchildren and successful marriage, 342–45; success of remarriage, 331–32

Reorientation, necessary for love and marriage, 6

Repression, resulting from masturbation, 102

Reproduction: cyclical events in the ovary, 233–34; embryo development, 252–53; formation of baby, 249; ovaries, 69, 72, 84, 244, 473, 474; ovulation, 72–73, 232–33; rhythm of, 232–33; testicles, 74, 80, 84, 478–80; diagram, 250–51. *See also* Conception; Pregnancy; Childbirth

Res judicata, 461

Retinoblastoma, mutation rate of, 226

Retroversion of uterus, explanation, 55

Rh factor (rhesus factor): explanation of, 223; importance to pregnancy, 247

Rhythm of reproductive function, 232–33. *See also* Safe period

Rice: customs regarding marriage ceremonies, 131–32; dangers of throwing, 131

Rife, Dr. D. C., 225

Robie, Dr. Walter F., 356

Roe, Clifford, 433

Roles: men's idea of women's duties, 11; sex behavior, 418; of women in life, 490–94; women's idea of men's duties, 11

Romance: overemphasis of sex appeal, 8; prefaces real love, 5; social factors, influence of, 8–9

Romeo and Juliet, represent change in modern standards of premarital relations, 41

Roosevelt, Mrs. Franklin Delano, 492

Rozier, 349

Rupture. *See* Hernia

Russia: death-rate abortions, 205; legalized abortion, 205

S

Sacrum, spinal bone, 70

Sadism, psychological perversion, 423

Safe period: biological contraception, 274; comments on, 73–74; conception possible on every day of cycle, 245; typical cycle, 235–38

alpingectomy, sterilization operation, 277

Sanger, Margaret, 492

Savings: among lower-income groups, 138; family demands on, 156; in relation to marital happiness, 122

Schizophrenia, 384

School of Infancy (Comenius), 299

Schools: need of courses in family living, 508; recreation, importance to sex education, 372; sex education in, 362–73; suggested courses in: biology, 369; English, 369; general science, 369; health and hygiene, 370; home economics, 370; mathematics, 370; physical education, 370; physiology, 369; social studies, 370; sociology, 370

Scouting, source of recreation for adolescents, 31, 32

Scrotum, 74

Security: financial and emotional security desirable for marriage, 137; motive in women stronger than in men, 160; purpose of marital relations, 182; sense of security arises out of trust and love, 6, 7

Seidert, Dr. Florence, 491

Self-abuse, faulty belief of, 349, 351. *See also* Masturbation

Self-analysis: first step in marriage counseling, 62; solution to question of love or infatuation, 4

Self-confidence, desirable trait for marital adjustment, 20

Self-consciousness, in children, 311

Self-expression, as a purpose of sex relations, 182

Self-gratification, 7

Self-relief. *See* Masturbation

Semen, fluid of ejaculation, 74

Seminal vesicle, secretion is part of ejaculation, 74

Seminal vesicles, gonorrhea infection of, 449

Senile. *See* Old age

Sensation, clitoris as seat of erotic, 69–70, 90

Separation. *See* Divorce

Sex: abnormal characteristics, 482; clitoris as seat of erotic response, 69–70; determined by type of sperm cell from father, 218; heredity, 217–30; normal development in adolescence, 397–98; norms in various cultures, 417–18, 420, 421, 423; predetermination of, 227; social customs and standards, 417–27

Sex adjustments: basis of conflicts, 489; books as an adjunct to counseling, 112; cases requiring a psychiatrist, 110–12; faulty attitudes, 99–100, 103–4; infant and its mother, 100–1; intramarital disturbances, 426–27; need for common sense in case where adjustment is good in the beginning, 104; newly married, 104–5; open-mindedness on the part of the one who has a problem in sexual adjustment, 106–7; physician as counselor, 109–10; puberty, 102–3; sexuality in the child, 101

Sex education: adolescent need in high school, 44; biology, course in, 369; clothes, 362; college courses, 373; dating conduct, 46–47; early childhood, 361; elementary level, 362–64; English, course in, 369; general science, course in, 369; health and hygiene, course in, 370; high school level, 367–68; home economics, course in, 370; integrated method, 368–69; lack of proper home training, 99; masturbation, 348–49; mathematics, course in, 370; parents and teachers, 364–67; physical education as a course, 370; physiology, course in, 369; premarital sex relations, 158; prevention of prostitution, 444–45; recreation, importance of, 372; school courses contributing to sex education, 369–70; social studies, course in, 370; sociology, course in, 370; special course method, 372–73; teaching problems of sex relations, 41

Sex hygiene: dangerous douches, 191; douches, suggested, 96; feminine, 96–97, 184; masculine hygiene, 96. *See also* Marriage; Health and hygiene